PREFACE

This edition of *Manual Drivetrains and Axles* is organized around the National Institute for Automotive Service Excellence (ASE) service area: Manual Drive Trains and Axles. The ASE Task List is included in Appendix A. The text information and task list should prepare you to take the A3, Manual Drive Trains and Axles, test.

This comprehensive textbook provides a diagnostic and repair approach to this area of automotive repair. It is organized to provide an understanding of the operating theory of automotive air conditioning, heating, and engine cooling systems in the theory chapters. The service chapters describe the most modern system maintenance, diagnostic, and repair procedures. Service Cautions, Service Tips, and Real-World Fixes are included in these chapters to aid your understanding.

ASE and NATEF Correlated

This textbook and and the accompanying worktext are designed to aid students who want to acquire the skills listed in the ASE task list for A3, Manual Drive Trains and Axles (see Appendix A). The worktext includes normal lab exercises needed to complete all of the NATEF tasks. A correlation chart for both ATTS and NATEF certification is provided in Appendix E.

Multimedia System

The multimedia CD-ROM that accompanies and supplements this textbook should make learning more fun. The CD includes:

1. PowerPoint presentations that illustrate both theory and service topics.
2. Flash animations that illustrate complex actions.
3. Sample ASE style test questions in an interactive form for immediate feedback.
4. Student worksheets.
5. A glossary of automotive terms.

Worktext

A separate worktext accompanies this textbook. Each exercise is a real-world task preformed by technicians in the manual drivetrains and axles service and repair field. The exercises help students and instructors apply the textbook information to everyday-type service and testing procedures. The exercises include typical results and where the problem might be if test results are not within the acceptable range. These exercises should help build diagnosis, testing, and repair skills.

Chapter Components

- Each chapter opens with a list of *Learning Objectives* for that chapter. They identify the goals to be achieved.
- Next is the *Terms To Learn*, which includes the new words commonly used in this field of repair.
- The chapter is divided numerically into topical sections that should help you understand the relationship of topics and move through the textbook easier.
- The service chapters contain *Service Cautions, Service Tips,* and *Real-World Fixes* to relate the printed information to real-world tasks encountered in manual drivetrains and axles service and repair.
- Each chapter ends with a *Chapter Quiz* and *Review Questions* that are written in an ASE-type question format.

Bold type is used for new terms as they appear for the first time. *Italic type* is used to emphasize important words and terms. These terms are often defined as they are introduced, and most of them are listed in the glossary at the back of the book.

New Features of the Fourth Edition

1. An index of How to Service Operations.
2. Expanded manual drivetrains and axles testing, diagnosis, and service procedures to reflect new tools, equipment, and service procedures.
3. Expanded electrical electronic content for testing, diagnosis, and repair.
4. A Spanish-language glossary.

Instructor Package

A comprehensive *instructor package* is available free when this text is adopted for classroom use. Instructors should contact Prentice Hall (call 1-800-526-0485 or online at www.prenhall.com). The instructor package includes the following:

- Instructor Manual with answers to all of the textbook questions
- Computerized testing program

Acknowledgments

This book has the support of much of the manual drivetrains and axles repair industry. I am grateful and wish to express sincere thanks to the following individuals and organizations for their special contributions:

Acra Electric Corporation
Advance Adapters
Alston Race Car Engineering
American Honda
ARB Air Locker
Band-It
Harold Beck, Yuba City
Borroughs
Tom Broxholm, Skyline College
BWD Automotive Corporation
Centerforce Clutches
Chassis Ear, Steelman

DaimlerChrysler Corporation
Cosmos International, Inc.
CR Services
Dana Corporation
Darrell Gwynn Racing Team
Dorman Products
Drive Line Service of Sacramento, Jim Scoggin
Durston/Vim Tools
Everco Industries
Fluke Corporation
Ford Motor Company
Joel Gelfand
General Motors Corporation
GKN Drivetech, Inc.
HeliCoil
James Halderman
Hyundai Motor America
Jerico Performance Products
John Deere
K-D Tools
Kent-Moore
L & T Slider Clutches, Lanny and Tony Miglizzi
LUK Clutches
Manual Transmission Warehouse, Richard Tinucci
Mark Williams Enterprises
McLeod Industries, Inc., George Koehler
Mighty Mover
Moog Automotive
Neapco
OTC Tools
Perfect Circle
Phoenix Systems
Plews
Quarter Master Industries
Racepak
RAM Automotive
Richmond Gear
Rockland Standard Gear
Sta-Lube
Bill Steen, Yuba College
Stock Car Products
Summer Brothers
Tilton Engineering, McLane Tilton
Tractech, Inc.
Transmission Technologies Corporation, TTC
Warner Electric
Warn Industries
Van Norman Equipment Company
Zexel Torsen, Inc.

MANUAL DRIVETRAINS AND AXLES

Fourth Edition

Tom Birch
Chuck Rockwood
Ventura College

PEARSON

Prentice
Hall

Upper Saddle River, New Jersey
Columbus, Ohio

Library of Congress Cataloging-in-Publication Data

Birch, Thomas W. (Thomas Wesley),
    Manual drivetrains and axles / Tom Birch, Charles Rockwood.–4th ed.
        p. cm.
    ISBN 0–13–118488–1
    1. Automobiles–Power trains. 2. Automobiles–Axles. I. Rockwood, Chuck. II. Title.

TL260.B57 2005
629.2'4–dc22

2004044408

Editor in Chief: Stephen Helba
Executive Editor: Ed Francis
Editorial Assistant: Jennifer Day
Production Editor: Holly Shufeldt
Production Coordination: Carlisle Publishers Services
Design Coordinator: Diane Ernsberger
Cover Designer: Ali Mohrman
Production Manager: Matt Ottenweller
Marketing Manager: Mark Marsden

This book was set in Century Book by Carlisle Communications, Ltd. It was printed and bound by Courier Kendallville, Inc. The cover was printed by Phoenix Color Corp.

Pearson Prentice Hall™ is a trademark of Pearson Education, Inc.
Pearson® is a registered trademark of Pearson plc
Prentice Hall® is a registered trademark of Pearson Education, Inc.

Pearson Education Ltd.
Pearson Education Singapore Pte. Ltd.
Pearson Education Canada, Ltd.
Pearson Education—Japan

Pearson Education Australia Pty. Limited
Pearson Education North Asia Ltd.
Pearson Educación de Mexico, S.A. de C.V.
Pearson Education Malaysia Pte. Ltd.

10 9 8 7 6 5 4 3 2 1
ISBN 0–13–118488–1

CONTENTS

HOW TO SERVICE OPERATIONS

Chapter 1

SERVICE INFORMATION, FASTENERS, TOOLS, AND SAFETY

LEARNING OBJECTIVES

After completing this chapter, you should be able to:

1. Retrieve vehicle service information.
2. Explain the strength ratings of threaded fasteners.
3. Discuss how to safely use hand tools.
4. Describe how to safely hoist a vehicle.
5. List the personal safety equipment that all service technicians should wear.
6. Know the ASE requirements for vehicle identification and the proper use of tools and shop equipment.

TERMS TO LEARN

aftermarket	OEM
bolt	pitch
bump cap	spontaneous combustion
cap screw	stud
dial indicator	telescopic gauge
grade	TSB
iATN	UNC
lock washer	UNF
Loctite	VCI
micrometer	vernier caliper washer
nut	VIN

1.1 VEHICLE IDENTIFICATION

All service work requires that the vehicle, including the engine and accessories, be properly identified. The most common identification method is knowing the make, model, and year of the vehicle.

> **Make:** e.g. Chevrolet, **Model:** e.g. Trailblazer, **Year:** e.g. 2003

The year of the vehicle is often difficult to determine exactly. Typically, a new model year starts in September or October of the year prior to the actual new year, but not always. A model may be introduced as the next year's model as soon as January of the previous year. This is why the **vehicle identification number**, usually abbreviated **VIN**, is so important (Figure 1-1). Since 1981 all vehicle manufacturers have used a VIN that is 17 characters long. Although every vehicle manufacturer assigns various letters or numbers within these seventeen characters, there are some constants, including:

- The first number or letter designates the country of origin.

1 = United States	K = Korea
2 = Canada	L = Taiwan
3 = Mexico	S = England
4 = United States	V = France
6 = Australia	W = Germany
9 = Brazil	Y = Sweden
J = Japan	Z = Italy

- The model of the vehicle is commonly the fourth or fifth character.
- The eighth character is often the engine code. (Some engines cannot be determined by the VIN number.)

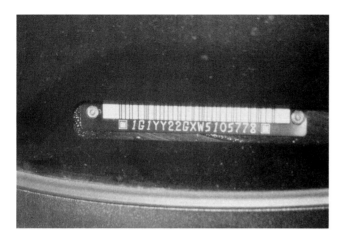

FIGURE I-I The VIN, vehicle identification number, is at the top front of the instrument panel and is visible through the windshield. (Courtesy of James Halderman)

■ The tenth character represents the year on all vehicles.

A = 1980	L = 1990	Y = 2000
B = 1981	M = 1991	1 = 2001
C = 1982	N = 1992	2 = 2002
D = 1983	P = 1993	3 = 2003
E = 1984	R = 1994	4 = 2004
F = 1985	S = 1995	5 = 2005
G = 1986	T = 1996	6 = 2006
H = 1987	V = 1997	7 = 2007
J = 1988	W = 1998	8 = 2008
K = 1989	X = 1999	9 = 2009

1.1.1 VECI Label

The **vehicle emissions control information (VECI)** label located under the hood of the vehicle shows informative settings and emission hose routing information (Figure 1-2). The VECI label (sticker) can be located on the underside of the hood, the radiator fan shroud, radiator core support, or on the strut towers. The VECI label usually includes the following information:

Engine identification	Base ignition timing
Emissions standard	(if adjustable)
for vehicle	Spark plug type and gap
Vacuum hose routing	Valve lash
diagram	Emission calibration code

1.1.2 Calibration Codes

Calibration codes are usually located on power train control modules (PCMs) or other controllers. When-

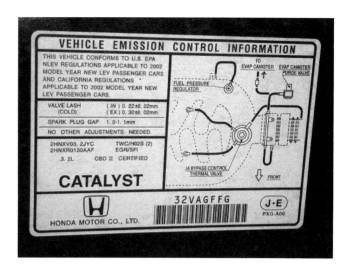

FIGURE I-2 The VECI, vehicle emission control information, label is attached to an underhood portion of the vehicle. (Courtesy of James Halderman)

ever diagnosing an engine operating fault, it may be necessary to know the calibration code to determine if the vehicle is the subject of a technical service bulletin or other service procedure (Figure 1-3).

FIGURE I-3 The sticker attached to this control module indicates the calibration code. (Courtesy of James Halderman)

1.1.3 Casting Numbers

Whenever an engine part such as a block is cast, a number is put into the mold to identify the casting (Figure 1-4). These casting numbers can be used to check dimensions such as the cubic inch displacement and other information such as year of manufacture. Sometimes changes are made to the mold, yet the casting number is not changed. The casting number is often the best piece of identifying information that the service technician can use.

1.2 SERVICE INFORMATION

Service information is needed by the service technician to determine specifications and service procedures and to learn about any necessary special tools needed.

1.2.1 Service Manuals

The original equipment manufacturer, **OEM**, and **aftermarket** service manuals contain specifications and service procedures. While OEM service manuals cover just one year and one or more model of the same vehicle, most aftermarket service manufacturers cover multiple years and/or models in one manual (Figure 1-5). Included in most service manuals are the following:

- Capacities and recommended specifications for all fluids
- Specifications including engine and routine maintenance items

- Testing procedures
- Service procedures including the use of special tools if needed

1.2.2 Electronic Service Information

Electronic service information is available mostly by subscription and provides access to an Internet site where service manual information is available (Figure 1-6). Most vehicle manufacturers also offer electronic service information to their dealers and to schools that offer corporate training programs.

FIGURE 1-5 The factory service manual is considered to be the most complete source of service and repair information for a vehicle. (Courtesy of James Halderman)

Casting Number   ID Tag

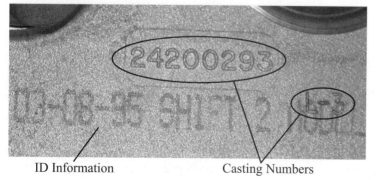

ID Information   Casting Numbers

FIGURE 1-4 The two transmission cases show casting numbers that are cast as part of the case. They also have an ID tag or painted-on ID information. (Courtesy of James Halderman)

FIGURE 1-6 Electronic service information, available from several independent sources, is read using a computer and monitor. (Courtesy of James Halderman)

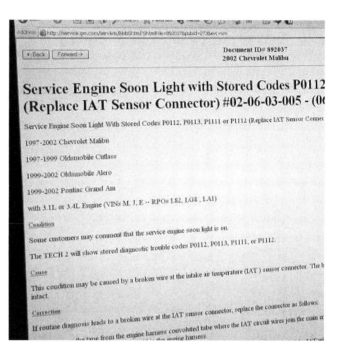

FIGURE 1-7 This TSB, technical service bulletin, describes a condition that causes the "Service Engine Soon Light" to come on for certain vehicles, and it describes the correction procedure for this concern. Note that it is in an electronic form. (Courtesy of James Halderman)

1.2.3   Technical Service Bulletins

Technical service bulletins, often called **TSBs**, are issued by the vehicle manufacturer to notify service technicians of a problem, and include the necessary corrective action. Technical service bulletins are designed for OEM dealership technicians but are republished by aftermarket companies and made available along with other service information to shops and vehicle repair facilities (Figure 1-7).

1.2.4   Internet

The Internet has opened the field for information exchange and access to technical advice. A very useful site is the international Automotive Technicians' Network (iATN) at www.iatn.net. This is a free site, but service technicians need to register to join. If a small monthly sponsor fee is paid, the shop or service technician can gain access to the archives, which include thousands of successful repairs in the searchable data base.

1.3   STEEL CLASSIFICATION

Steel is the base material for automotive parts that require high strength. Steel is iron that has been refined to the point where little carbon remains. Even a very small percentage of carbon in steel has a great deal of significance in the physical characteristics of any steel. The classifications of steel were established by the Society of Automotive Engineers (SAE) and are referred to as the SAE numbers.

The classification number usually contains four numbers, such as SAE 1040 steel. The first number (on the left) identifies the basic type (alloy) of the steel.

1   carbon steel (no other alloy)
2   nickel alloy
3   nickel-chromium (includes stainless steels)
4   molybdenum alloy (includes chromium-molybdenum alloys)
5   chromium
6   chromium-vanadium
9   silicon-manganese

(Other numbers are used to represent triple alloy steels.)

The second number represents the percent of alloy in the steel or is used to identify percentage ranges of alloy if more than one alloy is used in the steel.

The last two numbers represent the points of carbon and a small change in carbon content means a big difference in the characteristics of the steel (one percent contains 100 points; therefore, 35 points of carbon means the steel contains 0.35% carbon). Generally, the higher the carbon content of the steel, the harder the steel.

Low carbon steels	0.08% to 0.20% (8 to 20 points) carbon
Medium carbon steels	0.20% to 0.45% (20 to 45 points) carbon
High carbon steels	0.45% to 0.65% (45 to 65 points) carbon
Tool steel	above 0.65% (65 points) carbon

1.3.1 Steel Classification Examples

SAE 4130 is commonly used for high-strength tubing for race car roll cages:

4	chromium molybdenum
1	1% alloy
30	0.30% carbon

SAE 5140 is commonly used as the billet (block) of steel for some stabilizer bars:

5	chromium
1	1% alloy
40	0.40% carbon

Besides carbon content, the hardness of the steel is determined by heat treatment procedures, cooling times, temperatures, and even by what material is used to cool the steel. For example, *water-hardened* steel is quenched (cooled) by submerging the hot steel in water.

1.3.1.1 Rockwell Hardness Test The harder the steel, the more it resists the penetration of another object. A Rockwell hardness tester uses this principle by using a hard 1/16″ diameter ball on a diamond cone and measuring the distance this ball dents into the metal sample under a given load. Different scales are used to test various types of materials. The *C* scale is the most commonly used Rockwell hardness tester scale used for hardened and alloy steels. A typical camshaft lobe in an automotive engine should have a hardness of 45 on the Rockwell *C* scale. This is often abbreviated as 45 HRC.

1.4 THREADED FASTENERS

Most of the threaded fasteners used on vehicles are **cap screws**, which are fasteners that are threaded into a casting or part. Automotive service technicians usually refer to these fasteners as **bolts**, regardless of how they are used. In this book, they are called bolts although bolts are normally used with nuts. Sometimes, **studs**, a short rod with threads on both ends, are used for threaded fasteners. Often, a stud will have coarse threads on one end and fine threads on the other end. The end of the stud with coarse threads is screwed into the casting, and a nut is used on the opposite end to hold the parts together (Figure 1-8).

The fastener threads *must* match the threads in the casting or nut. The threads, which may be measured either in fractions of an inch (called *fractional*) or in metric units, are either coarse or fine. The coarse threads are called Unified National Coarse (**UNC**), and the fine threads are called Unified National Fine (**UNF**). Standard combinations of sizes and number of threads per inch (called **pitch**) are used. Pitch can be measured with a thread pitch gauge, as shown in Figure 1-9.

Bolts are identified by their diameter and length as measured from below the head, as shown in Figure 1-10. Fractional thread sizes are specified by the diameter in

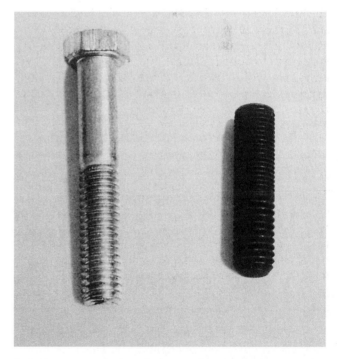

FIGURE 1-8 Typical bolt on the left and stud on the right. Note the different thread pitch on the top and bottom portions of the stud. (Courtesy of James Halderman)

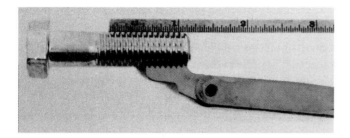

FIGURE 1-9 Thread pitch gauge used to measure the pitch of the thread. This is a 1/2-in. diameter bolt with 13 threads to the inch (1/2–13). (Courtesy of James Halderman)

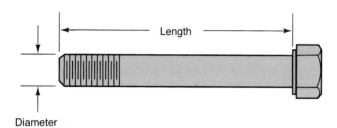

FIGURE 1-10 Bolt size identification. (Courtesy of James Halderman)

fractions of an inch and the number of threads per inch. For example, a 5/16–18 bolt has threads that are 5/16 of an inch in diameter and 18 threads per inch of length. Typical UNC thread sizes would be 5/16–18 and 1/2–13. Similar UNF thread sizes would be 5/16–24 and 1/2–20.

1.4.1 Metric Bolts

The size of a metric bolt is specified by the letter *M* followed by the diameter in millimeters (mm) across the outside (crest) of the threads. Typical metric sizes would be M8 and M12. Fine metric threads (pitch) are specified by the thread diameter followed by X and the distance between the threads measured in millimeters (M8 X 1.5). Typical metric sizes would be M8 X 1.5 (coarse thread), M8 X 1.25 (medium thread), and M8 X 1.0 (fine thread).

◀ SERVICE TIP ▶

Synthetic wintergreen oil, available at drugstores, makes an excellent penetrating oil. The next time you can't get that rusted bolt loose, head for the drugstore (Figure 1-11).

FIGURE 1-11 Synthetic wintergreen oil can be used as a penetrating oil to loosen rusted bolts or nuts. (Courtesy of James Halderman)

1.4.2 Bolt Grade

Bolts are made from many different types of steel, and for this reason some are stronger than others. The strength or classification of a bolt is called the **grade** and is marked on the bolt head. Fractional bolts have lines on the head to indicate the grade, as shown in Figure 1-12, the actual grade being two more than the number of lines on the bolt head. More lines or a higher grade number indicate a stronger bolt. Grade 5 and better bolts usually have threads that are rolled rather than cut, which also makes them stronger. In some cases, nuts and machine screws have similar grade markings. Metric bolts are marked with a decimal number to indicate the grade.

◀ CAUTION ▶

Never use hardware store (nongraded) bolts, studs, or nuts on any vehicle steering, suspension, brake, or clutch component (Figure 1-13). Always use the exact size and grade of hardware that is specified and used by the vehicle manufacturer.

1.4.3 Nuts

Most nuts used on bolts have the same hex size as the bolt head. Some inexpensive nuts use a hex size larger than the cap screw head. Metric nuts are often marked with dimples to show their strength—more dimples indicate stronger nuts. Some nuts, commonly called *self-locking nuts*, use interference fit threads to keep them from accidentally loosening. They are made so that the shape of the nut is slightly

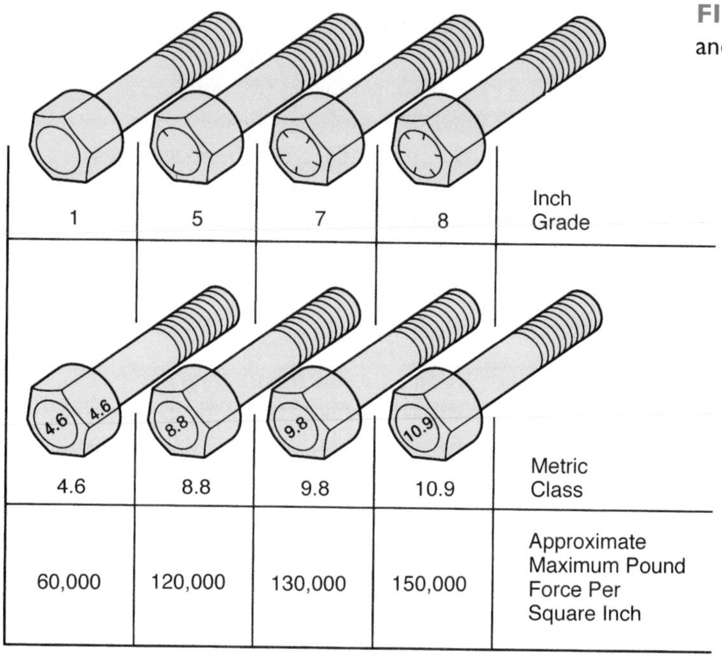

1	5	7	8	Inch Grade
4.6	8.8	9.8	10.9	Metric Class
60,000	120,000	130,000	150,000	Approximate Maximum Pound Force Per Square Inch

FIGURE 1-12 Typical bolt (cap screw) grade markings and approximate strength. (Courtesy of James Halderman)

◄ SERVICE TIP ►

A common mistake made by new technicians is to think that the size of a bolt or nut is the size of the head. The size of the bolt or nut (outside diameter of the threads) is usually smaller than the size of the wrench or socket that fits the head of the bolt or nut. Examples are given in the following table:

Wrench Size	Thread Size
7/16 in.	1/4 in.
1/2 in.	5/16 in.
9/16 in.	3/8 in.
5/8 in.	7/16 in.
3/4 in.	1/2 in.
10 mm	6 mm
12 mm or 13 mm*	8 mm
14 mm or 17 mm*	10 mm

* European (Système International d'Unités-SI) metric.

distorted or a section of the threads is deformed. Nuts can also be kept from loosening with a nylon washer fastened in the nut or with a nylon patch or strip on the threads (Figure 1-14).

FIGURE 1-13 Every shop should have an assortment of high-quality bolts and nuts to replace those damaged during vehicle service procedures. (Courtesy of James Halderman)

FIGURE 1-14 Types of lock nuts. On the left, a nylon ring; in the center, a distorted shape; and on the right, a castle used with a cotter key. (Courtesy of James Halderman)

◀ SERVICE TIP ▶

An open-end wrench can be used to gauge bolt sizes by placing the wrench opening across the threads. For example, a 3/8-in. wrench will closely fit the threads of a 3/8-in. bolt.

Most of these "locking nuts" are grouped together and are commonly referred to as *prevailing torque* nuts. This means that the nut will hold its tightness or torque and not loosen with movement or vibration. Most prevailing torque nuts should be replaced whenever removed to ensure that the nut will not loosen during service. Always follow manufacturer's recommendations. Anaerobic sealers, such as **Loctite**, are used on the threads where the nut or cap screw must be both locked and sealed.

1.4.4 Washers

Washers are often used under cap screw heads and under nuts. Plain, flat washers are used to provide an even clamping load around the fastener and to protect that part. Lock washers are added to prevent accidental loosening. Some manufacturers lock the washer onto a cap screw by placing it into position before rolling the threads.

1.5 BASIC TOOL LIST

Every automotive technician should possess the hand tools to turn fasteners (bolts, nuts, and screws). The following list does not include specialty tools, and items marked with an asterisk (*) are only needed if working on older vehicles.

Tool chest

1/4-in. drive socket set (Figure 1-15):
  1/4 to 9/16-in. standard and deep sockets (Figure 1-16)*
  6- to 15-mm standard and deep sockets
  1/4-in. drive ratchet
  1/4-in. drive 2-in. and 6-in. extension
  1/4-in. drive handle
3/8-in. drive socket set:
  *3/8 to 7/8-in. standard and deep sockets (Figure 1-17)
  10 to 19-mm standard and deep sockets
  3/8-in. drive Torx set, T40, T45, T50, and T55
  3/8-in. drive 5/8-in. and 13/16-in. spark plug socket

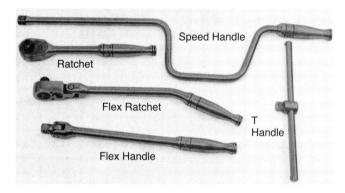

FIGURE 1-15 Typical drive handles for sockets (Courtesy of James Halderman)

FIGURE 1-16 Standard 12-point short socket (left), universal joint socket (center), and deep-well socket (right). Both the universal and deep-well are 6-point sockets. (Courtesy of James Halderman)

3/8-in. drive ratchet
3/8-in. drive 1 1/2-in., 3-in., 6-in., and 12-in. extension (Figure 1-18)
3/8-in. drive universal
Crowfoot set (fractional inch* and metric)
Hex/Allen socket
1/2-in. drive socket set:
    1/2 to 1-in. standard and deep sockets*
    1/2-in. drive ratchet
    1/2-in. drive breaker bar
    1/2-in. drive 5-in. and 10-in. extension
    3/8 to 1/4-in. adapter (Figure 1-19)
    1/2 to 3/8-in. adapter
    3/8 to 1/2-in. adapter
3/8 through 1-in. combination wrench set (Figure 1-20)
10- to 19-mm combination wrench set

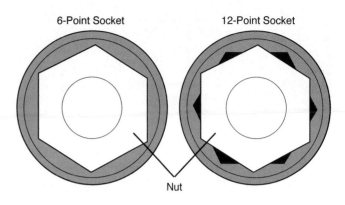

FIGURE 1-17 A 6-point socket fits the head of the bolt or nut on all sides. A 12-point socket can round off the head of a bolt or nut if a lot of force is applied. (Courtesy of James Halderman)

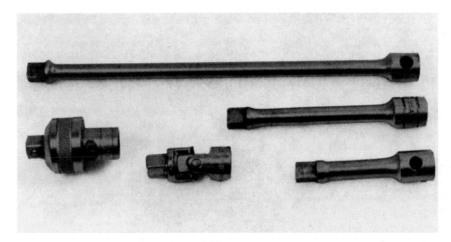

FIGURE 1-18 Various socket extensions. The universal joint (U-joint) in the center (bottom) is useful for gaining access in tight areas. (Courtesy of James Halderman)

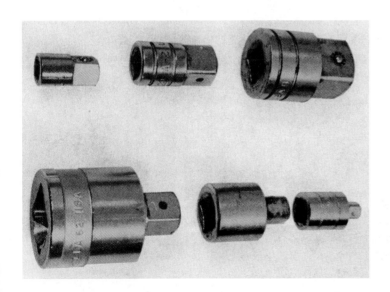

FIGURE 1-19 Socket drive adapters. These adapters permit the use of a 3/8-in. drive ratchet with 1/2-in. drive sockets, or other combinations as the various adapters permit. Adapters should *not* be used where a larger tool used with excessive force could break or damage a smaller-sized socket. (Courtesy of James Halderman)

1/16 to 1/4-in. hex wrench set
2 to 12-mm hex wrench set
5/16 to 9/16-in. flare-nut wrench set (Figure 1-21)*
10 and 12, 14 and 17-mm flare-nut wrench set
Diagonal, needle nose, adjustable-jaw, locking, snap-ring, and electrical stripping or crimping pliers (Figure 1-22)

Ball-peen, rubber, and dead-blow hammers (Figure 1-23)
Five-piece standard screwdriver set (Figure 1-24)
Four-piece Phillips screwdriver set
#15 and #20 Torx screwdriver
Awl
Mill file

FIGURE 1-20   Combination wrench. The openings are the same size at both ends. Notice the angle of the open end to permit use in close spaces. (Courtesy of James Halderman)

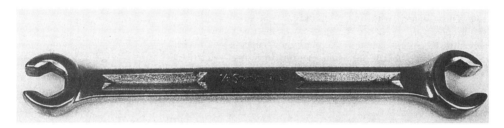

FIGURE 1-21   Flare-nut wrench. Also known as a *line wrench, fitting wrench,* or *tube-nut wrench.* This style of wrench is designed to grasp most of the flats of a six-sided (hex) tubing fitting to provide the most grip without damage to the fitting. (Courtesy of James Halderman)

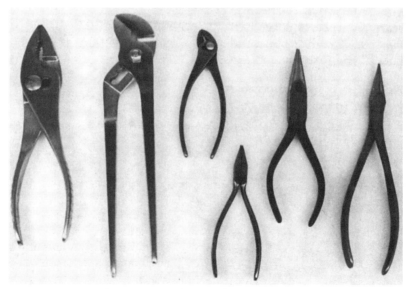

FIGURE 1-22   Assortment of pliers. Slip-joint pliers (far left) are often confused with water pump pliers (second from left). (Courtesy of James Halderman)

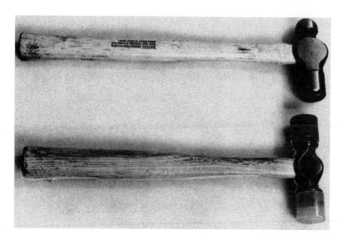

FIGURE 1-23   A ball-peen hammer (top) is purchased according to weight (usually in ounces) of the head of the hammer. At bottom is a soft-faced (plastic) hammer. Always use a hammer that is softer than the material being driven. Use a block of wood or similar material between a steel hammer and steel or iron engine parts to prevent damage to the engine parts. (Courtesy of James Halderman)

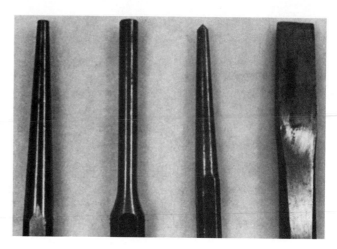

FIGURE 1-25   From the left, a starting punch, pin punch, center punch, and chisel. (Courtesy of James Halderman)

Center and pin punches (Figure 1-25)
Chisel
Utility knife
Valve core tool
Filter wrench (large and small filters)
Safety glasses
Circuit tester
Feeler gauge set
Gasket scraper
Pinch bar
Magnet

1.5.1   Tool Sets and Accessories

A beginning service technician may wish to start with a small set of tools before spending a lot of money on an expensive, extensive tool set (Figure 1-26).

◄ SERVICE TIP ►

An apprentice technician started working for a dealership and put his top tool box on a workbench. Another technician observed that along with a complete set of good-quality tools, the box contained several adjustable wrenches. The more experienced technician said, "Hide those from the boss." If any adjustable wrench is used on a bolt or nut, the movable jaw often moves or loosens and starts to round the head of the fastener. If the head of the bolt or nut becomes rounded, it becomes that much more difficult to remove.

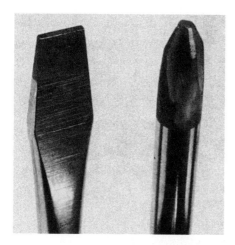

FIGURE 1-24   A flat-blade (or straight-blade) screwdriver (on the left) is specified by the length of the screwdriver and width of the blade. The width of the blade should match the width of the screw slot of the fastener. A Phillips-head screwdriver (on the right) is specified by the length of the handle and the size of the point at the tip. A #1 is a sharp point; #2 is most common (as shown), and a #3 Phillips is blunt and is only used for larger sizes of Phillips-head fasteners. (Courtesy of James Halderman)

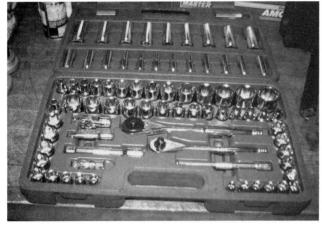

(a)

(b)

FIGURE 1-26   (a) A beginning technician can start with some simple basic hand tools. (b) An experienced, serious technician often spends several thousand dollars a year for tools such as found in this large (and expensive) tool box. (Courtesy of James Halderman)

◀ SERVICE TIP ▶

Most service technicians agree that it is okay for a beginning technician to borrow a tool occasionally. However, if a tool has to be borrowed more than twice, then be sure to purchase it as soon as possible. Also, whenever a tool is borrowed, be sure that you return the tool clean and show the technician you borrowed the tool from that you are returning the tool. These actions will help in any future dealings with other technicians.

◀ SERVICE TIP ▶

Apply a small amount of valve grinding compound to a Phillips or Torx screw or bolt head. The gritty valve grinding compound "grips" the screwdriver or tool bit and prevents the tool from slipping up and out of the screw head. Valve grinding compound is available in a tube from most automotive parts stores.

1.5.2   Brand Name versus Proper Term

Technicians often use slang or brand names of tools rather than the proper term. This results in some confusion for new technicians. Some examples are given in the following table.

Brand Name	Proper Term	Slang Name
Crescent wrench	Adjustable wrench	Monkey wrench
Vise Grips	Locking pliers	
Channel Locks	Water pump pliers or multigroove adjustable pliers	Pump pliers
	Diagonal cutting pliers	Dikes or side cuts

◄ SERVICE TIP ►

Whenever removing any automotive component, it is wise to quickly note the length, diameter, and thread pitch of each bolt so you will have a good idea of which bolt goes where.

◄ SERVICE TIP ►

Normally, a bolt should be long enough to thread into the part a distance that is equal to or about half-again the bolt diameter.

1.5.3   Safety Tips for Using Hand Tools

The following safety tips should be kept in mind whenever you are working with hand tools:

- Always *pull* a wrench toward you for best control and safety. Avoid pushing a wrench.
- Keep wrenches and all hand tools clean to help prevent rust and for a better, firmer grip.
- Always use a 6-point socket or a box-end wrench to break loose a tight bolt or nut.
- Use a box-end wrench for torque and the open-end wrench for speed.
- Never use a pipe extension or other type of "cheater bar" on a wrench or ratchet handle. If more force is required, use a larger tool or use penetrating oil and/or heat on the frozen fastener. (If heat is used on a bolt or nut to remove it, always replace it with a new part.)
- Always use the proper tool for the job. If a specialized tool is required, use the proper tool and do not try to use another tool improperly.
- Never expose any tool to excessive heat. High temperatures can reduce the strength ("draw the temper") of metal tools.
- Never use a hammer on any wrench or socket handle unless you are using a special wrench designed to be used with a hammer.
- Replace any tools that are damaged or worn.

◄ SERVICE TIP ►

If you must strike or pound on something, be sure to use a tool that is softer than what you are about to strike to avoid damage. Examples are given in the following table.

The Material Being Pounded	What to Pound With
Steel or cast iron	Brass or aluminum hammer or punch
Aluminum	Plastic or rawhide mallet or plastic-covered dead-blow hammer
Plastic	Rawhide mallet or plastic dead-blow hammer

◄ SERVICE TIP ►

Punches, made from soft materials like brass or aluminum, are available for striking a shaft, gear, or other object.

1.6   MEASURING TOOLS

The purpose of any repair is to restore the vehicle to factory-specified tolerance. Every repair procedure involves measuring. The service technician must measure twice:

- The original components must be measured to see if correction is necessary to restore the component or part to factory specifications.
- The replacement parts and finished machined areas must be measured to ensure proper dimension before the component is assembled or replaced on the vehicle.

1.6.1   Micrometer

A micrometer is a commonly used measuring instrument (Figure 1-27). The **thimble** rotates over the **barrel**

FIGURE 1-27 Typical micrometers used for dimensional measurements. (Courtesy of James Halderman)

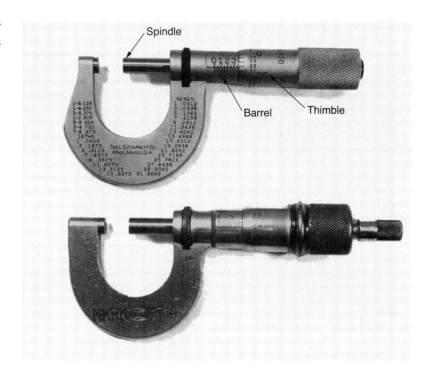

on a screw that has 40 threads per inch. Every revolution of the thimble moves the **spindle** 0.025 in. The thimble is graduated into 25 equally spaced lines; therefore, each line represents 0.001 in. Every micrometer should be checked for calibration on a regular basis (Figure 1-28).

1.6.2   Telescopic Gauge

A telescopic gauge is used with a micrometer to measure the inside diameter of a hole or bore.

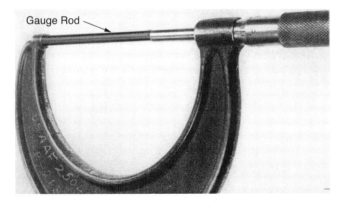

FIGURE 1-28 All micrometers should be checked and calibrated as needed using a gauge rod. (Courtesy of James Halderman)

◀ FREQUENTLY ASKED ▶ QUESTION

The word *gauge* means "measurement or dimension to a standard of reference." The word *gauge* can also be spelled *gage*. Therefore, in most cases, the words mean the same.

INTERESTING NOTE: One vehicle manufacturing representative mentioned that *gage* was used rather than *gauge* because even though it is the second acceptable spelling of the word, it is correct and it saved the company a lot of money in printing costs because the word *gage* has one less letter! One letter multiplied by millions of vehicles with gauges and the word *gage* used in service manuals adds up to a big savings to the manufacturer.

1.6.3   Vernier Dial Caliper

A vernier dial caliper can be used to measure gear diameter, bearing race inside diameter, as well as the depth of a bolt hole. Although not as accurate as a micrometer, a vernier caliper is faster and covers a wider measuring range (Figure 1-29).

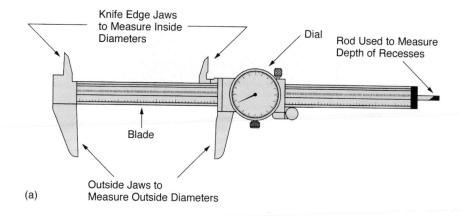

(a)

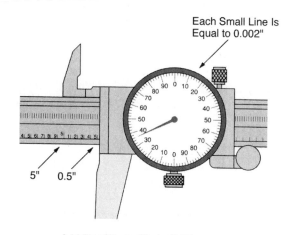

(b)

FIGURE 1-29 (a) A typical vernier dial caliper. This is a very useful measuring tool for automotive engine work because it is capable of measuring inside and outside measurements. (b) To read a vernier dial caliper, simply add the reading on the blade to the reading on the dial. (Courtesy of James Halderman)

1.6.4   Dial Indicator

A dial indicator is used to measure movement like shaft runout or gear lash/clearance (see Figure 5-20).

1.7   SAFETY TIPS FOR TECHNICIANS

Safety is not just a buzzword on a poster in the work area. Safe work habits can reduce accidents and injuries, ease the workload, and keep employees pain-free. Suggested safety tips include the following:

- *Wear safety glasses at all times while servicing any vehicle* (Figure 1-30).
- Watch your toes—always keep your toes protected with steel-toed safety shoes (Figure 1-31). If safety shoes are not available, then leather-topped shoes offer more protection than canvas or cloth.

- Wear gloves to protect your hands from rough or sharp surfaces. Thin rubber gloves are recommended when working around automotive liquids such as engine oil, antifreeze, transmission fluid, or any other liquids that may be hazardous.
- Service technicians working under a vehicle should wear a **bump cap** to protect the head against under-vehicle objects and the pads of the lift (Figure 1-32).
- Remove all jewelry that may get caught on something or act as a conductor to an exposed electrical circuit (Figure 1-33).
- Take care of your hands. Keep your hands clean by washing frequently with soap and hot water of at least 110°F (43°C).
- Avoid loose or dangling clothing.
- Ear protection should be worn if the sound around you requires that you raise your voice (sound level higher than 90 dB). (A typical lawn mower produces noise at a level of about 110 dB. This means that everyone who uses a lawn mower or other lawn or garden equipment should wear ear protection.)

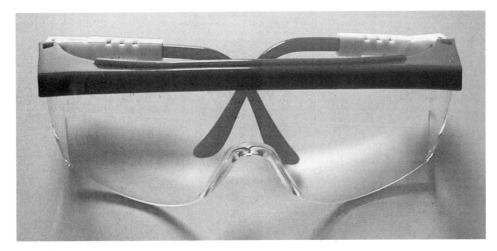

FIGURE 1-30 Safety glasses should be worn at all times when working on or around any vehicle or servicing any component. (Courtesy of James Halderman)

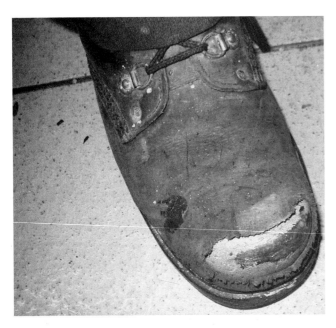

FIGURE 1-31 Steel-toed shoes are a worthwhile investment to help prevent foot injury due to falling objects. Even these well-worn shoes can protect the feet of this service technician. (Courtesy of James Halderman)

FIGURE 1-32 A bump cap provides a shield and padding to protect the head while working under a vehicle. (Courtesy of James Halderman)

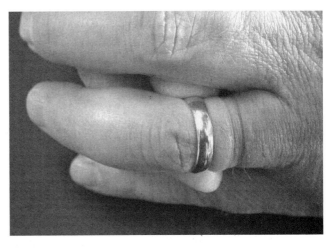

FIGURE 1-33 All jewelery like rings and watches should be removed when working on vehicles. (Courtesy of James Halderman)

- When lifting any object, get a secure grip with solid footing. Keep the load close to your body to minimize the strain. Lift with your legs and arms, not your back.
- Do not twist your body when carrying a load. Instead, pivot your feet to help prevent strain on the spine.
- Ask for help when moving or lifting heavy objects.
- Push a heavy object rather than pull it. (This is opposite to the way you should work with tools. Remember, never push a wrench! If you do and a bolt

or nut loosens, your entire weight is used to propel your hand(s) forward. This usually results in cuts, bruises, or other painful injury.)

- Always connect an exhaust hose to the tailpipe of any running vehicle to help prevent the buildup of carbon monoxide inside a closed garage space (Figure 1-34).
- When standing, keep objects, parts, and tools with which you are working between chest height and waist height. If seated, work at tasks that are at elbow height.
- Always be sure the hood is securely held open (Figure 1-35).

◀ SAFETY TIP ▶

Always dispose of oily shop cloths in an enclosed container to prevent a fire (Figure 1-36). Whenever oily cloths are thrown together on the floor or workbench, a chemical reaction can occur which can ignite the cloth even without an open flame. This process of ignition without an open flame is called **spontaneous combustion**.

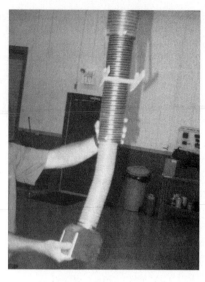

FIGURE 1-34   Always connect an exhaust hose to the tailpipe of the engine of a vehicle to be run inside a building. (Courtesy of James Halderman)

(a)

(b)

FIGURE 1-35   (a) A crude but effective method is to use locking pliers on the chrome-plated shaft of a hood strut. Locking pliers should only be used on defective struts because the jaws of the pliers can damage the strut shaft. (b) A commercially available hood clamp. This tool uses a bright orange tag to help remind the technician to remove the clamp before attempting to close the hood. The hood could be bent if force is used to close the hood with the clamp in place. (Courtesy of James Halderman)

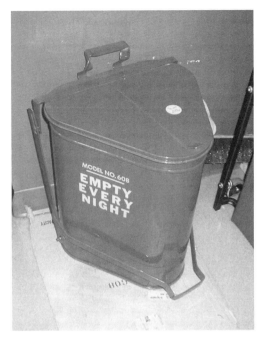

FIGURE 1-36   All oily shop cloths should be stored in a metal container equipped with a lid to help prevent spontaneous combustion. (Courtesy of James Halderman)

◀ TECH TIP ▶

SHOCK CONTROL

To avoid impact damage from your impact wrench on your hand, take the rubber covering from an old electric fuel pump and fit it on the handle of the gun to soften the blow.

1.7.1   Vehicle Lifting (Hoisting) Safety

Many chassis and underbody service procedures require that the vehicle be hoisted or lifted off the ground. The simplest methods involve the use of drive-on ramps or a floor jack and safety (jack) stands, whereas in-ground or surface-mounted lifts provide greater access. **Setting the pads is a critical part of the lifting procedure.**

   All automobile and light-truck service manuals include recommended locations to be used when hoisting (lifting) a vehicle. Newer vehicles have a triangle decal on the driver's door indicating the recommended lift points (Figure 1-37). The recommended standards for the lift points and lifting procedures are found in SAE

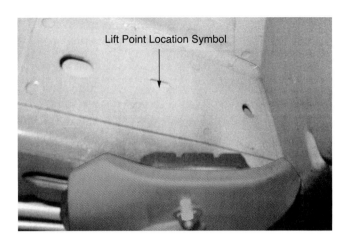

FIGURE 1-37   Most newer vehicles have a triangle symbol indicating the recommended hoisting lift points. (Courtesy of James Halderman)

Standard JRP–2184. These recommendations typically include the following points:

1. The vehicle, with the doors, hood, and trunk closed, should be centered on the lift or hoist so as not to overload one side or put too much force either forward or rearward.
2. The pads of the lift should be spread as far apart as possible to provide a stable platform.
3. Each pad should be placed under a part of the vehicle that is strong and capable of supporting the weight of the vehicle.
   a. Pinch welds at the bottom edge of the body are generally considered to be strong.

◀ CAUTION ▶

Even though pinch weld seams are the recommended location for hoisting many vehicles with unitized bodies (unit-body), care should be taken not to place the pad(s) too far forward or rearward. Incorrect placement of the vehicle on the lift could cause the vehicle to be imbalanced, and the vehicle could fall. This is exactly what happened to the vehicle in Figure 1-38. Be aware that a tall vehicle might hit the ceiling or suspended lights.

   b. Boxed areas of the body are the best places to position the pads on a vehicle without a frame. Be careful to note whether the arms of the lift might come into contact with other parts of the vehicle before the pad touches the intended

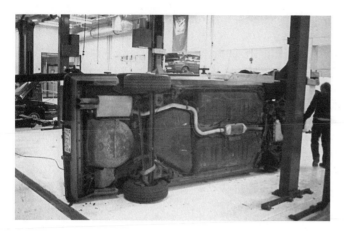

FIGURE 1-38 This vehicle fell from the hoist because the pads were not set correctly. No one was hurt, but the vehicle was a total loss. (Courtesy of James Halderman)

◀ CAUTION ▶

Do not look away from the vehicle while it is being raised (or lowered) on a hoist. One side or one end of the hoist can stop or fail, resulting in the vehicle being slanted enough to slip or fall, creating physical damage not only to the vehicle and/or hoist but also to the technician or others who may be nearby.

◀ HINT ▶

Most hoists can be safely placed at any desired height. For ease while working, the area in which you are working should be at chest level. When removing and replacing components like an axle, it is not necessary to work on them down near the floor or over your head. Raise the hoist so that the components are at chest level.

location. Commonly damaged areas include the following:

1. rocker panel moldings,
2. exhaust system (including catalytic converter), and
3. tires or body panels (Figure 1-39).

4. The vehicle should be raised about a foot [30 centimeters (cm)] off the floor, then stopped and shaken to check for stability. If the vehicle seems to be stable when checked at a short distance from the floor, continue raising the vehicle and watch until it has reached the desired height.

5. Before lowering the hoist, the safety latch(es) must be released and the direction of the controls reversed. The speed downward is often adjusted to be as slow as possible for additional safety.

(a)

(b)

FIGURE 1-39 (a) In this photo the pad arm is just contacting the rocker panel of the vehicle. (b) This photo shows what can occur if the technician places the pad too far inward underneath the vehicle. The arm of the hoist has dented the rocker panel. (Courtesy of James Halderman)

1.8 ELECTRICAL CORD SAFETY

Use correctly grounded three-prong sockets and extension cords to operate power tools. Use only double insulated power tools. Some modern tools use polarized two-prong plugs that have one wide and one narrow prong. When not in use, keep electrical cords off the floor to prevent tripping over them. Tape the cords to the floor if they are placed in high foot traffic areas.

◄ SAFETY TIP ►

Improper use of an air nozzle can cause blindness or deafness. If an air nozzle is used to dry and clean parts, make sure the air stream is directed away from anyone else in the immediate area. Clean, coil, and store air hoses when they are not in use.

1.9 FIRE EXTINGUISHERS

There are four classes of fire extinguishers. Each class should be used on specific fires only:

- **Class A** is designed for use on general combustibles, such as cloth, paper, and wood.
- **Class B** is designed for use on flammable liquids and greases, including gasoline, oil, thinners, and solvents.
- **Class C** is used only on electrical fires.
- **Class D** is effective only on combustible metals such as powdered aluminum, sodium, or magnesium.

The class rating is clearly marked on the side of every fire extinguisher. Many extinguishers are good for multiple types of fires (Figure 1-40).

When using a fire extinguisher, remember the word "PASS":

P = Pull the safety pin.
A = Aim the nozzle of the extinguisher at the base of the fire.
S = Squeeze the lever to actuate the extinguisher.
S = Sweep the nozzle from side-to-side at the base of the flame.

See Figure 1-41.

1.9.1 Types of Fire Extinguishers

The variety of fire extinguishers include:

- **Water**—A water fire extinguisher is usually in a pressurized container and is good to use on Class A

fires because it reduces the temperature to the point where a fire cannot be sustained.

- **Carbon Dioxide (CO_2)**—A carbon dioxide fire extinguisher is good for almost any type of fire, especially Class B or Class C materials. A CO_2 fire extinguisher works by removing the oxygen from the fire; the cold CO_2 also helps reduce the temperature of the fire.
- **Dry Chemical (yellow)**—A dry chemical fire extinguisher is good for Class A, B, or C fires by coating the flammable materials to eliminate the oxygen from the fire. A dry chemical fire extinguisher tends to be very corrosive and will cause damage to electronic devices.

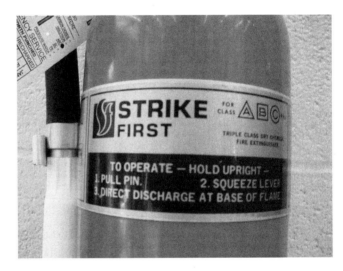

FIGURE 1-40 A typical fire extinguisher designed to be used on type A, B, or C fires. (Courtesy of James Halderman)

FIGURE 1-41 A CO_2 fire extinguisher being used on a fire set in an open steel drum during a demonstration at a fire department training center. (Courtesy of James Halderman)

(Photos courtesy of James Halderman)

PS-I The first step in hoisting a vehicle is to properly align the vehicle in the center of the stall.

PS-2 Most vehicles will be correctly positioned when the left front tire is centered on the tire pad.

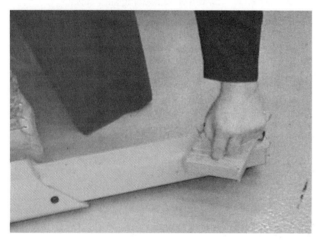

PS-3 Most pads at the end of the hoist arms can be rotated to allow for many different types of vehicle construction.

PS-4 The arms of the lifts can be retracted or extended to accommodate vehicles of many different lengths.

PS-5 Most lifts are equipped with short pad extensions that are often necessary to use to allow the pad to contact the frame of a vehicle without causing the arm of the lift to hit and damage parts of the body.

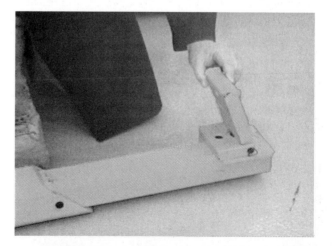

PS-6 Tall pad extensions can also be used to gain access to the frame of a vehicle. This position is needed to safely hoist many pickup trucks, vans, and sport utility vehicles (SUVs).

PS-7 An additional extension may be necessary to hoist a truck or van equipped with running boards to give the necessary clearance.

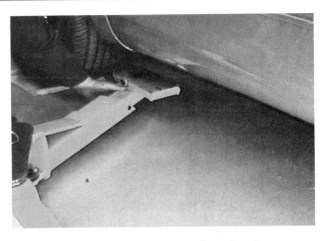

PS-8 Position the front hoist pads under the recommended locations as specified in the owner's manual and/or service information for the vehicle being serviced.

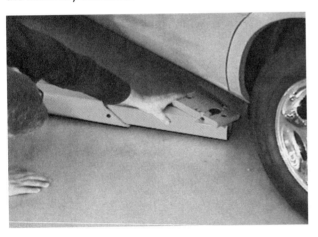

PS-9 Position the rear pads under the vehicle in the recommended locations.

PS-10 This photo shows an asymmetrical lift where the front arms are shorter than the rear arms. This design is best used for passenger cars and allows the driver to exit the vehicle more easily because the door can be opened wide without its hitting the vertical support column.

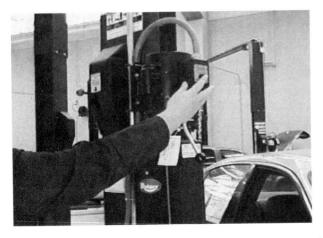

PS-11 After being sure all pads are correctly positioned, use the electromechanical controls to raise the vehicle.

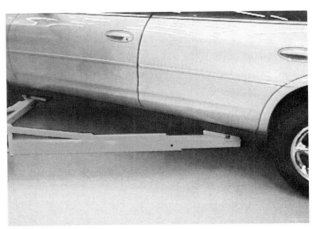

PS-12 Raise the vehicle about 1 foot (30 cm) and stop to double check that all pads contact the body or frame in the correct positions.

PS-13 With the vehicle raised about 1 foot off the ground, push down on the vehicle to check to see if it is stable on the pads. If the vehicle rocks, lower the vehicle and re-set the pads. If the vehicle is stable, the vehicle can be raised to any desired working level. Be sure the safety is engaged before working on or under the vehicle.

PS-14 This photo shows the pads set flat and contacting the pinch welds of the body. This method spreads the load over the entire length of the pad and is less likely to dent or damage the pinch weld area.

PS-15 Where additional clearance is necessary for the arms to clear the rest of the body, the pads can be raised and placed under the pinch weld area as shown.

PS-16 When the service work is completed, the hoist should be raised slightly and the safety released before using the hydraulic lever to lower the vehicle.

PS-17 After lowering the vehicle, be sure all arms of the lift are moved out of the way before driving the vehicle out of the work stall.

PS-18 Carefully back the vehicle out of the stall. Notice that all of the lift arms have been neatly moved out of the way to provide clearance so that the tires will not contact the arms when the vehicle is driven out of the stall.

REVIEW QUESTIONS

The following questions are provided to help you study as you read the chapter.

1. The two common types of bolt sizes are _____ and _____.

2. A 5/16–18 bolt has _____ threads and a _____ diameter of 5/16″.

3. A M8 X 1.5 bolt has a thread diameter of _____ _____ and a _____ of 1.5 mm.

4. A grade 8 bolt is _____ than a grade 5 bolt.

5. Loctite is an _____ compound used to _____ the nut on the bolt.

6. A Crescent wrench should properly be called an _____ _____.

7. When you loosen a tight nut or bolt, you should _____ on the wrench.

8. The best tool to loosen a really tight nut is either a _____ _____ socket or a _____ _____ wrench.

9. A _____ is a good tool to measure a shaft to see if it is worn.

10. A _____ _____ can be used to measure shaft end play or flywheel runout.

11. An oily shop cloth can ignite and burn without an open flame because of _____ _____.

12. A critical step in lifting a car on a hoist is to _____ the _____.

13. The third prong of a three-prong electrical plug is for _____.

14. Class B fire extinguishers are designed to extinguish _____ _____ fires.

15. A _____ _____ fire extinguisher is good for most types of fire.

CHAPTER QUIZ

The following questions will help you check the facts you have learned. Select the answer that completes each statement correctly.

1. Student A says that if a micrometer thimble is rotated two complete revolutions, the spindle will move 0.050″. Student B says the micrometer barrel has 40 threads per inch. Who is correct?
   a. Student A
   b. Student B
   c. Both A and B
   d. Neither A nor B

2. Two students are discussing bolts. Student A says that the wrench used with a bolt is the same size as the bolt. Student B says the thread diameter is the bolt size. Who is correct?
   a. Student A
   b. Student B
   c. Both A and B
   d. Neither A nor B

3. Two students are discussing measuring tools. Student A says that a micrometer can be used to measure parts to 0.001″. Student B says vernier calipers can be used to measure depth as well as the inside and outside diameter of a part. Who is correct?
   a. Student A
   b. Student B
   c. Both A and B
   d. Neither A nor B

4. Student A says that it is a good idea to get help when you need to lift a heavy object. Student B says that you should lift heavy objects using your legs, not your back. Who is correct?
   a. Student A
   b. Student B
   c. Both A and B
   d. Neither A nor B

5. Two students are discussing the hoisting of a vehicle. Student A says to put the pads of a lift under a notch at the pinch weld of a unit-body vehicle. Student B says to place the pads on the four corners of the frame of a full-frame vehicle. Who is correct?
   a. Student A
   b. Student B
   c. Both A and B
   d. Neither A nor B

6. The correct location for the pads when hoisting or jacking the vehicle can often be found in the _____.
   a. service manual
   b. shop manual
   c. owner's manual
   d. all of the above

7. For the best working position, the work should be _____.
   a. at neck or head level
   b. at knee or ankle level
   c. overhead by about 1 foot
   d. at chest or elbow level

8. When working with hand tools, always _____.
   a. push the wrench—don't pull toward you
   b. pull a wrench—don't push a wrench

9. Student A says that the fire extinguisher should be aimed at the base of a fire. Student B says that fire extinguishers remove either heat or oxygen from the burning material. Who is correct?

    a. Student A   **c.** Both A and B

    b. Student B   **d.** Neither A nor B

10. A high-strength bolt is identified by _____.

    a. a UNC symbol   **c.** strength letter codes

    b. lines on the head   **d.** the coarse threads

11. A fastener that uses threads on both ends is called a _____.

    a. cap screw   **c.** machine screw

    b. stud   **d.** crest fastener

12. The proper term for Channel Locks is _____.

    a. Vise Grips

    b. Crescent wrench

    c. locking pliers

    d. multigroove adjustable pliers

13. The proper term for Vise Grips is _____.

    a. locking pliers

    b. slip-joint pliers

    c. side cuts

    d. multigroove adjustable pliers

14. What is *not* considered to be personal safety equipment?

    a. air impact wrench   **c.** rubber gloves

    b. safety glasses   **d.** hearing protection

◄ Chapter 2 ►

ENVIRONMENTAL AND HAZARDOUS MATERIALS

LEARNING OBJECTIVES

After completing this chapter, you should be able to:

1. Define the Occupational Safety and Health Act (OSHA).
2. Explain the term Material Safety Data Sheet (MSDS).
3. Identify hazardous waste materials in accordance with state and federal regulations.
4. Describe the steps required to safely handle and store automotive chemicals and waste.
5. Follow proper safety precautions while handling hazardous waste materials.
6. Know the ASE requirements for all service technicians in order to adhere to environmentally appropriate actions and behavior.

TERMS TO LEARN

asbestosis	OSHA
DOT	Right-to-know laws
EPA	solvent
hazardous waste materials	used brake fluid
HEPA	used coolant
lung cancer	used oil
mesothelioma	WHIMS
MSDS	

2.1 INTRODUCTION

The safe handling of hazardous waste materials is extremely important in the automotive shop. The improper handling of hazardous material affects us all, not just those in the shop. Shop personnel must be familiar with their rights and responsibilities regarding hazardous waste disposal required by right-to-know laws. Shop personnel must also be familiar with hazardous materials in the automotive shop and the proper disposal methods for these materials according to state and federal regulations.

2.2 OCCUPATIONAL SAFETY AND HEALTH ACT

The United States Congress passed the **Occupational Safety and Health Act (OSHA)** in 1970. The purpose of this legislation is to assist and encourage the citizens of the United States in their efforts to assure safe and healthful working conditions by providing research, information, education, and training in the field of occupational safety and health, and to assure safe and healthful working conditions for working men and women by authorizing enforcement of the standards developed under the act. Since approximately 25% of workers are exposed to health and safety hazards on the job, the OSHA standards are necessary to monitor, control, and educate workers regarding health and safety in the workplace.

2.2.1   Health Care Rights

The OSHA regulations concerning on-the-job safety place certain responsibilities on the employer and give employees specific rights. Any person who feels there might be unsafe conditions in the workplace, whether asbestos exposure, chemical poisoning, or any other problem, should discuss the issue with fellow workers, the union representative (where applicable), and the supervisor or employer. If no action is taken and there is reason to believe the employer is not complying with OSHA standards, a complaint can be filed with OSHA, which will be investigated. The law forbids employers from taking action against employees who file a complaint concerning a health or safety hazard. However, if workers fear reprisal as the result of a complaint, they may request that OSHA withhold their names from the employer.

2.3   HAZARDOUS WASTE

Hazardous waste materials are chemicals, or components, that the shop no longer needs and that pose a danger to the environment and people if they are disposed of in ordinary garbage cans or sewers. However, one should note that no material is considered hazardous waste until the shop has finished using it and is ready to dispose of it. The **Environmental Protection Agency (EPA)** publishes a list of hazardous materials that is included in the Code of Federal Regulations. The EPA considers waste hazardous if it is included on the EPA list of hazardous materials or if it can be described in one or more of the following ways:

Reactive. Any material that reacts violently with water or other chemical is considered hazardous.

Corrosive. If a material burns the skin or dissolves metals and other materials, a technician should consider it hazardous. A pH scale is used, with the number 7 indicating neutral. Pure water has a pH of 7. Lower numbers indicate an acidic solution and higher numbers indicate a caustic solution. If when exposed to low pH acid solutions, a material releases cyanide gas, hydrogen sulfide gas, or similar gases, it is considered hazardous.

Toxic. Materials are hazardous if they leak one or more of eight different heavy metals in concentrations greater than 100 times the primary drinking water standard.

Ignitable. A liquid is hazardous if it has a flash point below 140°F (60°C), and a solid is hazardous if it ignites spontaneously.

Radioactive. Any substance that emits measurable levels of radiation is hazardouos. When individuals bring containers of highly radioactive substances into the shop environment, qualified personnel with the appropriate equipment must test them.

◄ CAUTION ►

When handling hazardous waste material, one must always wear proper protective clothing and use equipment detailed in the right-to-know laws, including respirator equipment when needed. All recommended procedures must be followed accurately. Personal injury may result from improper clothing, equipment, and procedures when handling hazardous materials.

◄ WARNING ►

Hazardous waste disposal laws include serious penalties for anyone responsible for breaking these laws.

2.4   RESOURCE CONSERVATION AND RECOVERY ACT (RCRA)

Federal and state laws control the disposal of hazardous waste materials. Every shop employee must be familiar with these laws. Hazardous waste disposal laws include the Resource Conservation and Recovery Act (RCRA), which states that hazardous material users are responsible for hazardous materials from the time they become a waste until the proper waste disposal is completed. Many shops hire an independent hazardous waste hauler to dispose of hazardous waste material. The shop owner, or manager, should have a written contract with the waste hauler. In this case, the user must store hazardous waste material properly and safely and be responsible for its transportation until it arrives at an approved hazardous waste disposal site and is processed according to the law. A shop may also choose to recycle the hazardous waste material in the shop rather than have it hauled to an approved hazardous waste disposal site. The RCRA controls these types of automotive waste:

- paint and body repair products waste,
- solvents for parts and equipment cleaning,
- batteries and battery acid,
- mild acids used for metal cleaning and preparation,
- waste oil and engine coolants or antifreeze,
- air conditioning refrigerants and oils, and
- engine oil filters.

The **right-to-know laws** state that employees have a right to know when the materials they use at work are hazardous. The right-to-know laws started with the **Hazard Communication Standard** published by the Occupational Safety and Health Administration (OSHA) in 1983. Originally, this document was intended for chemical companies and manufacturers that required employees to handle hazardous materials in their work situation. Meanwhile, the federal courts have decided to apply these laws to all companies, including automotive service shops. Under the right-to-know laws, the employer has responsibilities regarding the handling of hazardous materials by employees. All employees must be trained about the types of hazardous materials they will encounter in the workplace, and the employees must be informed about their rights under legislation regarding the handling of hazardous materials.

2.5 CLEAN AIR ACT

Air-conditioning (A/C) systems and refrigerant are regulated by the Clean Air Act, Title VI, Section 609. Technician certification and service equipment is also regulated. Any technician working on automotive A/C systems must be certified. A/C refrigerants must not be released or vented into the atmosphere, and used refrigerants must be recovered.

2.6 MATERIAL SAFETY DATA SHEETS (MSDS)

All hazardous materials must be properly labeled, and information about each hazardous material must be posted on **material safety data sheets (MSDS)**,

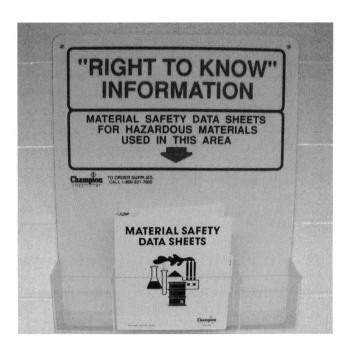

FIGURE 2-1 Material safety data sheets (MSDS) should be readily available for use by anyone in the area who may come into contact with hazardous materials. (Courtesy of James Halderman)

available from the manufacturer (Figure 2-1). In Canada, MSDS sheets are called **workplace hazardous materials information systems (WHIMS)**.

The employer has a responsibility to place MSDS sheets where they are easily accessible by all employees. The MSDS sheets provide the following information about the hazardous material: chemical name, physical characteristics, protective handling equipment, explosion/fire hazards, incompatible materials, health hazards, medical conditions aggravated by exposure, emergency and first-aid procedures, safe handling, and spill/leak procedures.

The employer also has a responsibility to make sure that all hazardous materials are properly labeled. The label information must include health, fire, and reactivity hazards posed by the material and the protective equipment necessary to handle the material. The manufacturer must supply all warning and precautionary information about hazardous materials, and this information must be read and understood by the employee before handling the material.

2.7 ASBESTOS EXPOSURE HAZARD

Friction materials such as brake and clutch linings may contain asbestos. Although asbestos has been eliminated from most original equipment friction materials, the automotive service technician cannot know whether the vehicle being serviced is or is not equipped with friction materials containing asbestos. It is important that all friction materials be handled as if they do contain asbestos.

Asbestos exposure can cause scar tissue to form in the lungs. This condition, called **asbestosis**, causes gradually increasing shortness of breath and permanent scarring of the lungs. Even low exposures to asbestos can cause **mesothelioma**, a type of fatal cancer of the lining of the chest or abdominal cavity. Asbestos exposure can also increase the risk of **lung cancer** as well as cancer of the voice box, stomach, and large intestine. It usually takes 15 to 30 years or more for cancer or asbestos lung scarring to show up after exposure. (Scientists call this the **latency period**.)

Government agencies recommend that asbestos exposure should be eliminated or controlled to the lowest level possible and have developed recommendations and standards that the automotive service technician and equipment manufacturers should follow. These agencies include the National Institute for Occupational Safety and Health (NIOSH), the Occupational Safety and Health Administration (OSHA), and the Environmental Protection Agency (EPA).

2.7.1 OSHA Asbestos Standards

The Occupational Safety and Health Administration (OSHA) has established three levels of asbestos exposure. Any vehicle service establishment that does either brake or clutch work must limit employee exposure to asbestos to less than 0.2 fibers per cubic centimeter (cc) as determined by an air sample. If the level of employee exposure is greater than specified, corrective measures must be taken and a large fine may be imposed.

◀ NOTE ▶

Research has found that worn asbestos fibers, such as from automotive brakes or clutches, may not be as hazardous as first believed. Worn asbestos fibers do not have sharp flared ends that can latch onto tissue, but rather are worn down to a dust form that resembles talc. Grinding or sawing operations on unworn brake shoes or clutch discs *will* contain *harmful* asbestos fibers. To limit health damage, always use proper handling procedures while working around any component that may contain asbestos.

2.7.2 EPA Asbestos Regulations

The federal Environmental Protection Agency (EPA) has established procedures for the removal and disposal of asbestos. The EPA procedures require that products containing asbestos be "wetted" to prevent the asbestos fibers from becoming airborne. According to the EPA, asbestos-containing materials can be disposed of as regular waste—asbestos is only considered hazardous when it is airborne.

2.7.3 Asbestos Handling Guidelines

The air in the shop area can be tested by a testing laboratory, but this can be expensive. Tests have determined that asbestos levels can easily be kept below the recommended levels by using a solvent or a special vacuum.

◀ NOTE ▶

Even though manufacturers are removing asbestos from brake and clutch lining materials, the service technician cannot tell whether the old brake pads or shoes or clutch discs contain asbestos. Therefore, to be safe, the technician should assume that all brake pads or shoes or clutch discs contain asbestos.

2.7.3.1 HEPA Vacuum   A special high-efficiency particulate air (HEPA) vacuum system has been proven to be effective in keeping asbestos exposure levels below 0.1 fibers per cubic centimeter.

2.7.3.2 Liquid/Solvent Brake Cleaners   Many technicians use an aerosol can of brake cleaning solvent to wet the brake dust and prevent it from becoming airborne. Some of the brake cleaning solvents may be hazardous; be sure to read the label on the product. Commercial brake cleaners are available that use a concentrated cleaner that is mixed with water (Figure 2-2). The waste liquid is filtered, and when dry, the filter can be disposed of as solid waste.

◀ CAUTION ▶

Never use compressed air to blow brake dust. The fine talclike brake dust can create a health hazard even if asbestos is not present or is present in dust rather than fiber form.

FIGURE 2-2   All brakes should be washed with liquid to help keep brake dust from becoming airborne. (Courtesy of James Halderman)

2.7.3.3 Disposal of Brake Dust and Brake Shoes   As mentioned, the hazard of asbestos occurs when asbestos fibers are airborne. Once the asbestos has been wetted down, it is (currently) considered to be solid waste, not hazardous waste. Old brake shoes and pads should be enclosed, preferably in a plastic bag, to help prevent any of the brake material from becoming airborne.

2.8   PROPER DISPOSAL

Always follow current federal and local laws considering disposal of all waste.

2.8.1   Used Brake Fluid

Most brake fluid is made from polyglycol; it is water soluble and can be considered hazardous if it has absorbed metals from the brake system.

- Collect brake fluid in containers clearly marked to indicate that they are dedicated for that purpose.
- If your waste brake fluid is hazardous, manage it appropriately and use only an authorized waste receiver for its disposal.
- If your waste brake fluid is nonhazardous, determine from your local solid waste collection provider how to dispose of it properly.

- Do not mix brake fluid with used engine oil.
- Do not pour brake fluid down drains or onto the ground.
- Recycle brake fluid through a registered recycler.

2.8.2   Used Oil

Used oil is any petroleum-based or synthetic oil that has been used. During normal use, impurities such as dirt, metal scrapings, water, or chemicals can get mixed in with the oil. Eventually, this used oil must be replaced with virgin or re-refined oil. The EPA's used oil management standards include a three-pronged approach to determine if a substance meets the definition of used oil. To meet this definition, a substance must satisfy each of the following three criteria:

1. **Origin.**   The first criterion for identifying used oil is based on the origin of the oil. Used oil must have been refined from crude oil or made from synthetic materials. Animal and vegetable oils are excluded from the EPA's definition of used oil.

2. **Use.**   The second criterion is based on whether and how the oil is used. Oils used as lubricants, hydraulic fluids, heat transfer fluids, and for other similar purposes are considered used oil. Unused oil, such as bottom clean-out waste from virgin fuel oil storage tanks or virgin fuel oil recovered from a spill, do not meet the EPA's definition of used oil because these oils have never been "used." The EPA's definition also excludes products used as cleaning agents or solely for their solvent properties, as well as certain petroleum-derived products like antifreeze and kerosene.

3. **Contaminants.**   The third criterion is based on whether the oil is contaminated with either physical or chemical impurities. In other words, to meet the EPA's definition, used oil must become contaminated as a result of being used. This aspect of the EPA's definition includes residues and contaminants generated from handling, storing, and processing used oil.

◄ NOTE ►

The release of only 1 gallon of used oil (a typical oil change) can make a million gallons of fresh water undrinkable.

If used oil is dumped down the drain and enters a sewage treatment plant, concentrations as small as 50–100 PPM (parts per million) in the wastewater can foul sewage treatment processes. Never mix a listed hazardous waste, gasoline, wastewater, hologenated solvents, antifreeze, or an unknown waste material with used oil. Adding any of these substances will cause the used oil to become contaminated, which classifies it as hazardous waste.

2.8.2.1 Disposal of Used Oil

Once oil has been used, it can be collected, recycled, and used over and over again. An estimated 380 million gallons of used oil are recycled each year. Recycled used oil can sometimes be used again for the same job or for a completely different task. For example, used motor oil can be re-refined and sold at the store as motor oil or processed for heating fuel. After collecting used oil in an appropriate container (for example, a 55-gallon steel drum), the material must be disposed of in one of two ways:

- Shipped off-site for recycling
- Burned in an on-site or off-site EPA-approved heater for energy recovery

2.8.2.2 Used Oil Storage

Used oil must be stored in compliance with existing **underground storage tank (UST)** or an **aboveground storage tank (AGST)** standards or kept in separate containers. Containers are portable receptacles, such as a 55-gallon steel drum.

Keep used-oil storage drums in good condition. This means that they should be covered, secured from vandals, properly labeled, and maintained in compliance with local fire codes. Frequent inspections for leaks, corrosion, spillage, and so on are an essential part of container maintenance.

Never store used oil in anything other than the proper tanks and storage containers. Used oil may also be stored in containers that are permitted to store regulated hazardous waste.

Follow used oil filters disposal regulations. Used oil filters contain used engine oil that may be hazardous. Before an oil filter is placed in the trash or sent for recycling, it must be drained using one of the following hot-draining methods approved by the EPA:

- Puncture the filter antidrain back valve or filter dome end and hot-drain for at least 12 hours.
- Hot-drain and crush.
- Dismantle and hot-drain.
- Use any other hot-draining method that will remove all the used oil from the filter

After the oil has been drained from the oil filter, the filter housing can be disposed of in any of the following ways:

- Recycling
- Pickup by a service contract company
- Disposed of in regular trash

2.8.3 Solvents

The major sources of chemical danger are liquid and aerosol brake cleaning fluids that contain chlorinated hydrocarbon solvents. The most common of these solvents are 1, 1, 1-trichloroethane, trichloroethylene, and tetrachloroethylene, which is also known as perchloroethylene, or "perk" for short. These solvents are all members of the same chemical family and share the same basic characteristics. They are colorless liquids with an odor of chloroform or ether. In large enough quantities these solvents can dull the senses, induce sleep, or cause a stupor. Very high levels of exposure over even a short period of time can be fatal. Repeated exposure to these solvents, in high concentrations and over long periods of time, can result in liver, kidney, and lung damage and may potentially cause cancer. Additionally, if these solvents are exposed to high heat or an open flame, they decompose into deadly gases such as hydrogen chloride, phosgene, and carbon monoxide.

Because 1,1,1-trichloroethane and trichloroethylene are know to be ozone depleters, the EPA prohibited their manufacture after January 1, 1996. Perks do not deplete the ozone and their use continues. Several other chemicals that do not deplete the ozone, such as heptane, hexane, and xylene, are now being used in nonchlorinated brake cleaning solvents. Some manufacturers are also producing solvents they describe as environmentally responsible that are biodegradable and noncarcinogenic.

Another solvent that can effect health is *n*-Hexane, a major component in several brands of automotive and industrial cleaners.

Some local areas like the South Coast Air Quality Management District in Southern California have regulations and standards for air quality and various chemicals that can affect air quality, including chemicals like solvents that evaporate into the air.

2.8.3.1 Sources of Chemical Poisoning

The health hazards presented by automotive cleaning solvents occur from three different forms of exposure: ingestion, inhalation, or physical contact. It should be obvious that swallowing automotive cleaning solvent is harmful, and such occurrences are not common. Automotive cleaning solvents should always be handled and stored properly and kept out of reach of children. The dangers of inhalation are perhaps the most serious problem—even very low levels of solvent vapors are hazardous. For example, the current OSHA standard (1910.1000) for airborne trichloroethylene is 100 parts per million (ppm) in the ambient air averaged over an 8-hour period. The ceiling level for exposure is 200 ppm, and there is a maximum acceptable peak level of 300 ppm for 5 minutes in any 2-hour period. The limits for other chlorinated hydrocarbon solvents, and for other chemicals replacing the chlorinated ones, are similar. These alternative chemicals are being used because they do not deplete the ozone layer, not because they are necessarily any safer to breathe, ingest, or touch.

Ingestion and inhalation are common forms of poisoning from many hazardous substances, but allowing automotive cleaning solvents to come in contact with the skin presents a danger unknown to many people. Not only do these solvents strip natural oils from the skin and cause irritation of the tissues, they also have the ability to be absorbed through the skin directly into the bloodstream. The transfer begins immediately upon contact and continues until the liquid is wiped or washed away.

There is no specific standard for physical contact with chlorinated hydrocarbon solvents or the chemicals replacing them. All contact should be avoided whenever possible. The law requires an employer to provide appropriate protective equipment and ensure proper work practices by an employee handling these chemicals.

2.8.3.2 Effects of Chemical Poisoning The effects of exposure to chlorinated hydrocarbon and other types of solvents can take many forms. Short-term exposure at low levels can cause headache, nausea, drowsiness, dizziness, lack of coordination, or unconsciousness. It may also cause irritation of the eyes, nose, and throat and flushing of the face and neck. Short-term exposure to higher concentrations can cause liver damage with symptoms such as yellow jaundice or dark urine. Liver damage may not become evident until several weeks after the exposure. Long-term or repeated exposure to perk may cause irritation or burning of the skin. It also increases the risk of damage to the liver or kidneys. If you experience any of these symptoms, seek medical treatment immediately, and tell the doctor about your exposure to brake cleaning solvents.

2.8.3.3 Chemical Precautions Unlike many industrial applications of chlorinated hydrocarbon solvents, automotive parts/brake cleaning sprays and liquids present relatively limited opportunity for exposure to dangerous levels of contamination. The possibility still exists, however, and just as with asbestos, there are safety precautions that should be followed to minimize the risk.

Always use any automotive cleaning solvent in an open, well-ventilated area and avoid breathing the vapors. Take precautions to prevent physical contact with the liquid solvent and clean any spills from the skin promptly using soap and water. Wear protective clothing and immediately remove any piece of clothing that becomes dampened with solvent. Do not wear the item again until it has been cleaned. Wear safety goggles or other eye protection when spraying brake cleaning solvents. The safest procedure is to avoid using these chemicals completely.

◀ SAFETY TIP ▶

HAND SAFETY

Service technicians should wear protective rubber or rubberlike gloves or wash their hands with soap and water after handling engine oil, differential or transmission fluids, or other shop chemicals (Figure 2-3).

The service technician should not wear watches or rings or other jewelry that could come in contact with electrical or moving parts of a vehicle.

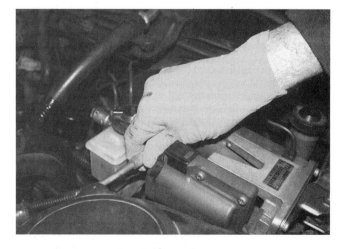

FIGURE 2-3 Protective gloves should be worn whenever working around grease or oil to help prevent possible skin problems. They help keep your hands clean, too! (Courtesy of James Halderman)

2.8.3.4 Status of Solvents as Hazardous and Regulatory Status   Most used solvents are classified as hazardous wastes. Other characteristics include:

- Solvents with flash points below 140°F are considered flammable and, like gasoline, are federally regulated by the Department of Transportation (DOT).
- Solvents and oils with flash points above 140°F are considered combustible and, like engine oil, are also regulated by DOT.

It is the responsibility of the repair shop to determine if their spent solvent is hazardous waste. Waste solvents that are considered hazardous waste have a flash point below 140°F (60°C). Hot water or aqueous parts cleaners may be used to avoid disposing of spent solvent as hazardous waste. Solvent-type parts cleaners with filters are available to greatly extend solvent life and reduce spent solvent disposal costs. Solvent reclaimers are available that clean and restore the solvent so that it lasts indefinitely.

2.8.3.5 Used Solvents   Used or spent solvents are liquid materials that have been generated as waste and may contain xylene, methanol, ethyl ether, and methyl isobutyl ketone (MIBK). These materials must be stored in OSHA-approved safety containers with tightly closed lids or caps (Figure 2-4). These storage receptacles must show no signs of leaks or significant damage due to dents or rust. In addition, the containers must be stored in a protected area equipped with secondary containment or spill protectors, such as a spill pallet. Additional requirements include:

- Containers should be clearly labeled "Hazardous Waste" and include the date the material was first placed into the storage receptacle.
- Labeling is not required for solvents being used in a parts washer.
- Used solvents will not be counted toward a facility's monthly output of hazardous waste if the vendor under contract removes the material.
- Used solvents may be disposed of by recycling with a local vendor, such as SafetyKleen, who removes the used solvent according to specific terms in the vendor agreement. See Figure 2-5.

2.8.4   Coolant Disposal

Coolant is a mixture of antifreeze and water. Proper coolant disposal applies to all types of antifreeze coolant, including the following:

- **Ethylene glycol**—This is the type that has been used almost exclusively since the 1950s. It is sweet-

FIGURE 2-4   Typical fireproof flammable storage cabinet. (Courtesy of James Halderman)

FIGURE 2-5   All solvents and other hazardous waste should be disposed of properly. (Courtesy of James Halderman)

tasting and can harm or kill humans, wild animals, or pets if swallowed (usually yellow–green).

◀ NOTE ▶

There is no universal color standard for antifreeze.

- **Propylene glycol**—Similar to ethylene glycol, this type of coolant is less harmful to pets and animals because it is not sweet-tasting, although it is still harmful if swallowed.
- **Organic acid technology (OAT)** antifreeze coolant (orange).
- **Hybrid organic acid technology (HOAT)** (orange or green).
- **VW/Audi pink**—Most of these coolants are HOAT (ethylene glycol-based with some silicate and containing an organic acid) and are phosphate-free.
- **Asian red**—This coolant is ethylene glycol-based and is silicate-free, yet contains phosphate.
- **Mercedes yellow**—This conventional ethylene glycol coolant has low amounts of silicate and no phosphates.
- **Korean or European blue**—This conventional ethylene glycol coolant has low amounts of silicate and no phosphates.

New antifreeze is not considered to be hazardous even though it can cause death if ingested. Used antifreeze may be hazardous due to dissolved metals from engine and other components of the cooling system. These metals can include iron, steel, aluminum, copper, brass, and lead (from older radiators and heater cores).

1. Coolant should be recycled either on-site or off-site.
2. Used coolant should be stored in a sealed and labeled container (Figure 2-6).
3. With a permit, used coolant can be disposed of by pouring into municipal sewers. Check with local authorities and obtain a permit before discharging used coolant into sanitary sewers.

2.8.5   Lead–Acid Battery Waste

About 70 million spent lead–acid batteries are disposed of each year in the United States alone. Lead is classified as a toxic metal and the acid used in lead–acid bat-

FIGURE 2-6 Used antifreeze coolants should be kept separate and stored in a leak-proof container until it can be recycled or disposed of according to federal, state, and local laws. Note that the storage barrel is placed inside another container to catch any coolant that may spill out of the inside barrel. (Courtesy of James Halderman)

teries is highly corrosive. The vast majority (95–98%) of these batteries are recycled through lead reclamation operations and secondary lead smelters for use in the manufacture of new batteries.

2.8.5.1 Status of Batteries as Hazardous and Regulatory Status   Used lead–acid batteries must be reclaimed or recycled. Leaking batteries must be stored and transported as hazardous waste. Some states have stricter regulations that require special handling procedures and transportation. According to the Battery Council International (BCI), battery laws usually include rules that:

- prohibit lead-acid battery disposal in landfills or incinerators,
- require batteries to be delivered to a battery retailer, wholesaler, recycling center, or lead smelter, and
- require all retailers of automotive batteries to post a sign that displays the universal recycling symbol and indicates the retailer's specific requirements for accepting used batteries.

◄ CAUTION ►

Battery electrolyte contains sulfuric acid, which is a very corrosive substance capable of causing serious personal injury, such as skin burns and eye damage. In addition, the battery plates contain lead, which is highly poisonous. For this reason, disposing of batteries improperly can cause environmental contamination and lead to severe health problems.

2.8.5.2 Battery Handling and Storage Batteries, whether new or used, should be kept indoors if possible. The storage location should be an area specifically designated for battery storage and must be well ventilated (to the outside). If outdoor storage is the only alternative, a sheltered and secured area with acid-resistant secondary containment is strongly recommended. It is also advisable that acid-resistant secondary containment be used for indoor storage. In addition, batteries should be placed on acid-resistant pallets and never stacked!

2.8.6 Fuel Safety and Storage

Gasoline is very explosive. The expanding vapors are extremely dangerous and are present even in cold temperatures. The vapors that form in many vehicle gasoline tanks are controlled, but vapors from stored gasoline may escape from the can, resulting in a hazardous situation. Therefore, place gasoline storage containers in a well-ventilated space. Although diesel fuel is not as volatile as gasoline, the same basic rules apply.

- Approved gasoline storage cans have a flash-arresting screen at the outlet. These screens prevent external ignition sources from igniting the gasoline within the can when someone pours the gasoline or diesel fuel.
- Technicians must always use approved *red* gasoline containers to allow for proper hazardous substance identification (Figure 2-7).
- Do not fill gasoline containers completely full. Always leave the level of gasoline at least 1 inch from the top of the container. This will allow room for the gasoline to expand at higher temperatures. If the containers are completely full, the expanding gasoline will be forced from the can and create a dangerous spill.

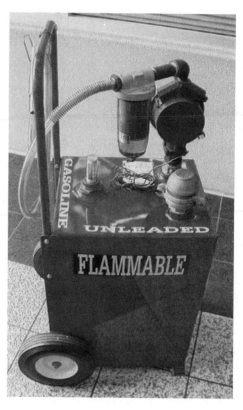

FIGURE 2-7 This portable gasoline supply is a sealed steel container that is painted red. (Courtesy of James Halderman)

- If gasoline or diesel fuel containers must be stored, place them in a designated storage locker or facility.
- Never leave gasoline containers open except while filling or pouring gasoline from the container.
- Never use gasoline as a cleaning agent.
- Always connect a ground strap to containers when filling or transferring fuel or other flammable products from one container to another, in order to prevent static electricity that could result in explosion and fire. These ground wires prevent the buildup of a static electric charge, which could result in a spark and a disastrous explosion.

2.8.7 Airbag Handling

Airbag modules are pyrometer devices that can be ignited if exposed to an electrical charge or if the front or sides of the vehicle are subjected to a sudden shock. Airbag safety should include the following precautions:

1. Disarm the air bag(s) if you will be working in the area where a discharged bag could make contact

with any part of your body. Consult service information for the exact procedure to follow for the vehicle being serviced.

2. Do not expose an airbag to extreme heat or fire.

3. Always carry an airbag pointing away from your body.

4. Place an airbag module facing upward.

5. Always follow the manufacturer's recommended procedure for air bag disposal or recycling, including the proper packaging to use during shipment.

6. Always wash your hands or body well if exposed to a deployed air bag. The chemicals involved can cause skin irritation and a possible rash to develop.

7. Wear protective gloves if handling a deployed air bag.

2.8.8 Used Tire Disposal

Used tires are an environmental concern for several reasons, including:

1. In a landfill, they tend to "float" up through the other trash and rise to the surface.

2. Tires trap and hold rainwater, which is a breeding ground for mosquitoes. Mosquito-borne diseases include encephalitis and dengue fever.

3. Used tires present a fire hazard and when they burn they create a large amount of black smoke that contaminates the air.

Used tires can be reused until the end of their useful life and then should be disposed of in one of the following ways:

1. Tires can be retreaded.

2. Tires can be recycled by shredding for use in asphalt.

3. Tires, removed from the wheel, can be sent to a landfill (most landfill operators will shred the tires because it is illegal in many states to landfill whole tires).

4. Tires can be burned in cement kilns or other power plants where the smoke can be controlled.

Use only a registered scrap tire handler to transport tires for disposal or recycling.

2.8.9 Air Conditioning Refrigerant Oil Disposal

Air conditioning refrigerant oil contains dissolved refrigerant and is therefore considered hazardous waste. This oil must be kept separate from other waste oil or the entire amount of oil must be treated as hazardous. Used refrigerant oil must be sent to a licensed hazardous waste disposal company for recycling or disposal (Figure 2-8).

◄ SAFETY TIP ►

INFECTION CONTROL PRECAUTIONS

Working on a vehicle can result in personal injury, including the possibility of being cut severely enough to cause serious bleeding. Some infections such as hepatitis B, HIV (which can cause acquired immunodeficiency syndrome, (AIDS), hepatitis C virus, plus others) are transmitted in the blood. These infections are commonly called **blood-born pathogens**. Report any injury that involves blood to your supervisor and take the necessary precautions to avoid coming in contact with blood from another person.

FIGURE 2-8 Used refrigerant oil should be stored in a clearly labeled, secure container. (Courtesy of James Halderman)

REVIEW QUESTIONS

The following questions are provided to help you study as you read the chapter.

1. OSHA is short for _____ _____ _____ and _____.

2. Hazardous waste materials are _____ or _____ that the shop no longer needs and that pose a danger.

3. EPA is short for _____ _____ _____.

4. A _____ material can burn skin or dissolve metal.

5. MSDS is short for _____ _____ _____ _____.

6. A MSDS contains information about a _____ _____.

7. _____ _____ or _____ _____ might contain asbestos.

8. Asbestos exposure can cause _____.

9. Used engine oil should be _____ so it can be used over and over.

10. Automotive solvents that contain _____ _____ solvents can cause health and environmental problems.

11. Cleaning solvents can strip _____ _____ from skin.

12. Some cleaning solvents have the ability to enter your _____ _____.

13. Technicians should wear _____ _____ and _____ _____.

14. Antifreeze can cause death if _____.

15. _____ is a very explosive liquid.

CHAPTER QUIZ

The following questions will help you check the facts you have learned. Select the answer that completes each statement correctly.

1. Student A says that the Occupational Safety and Health Act was passed in 1970 to protect workers. Student B says that the Environmental Protection Agency publishes a list of hazardous materials. Who is correct?
   a. Student A
   b. Student B
   c. Both A and B
   d. Neither A nor B

2. Hazardous materials include all of the following except _____.
   a. engine oil
   b. asbestos
   c. water
   d. brake cleaner

3. Student A says that employees have a right to know if materials that they are working with are hazardous. Student B says that all employees must be trained about hazardous materials. Who is correct?
   a. Student A
   b. Student B
   c. Both A and B
   d. Neither A nor B

4. Student A says that any technician working on an automotive A/C system must be certified. Student B says that all hazardous materials must be labeled. Who is correct?
   a. Student A
   b. Student B
   c. Both A and B
   d. Neither A nor B

5. To determine if a product or substance being used is hazardous, consult _____.
   a. a dictionary
   b. an MSDS
   c. EPA guidelines
   d. SAE standards

6. Student A says that right-to-know laws state that employees have the right to know when they are working with hazardous materials. Student B says that the right-to-know laws state that the employer has the responsibility to train employees about the hazardous wastes they will encounter in their workplace. Who is correct?
   a. Student A
   b. Student B
   c. Both A and B
   d. Neither A nor B

7. Student A says that hazardous waste is material that the shop no longer needs that can pose a danger to people and the environment. Student B says that material safety data sheets (MSDS) must be provided to all employees. Who is correct?
   a. Student A
   b. Student B
   c. Both A and B
   d. Neither A nor B

8. Student A says that exposure to asbestos can cause serious health problems. Student B says that all brake and clutch lining materials should be treated as if they contain asbestos. Who is correct?
   a. Student A
   b. Student B
   c. Both A and B
   d. Neither A nor B

9. Two students are discussing the disposal of used motor oil. Student A says that used motor oil should be recycled. Student B says that 1 gallon of used motor oil will make 1 million gallons of fresh water undrinkable. Who is correct?

    a. Student A
    b. Student B
    c. Both A and B
    d. Neither A nor B

10. Two students are discussing the solvents often used in automotive repair. Student A says that physical contact with solvents should be avoided. Student B says that all solvents should be used in open, well-ventilated areas. Who is correct?

    a. Student A
    b. Student B
    c. Both A and B
    d. Neither A nor B

11. Student A says that used coolant can be recycled or, with a permit, disposed of by pouring it down a drain. Student B says that new or used antifreeze can cause death if it is swallowed. Who is correct?

    a. Student A
    b. Student B
    c. Both A and B
    d. Neither A nor B

12. Student A says that the lead in batteries is toxic and battery acid is corrosive. Student B says that used batteries must be recycled. Who is correct?

    a. Student A
    b. Student B
    c. Both A and B
    d. Neither A nor B

13. Student A says that gasoline vapors are very dangerous. Student B says that gasoline should never be used to clean parts. Who is correct?

    a. Student A
    b. Student B
    c. Both A and B
    d. Neither A nor B

14. Two students are discussing how air bags should be handled. Student A says that air bag systems should always be disarmed when working near them. Student B says that air bags should never be exposed to extreme heat or fire. Who is correct?

    a. Student A
    b. Student B
    c. Both A and B
    d. Neither A nor B

15. Two students are discussing used tire disposal. Student A says that recycled tires can be added to asphalt for roads. Student B says that used tires are a fire hazard. Who is correct?

    a. Student A
    b. Student B
    c. Both A and B
    d. Neither A nor B

◀ Chapter 3 ▶

INTRODUCTION TO DRIVETRAINS

LEARNING OBJECTIVES

After completing this chapter, you should be able to:

1. Identify the major components of an automotive drivetrain.
2. Describe the purpose of the major components of the automotive drivetrain.
3. Understand gear ratios and their effect.
4. Calculate gear ratios.
5. Discuss the variety of drivetrains in use in today's vehicles.

TERMS TO LEARN

aerodynamic drag
all-wheel drive (AWD)
annulus gear
automatic transmission
bevel gear
clutch
constant-velocity joint (CV joint)
continuously variable transmission (CVT)
differential
drive axle
driveshaft
final drive
four-wheel drive (4WD)
front-wheel drive (FWD)
grade resistance
half shafts
helical gear
hypoid gear
internal gear
independent rear suspension (IRS)
manual transmission
overdrive
pinion gear
pitch diameter
pitch line
planetary gear set
rack and pinion gear set
reduction
rear-wheel drive (RWD)
ring gear
rolling friction
spiral bevel gear
spur bevel gear
spur gear
standard transmission
torque
torque converter
tractive effort
tractive resistance
transaxle
transfer case
transmission
universal joint (U-joint)
worm gear

3.1 INTRODUCTION

Every vehicle has a drivetrain that transfers power from the engine to the drive wheels. The drivetrain, also called a *power train*, serves several functions:

- It allows the driver to control the power flow.
- It multiplies the engine's torque.
- It controls the engine's speed.

Traditionally, the drivetrain delivered power to the rear wheels; this was called **rear-wheel drive** (RWD) (Figure 3-1). Most modern passenger vehicles drive the front wheels using **front-wheel drive** (FWD) (Figure 3-2). Some vehicles can drive two wheels all of the time and all four wheels part of the time; this is called **four-wheel drive** (4WD) (Figure 3-3). Older 4WD vehicles were intended for off-road use where traction is poor. A few vehicles will drive all four wheels all of the time; this is called **all-wheel drive** (AWD) or *full-time 4WD*. Many

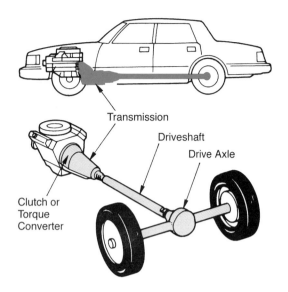

FIGURE 3-1 The drivetrain of a rear-wheel-drive (RWD) vehicle consists of a clutch, transmission, driveshaft, and rear axle. (Portions of materials contained herein have been reprinted with permission of General Motors Corporation, Service and Parts Operations, License Agreement #0310807)

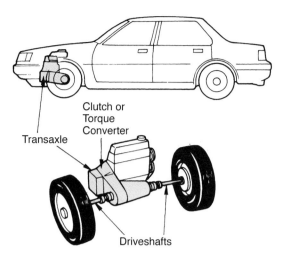

FIGURE 3-2 The drivetrain of a front-wheel-drive (FWD) vehicle consists of a clutch, transaxle, and a pair of driveshafts. (Portions of materials contained herein have been reprinted with permission of General Motors Corporation, Service and Parts Operations, License Agreement #0310807)

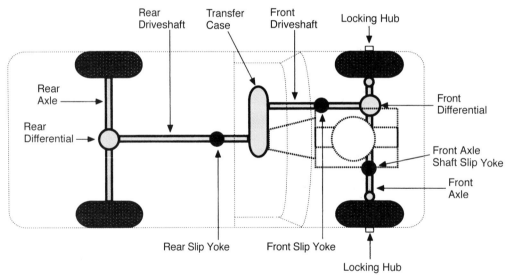

FIGURE 3-3 This four-wheel-drive (4WD) vehicle drivetrain consists of the components of a RWD drivetrain plus a transfer case, front driveshaft, and front drive axle. (Courtesy of Ford Motor Company)

modern AWD and full-time 4WD vehicles are designed for improved traction on wet or icy roads during daily use.

The drivetrain can use a clutch and manual transmission or a torque converter and automatic transmission. Either transmission is used with one or more driveshafts with universal joints or constant-velocity joints and drive axle reduction and differential gears. In most modern FWD vehicles, the transmission with the drive axle and differential gears are combined in a transaxle.

The clutch allows the engine's power flow to be stopped. The transmission provides the gear ratios to multiply the engine torque so a vehicle can be moved forward or backward from a stop. A transaxle and drive axle include a final drive ratio to help increase torque and also to determine engine speed at vehicle cruising speed. Differential gears in the drive axle and transaxle allow the drive wheels to be driven at different speeds while a vehicle turns a corner.

3.2 TORQUE

The rotating, mechanical power that is modified by the drivetrain is called **torque.** You exert torque each time you turn a doorknob or rotate a screwdriver. An automobile moves because of the torque that the drive axle exerts on the wheels and tires to make them rotate. Being a form of mechanical energy, torque cannot be created or destroyed—it is converted from one form of energy to a different form of energy.

An engine's torque is developed when combustion pressure pushes a piston downward to rotate the crankshaft (Figure 3-4). The amount of torque will vary depending on the size and design of the engine and the throttle opening. Torque is measured in newton-meters (N-m) or foot-pounds (ft-lb). One newton-meter of torque is equal to 0.737 ft-lb. A factor that greatly affects drivetrain design is that very little or no torque is developed at engine speeds below 1000 rpm. As shown in Figure 3-5, an engine begins producing a usable amount of torque at about 1200 rpm and a peak amount of torque at about 2500 to 3000 rpm, with an upper usable speed limit at about 4500 to 5000 rpm. The gear ratios in the transmission and drive axle are used to match the engine speed and torque output to the vehicle's speed and torque requirement.

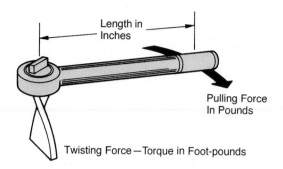

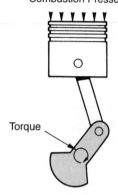

FIGURE 3-4 Torque, a twisting force, is produced when you pull on a wrench. An engine produces torque at the crankshaft as combustion pressure pushes the piston downward.

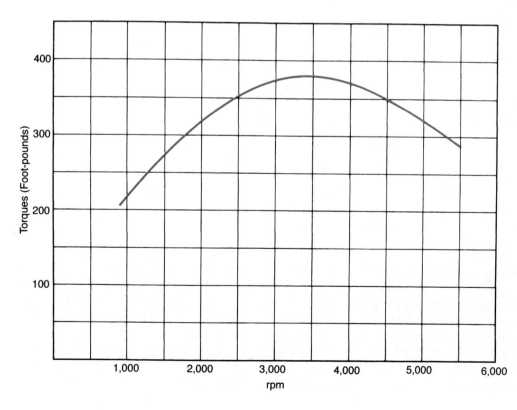

FIGURE 3-5 This curve shows the torque produced by a 350-in^3 (5.7-L) engine. Note that it begins producing usable torque at 1000 to 1200 rpm and a maximum torque (381 ft-lb) at 3500 rpm. The amount of torque drops off at higher rpm.

3.3 TORQUE MULTIPLICATION

Gears, belts and pulleys, and chains and sprockets can be used to change the speed or torque of a rotating shaft (Figure 3-6). These three devices are fairly similar in operation. In this book we concentrate on gears, the most popular method of torque multiplication used in drivetrains.

The teeth of gears in a gear set are cut proportional to the diameter of the gear. If one of two mating gears were twice as large as the other, it would have twice as many teeth. For example, if the smaller gear has 10 teeth,

the larger gear will have 20. If the teeth of these gears are intermeshed, 10 teeth of each gear will come into contact when the smaller gear rotates one revolution. This will require one revolution of the small gear and one-half revolution of the larger gear. It will take two revolutions of the small gear to produce one revolution of the larger gear. This is a gear ratio of 2:1, assuming that the small gear is the drive gear. To determine a gear ratio, we always divide the driven gear by the driving gear (Figure 3-7).

Torque is increased because of the length of the gear lever. Think of each tooth as a lever, with the fulcrum being the center of the gear. The lever lengths of the two gears can provide leverage much like that of a simple lever (Figure 3-8). Also, simple physics does not allow en-

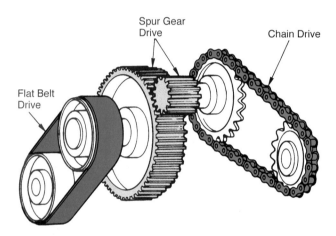

FIGURE 3-6 Torque can be transferred between shafts, and the amount of torque can be increased or decreased by belts and pulleys, gears, or chains and sprockets. (Reproduced with permission of Deere & Company, © 1972, Deere & Company. All rights reserved)

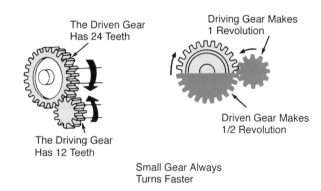

FIGURE 3-7 If the driving gear has one-half the number of teeth of the driven gear, the ratio will be 2:1 (24 ÷ 12 = 2) and the driven gear will rotate in a direction opposite to the driving gear. (Reproduced with permission of Deere & Company, © 1972, Deere & Company. All rights reserved.)

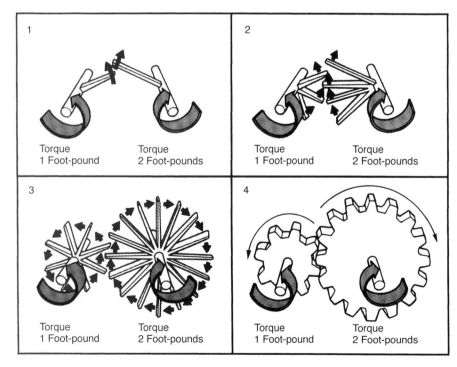

FIGURE 3-8 Torque is increased through a gear set because of the leverage of the gear teeth. Gears can be thought of as a series of levers. (Portions of materials contained herein have been reprinted with permission of General Motors Corporation, Service and Parts Operations, License Agreement #0310807)

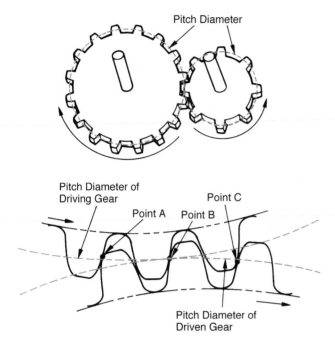

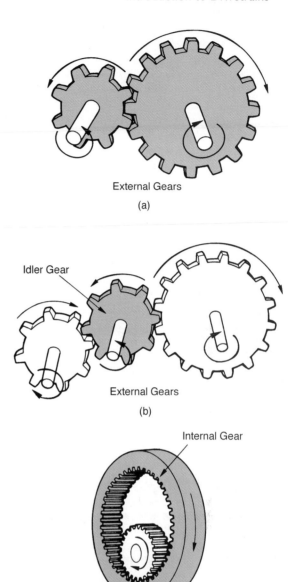

FIGURE 3-9   The pitch diameter is the effective diameter of the gear. Note how the contact points slide on the gear teeth as they move in and out of contact.

ergy to become lost in a gear set, other than what is changed to heat through friction; whatever power that comes in one shaft goes out the other. If the speed is reduced, the amount of torque will be increased a like amount, or vice versa. For example, if the driving gear has 20 ft-lb (27 N-m) of torque at 500 rpm and the ratio is 2:1, the driven gear will have 40 ft-lb (54 N-m) of torque (twice as much) at 250 rpm (half the speed).

The effective diameter of a gear is the **pitch diameter** or **pitch line** (Figure 3-9). The pitch diameter is the point where the teeth of the two gears meet and transfer power. The gear teeth are shaped to be able to slide in and out of mesh with a minimum amount of friction and wear.

Remember that the driven gear will rotate in a direction opposite to the driving gear. External gears will always reverse shaft motion (Figure 3-10). If same-direction motion is required, the power will be routed through two gear sets, or an internal and external combination of gears will be used. When power goes through a series of gears, an even number of gears (2, 4, 6, 8) will cause a reversal; an odd number of gears (3, 5, 7, 9) will produce same-direction rotation.

3.4   GEAR TYPES

Gears come in different types depending on the cut and relationship of the teeth to the shafts. **Spur gears,** the simplest gears, are on parallel shafts with teeth cut

FIGURE 3-10   (a) When one external gear drives another, the direction of rotation is always reversed. (b) An idler gear also reverses the direction of rotation so that the driving and driven gears rotate in the same direction. (c) When an external gear drives an internal gear, the two gears will rotate in the same direction.

straight or parallel to the shaft (Figure 3-11a). Most gears used in modern transmissions are **helical gears,** which have the teeth cut in a spiral or helix shape (Figure 3-11b). Helical gears are quieter than spur gears, but helical gears generate axial or end thrust under a load. Helical gears are stronger than a comparable-sized spur gear, and they have an almost continuous power flow because of the angled teeth.

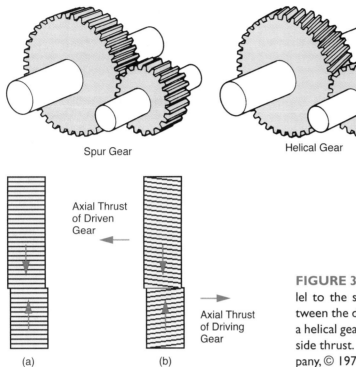

Spur Gear

Helical Gear

Axial Thrust
of Driven
Gear

Axial Thrust
of Driving
Gear

(a)   (b)

FIGURE 3-11   (A) The teeth of a spur gear are cut parallel to the shaft, and this produces a straight pressure between the driving and the driven gear teeth. (B) The teeth of a helical gear are cut on a slant, and this produces an axial or side thrust. (Reproduced with permission of Deere & Company, © 1972, Deere & Company. All rights reserved.)

A little-used version of a helical gear is the *herringbone gear*, which is essentially a right-hand and a left-hand helical gear mounted together so that the thrust loads are canceled (Figure 3-12). To identify a right-hand helical gear, the thumb of your right hand will align with the slant of the teeth if you put your hand on the gear with your fingers pointing in the direction of rotation. A left-hand gear is the opposite. When discussing gears, a **pinion gear** is the smaller gear of a pair.

Bevel gears are used on nonparallel shafts. The outer edge of the gear must be cut on the angle that bisects the angle of the two shafts (Figure 3-13). In

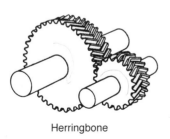

Herringbone

FIGURE 3-12   A herringbone gear looks like a combined left- and right-hand helical gear. It transfers force quietly with no axial thrust. (Reproduced with permission of Deere & Company, © 1972, Deere & Company. All rights reserved.)

other words, if the two shafts meet at a 90° angle and the two gears are the same size, the outer edge of the gears will be cut at a 45° angle. The simplest bevel gears have teeth cut straight and are called **spur bevel gears.** They are inexpensive but noisy. **Spiral bevel gears,** like helical gears, have curved teeth for quieter operation. A variation of the spiral bevel gear is the **hypoid gear**, also called an offset-bevel gear. Hypoid gears are used in most drive axles and some transaxles for longitudinal mounted engines. This design places the drive pinion gear lower in the housing than the ring gear and axle shafts.

Another gear set used with shafts that cross each other but do not intersect is the **worm gear** (Figure 3-13d). The worm gear or drive pinion is cut in a rather severe helix, much like a bolt thread, and the ring gear or wheel is cut almost like a spur gear. This gear set is commonly used to drive the speedometer shaft, and it provides a rather large ratio in one step. To determine the ratio, divide the number of teeth on the wheel by the pitch of the worm gear. For example, a single-pitch worm gear tooth driving a 20-tooth ring gear will have a ratio of 20:1, a very low ratio, and the wheel does not have to be 20 times larger than the worm gear. A 20:1 ratio in most gear sets requires the driven gear to be 20 times larger than the driving gear.

Most gears have external teeth. A few have the teeth cut on the inside of the gear's outer edge and are called **internal gears.** When they are used in a combination

(a) Bevel Gears

(b) Spiral Bevel
    Gears

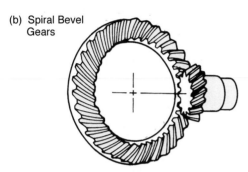

(c) Hypoid Gears

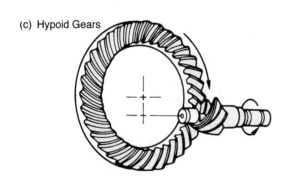

(d) Worm Gear

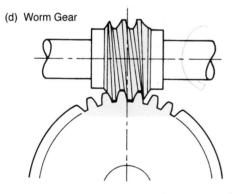

FIGURE 3-13 The three major styles of bevel gears are spur or plain bevel gears (a), spiral bevel gears (b), and hypoid gears (c). Note the differences in the shape of their teeth. A worm gear set (d) is also used to transmit power between angled shafts. (Portions of materials contained herein have been reprinted with permission of General Motors Corporation, Service and Parts Operations, License Agreement #0310807)

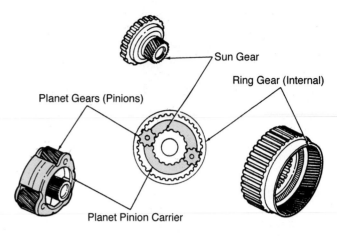

FIGURE 3-14 A planetary gear set is a combination of an internal ring gear, a sun gear, and a planet carrier with two or more planet pinion gears. (Courtesy of Ford Motor Company)

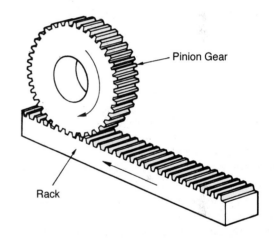

FIGURE 3-15 In a rack and pinion gear set, when the pinion gear rotates, the rack moves sideways. (Reproduced with permission of Deere & Company, © 1972, Deere & Company. All rights reserved.)

called a **planetary gear set,** the internal gear is called a **ring** or **annulus gear.** A planetary gear set is commonly used in automatic transmissions, and it consists of:

- a single sun gear in the center,
- two or more planet pinion gears meshed with the sun gear and mounted so they can rotate in the planet carrier, and
- the ring gear meshed with the planet pinions (Figure 3-14).

A **rack and pinion gear set** consists of a straight gear; the rack, which is meshed with the pinion gear (Figure 3-15). When the pinion gear rotates, the rack will slide sideways in the housing. This gear set changes the rotary motion of the pinion gear into a reciprocating, back-and-forth motion of the rack. This gear set is commonly used in steering systems with the rack connected to the tie-rods of the front wheels and the pinion gear connected to the steering wheel.

3.5 GEAR RATIOS

As mentioned earlier, most gear ratios are determined by dividing the number of teeth on the driven, output gear by the number of teeth on the driving, input gear. Most of the time, this means dividing a larger number, such as 20, by a smaller number, such as 5. In this case, $20 \div 5 = 4$, so the ratio will be 4:1. The driving gear will turn four times for each revolution of the driven gear. This results in a speed **reduction** and a torque increase. The higher the number, the lower the ratio. A 5:1 ratio is higher numerically, but in terms of speed of the driven gear it is a lower ratio than 4:1 (Figure 3-16).

If the driving gear has 20 teeth and the driven gear 5, there will be an increase in speed and a reduction in torque. This is called an **overdrive.** The ratio is com-

puted by dividing 5 by 20, $5 \div 20 = 0.25$; so the ratio would be 0.25:1. The driving gear will turn 0.25 or one-fourth of a revolution for each turn of the driven gear. Note that a gear ratio is always written so that the number 1 is to the right of the colon. This represents one turn of the output gear, while the number to the left represents the revolutions of the input.

Most of the time, the ratio will not end up in easy, whole numbers. It will be something like an 11-tooth driving gear and a 19-tooth driven gear, which gives a ratio of 19 divided by 11, which equals 1.7272727 and can be rounded off to 1.73. The automotive industry commonly rounds off gear ratios to two decimal points for consistency. A simple pocket calculator makes the mathematics very easy.

When power goes through more than one gear set, two or more ratios are involved. In most cases, the simplest way to handle this is to figure the ratio of each set and then multiply one ratio by the other(s). An example of this is a car with a first-gear ratio of 2.68:1 and a rear axle ratio of 3.45:1. The overall ratio in first gear is 2.68×3.45 or 9.246:1. The engine will rotate at a speed that is 9.246 times faster than the rear axle shafts. The overall ratios for the other transmission gears would be figured in the same manner (Figure 3-17).

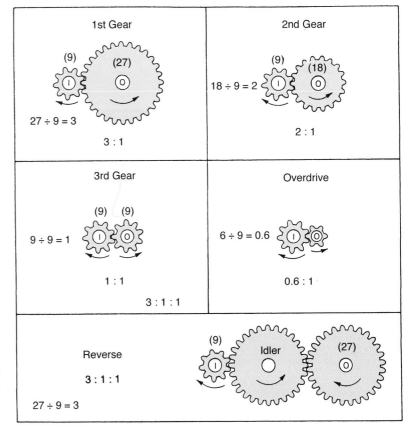

FIGURE 3-16 Dividing the number of teeth on the driven gear by the number of teeth on the driving gear gives the gear ratio for that gear pair. The gear sets for a typical transaxle are shown here. Note that a simple idler gear can be ignored when figuring the reverse gear ratio. (Portions of materials contained herein have been reprinted with permission of General Motors Corporation, Service and Parts Operations, License Agreement #0310807)

Axle ratio: 3.08:1								
Transmission: Close Ratio				*Mid Ratio*			*Wide Ratio*	
Gear	*Trans. Ratio*	*Overall Ratio*		*Trans. Ratio*	*Overall Ratio*		*Trans. Ratio*	*Overall Ratio*
1st	2.95:1	9.09:1		3.35:1	10.32:1		3.97:1	12.23:1
2nd	1.94:1	5.97:1		1.93:1	5.94:1		2.34:1	7.21:1
3rd	1.34:1	4.13:1		1.29:1	3.97:1		1.46:1	4.5:1
4th	1:1	3.08:1		1:1	3.08:1		1:1	3.08:1
5th	0.73:1	2.25:1		0.68:1	2.09:1		0.79:1	2.43:1

Axle ratio: 3.45:1								
Transmission: Close Ratio				*Mid Ratio*			*Wide Ratio*	
Gear	*Trans. Ratio*	*Overall Ratio*		*Trans. Ratio*	*Overall Ratio*		*Trans. Ratio*	*Overall Ratio*
1st	2.95:1	10.18:1		3.35:1	11.56:1		3.97:1	13.7:1
2nd	1.94:1	6.69:1		1.93:1	6.66:1		2.34:1	8.07:1
3rd	1.34:1	4.62:1		1.29:1	4.45:1		1.46:1	5.04:1
4th	1:1	3.45:1		1:1	3.45:1		1:1	3.45:1
5th	0.73:1	2.52:1		0.68:1	2.35:1		0.79:1	2.72:1

Axle ratio: 3.73:1								
Transmission: Close Ratio				*Mid Ratio*			*Wide Ratio*	
Gear	*Trans. Ratio*	*Overall Ratio*		*Trans. Ratio*	*Overall Ratio*		*Trans. Ratio*	*Overall Ratio*
1st	2.95:1	11:1		3.35:1	12.49:1		3.97:1	14.81:1
2nd	1.94:1	7.24:1		1.93:1	7.2:1		2.34:1	8.73:1
3rd	1.34:1	4.5:1		1.29:1	4.81:1		1.46:1	5.45:1
4th	1:1	3.73:1		1:1	3.73:1		1:1	3.73:1
5th	0.73:1	2.72:1		0.68:1	2.54:1		0.79:1	2.95:1

FIGURE 3-17   The overall gear ratio is determined by multiplying the transmission ratio by the axle ratio. This chart shows the overall ratios that result from combining three different transmissions with three different axle ratios. The left columns show a transmission with the close ratios; the right columns show the wide-ratio version. The highest drive axle ratio is at the top; the lowest is at the bottom.

3.6   TRACTIVE EFFORT

Tractive effort, also called *motive force* or *motive power*, is the engineering term that describes the amount of thrust that the engine and drivetrain can generate at the road surface. This is a product of how much torque is generated by the engine, how much this torque is increased by the drivetrain, and how much this torque is reduced by the size of the drive wheels. The formula used to determine the actual amount of tractive effort for a particular vehicle is

$$TF = \frac{T_e \times R_t \times R_a}{r}$$

where:

TF = tractive force in pounds

T_e = engine torque in foot-pounds

R_t = gear ratio, transmission

R_a = gear ratio, axle

r = effective loaded radius of drive wheel in feet

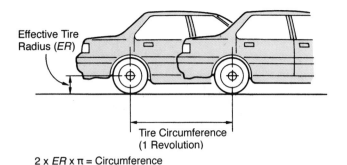

Effective Tire
Radius (ER)

Tire Circumference
(1 Revolution)

2 x ER x π = Circumference

FIGURE 3-18   Car speed is determined by the diameter and speed of the drive wheels. It can be computed as shown here.

This formula simply determines the amount of torque that is available at the drive wheels, and then it divides that amount of torque by the lever arm of the wheel. It is important to use the wheel loaded radius, the distance from the center of the wheel to the ground, because the weight of the vehicle and the pneumatic nature of the tire will shorten this distance. This distance also determines the speed of the car. For each revolution of the tire, the car will travel a distance

equal to the circumference of a circle with this radius (Figure 3-18). You can use the following formulas to determine the car's speed based on the gear ratio and engine speed, or vice versa:

$$mph = \frac{rpm \times tire\ diameter}{gear\ ratio \times 336}$$

$$engine\ rpm = \frac{mph \times gear\ ratio \times 336}{tire\ diameter}$$

If accuracy is important when using these formulas, you should use the loaded tire radius times 2 for the tire diameter.

By plotting the driveshaft torque in chart form, as in Figure 3-19, we get an interesting way to look at the torque available in the drivetrain. This chart is plotted for the torque curve shown in Figure 3-5 equipped with a six-speed transmission. In the chart shown in Figure 3-20, we plotted tractive effort and added the vehicle speed, which illustrates how the torque in each transmission gear relates to the speed of the vehicle. The torque in first gear is greatest but is usable

FIGURE 3-19a Multiplying the engine's torque (from Figure 3-5) by the transmission gear ratio gives the driveshaft torque for the various gears.

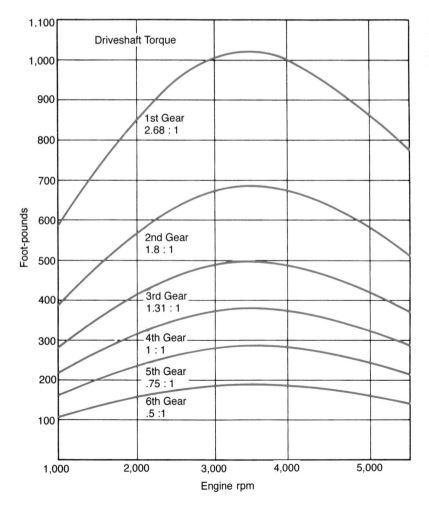

FIGURE 3-19b Multiplying the driveshaft torque by the axle ratio gives the torque available at the drive wheels. These curves are for a modern, domestic sports car.

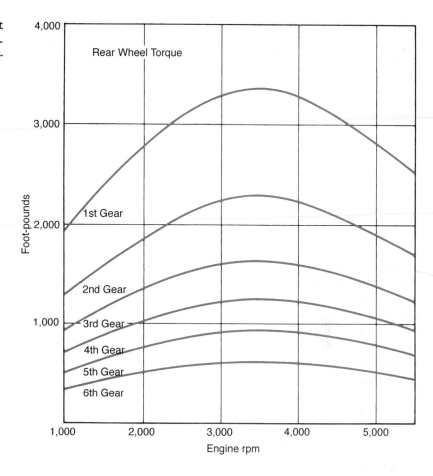

FIGURE 3-20 Dividing drive-wheel torque by the tire diameter gives the tractive force at the drive wheels. Combining this with the vehicle speed shows the available torque at the various speeds. Also note that five of the six gears can be used at 55 mph; second gear will produce the highest engine speed and sixth gear the slowest.

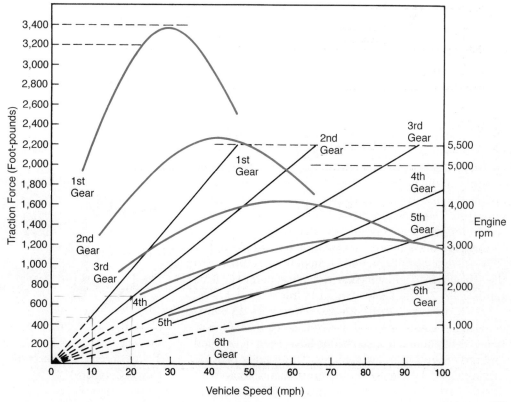

49

only up to about 45 mph if engine rpm is limited to 5500 rpm. Second gear gives a greater usable speed range but less torque, third gear gives still greater speed range but less torque, and so on.

The load that the drivetrain works against is called the **tractive resistance.** An engineer will use the formula

$$\text{tractive resistance} = F_r \times D_a \times G_r$$

where:

F_r = rolling friction
D_a = aerodynamic drag
G_r = grade resistance

Rolling friction is the drag of the tires on the road plus bearing friction. It increases at a constant rate, doubling as the speed is doubled. **Aerodynamic drag** is the wind resistance of air moving over the size and shape of the vehicle. It increases at a rapid rate, roughly four times as the speed is doubled (actually, velocity squared). **Grade resistance** is an amount equal to 0.01 times the vehicle weight times the angle of the grade in percent.

As you drive a vehicle, you adjust the throttle so that the engine produces the proper torque, and you select the gear needed to overcome the tractive resistance. If you are concerned with speed and acceleration rate, use lower gears and higher engine speeds. If you are concerned with fuel economy, use the highest gear to give the lowest practical engine speed.

3.6.1   Transmission Efficiency

Increased fuel costs and stringent emission requirements are forcing manufacturers to build more efficient vehicles. Five- and six-speed transmissions are more efficient than three- and four-speed transmissions. Manual transmission efficiency is affected by gear and bearing friction. An automatic transmission is also affected by the hydraulic pump and torque converter. Depending on the gear ratio, an automatic transmission is about 60 to 95% efficient actually, about 80 to 86% in average use. This means that about 14 to 20% of the power that enters the transmission is lost to friction and heat. In comparison, a manual transmission averages about 95% efficiency, so it generally transfers more power to the wheels. Efficiency in gear reduction and overdrive ratios is 92–97%, and 93–99% in a 1:1 ratio.

The driving public prefers automatic transmissions. Automated manual transmissions (AMT) and two-clutch manual transmissions have been developed and are offered in a few vehicles. These units provide driving ease, similar to automatic transmissions, with

the efficiency of a manual transmission. Continuously variable transmissions (CVT) that are currently used in some vehicles are more efficient than gear transmissions. These use either a steel belt with two variable-width pulleys or toroidal-shaped driving and driven members. CVTs promise to be more efficient than manual transmissions. CVTs are described in Section 3.9.

3.7   STANDARD TRANSMISSIONS

The **transmission** provides the various gear ratios necessary for a vehicle's operation, and it gives the driver a means of controlling the engine speed. It must have a ratio low enough (when multiplied by the axle ratio) to produce sufficient torque to get the vehicle moving. It must also have a ratio that will allow economical operation at cruise speeds without excessive engine rpm. There must also be enough intermediate ratios so that overrevving in the lower gear or lugging in the higher gear is not a problem. The weight of the vehicle, the amount of engine torque, the usable speed range of the engine, and the operating speed of the vehicle are used to determine if three, four, five, or even more speeds are necessary in the transmission. In addition to these forward-speed ratios, a transmission must provide a reverse for backing up and a neutral so the engine can run without moving the vehicle.

A **standard transmission,** also called a **manual transmission,** is constructed with a group of paths through which power can flow; each path is a different gear ratio (Figure 3-21). Synchronizer assemblies or sliding gears and the shift linkage are used to control or engage these power paths. Whenever one of these shifts is made, the power must be interrupted by a clutch. In Chapter 6 we provide a more thorough description of standard transmission operation.

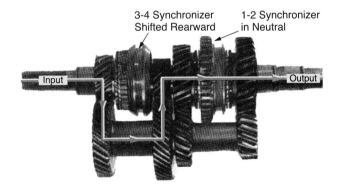

FIGURE 3-21 Gearset of a four-speed transmission showing the power flow for third gear. Shifting the 1–2 and 3–4 synchronizers selects the gear speed. (Courtesy of Ford Motor Company)

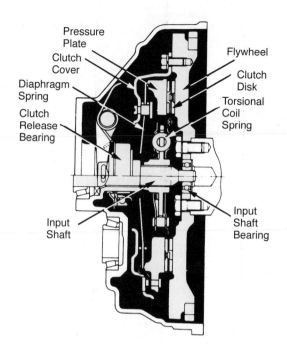

FIGURE 3-22 Cutaway view of a clutch assembly. The clutch disc drives the input shaft when the clutch is engaged. (Portions of materials contained herein have been reprinted with permission of General Motors Corporation, Service and Parts Operations, License Agreement #0310807)

The **clutch** interrupts the power flow to allow the transmission to be shifted. It is also used to ease the engagement of the power flow when the vehicle starts from a standstill. Remember that the engine does not produce usable torque until above 1000 rpm and that the engine speed with a vehicle in gear at 0 mph would be 0 rpm. The slight slippage as the clutch engages allows the engine speed to stay up where it produces usable torque as the car begins moving.

Most vehicles use a foot-pedal-operated single-plate clutch assembly that is mounted on the engine flywheel (Figure 3-22). When the pedal is pushed down, the power flow is disengaged; when the pedal is released, power can flow from the engine to the transmission through the engaged clutch. Clutch operation is described more completely in Chapter 4.

3.8 AUTOMATIC TRANSMISSIONS AND TORQUE CONVERTERS

An **automatic transmission** also has various gear ratios, but the paths of power flow are different from those of a standard transmission. Planetary gear sets are used and combined in a complex manner so that up to four or five speeds forward plus reverse are in one

complex gear set and the gears remain in constant mesh. Shifts are made by engaging or releasing one or more internal clutch packs that drive particular parts of the gear set, or by engaging or releasing other clutches or bands that hold particular parts of the gear set stationary. An automatic transmission might have as many as seven power control units. These are clutches or bands that are operated as needed to engage a certain gear. These control units can operate without an interruption of the power flow (Figure 3-23).

Automatic transmission control units are operated by hydraulic pressure. To make a shift, this system uses hydraulic valves to apply or release the proper clutch or band at the correct time. Many newer transmissions use an electronic computer control system, linked to the engine controls, which allows the engine and transmission to operate closer to each other's requirements.

A **torque converter** replaces the clutch. It is a type of fluid coupling that can release the power flow at slow engine speeds and also multiply the engine's torque during acceleration. Torque converters in newer vehicles include a friction clutch that locks up to eliminate slippage at cruising speeds, improving fuel economy and reducing emissions.

A few automatic transmissions have a gear arrangement resembling a standard transmission. A friction clutch is used with each forward gear. The friction clutch is applied to engage that particular vehicle's gear. One clutch is released and another is applied to shift into another gear. The one-way clutch, which self-releases and overruns when the next gear is engaged is also used in one or more of the gear ranges (Figure 3-24). A torque converter is used, and the operation of these clutches is by hydraulic pressure like other automatic transmissions.

3.9 CONTINUOUSLY VARIABLE TRANSMISSIONS

Some vehicles use a **continuously variable transmission** (CVT). A CVT transmission varies the gear ratio in a continuous manner instead of in a series of steps or gear ratios. The power flow is through a V-belt between two pulleys that change their width and effective diameter. When the car starts from a standing start, the driving pulley is small and the driven pulley is large. This gives a gear reduction identical to a small gear driving a large gear. As the speed increases, the effective diameter of the driving pulley increases because the sides of the pulley move together. While this happens, the driven pulley is made wider and therefore smaller in diameter. At cruising speeds, the driving pulley is larger than the driven pulley, which produces an overdrive ratio (Figure 3-25).

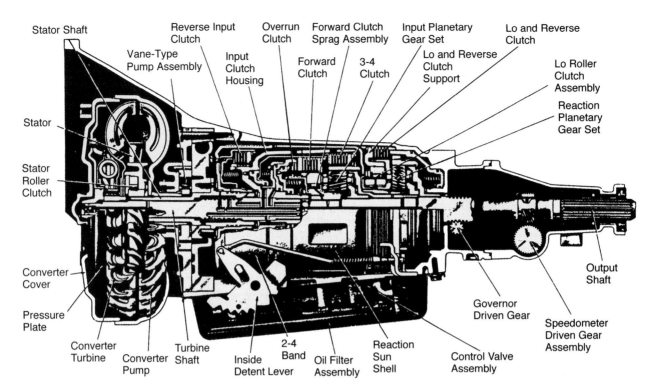

Stator Shaft · Vane-Type Pump Assembly · Reverse Input Clutch · Input Clutch Housing · Overrun Clutch · Forward Clutch · Forward Clutch Sprag Assembly · 3-4 Clutch · Input Planetary Gear Set · Lo and Reverse Clutch Support · Lo and Reverse Clutch · Lo Roller Clutch Assembly · Reaction Planetary Gear Set

Stator · Stator Roller Clutch · Converter Cover · Pressure Plate · Converter Turbine · Converter Pump · Turbine Shaft · Inside Detent Lever · 2-4 Band · Oil Filter Assembly · Reaction Sun Shell · Control Valve Assembly · Governor Driven Gear · Speedometer Driven Gear Assembly · Output Shaft

FIGURE 3-23 Cutaway view of a THM 700 transmission. This is a four-speed automatic transmission. Note the planetary gear sets and the eight control elements (clutches and bands) that produce the various speeds. (Portions of materials contained herein have been reprinted with permission of General Motors Corporation, Service and Parts Operations, License Agreement #0310807)

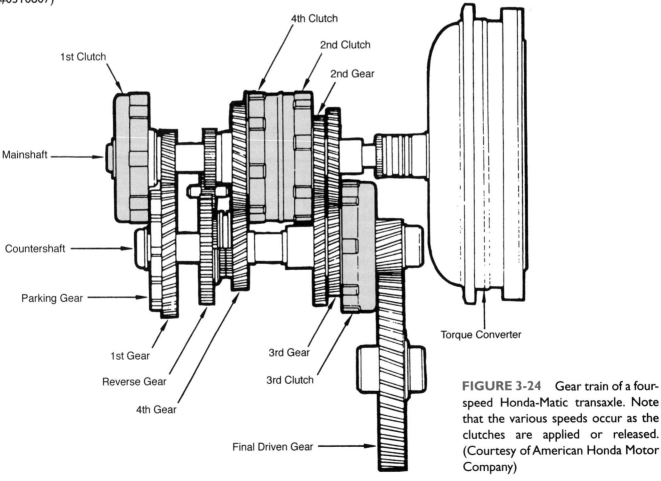

1st Clutch · 4th Clutch · 2nd Clutch · 2nd Gear · Mainshaft · Countershaft · Parking Gear · 1st Gear · Reverse Gear · 4th Gear · 3rd Gear · 3rd Clutch · Final Driven Gear · Torque Converter

FIGURE 3-24 Gear train of a four-speed Honda-Matic transaxle. Note that the various speeds occur as the clutches are applied or released. (Courtesy of American Honda Motor Company)

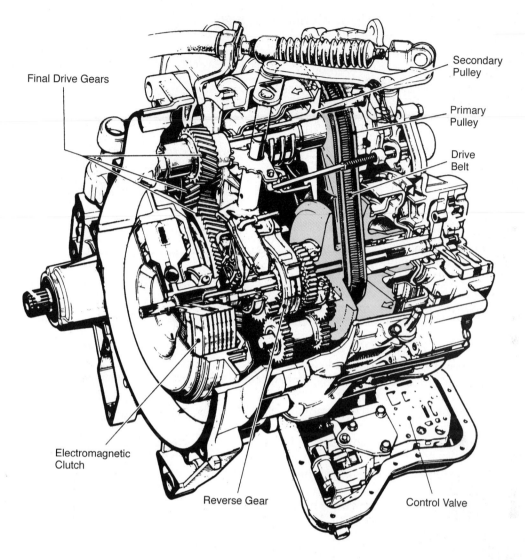

Final Drive Gears

Secondary Pulley

Primary Pulley

Drive Belt

Electromagnetic Clutch

Reverse Gear

Control Valve

(a)

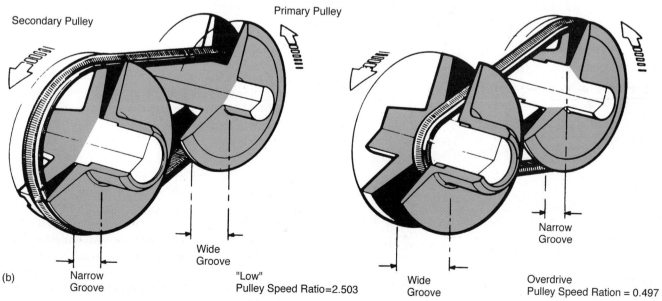

Secondary Pulley

Primary Pulley

Narrow Groove

Wide Groove

"Low" Pulley Speed Ratio=2.503

Wide Groove

Narrow Groove

Overdrive Pulley Speed Ration = 0.497

(b)

FIGURE 3-25 (a) CVT transaxle. (b) Note how the pulley diameters are changed to produce changes in the gear ratio. (Courtesy of Subaru of America, Inc.)

Pulley size changes smoothly and evenly, which produces a somewhat odd sensation while the car accelerates from a dead stop. When the throttle is pressed, first the engine speed increases to the point of good torque output, and then it stays at the same rpm while the vehicle accelerates. Many of you are more familiar with the series of engine speed increases in each gear along with a speed decrease when a shift is made.

Toroidal transmissions are also of the traction-drive type. A doughnut is an example of a toroidal shape. A toroidal transmission uses an input toroid and an output toroid that have the same shape, similar to part of a doughnut. There is a set of idler rollers, also called *variators*, that are pushed against the toroids. The rollers transmit power from one toroid to the other, and they can be twisted so the driving and driven radii can be changed (Figure 3-26). This design requires very exact machining of the two toroids and the variator rollers and is extremely sensitive to the type of lubricant used.

3.10   TRANSAXLES

A **transaxle** is a compact combination of a transmission and the final drive gear reduction and differential. It can be either a standard, automatic, or continuously variable transaxle. Transaxles are used in nearly all FWD vehicles, some midengine vehicles, and even a few RWD vehicles. A transmission normally has one output shaft that couples to the rear axle through the driveshaft. (Figure 3-27a) A transaxle has two output shafts that couple to the two front wheels through a pair of driveshafts (Figure 3-27b).

The **differential** used in transaxles or drive axles is a torque-splitting device that allows the two axle shafts to operate at different speeds so that a vehicle

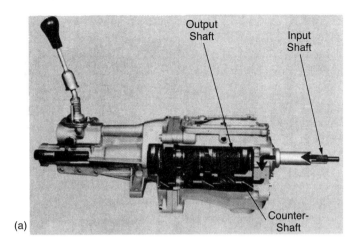

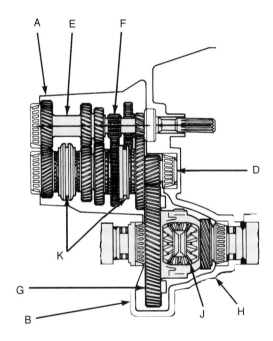

(b)

FIGURE 3-27   A transmission has one output shaft for the driveshaft to the rear axle (a). A transaxle combines a transmission section (a) and a reduction section (b) with the differential (J) for the two front driveshafts. (Courtesy of Ford Motor Company)

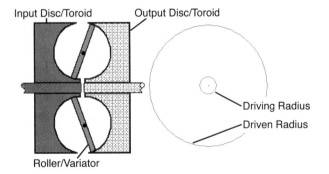

FIGURE 3-26   The rollers are pushed against the input and output toroids so they can transfer power. They are in low ratio as shown. The rollers will be twisted, the top one counterclockwise and the lower one clockwise to shift to a higher ratio.

can turn corners. When a vehicle turns a corner, the wheel on the outer side of the turning radius must travel farther than the inner wheel, but it must do this in the same period of time. Therefore, it must travel faster during this turning period. Most differentials are composed of a group of four or more gears. One gear is coupled to each axle and two are mounted on the differential pinion shaft (Figure 3-28). Differential operation is explained in Chapter 7.

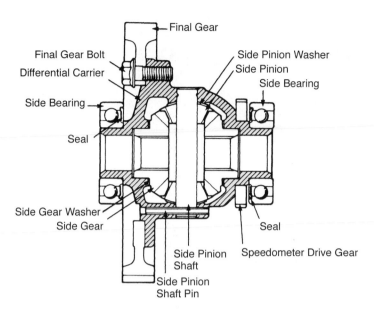

FIGURE 3-28 Cutaway view of the differential used in a transaxle. The transaxle drive pinion gear drives the final (ring) gear, and the side gears drive the wheels through the driveshafts. (Portions of materials contained herein have been reprinted with permission of General Motors Corporation, Service and Parts Operations, License Agreement #0310807)

3.11 DRIVESHAFTS

Driveshafts transfer power from one component to another. RWD driveshafts are usually made from steel tubing, and normally they have either a **universal joint** (U-joint) or a **constant-velocity** (CV) **joint** at each end (Figure 3-29). Most FWD driveshafts are a solid shaft; some are hollow tubing. A U-joint allows the shaft to bend as the drive axle moves up and down (relative to the vehicle's body) when the wheels travel over bumps. Speed fluctuations occur in the driveshaft as the U-joints transfer power at an angle, but these fluctuations are canceled out or eliminated by the joint at the other end of the shaft.

A FWD driveshaft must use a CV joint at its ends because the front wheels must be steered at sharp angles. Jerky steering wheel or drive wheel motion would occur if normal U-joints were used. As their name implies, CV joints transfer power without velocity change or speed fluctuation. Because CV joints are rather expensive and require a clean, well-lubricated environment, they are enclosed in a special boot. The short driveshafts used with transaxles and independent rear suspension drive axles are often called **half shafts.** Driveshafts, U-joints, and CV joints are described more completely in Chapter 9.

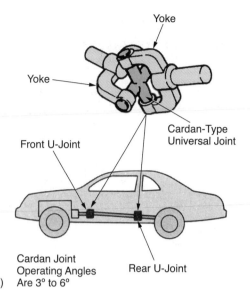

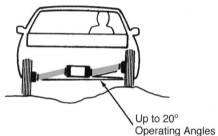

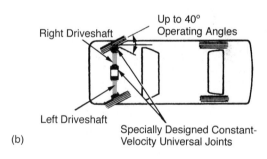

FIGURE 3-29 (a) An RWD driveshaft uses a pair of universal joints to allow the rear axle to move up and down. (b) A FWD driveshaft uses a pair of constant-velocity joints to allow the front wheels to move up and down and steer. (Courtesy of Ford Motor Company)

3.12 DRIVE AXLES

Most RWD vehicles use a drive axle assembly at the rear: (Figure 3-30). A **drive axle** serves several functions:

1. It supports the weight of the rear of the vehicle.
2. It contains the final drive reduction gears.
3. It contains the differential.

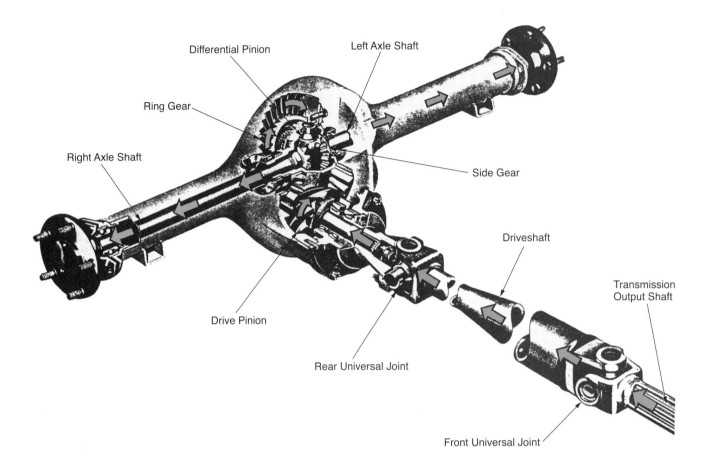

Differential Pinion

Left Axle Shaft

Ring Gear

Right Axle Shaft

Side Gear

Driveshaft

Transmission
Output Shaft

Drive Pinion

Rear Universal Joint

Front Universal Joint

FIGURE 3-30 A drive axle includes a ring and pinion gear to produce a lower gear ratio as it turns the power flow and a differential (differential pinion and side gears) to allow the drive wheels to rotate at different speeds. (Courtesy of Ford Motor Company.)

Many people call the drive axle assembly the *differential*. The drive axles used with **independent rear suspension** (IRS) (where one wheel can move vertically without moving the other) have separate wheel bearing assemblies and thus serve only the latter two functions.

Most axle assemblies use strong axle shafts to transfer the torque from the differential gears to the wheel and tire. A bearing at the outer end of the axle housing serves to transfer vehicle weight to the axle and then onto the wheel and tire while allowing the shaft to rotate.

The term **final drive** refers to the last set of reduction gears in a gear train. The term is commonly used when discussing truck and heavy equipment drivetrains. These reduction gears, along with the drive wheel diameter, determine the cruise speed engine rpm and, along with the transmission gear ratios, the tractive force of the drivetrain.

3.13   FOUR-WHEEL DRIVE

A vehicle will have more pulling power and traction if it drives all its wheels. This requires a drive axle at each end of the vehicle, another driveshaft, and a **transfer case** to drive the additional shaft and axle. A 4WD can be built into a front-engined RWD, a front-engined FWD, and a rear-engined RWD (Figure 3-31). The term 4×4 refers to a vehicle that has four wheels and that drives four wheels.

If 4WD is to be used all the time, a problem arises when a vehicle turns a corner, because each of the wheels rotates at a different speed (Figure 3-32). The fastest wheel will be the outer front, followed by the outer rear and the inner front, and the slowest is the inner rear. Three differentials must be used, one in each drive axle assembly plus an inner axle differential between the two drive axles. If a 4WD vehicle is operated on pavement in 4WD, the different speeds of the front

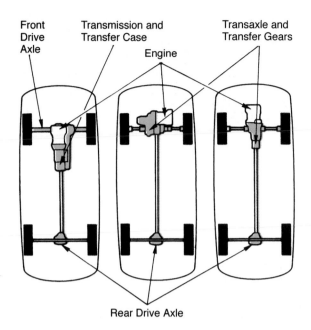

Front Drive Axle

Transmission and Transfer Case

Transaxle and Transfer Gears

Engine

Rear Drive Axle

FIGURE 3-31 Common 4WD drivetrain arrangements.

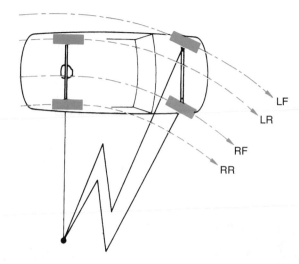

LF

LR

RF

RR

FIGURE 3-32 Each wheel travels at a different speed as a vehicle turns a corner. The outside front (LF) wheel must rotate the fastest, and the inside rear (RR) wheel moves the slowest. An all-wheel drive vehicle requires three differentials. (Courtesy of Ford Motor Company)

and rear tires will cause scuffing of the tires and a bindup of the gear train. Most 4WD vehicles are used in 2WD on pavement where the extra traction is not needed and shifted into 4WD when poor traction requires its use. When used with poor traction, tire slippage takes care of any tire scuffing or gear bind.

The added drive axle used with many 4WDs is almost the same as an RWD axle except that when used as a front axle, the outer ends must steer. This requires a steering knuckle at the outer end of the housing and a U-joint or CV joint at the outer end of the axle shaft. If a U-joint is used,

a steering wheel fluctuation and a fluctuation in the tires' rotation is usually noticeable on sharp turns.

The transfer case is normally attached to the rear of the transmission (Figure 3-33). It has a single input shaft from the transmission and two output shafts, one to the front and one to the rear drive axle. A dog clutch is used to engage the power flow to the second axle when 4WD is desired. A dog clutch is a simple mechanical clutch that resembles one internal gear that is slid over an external gear. Some newer transfer cases include a magnetic friction clutch that allows 4WD

FIGURE 3-33 This 4WD pickup uses a transfer case to provide the power flow to the front driveshaft and drive axle. (Courtesy of Ford Motor Company)

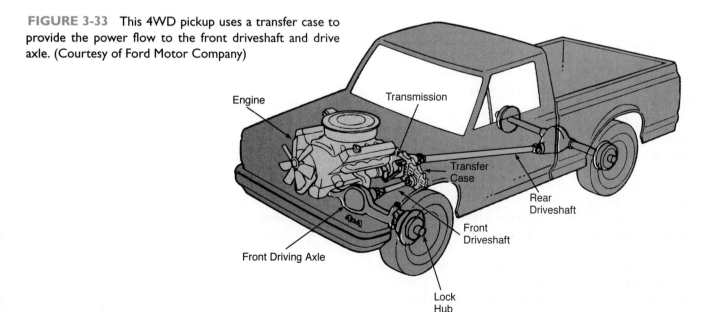

Engine

Transmission

Transfer Case

Rear Driveshaft

Front Driveshaft

Front Driving Axle

Lock Hub

engagement while the vehicle is moving. Some transfer cases are two-speed and include a set of reduction gears for lower-speed, higher-torque operation.

All-wheel drive (AWD), also called full-time 4WD, vehicles are 4WD vehicles equipped with CV joints on the front axles and an inner axle differential so they can be operated on pavement in 4WD. Some of the more expensive vehicles use a very sophisticated inner axle differential that can change the amount of torque going to each drive axle depending on traction conditions. 4WD and AWD are described more completely in Chapter 13.

REVIEW QUESTIONS

The following questions are provided to help you study as you read the chapter.

1. The gear ratios in the transmission are used to match the engine _____ and _____ to the requirements of the vehicle.

2. _____ gears have their teeth cut in a spiral.

3. _____ gears have their teeth cut straight.

4. _____ gears are used in most rear drive axles.

5. To determine a gear ratio, _____ the _____ gear by the _____ gear.

6. Which is the lower ratio: 5:1 or 3:1? _____

7. The transmission provides the gear ratio that will multiply the _____ sufficiently enough to move the vehicle.

8. The _____ allows the driver to interrupt the power flow to the transmission.

9. An automatic transmission is operated by _____ pressure.

10. The _____ _____ replaces the clutch in an automatic transmission.

11. A transaxle is a combination of a _____ and the final drive and _____.

12. _____ are used to transfer power from one component to another.

13. The driveshafts used with independent rear suspension are often called _____ _____.

14. A four-wheel drive vehicle has a _____ _____ attached to the rear of the transmission to drive the front axle.

15. All-wheel drive vehicles require an additional _____ to allow for the speed difference of the four tires.

CHAPTER QUIZ

The following questions will help you check the facts you have learned. Select the answer that completes each statement correctly.

1. A car's drivetrain can send power to the (A) rear wheels, (B) front wheels. Which is correct?
   a. A only
   b. B only
   c. Either A or B
   d. Neither A nor B

2. The turning form of mechanical power that passes through a rotating shaft is called (A) horsepower, (B) torque. Which is correct?
   a. A only
   b. B only
   c. Both A and B
   d. Neither A nor B

3. The power output from an automotive engine
   a. is almost constant from 0 rpm up to the maximum rpm.
   b. begins at about 1000 rpm and is almost constant up to the maximum rpm.
   c. begins at about 1000 rpm, increases until about 2500 rpm, and then decreases.
   d. begins at about 1000 rpm and increases up to the maximum rpm.

4. Gear ratios can be used to increase (A) horsepower, (B) torque. Which is correct?
   a. A only
   b. B only
   c. Both A and B
   d. Neither A nor B

5. If a gear with 20 teeth is driving a gear with 60 teeth, the gear ratio is
   a. 2:6.
   b. 3:1.
   c. 1:3.
   d. 0.33:1.

6. Two students are comparing spur and helical gears. Student A says a helical gear is stronger. Student B says a helical gear runs noisier. Who is correct?
   a. Student A
   b. Student B
   c. Both A and B
   d. Neither A nor B

7. A gear set used to transmit power between two shafts that meet at a right angle is the (A) hypoid gear set, (B) spiral bevel gear set. Which is correct?
   a. A only
   b. B only
   c. Both A and B
   d. Neither A nor B

8. The transmission is in first gear, which has a 2.5:1 ratio, and the rear axle has a ratio of 2:1. The overall gear ratio is (A) 4.5:1, (B) 5:1. Which is correct?

   a. A only
   b. B only
   c. Both A and B
   d. Neither A nor B

9. Drive-tire and wheel diameter will affect (A) vehicle speed, (B) tractive force. Which is correct?

   a. A only
   b. B only
   c. Both A and B
   d. Neither A nor B

10. Which car requires the most transmission gear ratios?

    a. light car, small engine
    b. light car, big engine
    c. heavy car, small engine
    d. heavy car, big engine

11. Two students are discussing clutch application. Student A says they must engage completely, all at once. Student B says there must be a small amount of slipping. Who is correct?

    a. Student A
    b. Student B
    c. Both A and B
    d. Neither A nor B

12. A continuously variable transmission uses (A) planetary gears like an automatic transmission, (B) special gears that can change diameter. Which is correct?

    a. A only
    b. B only
    c. Both A and B
    d. Neither A nor B

13. Two students are discussing front driveshafts. Student A says CV joints are used so the front wheels can turn sharp corners. Student B says CV joints are used to prevent jerky steering wheel motions while turning. Who is correct?

    a. Student A
    b. Student B
    c. Both A and B
    d. Neither A nor B

14. A differential (A) provides the gear reduction needed in the drive axle, (B) drives two wheels at different speeds. Which is correct?

    a. A only
    b. B only
    c. Both A and B
    d. Neither A nor B

15. An AWD car must have a differential (A) in each drive axle, (B) between the two drive axles. Which is correct?

    a. A only
    b. B only
    c. Both A and B
    d. Neither A nor B

Chapter 4

CLUTCH THEORY

LEARNING OBJECTIVES

After completing this chapter, you should be able to:

1. Identify the parts of a clutch assembly and know the purpose of each.
2. Understand the requirements for good, smooth clutch operation.
3. Identify the components used to operate a clutch.

TERMS TO LEARN

Auburn
Borg and Beck
clutch cable
clutch disc
clutch fork
clutch housing
clutch plate
coefficient of friction
cone clutch
cover
cushioned disc
damper
diaphragm
dog clutch
dual mass flywheel
engagement modulation
facing
fluid clutch

flywheel
hub and damper assembly
hydraulic
hydraulic clutch
lining
linkage
Long
magnetic clutch
Marcel
modular clutch
one-way clutch
pilot bearing
pivot shaft
pressure plate assembly
pressure ring
pressure springs
release bearing
release bearing support

release levers
sprag clutch
stepped flywheel

throw-out bearing
wet clutch

4.1   INTRODUCTION

The clutch connects the engine to the transmission. It is disengaged to allow the driver to select the appropriate gear range. You may remember the first time you drove a vehicle with a manual transmission. The first few times you let the clutch out the engine stalled or the vehicle jumped forward. You soon learned to feather the clutch. Engaging the clutch slowly and increasing the engine speed allowed the vehicle to move smoothly from a stop.

The major parts of a clutch assembly are the **pressure plate assembly, flywheel,** and **clutch disc** (Figure 4-1). The pressure plate and flywheel are the clutch input members and revolve at engine speed. The clutch disc is the clutch output member. It is splined to the transmission input shaft and provides input to the transmission.

The clutch disc is firmly clamped between the flywheel and pressure plate when the clutch is engaged. This will allow the engine's torque to be transferred to the transmission (Figure 4-2). When the clutch is disengaged, the pressure plate will move away from the disc and flywheel, which releases the pressure on the disc. The power flow through the clutch will be interrupted.

The clutch must transmit the engine torque without slipping when completely engaged but allow con-

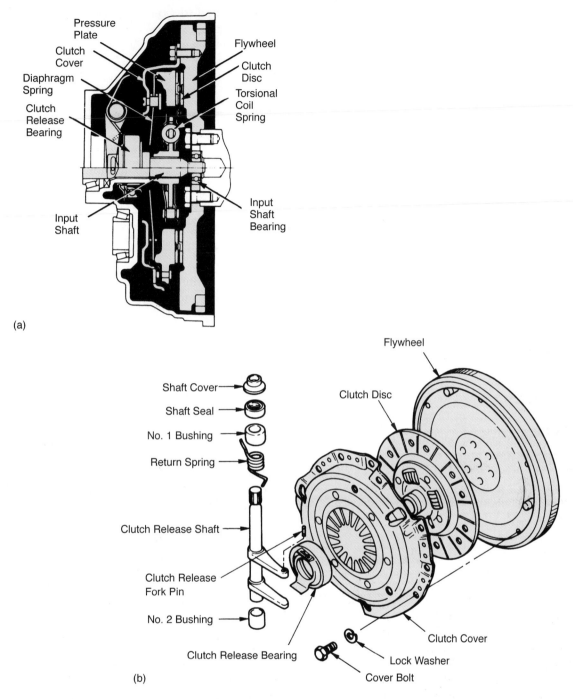

FIGURE 4-1 Cutaway (a) and exploded (b) view of a clutch assembly, showing the various components. (Portions of materials contained herein have been reprinted with permission of General Motors Corporation, Service and Parts Operations, License Agreement #0310807)

trolled slippage as the clutch is being engaged. Clutch engagement begins as the clutch disc is squeezed between the flywheel and pressure plate. The torque transfer through the clutch increases until the clutch is completely engaged. The controlled

slip is known as clutch **engagement modulation** (Figure 4-3).

The amount of torque that a clutch can transmit is a product of the contact surface area that exists between the clutch disc, pressure plate and flywheel, the

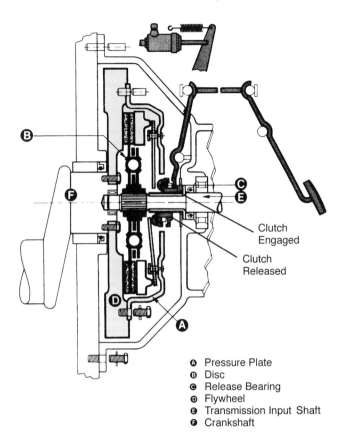

A Pressure Plate
B Disc
C Release Bearing
D Flywheel
E Transmission Input Shaft
F Crankshaft

FIGURE 4-2 A clutch is applied when the spring(s) pushes the pressure plate toward the flywheel, squeezing the disc against the flywheel (top). Pushing on the clutch pedal forces the release bearing to pull the pressure plate away from the disc, releasing the clutch (bottom). (Courtesy of LUK Clutches)

coefficient of friction of the disc lining, and how tightly the disc is squeezed. The formula used to the compute the clutch capacity is:

$$T = n \times f \times F \times r$$

where:

T = torque in foot-pounds

n = number of friction surfaces (two per disc)

f = facing coefficient of friction (0.25 is average)

F = total effective pressure (clamping force) in pounds

r = mean effective radius of lining in feet [(inside radius + outside radius) ÷ 2]

From this formula, torque capacity will increase if friction surfaces are added (two or three disc clutches are sometimes used), the coefficient of friction is increased (clutch grab might occur), the spring pressure is increased (clutch pedal effort will increase), or a larger mean radius (larger disc, pressure plate, and flywheel) is used.

Coefficient of friction describes the relative amount of friction between two surfaces. A simple explanation of this is shown in Figure 4-4, which compares the force that it takes to slide a block of rubber (the tire) over dry pavement, wet pavement, and ice. Tire traction suffers from friction loss when a road becomes wet and almost disappears when ice forms. Similarly, if the coefficient of friction of the clutch were

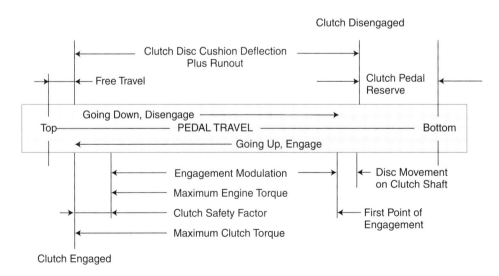

FIGURE 4-3 Clutch pedal travel (center) causes several things to occur during disengagement (top, at left) and engagement (bottom, at right).

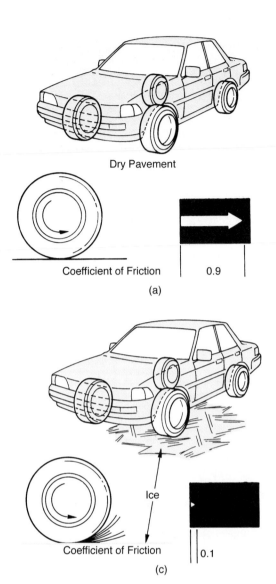

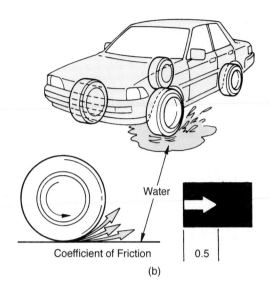

FIGURE 4-4   (a) The coefficient of friction between a tire and dry pavement is about 0.9, providing enough traction to steer and stop safely. (b) Rain will drop this friction coefficient to about 0.5, limiting traction. (c) Ice will reduce the coefficient of friction to about 0.1, making stopping and steering difficult and somewhat dangerous.

less, it might slip and not transmit the required torque. If the friction coefficient were greater, the clutch would become more aggressive and grabby, and engagement would be harsh and severe.

In addition to the pressure plate assembly and disc, the clutch needs a method to release it; this is accomplished by the **release bearing, clutch fork,** and **linkage.** The release bearing, also called a **throw-out bearing,** is mounted on the **release bearing support,** also called a *bearing guide, candlestick,* or *quill.* This is built into the transmission front bearing retainer. When the clutch pedal is depressed, the linkage and clutch fork force the release bearing against the release levers or diaphragm fingers of the pressure plate assembly. This causes the pressure plate to move rearward, releasing the clutch.

4.2 CLUTCH DISCS

A variety of discs are available, with each disc incorporating design features that make it most suitable for a particular installation. A disc is made up of several major parts: the **hub and damper assembly, facing** or **lining,** and plate or web with Marcel (Figure 4-5). Disc size is measured at the outside diameter of the friction material.

4.2.1 Clutch Hub and Damper Assembly

The clutch hub has internal splines (from 10 to 26) that slide over the external splines of the transmission input/clutch shaft. Each time the clutch is applied, the disc must slide forward slightly to contact the flywheel;

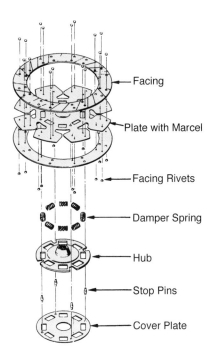

FIGURE 4-5   Exploded view of a clutch disc showing the various parts. (Courtesy of McLeod Industries, Inc.)

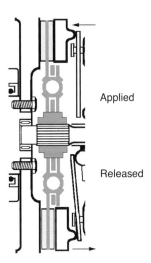

FIGURE 4-6   During apply and release, the clutch hub must slide slightly on the transmission shaft, as the facing moves toward or away from the flywheel.

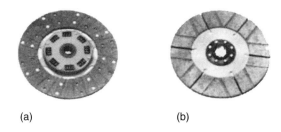

FIGURE 4-7   Cushioned disc (a) and rigid disc (b) that has the plate connected directly to the hub. (Courtesy of McLeod Industries, Inc.)

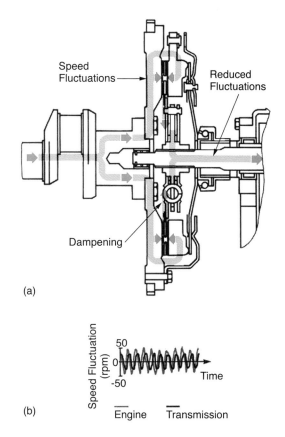

FIGURE 4-8   (a) When an engine runs, the crankshaft and flywheel must speed up and slow during each revolution. (b) The torsional springs and damper assembly reduce these speed fluctuations. (Courtesy of LUK Clutches)

it must slide back to prevent drag on the flywheel when the clutch is released (Figure 4-6).

Most discs include a damper assembly as part of the hub, and these are called cushioned (or dampened) discs. A few discs have the hub secured solidly to the web and are called rigid discs (Figure 4-7). An engine produces uneven power impulses that cause tortional vibration. The **damper** reduces and tries to eliminate the torsional vi-

brations that result from the uneven power impulses in the engine from the rest of the drivetrain. As an engine goes through its power cycle, the crankshaft will try to speed up and slow down during portions of each revolution. If these slight speed fluctuations are not removed by the damper, they will cause "gear rattle," vibration, noise, and increased wear (Figure 4-8). The damper assembly is composed of the hub with four to eight openings or fingerlike extensions, one or more springs for each extension, a spring washer, and a friction washer. These parts are fitted between the web of the disc and a metal retainer and are held together by a series of rivets called *stop pins*, which also keep the hub from revolving too far. The damper springs are positioned by a series of windows in the web and retainer. The torque must pass through the damper springs on its way from the engine to the transmission, and any power impulses that tend to speed up the clutch hub will compress the springs. The springs will reextend when there is a torque lag. The springs and washer portion of a damper assembly are designed to absorb the torsional vibrations of a particular engine.

4.2.2 Clutch Facing

The clutch friction material must be able to withstand the heat generated by that friction during engagement and disengagement. Traditionally, a mixture of asbestos has been used with various filler and binder materials in either a molded or woven form. You can see the fibers in a woven disc. Asbestos is nearly an ideal friction material for brake lining and clutch facing because it has a very good coefficient of friction, excellent heat characteristics, and low cost. However, the possibility of getting cancer from inhaling asbestos fibers has greatly reduced its use. Federal law banned the manufacture of asbestos-containing clutch facings after August 1992. This ban is currently under review. Asbestos is being replaced with fiberglass and aramid nonmetallic compounds and metallic materials. Various mixtures of powdered iron, copper, graphite, and ceramics are used to obtain the desired friction and wear characteristics. At one time, asbestos-based facings were classed as organic materials.

The wear rate and coefficient of friction of nonmetallic facings is greatly affected by temperature, as shown in Figure 4-9. If the facing is overheated, its capacity to transmit torque is lowered, and this will probably cause slippage and more heat. As the temperature increases, the binders holding the facing material together will lose their strength, greatly increasing the wear rate. It is possible for the facing to last many thousands of miles and then become worn out in one prolonged period of slipping and heating.

The facing is attached to the Marcel portion of the plate by a series of rivets installed in counterbored holes or by bonding (Figure 4-10). Some metallic facings are formed directly onto a steel backing. If there is less than 0.015 in. (0.38 mm) of facing above the rivets or backing, a disc is considered worn out.

Most nonmetallic facings have a series of radial grooves cut across their surface (Figure 4-11). These

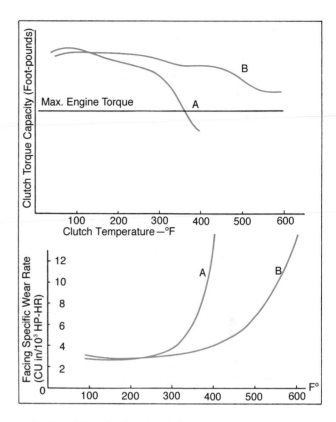

FIGURE 4-9   As the clutch facing temperature increases, its ability to transfer torque decreases (top) and its wear rate increases (bottom). Facing A is a normal production facing material; facing B is a heavy-duty, high-performance facing. (Courtesy of Ford Motor Company)

◀ SAFETY TIP ▶

As asbestos facing wears, minute particles of lightweight asbestos fibers break off. If one or more of these fibers lodge in the lining of your nose, throat, nasal passage, or lungs, they can produce cancer. When working around automotive clutch or brake assemblies, you should be extra careful not to let the dust particles enter the air or inhale any of these airborne particles.

grooves wipe dust and dirt from the surfaces of the flywheel and pressure plate, and they promote an airflow to help cool the friction surfaces and break a vacuum that might cause the friction surfaces to stick together during release. Some metallic discs have a series of radial slots cut across the facing; these slots allow the disc to expand without warping when it gets hot.

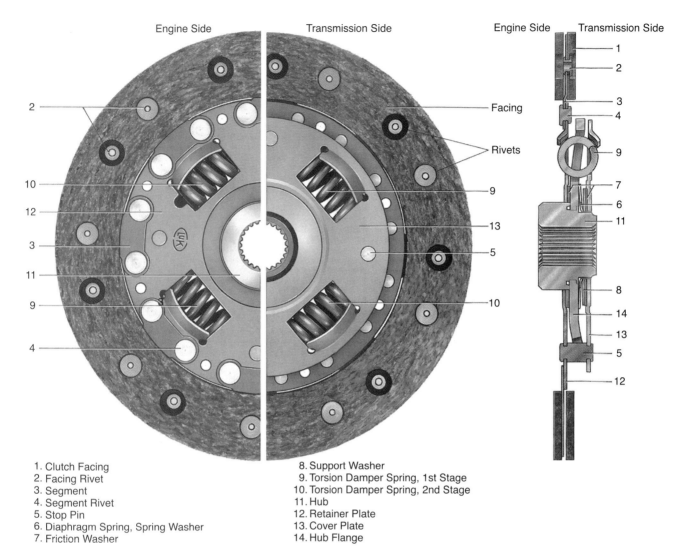

1. Clutch Facing
2. Facing Rivet
3. Segment
4. Segment Rivet
5. Stop Pin
6. Diaphragm Spring, Spring Washer
7. Friction Washer
8. Support Washer
9. Torsion Damper Spring, 1st Stage
10. Torsion Damper Spring, 2nd Stage
11. Hub
12. Retainer Plate
13. Cover Plate
14. Hub Flange

FIGURE 4-10   The facing is riveted to one end of the Marcel segments in an alternating manner. This allows the Marcel to expand while the clutch is released and compress during clutch engagement. (Courtesy of LUK Clutches)

4.2.3   Plate

The plate of the disc connects the facing (where the torque enters) to the hub (where it leaves). It also contains the Marcel, which is a large series of wave springs. Figure 4-12 shows how the facing is attached to the **Marcel** so that the disc can compress as the clutch is applied. This causes a slight time lag that allows the clutch to apply more smoothly. Clutch discs used for racing, where smooth operation is not necessary, often do not have Marcels.

4.3   PRESSURE PLATE ASSEMBLIES

The **pressure plate assembly** is a combination of the **pressure ring (plate)**, **cover** (also called a *hat*), **pressure springs,** and **release levers** (also called *fingers*). There are four basic styles of pressure plates: **Auburn, Borg and Beck, diaphragm,** and **Long** (Figure 4-13). Three of these styles are named for their early manufacturer, and one is named for the type of spring used. The major characteristics of each design are as follows:

FIGURE 4-11 Most asbestos and nonasbestos organic facings have a series of grooves cut across the surface. (Courtesy of LUK Clutches)

- **Auburn:** very open cover; springs act through the leverage of the release levers; uses three or six springs; mounting holes are three groups of one or two holes.
- **Borg and Beck:** the most closed cover; three wide stamped-steel release levers; up to 12 springs; usually has six evenly spaced mounting holes.
- **Diaphragm:** a ringlike cover; uses a many-fingered diaphragm spring, which also serves as the release lever; usually has six evenly spaced mounting holes.
- **Long:** a somewhat triangular cover; three narrow, forged-steel release levers, which extend through the cover and often have weights on them; usually uses nine springs; usually has mounting bolt holes in three groups of two.

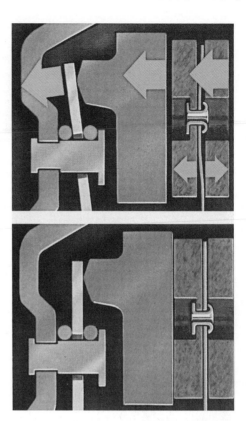

FIGURE 4-12 When a clutch is released, the Marcel springs expand the thickness of the facing (bottom). During reapplication of the clutch, these segments compress, causing a slight lag and much smoother application (top). (Courtesy of LUK Clutches)

The Borg and Beck and diaphragm designs are the most common at this time. The Auburn design is not commonly used on modern passenger vehicles. The relatively low height of the diaphragm design is highly favored for modern transverse engine vehicles where engine and transaxle length are critical.

The pressure plate used on a few FWD vehicles is bolted directly onto the engine's crankshaft, and the flywheel is bolted onto the pressure plate. This allows the release bearing to be placed inside the pressure plate and operated by a pull rod through the transmission input shaft. It is often called a *pull-type* clutch (Figure 4-14a).

Another pull-type clutch style is a modification of a diaphragm clutch. The mounting of the diaphragm spring is moved in the cover and at the pressure ring so a pulling force is used to release the clutch instead of the normal pushing force (Figure 4-14b and c). This change produces an improvement in clutch system efficiency and a lower clutch pedal effort.

Borg & Beck Style

Diaphragm Style

Long Style

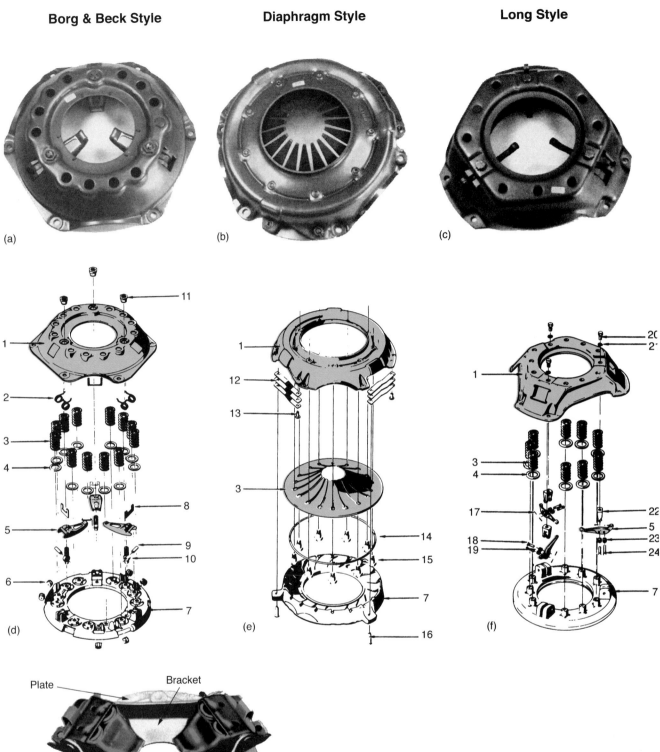

(a)

(b)

(c)

(d)

(e)

(f)

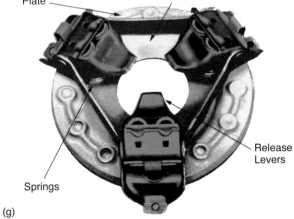

Plate

Bracket

Springs

Release
Levers

(g)

FIGURE 4-13 The major styles of pressure plate assembly are Borg and Beck (a and d), diaphragm (b and e), and Long (c and f); the Auburn design (g) is used occasionally. d, e, and f are exploded views. (a, b, and c are courtesy of RAM Automotive; d, e, and f are courtesy of McLeod Industries, Inc.; g is reproduced with permission of Deere & Company, © 1972 Deere & Company. All rights reserved.)

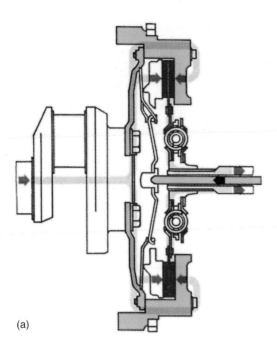

(a)

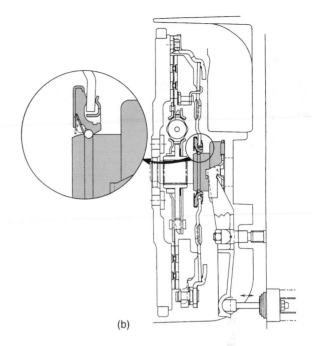

(b)

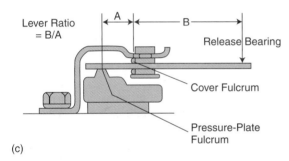

(c)

FIGURE 4-14   (a) One older design, pull-type pressure plate assembly is operated through a push rod that slides through the transaxle shaft; note how the clutch cover attaches to the crankshaft. (b) A more common pull style connects the release bearing to the diaphragm fingers so that the release bearing can pull on them. A pull clutch has a better lever ratio, as shown in c. (a is courtesy of LUK Clutches; b: Portions of materials contained herein have been reprinted with permission of General Motors Corporation, Service and Parts Operations, License Agreement #0310807)

4.3.1   Pressure Ring

A pressure ring is simply a flat, fairly heavy ring usually made from cast iron. The heavy weight is necessary to dissipate heat and have sufficient heat sink so as not to warp. It also provides sufficient strength so it will spread the spring force evenly onto the disc. For high-rpm use, the ring is made from cast steel because centrifugal force can cause a cast iron ring to explode.

When a clutch slips, heat is generated at the friction surfaces, and this heat will warm up both the facing and the pressure ring. Excess heat will cause the pressure ring to expand to the point of warpage, destroying its flatness and causing poor ring-to-facing contact. The greater the mass of the pressure ring, the less the tem-perature will rise because the heat will spread through more metal.

Torque enters the pressure ring from the cover, either through a drive strap or a boss where the release levers extend through openings in the cover. Torque passes out through the friction contact with the facing on the disc.

Pressure plate diameter is measured at the outside diameter of the pressure plate ring. It should always be the same size or slightly larger than the disc diameter.

4.3.2   Cover

The cover is the stamped-steel housing that transmits the torque from the flywheel to the pressure ring. It also provides a mounting place for the springs and release levers and must be strong enough to contain the various forces without distorting.

4.3.3   Pressure Springs

A diaphragm spring or a group of coil springs provides the clamping force needed to transmit the torque through the clutch assembly. Coil springs are wound from a metal with good high-temperature characteristics. The strength or rate of the spring is determined by the diameter of the wire, the diameter of the coil, the overall length, and the number of coils. Referring to the formula in Section 4.1, it would take 800 lb (364 kg) of force on a single-plate, 10-in. clutch to transmit the 300 ft-lb (407 N-m) of torque that a 305-in^3 (5-L) V8 engine can produce. The springs used in the pressure plate are of the size and number to produce the clamping force needed to keep the clutch from slipping.

A diaphragm spring is a type of Belleville spring that can also produce the needed clamping force. The conical shape of the diaphragm spring resists flattening, and this resistance produces the spring's force. It also produces an interesting strength-to-compression curve in that it produces a lot of spring force during the first part of compression and less after a certain point. A diaphragm spring has a very high rate during the first part of compression (Figure 4-15). This results in a higher clutch pedal effort as the pedal is first depressed, and then a lower effort at midtravel.

The force on a coil spring increases in direct proportion to its compressed length; this is called the *spring rate*. A coil spring pressure plate starts with a lower pedal effort that increases steadily as the pedal is depressed.

As a disc wears and becomes thinner, coil springs will have less clamping force because they are not compressed as far as when the disc was new. Oddly, a diaphragm pressure plate will have more clamping power because of the spring's force characteristics.

A recent development to extend clutch wear life is a self-adjusting fulcrum ring. As the disc facing wears, three springs between the plastic fulcrum ring and the clutch cover move the ring, and this changes the fulcrum point. This maintains a constant finger geometry to keep pedal effort the same over the life of the disc (Figure 4-16).

4.3.4   Release Levers

The release levers provide a means of compressing the spring(s) and pulling the pressure ring away from

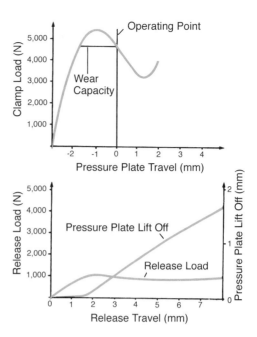

FIGURE 4-15   The pressure plate clamping load of a diaphragm spring clutch actually increases slightly as the facing wears (top). The release bearing load increases only slightly after the point of pressure plate lift-off (bottom). (Courtesy of LUK Clutches)

the disc. This movement is called *plate lift*. Along with the leverage of the clutch linkage, release levers provide a lever that will produce the necessary 500 to 1500 lb (227 to 682 kg) of force needed at the pressure plate from the 20 lb (9 kg) or so used to push the clutch pedal. A 1000-lb spring load at the pressure ring to a pedal load of 20 lb is a ratio of 1000 to 20, or 50:1. The pressure plate lever ratio is somewhere between 3.5:1 and 5:1; the linkage between the pedal and the release bearing must provide the remaining leverage (Figure 4-17). The 3.5:1 ratio will produce more pressure plate lift but will require a greater pedal effort. The 5:1 ratio provides less pedal effort but either requires longer pedal travel or provides less plate lift. Also, remember that with a 50:1 ratio, 4 in. (101.6 mm) of clutch pedal travel will produce only 0.080 in. (2.032 mm) of pressure ring travel, just enough to allow the Marcel to expand and produce enough plate lift for a slight air gap.

The Long style of release levers provides an advantage in that the weights on the levers allow weaker springs to be used. Centrifugal force on these weights increases disc clamping force (Figure 4-18). When the clutch is first engaged, engine speed is low, so the engine is not producing full torque. As the engine speed and torque output increase, centrifugal force acting

Conventional Clutch Pressure Plate

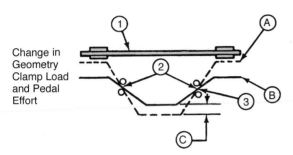

Change in Geometry Clamp Load and Pedal Effort

Self-Adjusting Pressure Plate

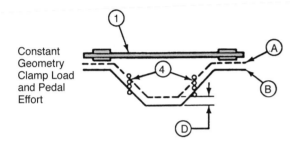

Constant Geometry Clamp Load and Pedal Effort

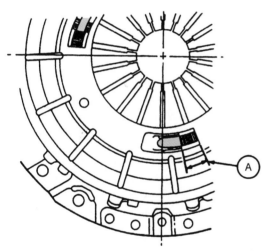

FIGURE 4-16 This pressure plate assembly (top) includes an adjustable fulcrum that moves to compensate for disc facing wear (bottom). The fulcrum (4) rotates slightly to keep the finger geometry and pedal effort consistent. (Courtesy of Ford Motor Company)

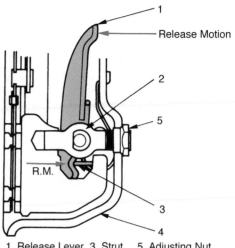

1. Release Lever 3. Strut   5. Adjusting Nut
2. Eyebolt   4. Cover

(a)

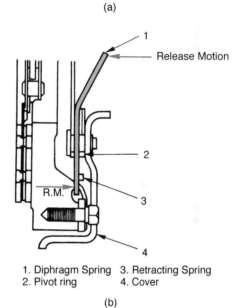

1. Diphragm Spring 3. Retracting Spring
2. Pivot ring   4. Cover

(b)

FIGURE 4-17 (a) In a Borg and Beck clutch, release motion of the throw-out bearing forces the release lever to pivot at the eyebolt and move the pressure plate toward the cover. (b) A similar motion occurs at the diaphragm spring in a diaphragm clutch. (Portions of materials contained herein have been reprinted with permission of General Motors Corporation, Service and Parts Operations, License Agreement #0310807)

through the levers increases clutch torque capacity. This also increases the effort needed to depress the pedal at higher rpm. It is also the reason why the engine is run at a specified rpm when checking clutch pedal free travel on some vehicles.

Centrifugal force can also affect a diaphragm clutch. During a very high rpm disengagement, if the fingers are moved far enough forward so that they pass

over center (beyond flat), centrifugal force will try to throw the weight of the fingers in the other direction. Some people have seen this as a shift at high rpm in which the pedal stays on the floor while the engine over-revs. To prevent this, "bent finger" diaphragms are used for installations where high-rpm shifts might occur (Figure 4-19). The bent feature of the fingers keeps them from traveling over center.

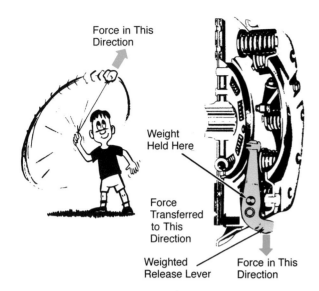

Force in This Direction

Weight Held Here

Force Transferred to This Direction

Weighted Release Lever

Force in This Direction

FIGURE 4-18   At speed, the weights on the release levers of a Long clutch try to fly outward. This action increases the clamping force on the clutch disc. (Courtesy of Ford Motor Company)

4.3.5   Stepped Flywheels

Some manufacturers use a **stepped flywheel.** These are combined with a pressure plate that has either a flat or almost flat cover (Figure 4-20). Stepped flywheels have more of the mass at the outer edge, and this increases the amount of rotational inertia for the amount of mass.

4.3.6   Modular Clutch Assembly

A **modular clutch** is a combination of a flywheel, pressure plate, and disc in one assembly; the pressure plate is riveted onto the flywheel with the disc in-between. This assembly bolts onto a flex plate like the torque converter of an automatic transmission.

FIGURE 4-19   A bent finger diaphragm clutch. The shape of the fingers keeps the fingers and release bearing from going past center during clutch release. (Portions of materials contained herein have been reprinted with permission of General Motors Corporation, Service and Parts Operations, License Agreement #0310807)

If a modular clutch fails, it is removed and replaced with a new assembly, which has the disc centered, and also, the new assembly is balanced as a unit (Figure 4-21).

4.3.7   Double Disc Clutches

A relatively inexpensive method of increasing clutch capacity is to use two or more clutch discs. All that is required is another disc (much like the first), a floater plate, and a lengthened pressure plate cover with provision for

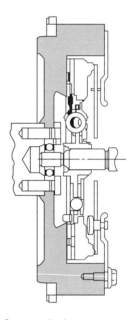

FIGURE 4-20   Some vehicles use a stepped flywheel with a rim that is thicker than the center portion where the clutch disc runs.

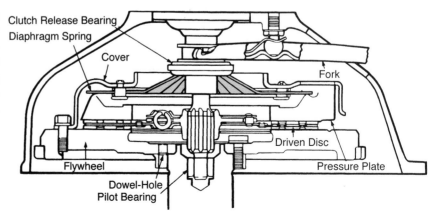

Clutch Release Bearing

Diaphragm Spring

Cover

Fork

Driven Disc

Flywheel

Pressure Plate

Dowel-Hole Pilot Bearing

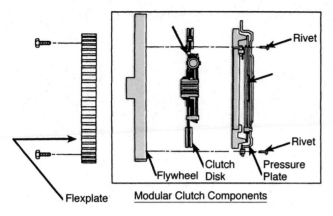

FIGURE 4-21 This modular clutch assembly combines the flywheel, clutch disc, and pressure plate in one assembly that is riveted together. The assembly is attached to a flexplate just like the torque converter with an automatic transmission. (Courtesy of Daimler Chrysler Corporation)

the floater plate (Figure 4-22). The floater plate must be able to move forward to squeeze the front disc against the flywheel and rearward during release to provide an air gap at this disc. Movement of the pressure plate provides the clamping force for both discs, and there must be enough movement to provide air gaps at both discs.

4.4 RELEASE BEARINGS

The release bearing is a thrust bearing that transmits the force from the clutch linkage to the spinning pressure plate release levers to release the clutch. It is a ball bearing that is lubricated during manufacture, then sealed. The bearing is often pressed onto a hub that attaches to the clutch fork and has a center hole sized to slide over the transmission bearing retainer quill (Figure 4-23). The release bearing is connected to the fork, which is mounted on a pivot shaft or a pivot point in the **clutch**

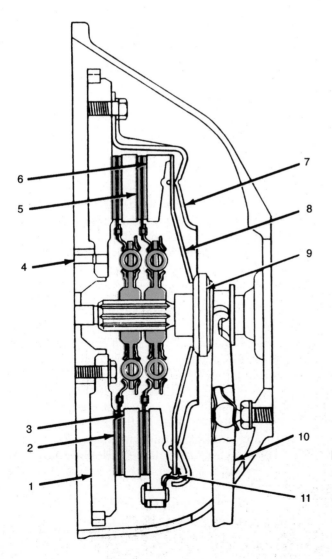

1. Flywheel
2. Front Driven Disc
3. Front Pressure Plate
4. Dowel Hole
5. Rear Driven Disc
6. Rear Pressure Plate
7. Cover
8. Diaphragm Spring
9. Throwout Bearing
10. Fork
11. Retracting Spring

FIGURE 4-22 Double disc clutch; note the front pressure plate (floater plate) between the two discs. The second **disc** doubles the torque capacity of the clutch. (Portions of materials contained herein have been reprinted with permission of General Motors Corporation, Service and Parts Operations, License Agreement #0310807)

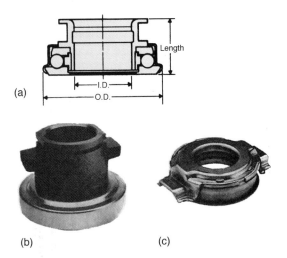

(a)

(b)   (c)

FIGURE 4-23   (a) Cutaway view of a clutch release bearing with the critical dimensions. A release bearing can be mounted onto a hub (b) or made integral with the hub (c). (Courtesy of CR Services)

housing (also called a **bell housing**). If a **pivot shaft** (also called a **cross shaft**) is used it extends out of the clutch housing, ending at a lever (Figure 4-24).

In many installations, the clutch linkage pulls the release bearing slightly away from the pressure plate levers when the clutch is released. This results in a slight free play at the clutch pedal, less wear of the bearing and release levers, and the assurance that the clutch is completely engaged. Many newer vehicles with self-adjusting mechanical or hydraulic linkage maintain a light contact between the release bearing and the release levers at all times.

There are several types of bearings. Many bearings are of the thrust type; others are self-aligning or self-centering, which can compensate for slight misalignment errors (Figure 4-25). In another variation, the face of the bearing is flat. This style is normally used with pressure plate release levers that have a curved contact surface (Figure 4-26a). Some release bearings have a curved face and are normally used with release levers that have flat contact surfaces (Figure 4-26b). A curved-face release bearing should never be used with curved-lever pressure plates.

The release bearing used on some older British and European vehicles is a circular carbon ring that presses against a polished steel ring attached to the clutch release levers. As expected, the carbon wears slightly each time the clutch is used (Figure 4-27).

While the clutch is released, the force being exerted by the release bearing onto the pressure plate is transmitted through the flywheel to the thrust bearing on the engine crankshaft. This bearing holds the crankshaft and flywheel in the proper lengthwise position.

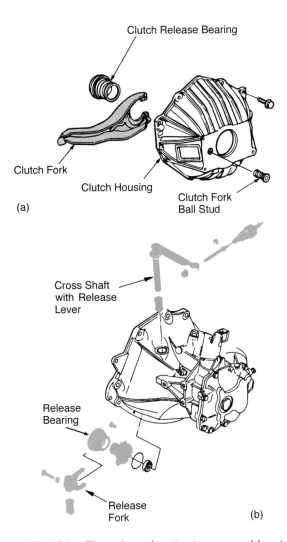

(a)

(b)

FIGURE 4-24   The release bearing is operated by either a release fork (a) or a cross shaft (b). (Portions of materials contained herein have been reprinted with permission of General Motors Corporation, Service and Parts Operations, License Agreement #0310807)

4.5 PILOT BEARINGS

The engine end of a transmission clutch shaft needs to be supported, and this is done by a **pilot bearing** that is pressed into the end of the crankshaft (Figure 4-28). This can be a sintered bronze oilite bearing, a needle bearing, or a ball bearing. The oilite bearing is impregnated with oil to lubricate it; the other types of bearings are usually lubricated and then sealed.

Some transaxles do not use pilot bearings because the input shaft is well supported by a pair of bearings inside the transmission.

Clutch service normally requires the replacement of worn or faulty parts. In most cases, a new clutch disc, pressure plate, release bearing, and pilot bearing

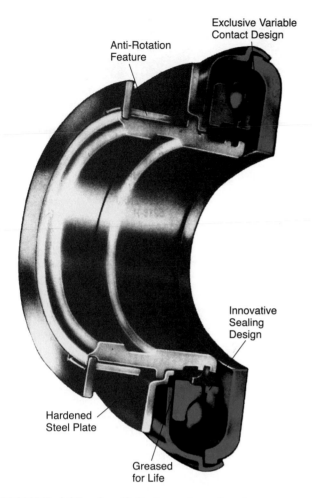

FIGURE 4-27 This release bearing has a disc of carbon on the face where it contacts a polished disc attached to the release levers. (Courtesy of CR Services)

4.6 CLUTCH LINKAGE

Three types of linkage are commonly used to transmit the movement and force from the pedal to the release bearing and pressure plate. They are: mechanical rods and levers, a mechanical cable, and hydraulic linkage. With each type, the motion moves the pressure plate away from the flywheel to release the clutch, or toward the flywheel to engage the clutch (Figure 4-29). The linkage provides a significant mechanical advantage so the driver can easily release the clutch (see Figure 16-19a).

Many modern vehicles are equipped with a clutch–starter interlock switch that prevents cranking and starting of the engine unless the clutch pedal is depressed. This switch is normally mounted at the clutch pedal.

4.6.1 Mechanical Rod Linkage

A mechanical rod linkage is a series of rods that transmits a pushing motion to the release fork/lever (Figure 4-30). If the motion needs to make a significant change in direction, bellcranks mounted on pivot shafts are used. This type of linkage ends at the clutch fork after it passes through an equalizer shaft that pivots from both the engine/bell housing and the car body. Because the clutch assembly and engine are on rubber mounts, the engine can move relative to the body and clutch pedal, and any movement during clutch operation can cause an unwanted apply, release, or chatter.

The clutch pedal used with this linkage usually includes an over-center, or assist, spring (Figure 4-31). This spring is mounted to pull the pedal upward during the first half of pedal travel and downward during the second half. This last action reduces pedal effort and helps release the clutch. You can demonstrate this by pushing on the clutch pedal with the linkage disconnected, *but be careful.* In most cases, the pedal will move downward rather violently.

FIGURE 4-25 A self-aligning release bearing can compensate for slight misalignments between the bearing and the pressure plate levers. (Courtesy of CR Services)

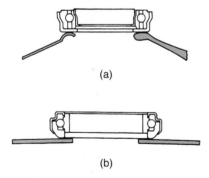

FIGURE 4-26 (a) A flat-faced release bearing is used with curled or curved release levers. (b) A radiused, or curved-face, bearing is used with flat fingers. (Courtesy of Tilton Engineering)

are installed during a "clutch job." In vehicles using a modular clutch, the clutch disc and pressure plate assembly are replaced as a unit. Clutch service and repair are described more completely in Chapter 5.

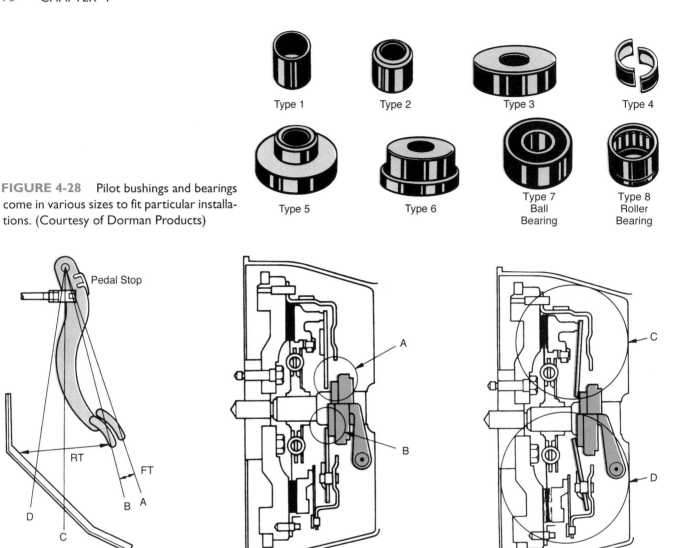

FIGURE 4-28 Pilot bushings and bearings come in various sizes to fit particular installations. (Courtesy of Dorman Products)

Type 1 Type 2 Type 3 Type 4

Type 5 Type 6 Type 7 Ball Bearing Type 8 Roller Bearing

(a)   (b)   (c)

FIGURE 4-29 When the clutch pedal is at its released position (a), there is clearance between the release bearing and the release levers. As the pedal moves through its free travel (b), the release bearing contacts the release levers. The pressure plate moves away from the disc (with the Marcel expanded) at point C, and further travel of the pedal to point D produces an air gap between the disc and the pressure plate and flywheel. Self-adjusting clutches release to point B.

Mechanical linkage includes an adjustment at some point so that free travel can be adjusted. This is merely a method of changing the length of one of the rods so that it is a bit shorter and a slight clearance exists [about 1 in. (25.4 mm) measured at the pedal, or about 1/16 in. (1.6 mm) measured at the clutch fork].

4.6.2 Mechanical Cable Linkage

Cable linkage consists of a steel cable attached to the clutch pedal. The clutch cable is routed to the en-

gine/bell housing, where it can pull on the clutch fork/lever (Figure 4-32). Much of the cable is enclosed in a housing or conduit so that it can be routed around corners or obstacles. Although simple and inexpensive, cables have a drawback in that they develop internal friction through time, which makes them harder to operate.

Many vehicles include a *self-adjuster mechanism* at the clutch pedal. Older vehicles include a method of manual adjustment, at the end of either the cable or cable housing. The self-adjuster is usually a spring-loaded cam that is locked onto the pedal when a spring-loaded

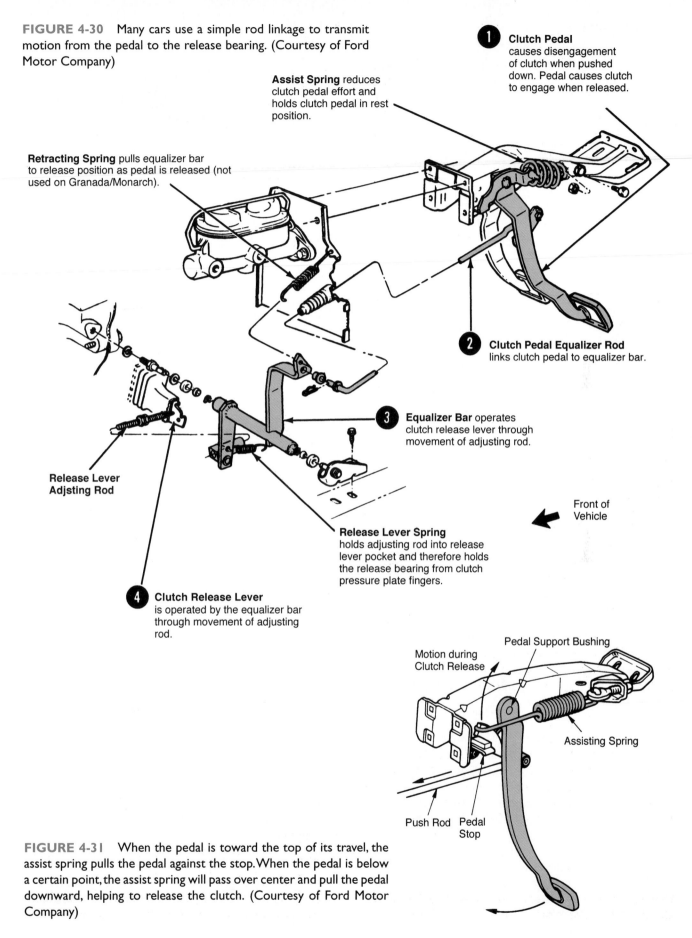

FIGURE 4-30 Many cars use a simple rod linkage to transmit motion from the pedal to the release bearing. (Courtesy of Ford Motor Company)

1 Clutch Pedal causes disengagement of clutch when pushed down. Pedal causes clutch to engage when released.

Assist Spring reduces clutch pedal effort and holds clutch pedal in rest position.

Retracting Spring pulls equalizer bar to release position as pedal is released (not used on Granada/Monarch).

2 Clutch Pedal Equalizer Rod links clutch pedal to equalizer bar.

3 Equalizer Bar operates clutch release lever through movement of adjusting rod.

Release Lever Adjsting Rod

Front of Vehicle

Release Lever Spring holds adjusting rod into release lever pocket and therefore holds the release bearing from clutch pressure plate fingers.

4 Clutch Release Lever is operated by the equalizer bar through movement of adjusting rod.

Motion during Clutch Release

Pedal Support Bushing

Assisting Spring

Push Rod Pedal Stop

FIGURE 4-31 When the pedal is toward the top of its travel, the assist spring pulls the pedal against the stop. When the pedal is below a certain point, the assist spring will pass over center and pull the pedal downward, helping to release the clutch. (Courtesy of Ford Motor Company)

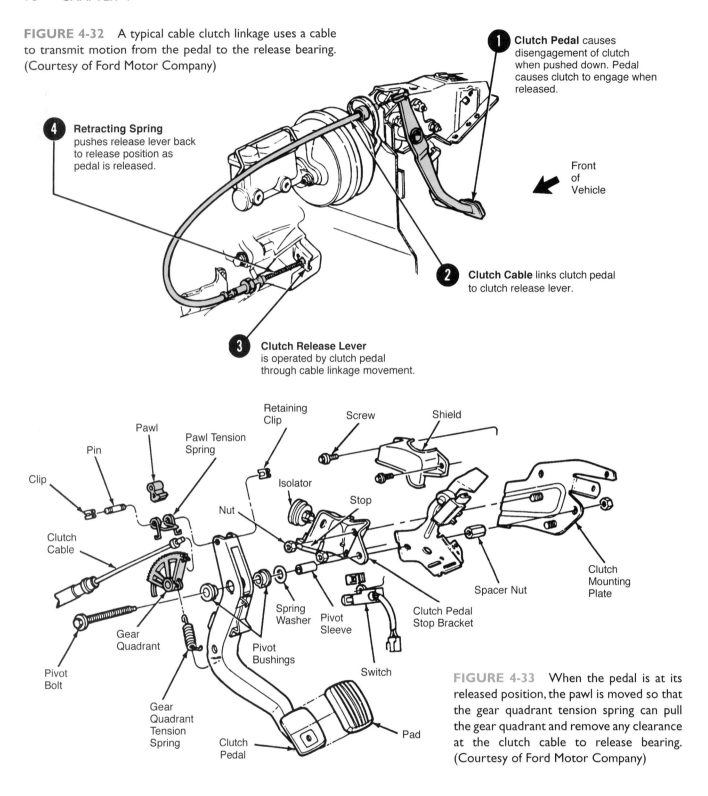

FIGURE 4-32 A typical cable clutch linkage uses a cable to transmit motion from the pedal to the release bearing. (Courtesy of Ford Motor Company)

1 Clutch Pedal causes disengagement of clutch when pushed down. Pedal causes clutch to engage when released.

4 Retracting Spring pushes release lever back to release position as pedal is released.

Front of Vehicle

2 Clutch Cable links clutch pedal to clutch release lever.

3 Clutch Release Lever is operated by clutch pedal through cable linkage movement.

FIGURE 4-33 When the pedal is at its released position, the pawl is moved so that the gear quadrant tension spring can pull the gear quadrant and remove any clearance at the clutch cable to release bearing. (Courtesy of Ford Motor Company)

pawl engages it (Figure 4-33). The pawl is lifted each time the clutch is released so that the cam's spring can rotate and remove any slack or clearance in the cable. When the pedal is applied, the pawl's spring returns it to lock the cam to the pedal.

4.6.3   Hydraulic Linkage

A **hydraulic** system transmits force through fluid. Liquids cannot be compressed, and if a force is put on liquid at one end of a passage, liquid at the other end

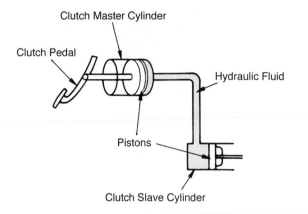

FIGURE 4-34 Simple hydraulic clutch system. The hydraulic fluid will transmit force and motion from the clutch pedal to the slave cylinder.

of the passage will exert the same force (Figure 4-34). Normally in a simple hand- or foot-operated system, force is exerted on a piston in the input cylinder, or pump, and leaves at the output cylinder. If these pistons are the same size, they will have equal force and movement. Whatever movement goes in one end will be at the other. If the input and output pistons are of different sizes, a hydraulic lever is created. If the input piston is smaller (which is normal), force will increase, but travel of the output piston will be reduced, just like a lever.

In a **hydraulic clutch** system, the input piston is located in the clutch master cylinder and will be connected to the clutch pedal (Figure 4-35). The output piston is located in the slave cylinder, and it will operate the clutch fork/lever. These two pistons will be

FIGURE 4-35 Hydraulic clutch system showing the clutch master cylinder and slave cylinder (1). (Portions of materials contained herein have been reprinted with permission of General Motors Corporation, Service and Parts Operations, License Agreement #0310807)

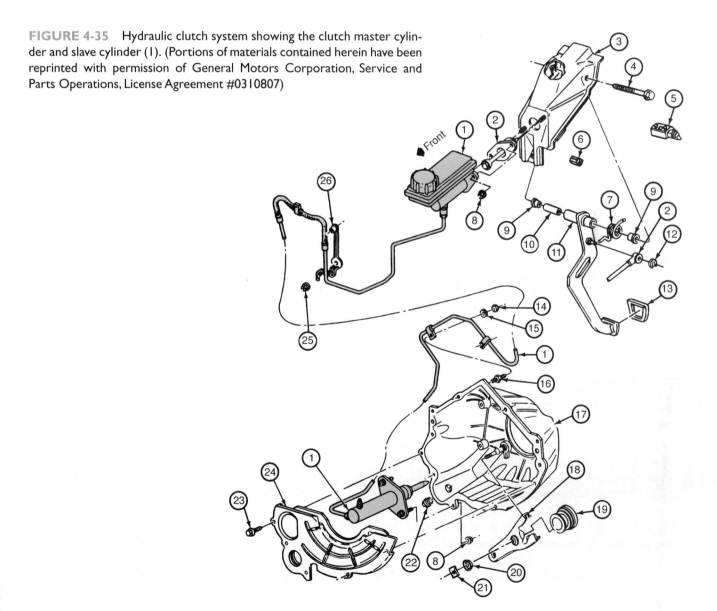

connected by metal, reinforced rubber, or plastic tubing. When the clutch pedal is depressed, the master cylinder piston forces fluid through the tubing to the slave cylinder, where the pressure forces the piston to move the clutch fork/lever. When the pedal is released, the pressure plate forces the slave cylinder piston to return the fluid to the master cylinder. When the master cylinder is released, a compensating port is opened up between the cylinder bore and the fluid reservoir. This allows for fluid expansion or contraction due to temperature changes, for any air to leave the fluid, and in many cases, for self-adjustment for disc wear. Because air can be compressed, any trapped in a hydraulic system will cause mushy, spongy, or incomplete operation.

DOT 3 brake fluid is generally used in clutch hydraulic systems. The slave cylinder used in some systems is concentric to the quill on the transmission bearing retainer and has the release bearing connected directly to it (Figure 4-36).

4.6.4   Clutch Pedal Switch

Modern vehicles have a clutch pedal position switch that is used to signal the starter circuit that the clutch is released; this prevents starter operation unless the clutch pedal is depressed. The switch is normally open, and it closes when the pedal is completely depressed. This completes the circuit from the ignition switch to the starter relay, and when the circuit is completed, the starter relay energizes the starter, cranking the engine (Figure 4-37). This safety feature prevents the vehicle from moving accidentally when the starter is engaged.

4.7   OTHER TYPES OF CLUTCHES

Other types of clutches are used for different purposes in the vehicle.

- **Wet clutch.** A clutch assembly enclosed in a chamber with fluid is a wet clutch (Figure 4-38a). The fluid keeps the friction surfaces cooler and can produce a better coefficient of friction.
- **Fluid clutch.** This is similar to the torque converter used in automatic transmissions, but it cannot increase torque (Figure 4-38b). It has two members, an input impeller, or torus, and an output torus (turbine).

- **Magnetic clutch.** One style of magnetic clutch is commonly used with air-conditioning compressors. A similar clutch is used in some transfer cases that shift into 4WD with the vehicle moving. This style uses a flat iron disc mounted next to another flat metal surface with a coil of wires behind it. When electric current passes through the coil, the metal plates are attracted to each other, transferring power. The other style of magnetic clutch uses a flat iron disc mounted in an enclosure between two surfaces with iron powder in the areas between them. Again, electric current passes through a coil of wires to create a magnetic field to transfer power (Figure 4-39).
- **Dog clutch.** This is a purely mechanical clutch in which one set of internal teeth are slid over a matching set of external teeth (Figure 4-40). A dog clutch can be engaged only if the two parts are at the exact same speed. Synchronizers in a standard transmission use a version of a dog clutch.
- **One-way clutch.** Also called a *roller* or *overrunning clutch*, this clutch can drive through a set of rollers, each with a cam (Figure 4-41a). The rollers will release or freewheel if the output tries to drive the input.
- **Sprag clutch.** The operation is similar to a one-way clutch except that the driving action is through a set of camlike sprags that rotate slightly to wedge and transmit power, or not wedge to release (Figure 4-41b).
- **Cone clutch.** This clutch was used with some older vehicles. Transmission synchronizer rings are a variation of a cone clutch. It consists of an internal cone and a matching external cone that can transmit power when pushed together (Figure 4-42).
- **Internal expanding shoe clutch.** This clutch, commonly called a centrifugal clutch and used on chain saws and go-carts, has a set of lined shoes that will expand from centrifugal force to engage a drum to transmit power. The shoes will release when the engine slows down and the springs can pull them away from the drum (Figure 4-43).
- **Automatic clutch actuation.** A standard transmission and friction clutch are more fuel efficient than an automatic transmission, but today's drivers prefer the convenience and driving ease of automatic transmissions. Automatic clutch controls are under development to make friction clutch vehicles easier to drive; these use an electronic control unit and a servomotor to operate the clutch (Figure 4-44).

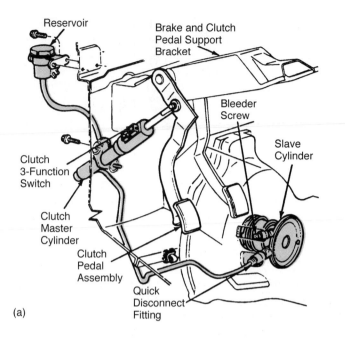

Reservoir

Brake and Clutch
Pedal Support
Bracket

Bleeder
Screw

Slave
Cylinder

Clutch
3-Function
Switch

Clutch
Master
Cylinder

Clutch
Pedal
Assembly

Quick
Disconnect
Fitting

(a)

FIGURE 4-36 The slave cylinder of some systems is concentric to the transmission input bearing retainer (a). When the clutch pedal is depressed, pressurized fluid is forced from the clutch master cylinder to the slave cylinder to release the clutch (b). (Courtesy of Ford Motor Company)

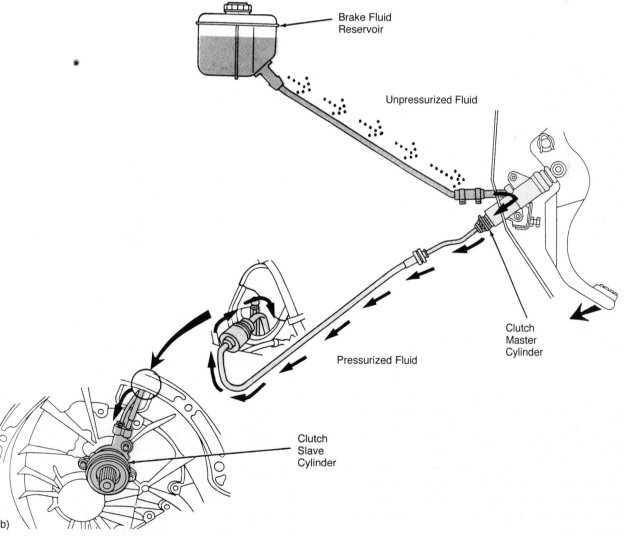

Brake Fluid
Reservoir

Unpressurized Fluid

Clutch
Master
Cylinder

Pressurized Fluid

Clutch
Slave
Cylinder

(b)

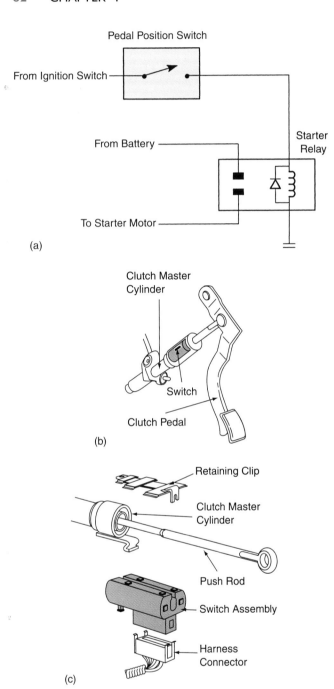

FIGURE 4-37 The pedal position switch closes when the clutch pedal is depressed, and this energizes the starter relay so that the starter motor can operate (a). Some switches are mounted onto the pedal push rod (b); they can be removed for replacement (c). (A is courtesy of Chrysler Corporation)

4.8 DUAL MASS FLYWHEEL

The **dual mass flywheel** is a two-piece flywheel that incorporates a damper assembly and attempts total elim-

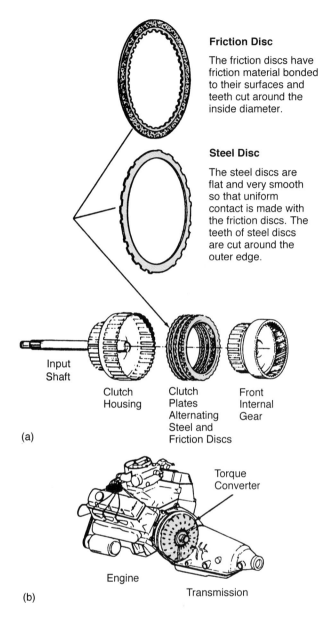

FIGURE 4-38 (a) A wet clutch, like this one from an automatic transmission, runs in a bath of fluid. (b) A fluid clutch and torque converter transfer power through fluid. (Portions of materials contained herein have been reprinted with permission of General Motors Corporation, Service and Parts Operations, License Agreement #0310807)

ination of torsional vibrations. Introduced on the 1989 ZR1 and L98 Corvettes, this unit provides better isolation of engine vibrations from the drivetrain.

The dual mass flywheel consists of two flywheels: the primary one is bolted to the engine crankshaft in the normal manner, and the secondary one is mounted on the primary flywheel through a ball bearing (Figure 4-45). The clutch assembly is mounted on the secondary flywheel, and engine torque must pass from the

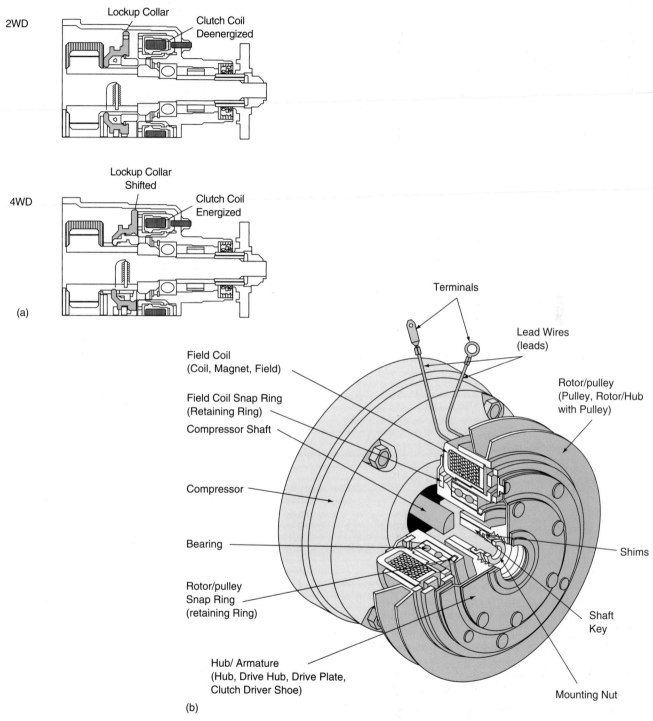

2WD

Lockup Collar

Clutch Coil
Deenergized

4WD

Lockup Collar
Shifted

Clutch Coil
Energized

(a)

Terminals

Lead Wires
(leads)

Field Coil
(Coil, Magnet, Field)

Field Coil Snap Ring
(Retaining Ring)

Compressor Shaft

Compressor

Bearing

Rotor/pulley
Snap Ring
(retaining Ring)

Hub/ Armature
(Hub, Drive Hub, Drive Plate,
Clutch Driver Shoe)

Rotor/pulley
(Pulley, Rotor/Hub
with Pulley)

Shims

Shaft
Key

Mounting Nut

(b)

FIGURE 4-39 Some transfer cases use a magnetic clutch coil to shift into 4WD (a). Magnetic clutches are commonly used with air-conditioning compressors (b). (b is courtesy of Warner Electric. All rights reserved.)

primary flywheel through a set of very long damper springs to the secondary flywheel and clutch. Vibration dampening is improved because of the very long damper springs, which have a low natural vibration frequency, and the mass of the secondary flywheel, which adds to the mass of the pressure plate and clutch assembly.

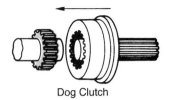

Dog Clutch

FIGURE 4-40 Most dog clutches are simply matching male and female splines. They transmit power when one is slid over the other. (Reproduced with permission of Deere & Company, © 1972 Deere & Company. All rights reserved.)

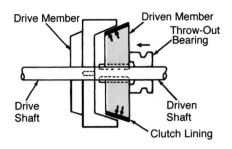

FIGURE 4-42 A cone clutch is engaged when the inner and outer cones are forced together. (Reproduced with permission of Deere & Company, © 1972 Deere & Company. All rights reserved.)

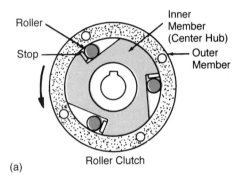

(a)   Roller Clutch

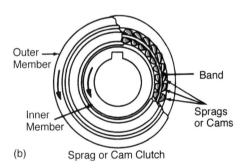

(b)   Sprag or Cam Clutch

FIGURE 4-41 Both roller (a) and sprag (b) clutches are one-way clutches. They transmit power when the inner drive member rotates to cause the rollers to lock against the outer member or to cause the sprags to rock and lock against the outer member. (Reproduced with permission of Deere & Company, © 1972 Deere & Company. All rights reserved.)

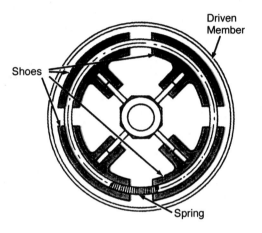

FIGURE 4-43 Centrifugal force from increased rpm causes the spring-loaded shoes to move outward and drive the outer driven member on this internal expanding clutch. (Reproduced with permission of Deere & Company, © 1972 Deere & Company. All rights reserved.)

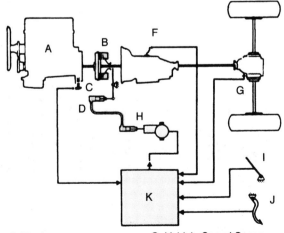

FIGURE 4-44 An automatic clutch uses a servomotor (H) to operate the clutch, and this motor is controlled by an electronic control module (K), which receives input from a group of sensors.

A. Engine
B. Clutch
C. RPM Sensor
D. Slave Cylinder
E. Transmission
F. Gear Shift Sensor

G. Vehicle Speed Sensor
H. Servo Motor & Clutch Master Cylinder
I. Throttle Sensor
J. Clutch Pedal Sensor
K. Eletronic Control Module

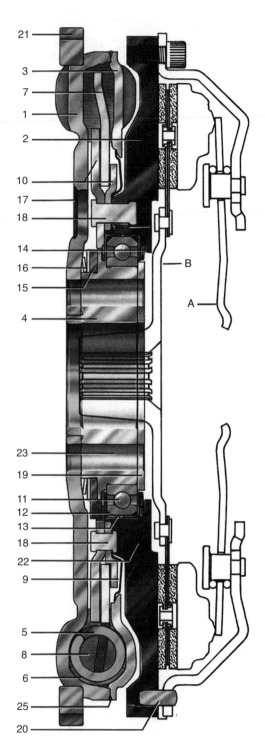

1. Primary Flywheel
2. Secondary Flywheel
3. Cover (Primary Inertia)
4. Hub
5. Damper Spring
6. Spring Guide
7. Flange and Diaphragm Spring
8. Grease-Filled Area
9. Seal
10. Friction Washers and Support Washers
11. Radial Ball Bearing
12. 'O' Ring
13. Seal
14. Diaphragm Springs for Base Friction
15. Friction Control Plate
16. Diaphragm Spring
17. Cap
18. Rivet
19. Washer
20. Dowel Pin
21. Ring Gear
22. Airflow Opening
23. Mounting Hole
24. Locating Hole
25. Laser Welded
A. Diaphragm Spring Clutch with Elastic Spacer Bolt Design
B. Rigid Disc

FIGURE 4-45 In a dual mass flywheel, the primary flywheel (1) is mounted to the crankshaft and drives the secondary flywheel (2) through a set of damper springs (5). The mass of the second flywheel and the long length of the damper springs remove more torsional vibrations than a conventional clutch disc damper. (Courtesy of LUK Clutches)

REVIEW QUESTIONS

The following questions are provided to help you study as you read the chapter.

1. The clutch is _____ to allow the driver to select the appropriate gear range.

2. The _____ _____ describes the relative amount of friction between two surfaces.

3. The clutch disc _____ reduces the torsional vibrations from the engine.

4. The clutch disc may contain _____, which is a known cancer-causing material.

5. The clutch disc facing is attached to the _____ part of the clutch disc by rivets.

6. The _____ _____ _____ bolts to the flywheel.

7. The pressure plate releases the clutch disc when the clutch is _____.

8. The clutch is _____ when the clutch pedal is depressed.

9. The _____ _____ transmits force from the clutch linkage to the spinning pressure plate.

10. The _____ _____ supports the end of the transmission clutch shaft.

11. Three types of clutch linkage are common. They are:

    a. _____

    b. _____

    c. _____

12. A clutch pedal _____ is used to prevent the vehicle from starting with the clutch engaged.

13. When the clutch pedal is released the clutch is _____.

14. A _____ clutch is commonly used in automotive air conditioning systems.

15. A multidisc _____ clutch is commonly used in automatic transmissions.

CHAPTER QUIZ

The following questions will help you check the facts you have learned. Select the answer that completes each statement correctly.

1. When the clutch is applied,

    a. springs force the pressure ring toward the clutch cover.

    b. springs force the pressure ring toward the flywheel.

    c. a substantial pressure exists between the release bearing and the pressure plate release levers.

    d. all of these.

2. Two students are discussing the springs at the center of a clutch disc. Student A says they are used to help cushion clutch engagement. Student B says they absorb engine torsional vibrations. Who is correct?

    a. Student A   c. Both A and B

    b. Student B   d. Neither A nor B

3. Two students are discussing the Marcel portion of a clutch disc. Student A says the lining is riveted to the Marcel at one side of each wavy portion. Student B says the lining is bonded solidly to the Marcel. Who is correct?

    a. Student A   c. Both A and B

    b. Student B   d. Neither A nor B

4. When a clutch is released, the A. release bearing is pushing against the release levers; B. pressure plate springs are compressed. Which is correct?

    a. A only   c. Both A and B

    b. B only   d. Neither A nor B

5. When a clutch is released, A. the Marcel in the disc will flatten; B. an air gap will be on each side of the facing. Which is correct?

    a. A only   c. Both A and B

    b. B only   d. Neither A nor B

6. While discussing clutch lining, Student A says that asbestos lining is no longer used because it is too expensive. Student B says asbestos lining has been phased out because it presents a health hazard. Who is correct?

    a. Student A   c. Both A and B

    b. Student B   d. Neither A nor B

7. Clutch chatter is eliminated by

    a. cushion springs at the center of the disc.

    b. Marcel in the disc.

    c. pressure plate springs.

    d. none of these.

8. The clutch pedal over-center spring is used to help

    A. return the clutch pedal to the released position.

    B. release the clutch. Which is correct?

    a. A only   c. Both A and B

    b. B only   d. Neither A nor B

9. In a hydraulic clutch, the slave cylinder A. is connected to the clutch pedal; B. is pushed by fluid pressure. Which is correct?

   a. A only   **c.** Both A and B

   b. B only   **d.** Neither A nor B

10. The weights attached to the release levers of a Long-style clutch are used to A. increase the clamping pressure on the disc; B. reduce the amount of effort required for pedal depression. Which is correct?

   a. A only   **c.** Both A and B

   b. B only   **d.** Neither A nor B

11. The amount of torque that a clutch can transmit is determined by the

   a. diameter of the disc.

   b. strength of the pressure plate springs.

   c. number of discs.

   d. all of these.

12. A diaphragm clutch uses A. three wide release levers. B. 12 strong coil springs. Which is correct?

   a. A only   **c.** Both A and B

   b. B only   **d.** Neither A nor B

13. The major bearing(s) used with a clutch assembly is (are) the A. release bearing that is mounted at the front of the transmission; B. pilot bearing that supports the end of the transmission input shaft. Which is correct?

   a. A only   **c.** Both A and B

   b. B only   **d.** Neither A nor B

14. Clutch pedal free travel is an adjustment that ensures that the A. release bearing rides constantly against the pressure plate release levers; B. clutch is completely engaged. Which is correct?

   a. A only   **c.** Both A and B

   b. B only   **d.** Neither A nor B

15. Of the following, which type of clutch is not commonly used in modern vehicles?

   a. wet clutch

   b. dog clutch

   c. cone clutch

   d. internal expanding shoe clutch

16. The single-disc clutch has a 9-in. outside diameter and uses a facing that is 2 in. wide. The clamp load strength is 300 lb. How much torque can it transmit?

17. During the 4 in. of clutch pedal travel, the pressure plate moves 0.100 in. What is the linkage leverage ratio?

◀ Chapter 5 ▶

CLUTCH SERVICE

LEARNING OBJECTIVES

After completing this chapter, you should be able to:

1. Perform the maintenance operations needed to keep a clutch operating properly.
2. Diagnose the cause of common clutch problems and recommend the proper repair method.
3. Remove and replace a clutch assembly.
4. Inspect used clutch components to determine if they are usable.
5. Complete the ASE tasks for clutch diagnosis and repair (see the Appendix).

TERMS TO LEARN

axial runout	clutch spin down
Blanchard grinding	disc alignment
bench bleed	disc runout
bleed	drag
bore runout	face runout
chatter	grab
clutch pedal free travel	gravity bleeding
clutch slippage	radial runout

5.1   INTRODUCTION

Most automotive technicians will perform three different levels of clutch service operations:

1. **Preventive maintenance level:** check pedal free travel and fluid levels and make the necessary adjustments to ensure proper operation.
2. **Troubleshooting and diagnosis:**   determine the cause of a particular concern and make recommendation for repair.
3. **Repair or overhaul:**   make the actual repair to get the vehicle back in proper operation.

This chapter, as well as the following service chapters, will be arranged in this order: description of the maintenance and adjustment operations, the troubleshooting procedures, and the normal repair procedures in this service field.

5.2   CLUTCH SERVICE

Typical service for a clutch includes checking **clutch pedal free travel**, or *free play*, of mechanical linkage systems and checking the fluid level in hydraulic systems. These two operations are normally performed along with the other routine service checks.

Too much free travel might cause the clutch to not release completely, and too little free travel might cause the clutch to not engage completely. The second case is much more common because clutch pedal free travel will decrease as the clutch disc facing wears. There is no free travel on some self-adjusting or hydraulic clutches used on many vehicles. When diagnosing a clutch or transmission concern, the first step is always a clutch pedal free travel check.

5.2.1 Clutch Pedal Free Travel

To check and adjust clutch pedal free travel:

1. Push the clutch pedal downward by hand. As the pedal moves, you should feel a light resistance of the clutch pedal return spring, and after a short period of travel, you should feel a much greater resistance as the release bearing contacts the release levers of the pressure plate assembly. The first travel portion is free travel (Figure 5-1). Some manufacturers recommend checking and measuring free travel at the clutch fork or lever. In this case, push on the end of the fork in the direction of release travel, and again, you should feel a small amount of resistance for a short distance, which is the free travel.

2. Measure the amount of free travel using a ruler or tape measure. Compare the distance measured with the specifications (Figure 5-2). A free travel amount that is more or less than the specifications indicates the need for a clutch adjustment. It should be noted that some manufacturers recommend measuring free travel with the engine running. If no specifications are available, many technicians will use 3/4 to 1 in. (20 to 25 mm) at the clutch pedal and 1/8 to 1/4 in. (3 to 6 mm) at the clutch fork as a rule of thumb.

◀ SERVICE TIP ▶

Hook the end of a tape measure onto the pedal or the sole of your shoe, and run it through the steering wheel as shown in Figure 5-2b. Note the reading at the steering wheel as you move the pedal through its travel.

3. If an adjustment is necessary, locate the adjustable portion of the linkage, and shorten the linkage as necessary to obtain the correct amount of free travel (Figure 5-3). As a final check, operate the clutch pedal through its full range of travel. It should operate smoothly without any unusual lags, skips, roughness, or noise.

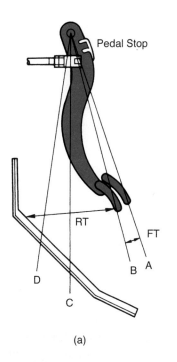

(a)

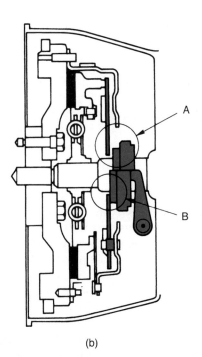

(b)

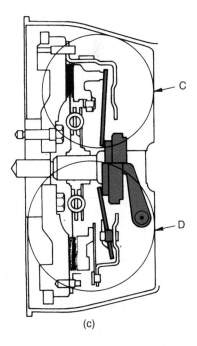

(c)

FIGURE 5-1 As the clutch pedal is depressed from the released position (a), it will move through its free travel as the release bearing moves to contact the release levers (b). (c) The pressure plate then moves away from the flywheel, allowing the Marcel of the disc to expand and an air gap to begin. When the pedal reaches the floor, there should be an air gap at both sides of the disc.

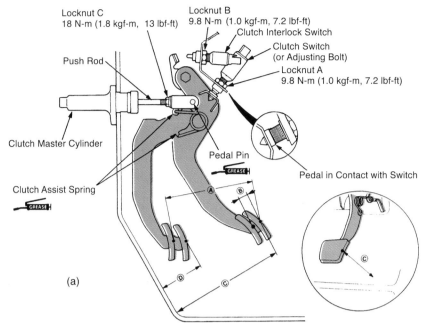

(a)

Ⓐ (Stroke at Pedal): 142.5 - 152.5 mm (5.61 - 6.00 in)
Ⓑ (Total Clutch Pedal Free Play): 9.0 - 15.0 mm (0.35 - 0.59 in) includes the pedal play 1 - 7 mm (0.04 - 0.28 in)
Ⓒ (Clutch Pedal Height): 184 mm (7.24 in) to the Floor
Ⓓ (Clutch Pedal Disengagement Height): 74 mm (2.9 in) Minimum to the Floor

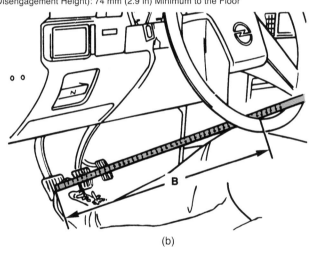

(b)

FIGURE 5-2 Clutch pedal movements are measured at the pedal, and the distances are specified by the vehicle manufacturer (a). A handy way to make these measurements is with a tape measure hooked on the pedal or your shoe (b). (a is courtesy of American Honda Motor Company; b: Portions of materials contained herein have been reprinted with permission of General Motors Corporation, Service and Parts Operations, License Agreement #0310807)

◀ **SERVICE TIP** ▶

With modern self-adjusting clutches, a decrease in free travel indicates excessive clutch wear, and this vehicle is due for a clutch replacement.

5.2.2 Clutch Fluid Level

Clutch hydraulic fluid level is checked by looking at the fluid level at the clutch master cylinder reservoir (Figure 5-4). Many reservoirs will be marked to indicate the correct fluid level. If there are no markings, assume that the fluid level should be between 1/4 and 1/2 in. (6 and 13 mm) from the top. Normally, the fluid level will

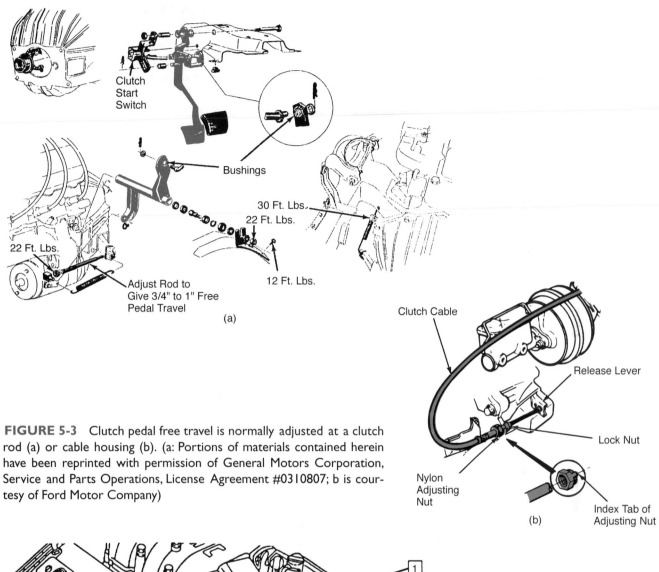

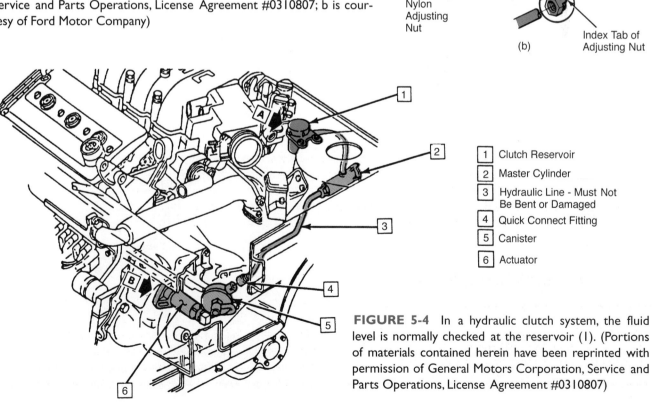

FIGURE 5-3 Clutch pedal free travel is normally adjusted at a clutch rod (a) or cable housing (b). (a: Portions of materials contained herein have been reprinted with permission of General Motors Corporation, Service and Parts Operations, License Agreement #0310807; b is courtesy of Ford Motor Company)

1	Clutch Reservoir
2	Master Cylinder
3	Hydraulic Line - Must Not Be Bent or Damaged
4	Quick Connect Fitting
5	Canister
6	Actuator

FIGURE 5-4 In a hydraulic clutch system, the fluid level is normally checked at the reservoir (1). (Portions of materials contained herein have been reprinted with permission of General Motors Corporation, Service and Parts Operations, License Agreement #0310807)

rise slightly as the clutch facing wears. A low fluid level usually indicates a leak in the system.

◀ SERVICE TIP ▶

Clutch hydraulic fluid is hygroscopic (it absorbs water), so the hydraulic system should be drained, flushed, and filled with new fluid to prevent corrosion and increase the service life of the components.

5.3 PROBLEM DIAGNOSIS

Problem solving for clutches is difficult because most clutch assemblies are inaccessible and normally operate silently. You can perform operational checks, however, to determine if the clutch is operating properly and from these results, determine if a disassembly for visual inspection is necessary. Disassembly is usually the last resort because of the time required to remove the transaxle or transmission (Figure 5-5).

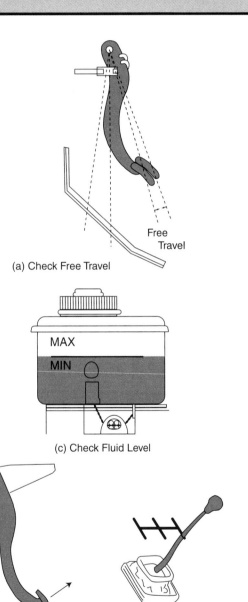

(a) Check Free Travel

(c) Check Fluid Level

(e) Release Clutch Operation

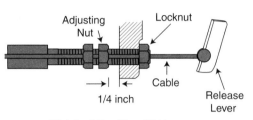

(b) Adjust Free Travel if Necessary

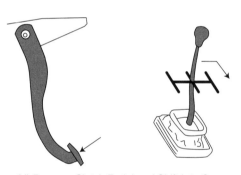

(d) Depress Clutch Pedal and Shift Into Gear

(f) Operate Clutch Pedal by Hand to Feel

FIGURE 5-5   When diagnosing clutch problems, begin by checking clutch pedal feel and the amount of free travel (a). Adjust the free travel if it is wrong (b). On hydraulic clutches, check the fluid level and condition (c). Next, start the engine; depress the clutch pedal; and check for gear clash as you shift into reverse (d). Now let up on the clutch to check the engagement (e); if checking for slippage, use high gear. If any problems are indicated, operate the pedal by hand to feel the operation better (f).

5.3.1   Clutch Slippage

Clutch slippage can be checked fairly easily in a shop; a more thorough check can be made on a road test.

To check for slippage in a shop:

1. Check and adjust clutch pedal free travel.
2. Warm up the engine to operating temperature, block the wheels, and apply the parking brake completely.
3. Shift the transmission into its highest gear and let out the clutch pedal in a smooth, normal manner. The engine should stall immediately. A delay indicates slow engagement and slipping.

To check for slippage on a road test:

1. Check and adjust clutch pedal free travel.
2. Drive to an area with very little traffic. Accelerate slowly and drive at 15 to 20 mph (24 to 32 kph) in the highest transmission gear. Use the lowest speed at which the vehicle will operate smoothly.
3. Depress the accelerator completely to make a wide-open throttle acceleration, and listen to the engine rpm or watch the tachometer. The engine speed should increase steadily as the vehicle speeds up. Any clutch slipping will occur as the engine enters its power band, where it produces maximum torque, around 1500 to 3000 rpm, depending on engine design. If the engine speed flares upward, the clutch is slipping and needs service. Slipping becomes even more evident if this test is made while driving up an incline.

5.3.2   Clutch Spin Down

Hard shifting into gear from neutral, sometimes accompanied with gear clash, can be caused by a clutch that is not releasing completely. This is called **drag** and is easily checked by a spin-down test. Spin down is the time it takes for the clutch disc and transmission gears to spin to a stop when the clutch is released. This time will vary depending on clutch disc diameter and transmission drag.

To check clutch spin down:

1. Check and adjust clutch pedal free travel.
2. Warm up the engine and transmission to operating temperatures.
3. With the engine running at idle speed and the transmission in neutral, push in the clutch pedal,

wait 9 seconds, and shift the transmission into reverse (a nonsynchronized gear). The shift should occur silently. Gear clash or grinding indicates a dragging clutch that has not released completely.

The 9-second time period is very long; you will find some cars that will shift quietly and cleanly into reverse in 3 or 4 seconds. If a clutch fails a spin-down check, it probably needs to be replaced.

5.3.3   Clutch Diagnosis Chart

Most clutch problems can be cured only by replacing some or all of the clutch components. About the only exception is when there is a problem with the linkage, which is on the outside and can be easily repaired or replaced. A trouble chart like the one in Figure 5-6 can be used as a final check before replacing a clutch. The service performed to diagnose each problem follows almost the same procedure: check for proper free travel and for proper linkage operation; if the problem has not been corrected, remove and replace (R&R) the clutch.

5.3.4   Clutch Pedal Operation Check

This check requires an assistant, but it is fairly quick and easy.

To perform a clutch pedal operation check:

1. With the hood open and the engine off, work the clutch pedal slowly through full apply and release while you check for noises and inspect for improper movement of the linkage and pivot points. You can often pinpoint the location of noises by placing your hand at different points to feel for the vibration that accompanies some noises or to dampen a noise. The noise will often go away when you apply pressure to the problem area (Figure 5-7).
2. As an assistant moves the pedal slowly and evenly, inspect the linkage points from under the hood or vehicle for improper movement, binding, or noise. Also, check for excessive flexing of the engine bulkhead or firewall. On vehicles with self-adjusting clutches, check to ensure that the adjuster cam and locking mechanism is operating correctly (Figure 5-8). On vehicles with hydraulic clutches, check to ensure that the slave cylinder is moving an adequate distance (Figure 5-9).
3. When checking a vehicle equipped with a clutch–starter interlock switch, turn the ignition

Chart A

Problem	Description	Diagnosis/Service
Noise	Squeaks or scrapes as the pedal is depressed, engine off	5.3.4
	Squeals as the pedal is depressed, engine running	5.3.5
	Unusual noises during operation	5.4
Grab	Chatters during engagement	5.2.1 to 5.3.4, broken engine mount, 5.4
	Abrupt/severe engagement	Same as for "Grab"
Drag	Does not disengage completely	5.2.1 to 5.3.4, 5.4
Slip	Does not engage completely	5.2.1 to 5.3.4, 5.4
Vibrations	Speed-related vibrations that increase in intensity as the engine speeds up	Confirm that another engine system is not the cause; balance or R & R flywheel and pressure plate.
Hard pedal	Requires a high amount of force to operate the pedal	Check for binding cable or pivots; lube or R & R

Chart B

Possible Cause of Problem	Slip	Grab	Chatter	Drag	Noise
Worn or glazed facings	X	X	X		
Broken facing				X	
Facing stuck to flywheel or pressure plate					X
Warped disc				X	
Broken damper springs					X
Flattened Marcel springs		X			
Excessive disc runout				X	
Disc binding on clutch shaft				X	
Worn splines in disc			X	X	X
Grease or oil on facings	X	X	X		
Clutch cover distorted			X	X	
Weak or broken pressure plate springs	X				
Warped or grooved pressure plate	X	X	X		
Broken release lever or pivot				X	
Pressure plate binding on stands	X	X			
Uneven release levers			X	X	
Worn levers	X			X	
Excessive free travel				X	
Insufficient free travel	X				
Insufficient pedal or bearing travel		X		X	
Worn linkage			X	X	X
Worn fork					X
Worn throw-out bearing					X
Leaky hydraulic system				X	
Air in hydraulic system			X		
Worn pilot bearing					X
Flywheel step height out of specs	X				
Bad motor mounts		X	X		
Firewall/pedal mount flex				X	

FIGURE 5-6 Chart A indicates the checks that are made to determine the cause of common clutch problems; the numbers at the right refer to the sections in this chapter. Chart B indicates the probable causes for the five most common complaints.

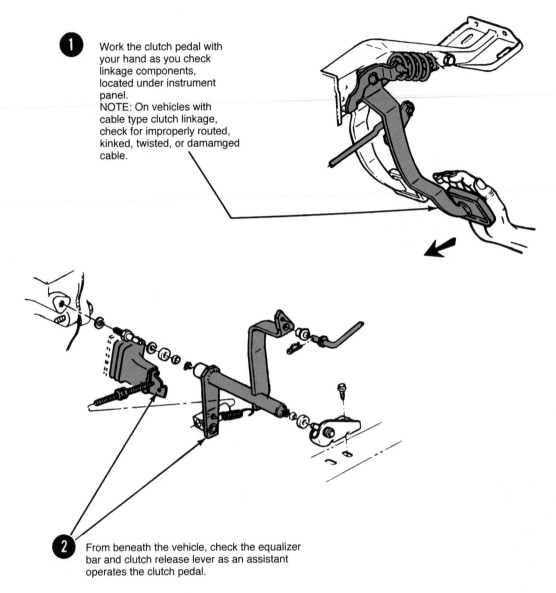

① Work the clutch pedal with your hand as you check linkage components, located under instrument panel.
NOTE: On vehicles with cable type clutch linkage, check for improperly routed, kinked, twisted, or damamged cable.

② From beneath the vehicle, check the equalizer bar and clutch release lever as an assistant operates the clutch pedal.

FIGURE 5-7   Check for noises by moving the pedal by hand as you check the various parts of the linkage. If necessary, the linkage can be disconnected to isolate different portions. (Courtesy of Ford Motor Company)

switch to the crank position and depress the clutch pedal. As the pedal nears the end of its travel, the starter should begin cranking.

REAL-WORLD FIX The clutch on a 1991 Dodge Ram pickup (260,000 km) did not release completely. Adjusting the cable helped, but the end of the adjustment was reached. The transmission and clutch were removed, and the clutch was inspected.

FIX

Following advice, a new cable was purchased, and it was determined that the old cable had stretched. Installation of the new cable repaired this problem.

5.3.5   Clutch Pedal Noise Check, Engine Running

This check is used to pinpoint the causes of squeaks or growling noises that occur and may change as the

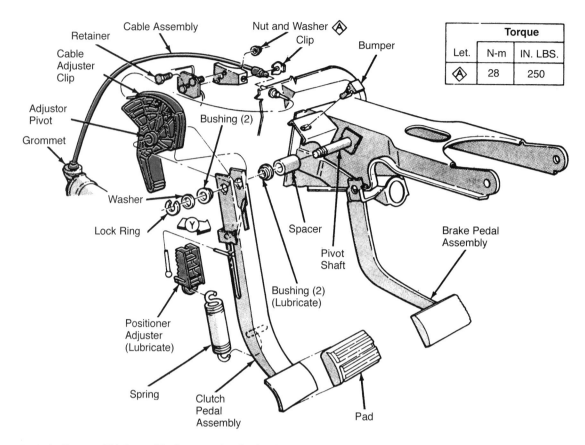

Torque		
Let.	N-m	IN. LBS.
Ⓐ	28	250

FIGURE 5-8 With a self-adjusting clutch, check the cable, cable adjuster clip (cam), and positioner adjuster for proper operation. (Courtesy of DaimlerChrysler Corporation)

Bearing Travel Measurement

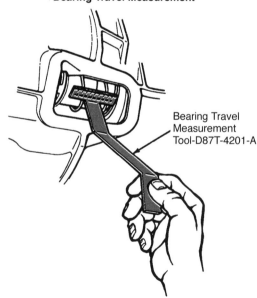

FIGURE 5-9 If the problem on this hydraulic clutch is failure to release, check for proper bearing travel. Insufficient bearing travel indicates a faulty hydraulic system. (Courtesy of Ford Motor Company)

clutch pedal is depressed (Figure 5-10). During the check, the engine should be running at idle speed and the clutch linkage must be adjusted to the correct free travel. On self-adjusting or hydraulic zero-free-play systems, it will be necessary to pry back the release lever or fork to isolate transmission bearing noise from release bearing noise, and this may be impractical on some vehicles. The common bearing noise problems fall into one of four categories:

1. Noise stops as clutch pedal is released completely—transmission bearing or gear rollover problem. This problem is covered in Chapter 8.
2. Noise begins as the clutch pedal is depressed just beyond free travel—faulty release bearing.
3. Noise and vibration occur at one-fourth to one-half pedal travel—faulty pressure plate-to-release bearing contact.
4. Noise after clutch is released completely—faulty pilot bearing.

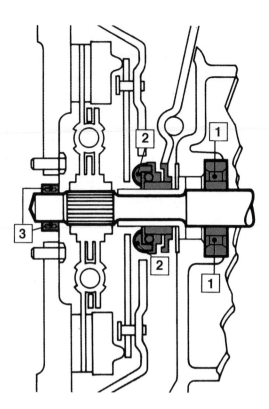

FIGURE 5-10 Any of these three bearings can cause noise. A faulty transmission input shaft bearing (1) will cause noise while the clutch is engaged; a faulty release bearing (2) will cause noise with the pedal depressed; and a faulty pilot bearing (3) will cause noise while the clutch is released. (Courtesy of LUK Clutches)

To perform a clutch pedal noise check:

1. Check and adjust clutch pedal free travel.
2. Warm up the engine and transmission to operating temperatures.
3. Set the parking brake, and with the engine at idle speed and the transmission in neutral, depress the clutch pedal slowly and steadily as you listen for unusual noises.

If noise begins as the clutch releases and the transmission gears spin down in speed, shift the transmission into gear to ensure that they are stopped. Noise at this time is definitely coming from the pilot bearing or release bearing. Shift back into neutral, and let the clutch out slightly so that the transmission gears are spinning again. Now the pilot bearing will have stopped with the release bearing still spinning. If the noise stops, it is being caused by a faulty pilot bearing; if the noise continues, it is a faulty release bearing.

◄ **PROBLEM SOLVING** ►

Imagine that you are working in a general automotive repair shop and these problems are brought to you.

Case 1

The vehicle is a 15-year-old pickup, and the complaint is an engine speed flare-up under load. You suspect that it is a slipping clutch, and your road test confirms an improper engine speed increase at 20 mph as you make a full-throttle acceleration in fourth gear. When you check for clutch pedal free travel, you find there is none. What should you do next?

Case 2

The vehicle is a 6-year-old FWD compact sedan, 85,000 mi on the odometer, and a noise complaint. As you apply the clutch to change gears, a squealing, sometimes growling noise occurs, and this noise continues until the pedal is completely released. What is probably wrong? What will you need to do to fix it? What should you recommend to the customer?

REAL-WORLD FIX The clutch and release bearing in a 1995 Mustang (122,000 mi) were replaced six months ago, but it came back with a release bearing squeal complaint. The clutch and release were replaced again, but three days later, it returned again with the same complaint.

FIX

The vehicle was raised and operated on a lift, and the release fork could be seen to vibrate as the noise was occurring. Lifting the fork slightly would stop the noise. Removing the transmission allowed lubrication of the release fork pivot, and fixed this problem.

5.4 CLUTCH REPLACEMENT

Clutch replacement, commonly called a *clutch job*, is a fairly expensive repair that should include a number of checks to ensure proper completion. During disassembly, the parts should be checked to determine if they were the cause of the failure and if they are suitable for reuse. During reassembly, each phase is normally accompanied by checks for proper clearances or operation so that any faulty parts or assemblies can be corrected as early in the assembly as possible.

REAL WORLD FIX   The clutch in a 1988 Chevrolet Corsica (119,000 mi) would not disengage. A broken pressure plate or clutch disc was suspected, so the transaxle was removed. Inspection showed normal clutch wear, nothing to prevent disengagement. A new pressure plate, disc, and throw-out bearing were installed, and the flywheel was turned. The clutch still would not disengage. A small leak was found at the slave cylinder, so the entire hydraulic system was replaced with an OEM assembly. The new assembly was full of fluid, so bleeding was not necessary. The slave cylinder push rod has a normal amount of movement during clutch pedal travel. At the suggestion of the parts supplier, a flywheel shim was installed to compensate for the thinner flywheel, and this did not help.

FIX

Close inspection revealed that the release fork was bent and worn. Replacement of this fork and its bushings fixed this problem. It is important to spend a few minutes inspecting all of the clutch components to ensure a complete and proper repair.

◀   SERVICE TIP   ▶

The technician should serve as the final quality control check of all the parts as they are assembled. Having to redo a job means lost time and money. Thoroughness while making a repair may take a little more time, but it will ensure a first-rate operation. The goal for a clutch job should be "new vehicle" operation (Figure 5-11). A good technician does not need to blame failures on faulty parts.

Clutch replacement normally involves replacing four items: the pressure plate assembly, clutch disc, release bearing, and pilot bearing. If there is a problem with the clutch operation, the pressure plate and disc are usually damaged in some way and need replacement. With today's labor cost, it is unwise to install a part that is not operating completely right. The release and pilot bearings are often replaced for insurance purposes. These two

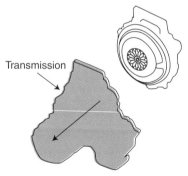

(a) Remove Transmission/Transaxle

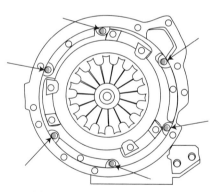

(b) Remove Retainer Bolts Evenly

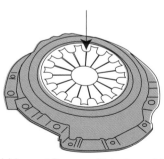

(c) Inspect Pressure Plate Assembly

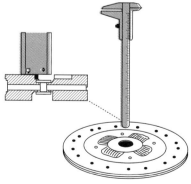

(d) Inspect Disc

FIGURE 5-11   The sequence to do a clutch job is to remove the transmission/transaxle (a); remove the clutch components (b); inspect the pressure plate assembly (c), disc *(continued)*

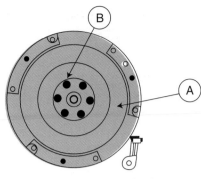

(e) Inspect Flywheel

(f) Replace Pilot Bearing

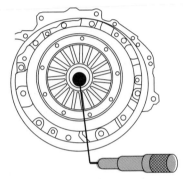

(g) Align Disc and Install Pressure Plate Assembly

(h) Tighten Retaining Bolts to the Correct Torque

FIGURE 5-11, Continued   (d) flywheel (e); replace the pilot bearing (f); install and align the disc and pressure plate assembly (g); and tighten the bolts to the correct torque and in the correct sequence (h).

parts are not very expensive, and their replacement will ensure correct operation for the life of the new disc and pressure plate. For convenience, some parts suppliers package all four parts in one package (Figure 5-12).

A clutch job begins with removal of the transaxle/transmission; this operation is described in Chapter 8. The service operation described here is very general. As you remove and replace the clutch, you should follow the procedure given in a service manual for the vehicle you are repairing.

5.4.1   Clutch Removal

To remove a clutch:

1. With the transmission removed, mark the flywheel and pressure plate cover with index marks so that you can realign them if the original pressure plate assembly is to be reused (Figure 5-13). Many manufacturers balance the pressure plate and flywheel assembly; repositioning the pressure plate on the flywheel can cause an annoying vibration.

◄ **SERVICE TIP** ►

Caution: Because the old disc might have used asbestos-based facing, try not to cause dust to enter the air. Do not breathe any of this dust. Never blow the dust from the assembly using compressed air and an air gun. To remove the dust, some technicians will vacuum the assembly provided that the vacuum cleaner is equipped with a HEPA (high-efficiency particulate filter). Asbestos fibers can pass right through a normal shop vacuum. The clutch dust can also be removed by one of the various wet washing systems available (Figure 5-14).

◄ **SERVICE TIP** ►

Install an alignment tool or dummy clutch shaft into the clutch disc to support it while you remove the pressure plate.

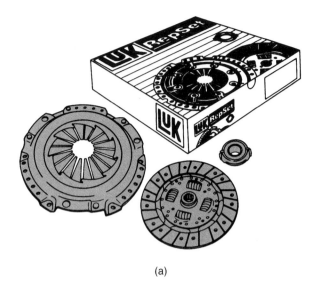

(a)

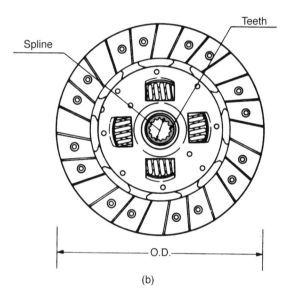

(b)

FIGURE 5-12 Some suppliers package a replacement disc and pressure plate assembly along with the release bearing in one package (a). Sometimes the pilot bearing is also included. The critical dimensions for the replacement disc are shown in (b). (Courtesy of LUK Clutches)

2. Remove the bolts securing the pressure plate cover to the flywheel two turns at a time and in an alternating fashion, back and forth across the pressure plate. If one or two of the bolts are tight while the others are removed completely, the springs forcing the pressure plate away from the cover can cause a distortion of the cover (Figure 5-15). Note the bolts as they are removed. Pressure plate bolts are normally grade 8 bolts and usually have a special shank portion to help center and drive the pressure plate cover. As the last bolt is removed, be prepared to support the pressure plate assembly and clutch disc; they can be heavy. Remove the pressure plate and disc.

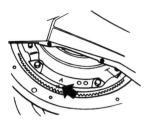

FIGURE 5-13 If the pressure plate assembly is to be re-installed, index marks should be put on the flywheel and cover so that they can be realigned in the same position. (Portions of materials contained herein have been reprinted with permission of General Motors Corporation, Service and Parts Operations, License Agreement #0310807)

FIGURE 5-14 Before disassembly, it is a good practice to wash the pressure plate assembly and flywheel with a mixture of soap and water. This will hold down or remove any asbestos dust or fibers and help clean things.

3. Remove the pilot bearing from the crankshaft (Figure 5-16). A puller is normally used for this. Most pullers are designed to enter the pilot bearing, expand to lock into it, and pull the bearing out as force from a slide hammer or puller bolt is exerted on it.

4. Remove the release bearing from the clutch fork and bearing retainer quill.

◀ **SERVICE TIP** ▶

Another pilot bushing removal method is to thread a coarse bolt into the bushing so it bottoms against the crankshaft. Further tightening will move the bushing outward.

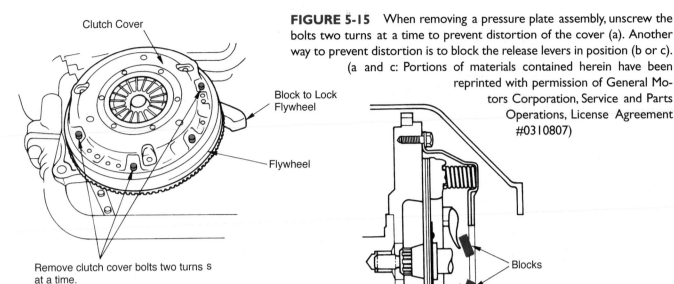

Clutch Cover

Block to Lock Flywheel

Flywheel

Remove clutch cover bolts two turns  at a time.

(a)

FIGURE 5-15 When removing a pressure plate assembly, unscrew the bolts two turns at a time to prevent distortion of the cover (a). Another way to prevent distortion is to block the release levers in position (b or c). (a and c: Portions of materials contained herein have been reprinted with permission of General Motors Corporation, Service and Parts Operations, License Agreement #0310807)

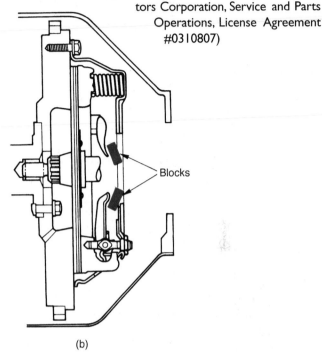

Blocks

(b)

(c)

◀ SERVICE TIP ▶

A somewhat messy alternative method is to fill the cavity behind the bearing with chassis grease and drive a close-fitting round rod or dowel into the grease. This will create a hydraulic force behind the bearing, forcing it outward. Soap or wet tissue can also be used.

REAL-WORLD FIX The clutch in a Chevrolet Camaro (68,000 mi) did not disengage completely. The master cylinder fluid level was correct, and the clutch fork travel was measured at 1 1/8".

FIX

Removal of the transmission and clutch assembly showed a clutch disc falling apart; pieces of lining were wedged in the pressure plate and disc. Replacement of the disc fixed this problem.

AUTHOR'S NOTE

Clutch lining breakup is often a sign of severe clutch operation.

REAL-WORLD FIX A 1994 Nissan Pathfinder (125,000 mi) made a groaning, whirring noise as the clutch was engaged. The clutch was replaced, but the noise came back after 12,000 miles. A new clutch disc, pressure plate, release bearing, and pilot bushing were installed during the clutch replacement.

FIX

Pulling the transmission allowed inspection of the parts, and a faulty pilot bushing was found. An updated pilot bushing was installed and lubricated.

5.4.2 Clutch Component Inspection

Many technicians check each part as it is disassembled to try to determine if it failed earlier than it should have. They do this to locate any condition that needs correcting before the clutch is reassembled. Any components to be reused should be checked to ensure that they are completely serviceable. As mentioned earlier, if the clutch is slipping, the disc and the pressure plate should be replaced. The following

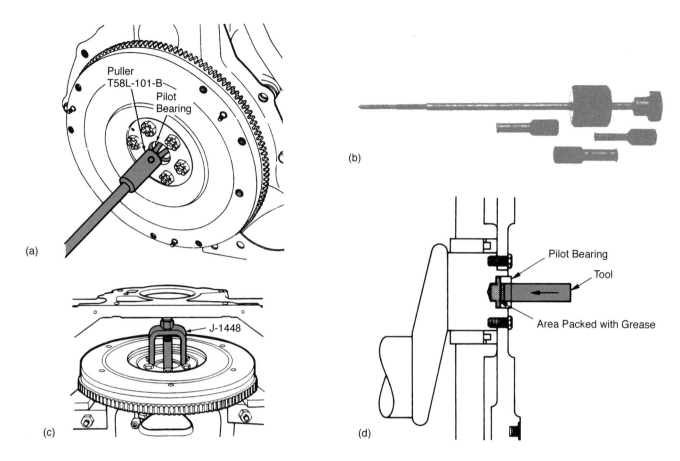

FIGURE 5-16   A pilot bearing is removed by catching it with an expanding puller attached to a slide hammer (a)—a puller set is shown at (b)—using a special-purpose puller (c), or filling it with grease and driving a round tool into the bearing (d). (a is courtesy of Ford Motor Company; b is courtesy of LUK Clutches; c: Portions of materials contained herein have been reprinted with permission of General Motors Corporation, Service and Parts Operations, License Agreement #0310807)

sections explain the normal checks to be made during a clutch job.

5.4.2.1 Flywheel The friction surface of the flywheel should be checked for grooves, nicks, and heat checks, which indicate a need for resurfacing or replacement (Figure 5-17). **Blanchard grinding,** which moves a spinning grinding stone around the flywheel surface, is the recommended method of resurfacing because it leaves a truly flat surface with a series of circular, nondirectional scratches (Figure 5-18). These scratches are the same as those found on some new flywheel or pressure plate surfaces, and they promote rapid disc facing-to-flywheel break-in. With a stepped flywheel, be sure that the same thickness of metal is removed from each of the two surfaces.

◄   **SERVICE TIP**   ►

If the friction surface is flat and smooth but highly polished or glazed, some technicians will sand the friction surface using a disc sander with 80- to 120-grit paper (Figure 5-19). When doing this, the sander is kept in motion while attempting to duplicate the ground finish of a new unit without cutting grooves.

Many modern flywheels are forged steel, which tends to warp (potato chip shape) or dish if overheated. This is checked by placing a straightedge across the flywheel in several locations. Over 0.0005 in. (0.013 mm) of warpage per inch of diameter is

FIGURE 5-17 A new (left) and typical worn flywheel (right). This worn flywheel should be resurfaced. (Courtesy of McLeod Industries, Inc.)

considered excessive. This means that a 12-in.-diameter flywheel can have 0.006 in. (12 × 0.0005) of warpage error.

If there are complaints of vibration or an odd wear pattern at the hub of the disc or pressure plate release levers, the flywheel should be checked for excessive runout. **Face** or **axial runout** is checked by positioning a dial indicator with the indicating stylus at the outer edge of the flywheel face (Figure 5-20).

◀ **SERVICE TIP** ▶

With the dial indicator set up, push and pull on the flywheel and crankshaft in a direction that is parallel to the crankshaft. The dial indicator is now measuring crankshaft end play. Normal crankshaft end play should be about 0.002 to 0.010 in. (0.05 to 0.25 mm). Movement greater than the specified amount indicates worn crankshaft thrust bearings.

While rotating the crankshaft to measure flywheel runout, be sure to keep an inward pressure on the flywheel to prevent end play from affecting the runout readings.

To measure flywheel axial runout, you should:

1. Mount the dial indicator so the measuring stem is parallel to the crankshaft and pointing directly toward the flywheel, and adjust the indicator to read zero.
2. Rotate the flywheel while watching the dial indicator. Maintain an even pressure, either inward or outward, to maintain zero crankshaft end play.
3. The variation in reading is the amount of axial runout.

1. The Master Control Panel—Includes All Switches
2. Grinding Head Swivel Lock Lever
3. Depth of Grind Dial
4. Grinding Head Down Feed Wheel
5. Wheel Dresser
6. Grinding Head Swivel Handle
7. Coolant Nozzle

FIGURE 5-18 A flywheel grinder rotates the flywheel as a spinning stone is lowered onto the surface. Various styles of flywheels, including stepped ones (inset), can be resurfaced using this machine. (Courtesy of Van Norman Equipment Co., Inc.)

(a)

(c)   After

(b)   Before

FIGURE 5-19 If not too badly scored (a), a glazed flywheel can be refinished using a sanding disc (b); the finished surface should show nondirectional sanding scratches (c).

To measure flywheel radial runout, you should:

1. Remount the dial indicator so it is at the edge of the flywheel, pointing directly toward the center of the flywheel.
2. Adjust the dial indicator to read zero.
3. Rotate the flywheel while watching the dial indicator.
4. The variation in reading is the amount of radial runout.

Radial runout has a greater effect on balance and vibration than on clutch operation. Runout in either direction greater than 0.010 in. (0.25 mm) is considered excessive; runout as little as 0.005 in. (0.1 mm) can cause **chatter.**

If the flywheel is to be removed, it is a good practice to place index marks at the crankshaft flange for faster alignment during reassembly.

◄ **SERVICE TIP** ►

It is easy to cut your hand or fingers if you handle a flywheel by the edges. Long bolts can be threaded into the pressure plate bolt holes to provide convenient handles (Figure 5-21).

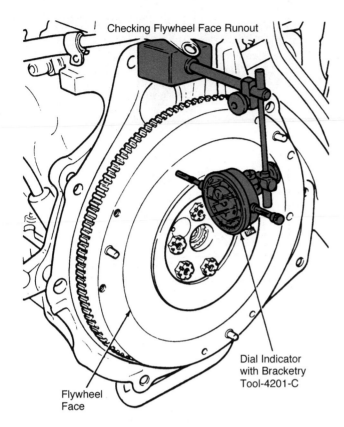

Checking Flywheel Face Runout

Dial Indicator with Bracketry Tool-4201-C

Flywheel Face

FIGURE 5-20 This dial indicator is set up to measure flywheel face or axial runout. (Courtesy of Ford Motor Company)

It is also a good practice to inspect the starter ring gear teeth. If they are damaged, replace either the starter gear or flywheel.

REAL-WORLD FIX The clutch in a 1995 VW GTI (107,000 mi) has been replaced and the flywheel was resurfaced at the same time. But now there is a noticeable clutch chatter. The technician was told that during the resurfacing, only the clutch mating surface was machined. The technician feels that the step height could be wrong, but he cannot find a specification for this.

FIX

After contacting iATN, international Automotive Technician Network, a fellow technician provided the step-height specification. A check of the flywheel showed that it's step was at the limit, but the clutch surface also had 0.003 in. of runout. Remachining the flywheel fixed this problem.

5.4.2.2 Pressure Plate Assembly A used pressure plate assembly should be inspected visually for friction surface damage, release lever wear, lever pivot wear, and cover distortion, but there is no way to check effectively for proper spring strength. Like the flywheel, the friction surface will tend to polish or glaze from normal use. If there is excessive slippage, grooves, heat checks, and warping can occur (Figure 5-22). Warpage can be checked by placing a straight-edge across the friction surface and will show up as a gap between the straightedge and the inner portion of the pressure plate ring.

Set the pressure plate on the flywheel. All of the mounting points should meet the flywheel evenly and completely. Any air gaps indicate a distorted clutch cover. Release lever wear occurs at the contact surface with the

FIGURE 5-21 Two long bolts (arrows) have been threaded into the flywheel to serve as handles for carrying and positioning.

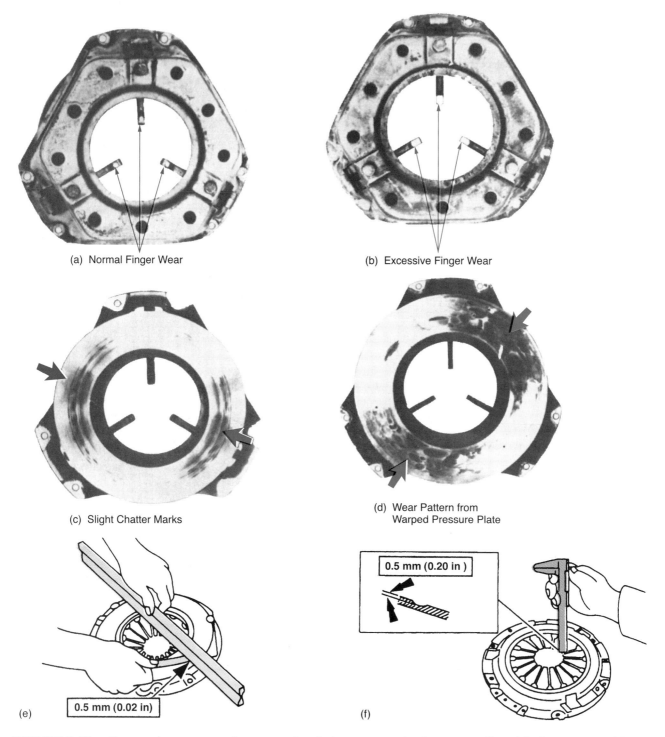

(a) Normal Finger Wear

(b) Excessive Finger Wear

(c) Slight Chatter Marks

(d) Wear Pattern from Warped Pressure Plate

(e)   0.5 mm (0.02 in)

0.5 mm (0.20 in)

(f)

FIGURE 5-22   Commonly encountered pressure plate faults are excessive finger wear (b and f), chatter marks (c), and excessive warpage (d and f). (Courtesy of Ford Motor Company)

release bearing; this area should appear smooth and polished with no metal removed. Release lever height should be checked after the pressure plate and disc are bolted to the flywheel. Soft reddish-brown rust and highly polished or shiny rough areas around the lever pivots are indica-

tions of wear at these points. If any problems are noticed, the pressure plate assembly should be replaced.

5.4.2.3 Clutch Disc   If installing a used disc, it should be checked for facing thickness, damper spring condi-

FIGURE 5-23 Clutch disc failure comes in many forms; a good technician will determine and correct the cause of abnormal failures so they won't occur again. (Courtesy of LUK Clutches)

tion, wear of the hub splines, and warpage or axial runout (Figure 5-23). The thickness of the facing can be checked by two different methods. The most popular method is to measure the height of the facing surface above the rivets; this is also called *rivet head depth* (Figure 5-24).

◀ SERVICE TIP ▶

With a new disc, rivet head depth will be about 0.050 in. (1.2 mm); a disc with less than 0.015 to 0.020 in. (0.38 to 0.5 mm) should be replaced.

The second method is to place cardboard or a shop cloth over the facing to keep it clean and squeeze the facings together to compress the Marcel spring. If no specifications are available, the minimum thickness of the compressed disc should be 0.280 in. (7.1 mm).

The damper springs and hub splines are checked visually for reddish rust and shiny worn areas as well as broken or missing springs. **Disc runout** warpage is checked by making an axial runout check. This usually requires a pair of tapered centers or an expanding arbor at true center to the hub splines; a tight-fitting clutch shaft spline will work. The disc is rotated while watching for runout or wobbling of the facing surfaces (Figure 5-25). More than 0.020 in. (0.5 mm) is excessive, and the disc should be replaced.

◀ SERVICE TIP ▶

A similar check for warpage is to set the disc against the flywheel. The facing should contact the flywheel evenly all around the disc.

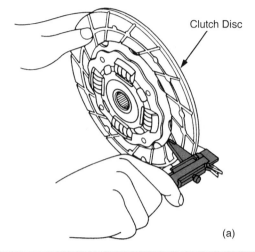

Clutch Disc

(a)

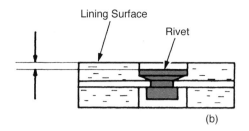

Lining Surface

Rivet

(b)

(c)

(d) Wear Pattern from
Warped Pressure Plate

FIGURE 5-24 Clutch disc thickness can be measured using a vernier or dial caliper (a) to measure rivet depth (b) or a micrometer (c) or vernier caliper to measure the overall thickness (d). There is no need to measure a disc that is worn to the bottom of the grooves (d). (a: Portions of materials contained herein have been reprinted with permission of General Motors Corporation, Service and Parts Operations, License Agreement #0310807; b is courtesy of American Honda Motor Company; d is courtesy of Ford Motor Company)

5.4.2.4 Clutch/Bell Housing There should be no oil or grease residue inside the bell housing. If oil is present, check the crankshaft seal or the plugs sealing the camshaft or oil galleys. If there has been early failure of the pilot or release bearings or a complaint of clutch pedal vibration or the transmission jumping out of gear, the face and bore surfaces of the bell housing should be checked for excessive runout. These checks are made with a dial indicator that is attached to the crankshaft, flywheel, pressure plate, or disc, depending on the equipment available and how far the clutch is disassembled.

To check bell housing face runout, you should:

1. Mount a dial indicator onto the flywheel with its mounting post running through the bell housing bore. The measuring stem should be against the transmission mounting surface with the measuring stem parallel to the crankshaft.

2. Adjust the dial indicator to read zero.

3. Rotate the crankshaft while watching the indicator reading (Figure 5-26). Maintain a forward or rearward pressure to eliminate crankshaft end play.

4. Any variation in reading is the amount of face runout.

◄ **SERVICE TIP** ►

The limit for face runout is about 0.010 in. (0.25 mm). If there is excessive runout, check for loose mounting bolts or dirt between the bell housing and the engine block. If the runout cannot be corrected, normally the bell housing is replaced, but it is possible to put shims between the bell housing and the engine block for correction.

(a)

(b)

FIGURE 5-25 (a) It is a good practice to check a disc for lateral runout by rotating it on the transmission clutch shaft or in a tool for that purpose. (b) Also check to make sure that the disc slides freely on the shaft splines. (a is courtesy of LUK Clutches; b: Portions of materials contained herein have been reprinted with permission of General Motors Corporation, Service and Parts Operations, License Agreement #0310807)

To check bell housing bore runout, you should:

1. Reposition the dial indicator so the measuring stem is inside the bore and pointing outward.
2. Adjust the dial indicator to read zero.
3. Rotate the crankshaft while watching the indicator reading.
4. Any variation in reading is the amount of bore runout.

◀ SERVICE TIP ▶

Because of the small area in a bore, a wiggle bar is often used (Figure 5-27a). The limit for bore runout is about 0.010 in. (0.25 mm).

Bore runout can be corrected by using eccentric dowel pins to reposition the bell housing (Figure 5-27b). These are available in different sizes and positioned to move the bell housing the right distance in the correct direction to center the bore to the crankshaft.

5.4.2.5 Release Bearing   Other than feeling for roughness or seeing obvious wear or burning, there are no effective bench checks for release bearings. This is one reason why they are normally replaced with the disc and pressure plate.

The release bearing used on some older vehicles is a two-part assembly. The old bearing is pressed off the sleeve, and the new bearing is pressed onto it (Figure 5-

28). Some vehicles use different lengths of release bearings. You should always check the replacement for correct length and type (Figure 5-29). Remember that a curved face bearing should never be used with a pressure plate with curved fingers.

REAL-WORLD FIX   The clutch in a 1991 Acura (65,000 mi) did not release. Even though the clutch was replaced 10,000 miles ago and still appeared good, the pressure plate and disc were replaced and the flywheel resurfaced. The clutch now released, but it had a chatter problem. The pedal did not feel right. Closer inspection showed a slight binding in the clutch cable. It was replaced, but this did not help.

FIX

Closer inspection revealed an improper return spring connection to the release bearing. Smoothing a damaged area where the release bearing operated and replacement of the release bearing and spring fixed this problem.

AUTHOR'S NOTE

A thorough inspection during the clutch repair would have caught this problem.

5.4.3 Clutch Replacement

During replacement, the clutch components must be kept clean and dry. All grease and oil that contacts the friction surfaces must be cleaned off. Small amounts of oil on the clutch facing will cause the clutch to grab or chatter.

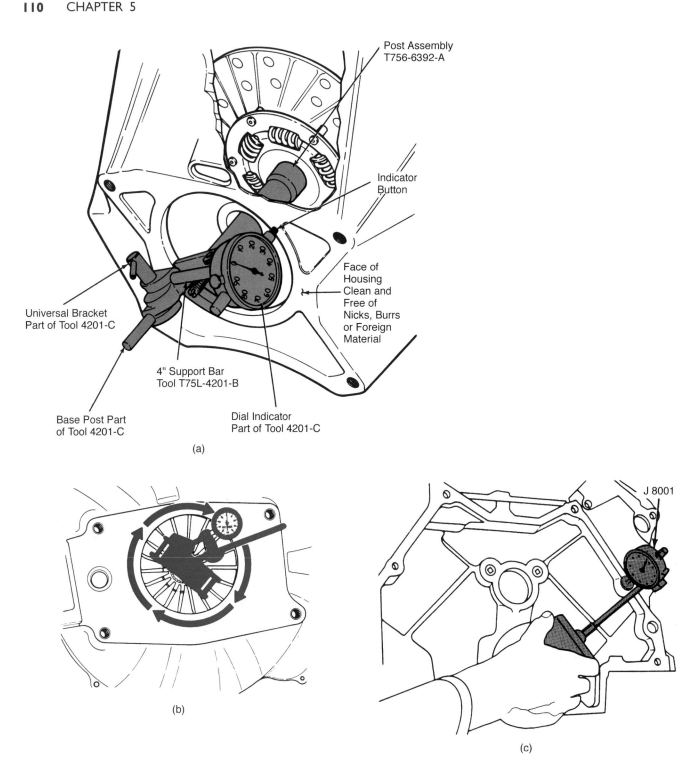

Post Assembly
T756-6392-A

Indicator
Button

Face of
Housing
Clean and
Free of
Nicks, Burrs
or Foreign
Material

Universal Bracket
Part of Tool 4201-C

4" Support Bar
Tool T75L-4201-B

Base Post Part
of Tool 4201-C

Dial Indicator
Part of Tool 4201-C

(a)

(b)

J 8001

(c)

FIGURE 5-26 A dial indicator is mounted to the clutch disc (a) or the pressure plate assembly (b) and the crankshaft is rotated to check for runout at the face of the clutch housing. It can also be mounted to the crankshaft to check for runout of the clutch housing surface (c). (a is courtesy of Ford Motor Company; b and c: Portions of materials contained herein have been reprinted with permission of General Motors Corporation, Service and Parts Operations, License Agreement #0310807)

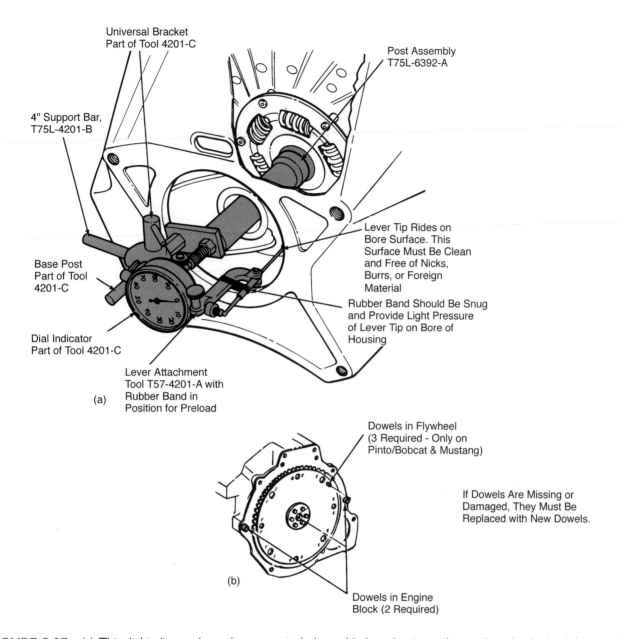

Universal Bracket
Part of Tool 4201-C

Post Assembly
T75L-6392-A

4" Support Bar,
T75L-4201-B

Lever Tip Rides on
Bore Surface. This
Surface Must Be Clean
and Free of Nicks,
Burrs, or Foreign
Material

Base Post
Part of Tool
4201-C

Rubber Band Should Be Snug
and Provide Light Pressure
of Lever Tip on Bore of
Housing

Dial Indicator
Part of Tool 4201-C

Lever Attachment
Tool T57-4201-A with
Rubber Band in
Position for Preload

(a)

Dowels in Flywheel
(3 Required - Only on
Pinto/Bobcat & Mustang)

If Dowels Are Missing or
Damaged, They Must Be
Replaced with New Dowels.

(b)

Dowels in Engine
Block (2 Required)

FIGURE 5-27 (a) This dial indicator has a lever or wiggle bar added so that it can be used to check clutch housing bore runout. (b) Excessive runout can be caused by damaged or missing dowels; if the dowels are good, runout can be corrected by installing eccentric dowels. (Courtesy of Ford Motor Company)

Old Bearing

Release
Bearing
Sleeve

New Bearing

NR134

FIGURE 5-28 Some release bearings are mounted on a sleeve, and the old bearing can be used to install the new one, as shown here. (Courtesy of DaimlerChrysler Corporation)

A. Height
B. I.D.
C. Bearing Face

Part No.	16001	16010	16021
Dim. A	1.485"	1.290"	1.635"
Dim. B	1.375"	1.375"	1.375"
Dim. C	2.930"	2.560"	2.930"
Application	GM., Used When Replacing Diaphragm Pressure Plate w/ 3-Finger Type	GM., All High-Cone Diaphragms & 12" B&B	GM., Used when 1600 Is Too Short for Proper Adjustment

FIGURE 5-29 Some cars use release bearings of different lengths; the critical dimensions are shown here. (Courtesy of McLeod Industries, Inc.)

◄ SERVICE TIP ►

Many technicians pick up and hold a new disc by the very outside edge or center hole, never touching the facing (Figure 5-30). A pressure plate assembly is handled by the cover, not the face of the pressure ring.

When replacing the clutch on a vehicle with a modular assembly, after removing the transmission/transaxle, the entire assembly is unbolted from the flexplate and a new assembly is installed. The new modular assembly has the clutch disc already centered between the flywheel and pressure plate (Figure 5-31).

The procedure described here begins with new or thoroughly checked and cleaned parts. Again, it is recommended that you follow the procedure described in a service manual when replacing the clutch on a particular vehicle. Before beginning assembly, check the new parts to ensure that they are the correct size and type.

To replace a clutch assembly:

1. Check the flywheel bolts to make sure that they are tight and torqued to specifications. Check the pilot bearing recess to ensure that it is clean, and drive the new pilot bearing into the crankshaft recess. The best tool for this is a commercial or shop-made

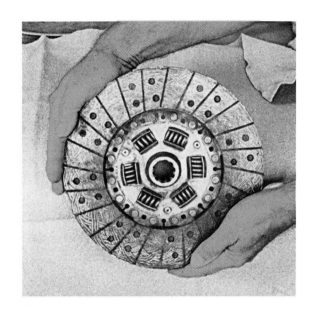

FIGURE 5-30 A new disc should be held by the edges or center spline to prevent contamination of the facing, which can cause chatter.

driver with a stem the same size as the bearing bore and a face that is larger than the diameter of the bearing (Figure 5-32a).

◄ SERVICE TIP ►

A substitute for a special tool is a bushing driver with these dimensions or an old clutch shaft with a flat washer positioned between the bearing and the clutch shaft splines (Figure 5-32b).

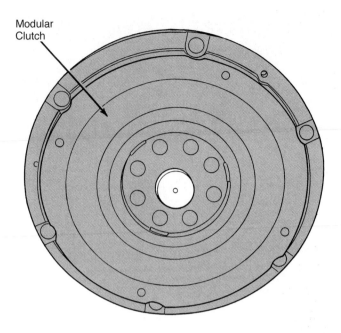

Engine Side Shown

FIGURE 5-31 When replacing a modular clutch, the new modular assembly, with the new flywheel, clutch disc, and pressure plate, is bolted onto the flexplate. (Courtesy of DaimlerChrysler Corporation)

The new pilot bearing is driven in until it is fully seated or has entered completely into the crankshaft. Most pilot bearings do not require lubrication.

◄ SERVICE TIP ►

Roller bearings with exposed rollers should be lubricated with a thin film of grease; a few drops of motor oil is all you should put on a sintered bushing.

2. Place the new clutch disc over the transmission clutch shaft and make sure that it slides freely over the splines. Next, determine which side of the disc goes against the flywheel; it will often be marked "flywheel side." If not, the damper assembly normally faces the pressure plate.

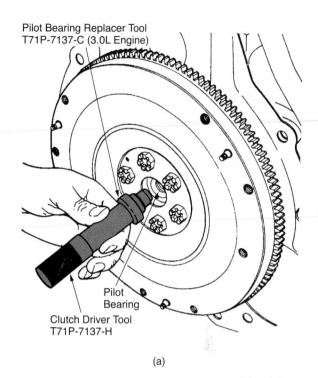

(a)

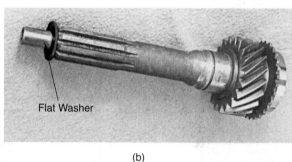

(b)

FIGURE 5-32 (a) A new pilot bearing should be installed using a driver. (b) If a clutch shaft is used as a driver, a flat washer should be placed on the shaft to prevent damaging the bearing. (a is courtesy of Ford Motor Company)

REAL-WORLD FIX A 1994 Honda Civic (216,000 mi) was towed into the shop with a bad clutch. The slave cylinder was leaking, and disassembly showed a completely worn-out disc. A new clutch disc, release bearing, and slave cylinder were installed, and the flywheel was resurfaced at this time. On engine start-up, the clutch would not release. The pedal felt good, and the release lever moved properly.

FIX

Disassembly showed that the disc was installed correctly, but the splines were wrong so the disc did not slide easily on the transmission shaft. Installation of the correct disc fixed this problem.

REAL-WORLD FIX A 1994 Acura NSX (65,000 mi) had a bad clutch. Because of the cost of the replacement parts, the vehicle owner requested that only the friction discs be replaced. The flywheel and intermediate plate (two-plate clutch) were touched up using an abrasive pad. The transmission splines were lubricated using synthetic grease as the parts were replaced. But, the clutch would not release.

FIX

This two-plate clutch requires an initializing adjustment to set the clearance between the mid plate and the flywheel. Making this adjustment fixed this problem.

◄ SERVICE TIP ►

To determine the correct clutch disc position, place each side of the disc against the flywheel and rotate it; the side that contacts the flywheel bolts or does not let the clutch facing contact the flywheel is the wrong side (Figure 5-33).

3. Position the **disc alignment** tool through the disc and into the pilot bearing so the disc is centered (Figure 5-34). Many shops will normally use a tool with expanding collets that will lock into the pilot bearing and tapered centering cones for the disc. An old transmission clutch shaft is a good substitute. If using commercial wooden or plastic align-

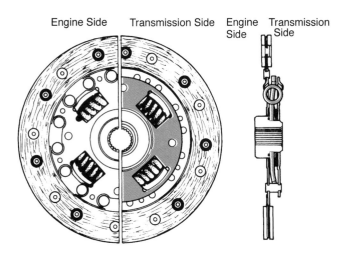

FIGURE 5-33 Many replacement discs will have a marking indicating the flywheel or pressure plate side; the damper assembly is normally on the pressure plate or transmission side. (Courtesy of LUK Clutches)

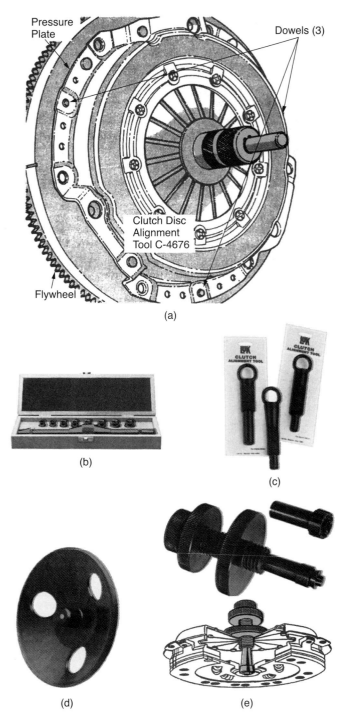

FIGURE 5-34 (a) Most manufacturers use special tools to hold the disc in alignment while the pressure plate bolts are tightened. These tools are also available from aftermarket sources in sets to fit many cars (b) or a single purpose (c and d). The tool shown in d is used for edge-centered discs. (e) A recently developed tool holds the disc centered to the pressure plate. (a is courtesy of DaimlerChrysler Corporation; b, c, and d are courtesy of LUK Clutches; e is courtesy of Vim Tools)

ment tools, make sure they fit closely enough to center the disc. Clutches without a pilot bearing are OD (outside diameter) centered; the centering edge (outside) of the disc must be perfectly aligned with the flywheel. Another style of alignment tool holds the disc centered onto the pressure plate while the pressure plate is installed.

4. Install the pressure plate over the disc, making sure that it is properly aligned with the dowel pins and mounting bolt holes, and install the mounting bolts. If reusing a pressure plate, align your index marks made earlier. In some cases, you will need to do this before step 3.

◄ SERVICE TIP ►

A simple disc alignment tool can be made to aid clutch installation if a disc alignment tool is not available. This tool holds the disc in a centered position against the pressure plate as the pressure plate is installed. The materials needed to make the tool are a short length of 3/8″ or 5/16″ threaded rod, a large washer, and a nut, as shown in Figure 5-35. A hook to catch the center of the disc is formed at one end of the rod, and this hook should be flattened so it will be easier to remove. The washer must be large enough to press against the pressure plate levers/fingers. To use this tool, center the disc on the pressure plate, install the tool as shown, and tighten the nut enough to hold them together. Make sure the outer edge of the disc is centered to the pressure plate. Next, install the pressure plate, and then remove the tool.

REAL-WORLD FIX   A Volkswagen Fox (127,000 mi) clutch would not release. The clutch components were replaced, but the clutch still would not release. The clutch pedal and cable were okay.

FIX

Removal of the clutch and comparing it with a new set of clutch components revealed that the wrong parts were used on the original replacement. Using the right parts fixed this problem.

AUTHOR'S NOTE

The technician is always the final quality control check. Each part should be checked to make sure it fits properly as it is installed.

NOTE: If installing a pressure plate equipped with a self-adjusting fulcrum ring, check the length of the adjusting ring actuation springs (Figure 5-36). If the length exceeds specifications, place the assembly in a press or drill press, and using a suitable release bearing substitute, compress the diaphragm fingers to a released position.

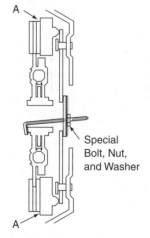

FIGURE 5-35   A simple, shop-made tool can be used to hold the disc centered against the pressure plate as the pressure plate is installed. The gaps at the edge of the disc and pressure plate (a) should be equal.

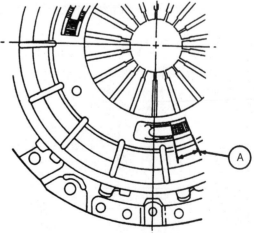

FIGURE 5-36   When installing a pressure plate with a self-adjusting fulcrum ring, check dimension A. If the distance exceeds the specification, follow the proper procedure to adjust it. (Courtesy of Ford Motor Company)

Then rotate the adjusting ring so that the springs are compressed to the proper length, release the press pressure, and install the pressure plate assembly.

5. Tighten the mounting bolts two turns at a time and in an alternating fashion, back and forth across the pressure plate (Figure 5-37). They should be tightened to the correct torque.

◀ SERVICE TIP ▶

Remove the alignment device and check to make sure that the pilot bearing is in the exact center of the disc (Figure 5-38).

◀ SERVICE TIP ▶

The height variation of the release levers can be checked after the pressure plate is installed. Using a vernier or dial caliper, measure from the contact face for the release bearing to the clutch disc. All of the heights should be within 0.020 in. (50 mm) of each other (Figure 5-39). The readings will be more accurate after the clutch has been applied a few times. Some technicians will assemble a pressure plate, disc, and flywheel off the vehicle, and then apply and release the clutch in a press before checking finger height.

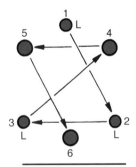

Tightening Sequence

FIGURE 5-37 With the disc held centered, the pressure plate bolts should be tightened two turns at a time in a pattern like this. (Portions of materials contained herein have been reprinted with permission of General Motors Corporation, Service and Parts Operations, License Agreement #0310807)

◀ SERVICE TIP ▶

Watch the release levers as the pressure plate is tightened onto the flywheel. They should start to move toward the flywheel when the clutch cover is about 1/8" to 3/16" from the flywheel.

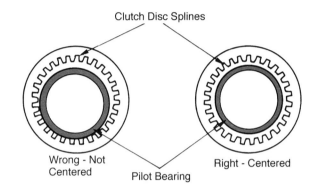

FIGURE 5-38 After the bolts have been tightened to the correct torque, sight down the splines to make sure that they are centered to the pilot bearing.

FIGURE 5-39 The height of the release levers can be measured after the pressure plate assembly has been installed by measuring from the fingers to the hub of the disc. The readings should all be the same.

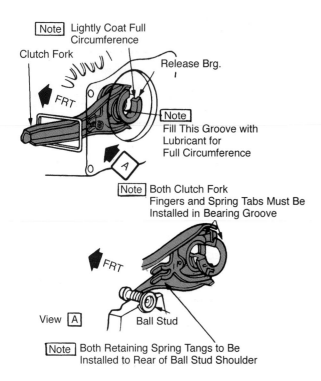

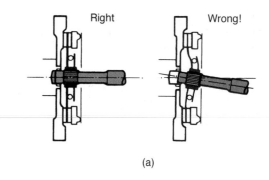

FIGURE 5-40 A release bearing should be lubricated before installation, as shown here. (Portions of materials contained herein have been reprinted with permission of General Motors Corporation, Service and Parts Operations, License Agreement #0310807)

6. Check the clutch linkage to make sure that it operates smoothly. On cable-operated clutches, this is a good time to remove, clean, and lubricate the cable.

7. Fill the groove inside the bore of the release bearing with grease, apply a thin film of grease on the fork contact areas, and slide the release bearing onto the transmission quill, making sure that the bearing collar slides smoothly (Figure 5-40). The quill portion of the transmission bearing retainer should be smooth and unworn. On clutch forks that use pivot balls, a thin film of grease should be put on the ball. On forks mounted on pivot shafts, the pivot bushings should be lubricated.

8. Replace the transmission, being sure to observe these points:
   - Place a very thin film of grease on the clutch splines.
   - Never let the transmission hang on the clutch disc splines. A simple way to prevent this and also make the installation easier is to use a pair of guide pins to support the transmission while it is slid into place (Figure 5-41).

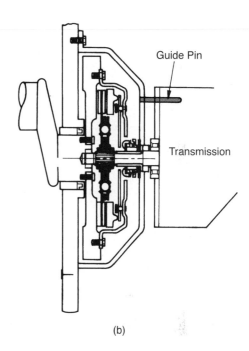

FIGURE 5-41 (a) "Hanging" a partially installed transmission on the disc will bend the center of the disc. (b) Installation of guide pins will support the transmission as you slide it into place. (a is courtesy of LUK Clutches)

- Make sure that no wires, cables, or hoses are trapped under the clutch housing or transmission as it is installed.
- The transmission should be completely checked against the clutch housing or engine before the mounting bolts are tightened.
- Tighten the transmission mounting bolts two turns at a time, working back and forth across the transmission until they are tightened to the correct torque. It should not be necessary to force the transmission into place.
- Complete the transmission installation as described in Section 8.4.2.
- Adjust the free travel before operating the clutch.

◄   PROBLEM SOLVING   ►

Imagine that you are working in a general automotive repair shop and these problems are brought to you.

CASE 1

Your boss has taken in a job to replace the clutch disc in a fairly high mileage FWD car and you have just removed the pressure plate assembly. The clutch disc is worn out, and both the pressure ring and the flywheel are grooved, checked, and polished from slippage. What parts should you replace or recondition as you complete this job?

CASE 2

The mechanic in the bay next to you is completing a clutch job on a pickup and has asked you to help install the transmission. The two of you place the transmission on the guide pins. It slides in easily but stops about 3/4 in. from the clutch housing; it won't go any farther. What is wrong? What should you recommend to your partner?

REAL-WORLD FIX A 1992 Isuzu Rodeo (174,000 mi) came in with no clutch. A leaking clutch master cylinder was found and replaced, but this did not help. The transmission was difficult to shift. The transmission was removed and a new slave cylinder, clutch disc, pressure plate, release bearing, fork, and fork pivot stud were installed. The clutch still did not work properly.

FIX

An adjustable slave cylinder rod was located and installed. Adjustment of the clutch pedal free travel fixed this problem.

REAL-WORLD FIX A Mitsubishi pickup (173,000 mi) clutch was replaced, but the truck soon came back with a broken clutch lever. The customer stated that this was the second time the lever had broken. The clutch appeared okay, and it worked properly after the lever was replaced. What caused the unusual lever breakage?

FIX

An inspection showed that the engine balance shaft was out of time. Replacement of the camshaft timing belt and properly timing the balance shaft fixed this problem.

REAL-WORLD FIX The clutch (pressure plate, disc, throw-out bearing, and master cylinder) on a 1995 Camaro was replaced by another shop, but it did not release until the pedal was at the floor. The system was bled, but the slave cylinder did not travel far enough to allow disengagement.

FIX

Disassembly of the clutch revealed that the mechanic had installed the throw-out bearing backwards.

5.5   HYDRAULIC SYSTEM REPAIR

Fluid leaks or failure to release completely indicate the need for hydraulic system service. Clutch hydraulic systems have evolved from the early systems that had free travel adjustment and required clearance at the release bearing to newer systems that maintain a slight preload. The older systems used rebuildable master and slave cylinders much like brake components, while the newer systems use nonrebuildable cylinders that are serviced by replacement. The older systems used steel and reinforced rubber lines with threaded fittings, while the newer systems use plastic tubing sealed by O-rings and held together by locking pins at the connections (Figures 5-42 and 5-43).

A drop in fluid level at the reservoir indicates a fluid leak. Normally, facing wear will cause an increase, or rise, in the fluid level, so topping off the reservoir is not necessary or recommended. The cause of a fluid leak is usually found through visual inspection of the cylinders and lines to locate the wetness. Fluid leak repair is done by correcting the fault: tightening a line fitting, replacing an O-ring, or rebuilding or replacing a defective part (Figure 5-44).

Inability to release the clutch completely can be checked by observing slave cylinder travel as the clutch pedal is depressed. The slave cylinder should begin moving immediately and travel in a smooth, steady manner. Some manufacturers provide slave cylinder travel or extension specifications. For example, one manufacturer specifies 0.53 in. (13.5 mm) of slave cylinder motion for one complete stroke of the clutch pedal (see Figure 5-9). Insufficient slave cylinder travel indicates air in the system or a faulty slave or master cylinder.

In many cases, a clutch hydraulic system can be bled by **gravity bleeding;** in others, a helper is needed.

To bleed a clutch hydraulic system using the gravity method:

1. Clean the bleeder valve at the slave cylinder and place a shop cloth under it to catch escaping fluid.
2. Open the bleed valve by loosening the bleeder screw and observe the flow out of it (Figure 5-45). If no flow occurs, have a helper depress the

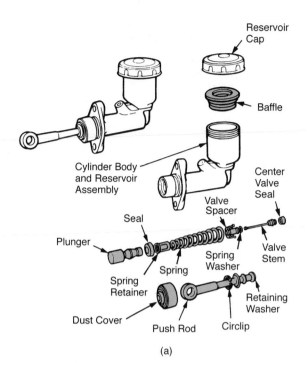

(a)

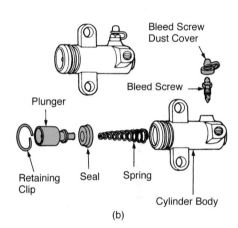

(b)

FIGURE 5-42   On some cars, the clutch master (a) and slave (b) cylinders can be disassembled and rebuilt. (Portions of materials contained herein have been reprinted with permission of General Motors Corporation, Service and Parts Operations, License Agreement #0310807)

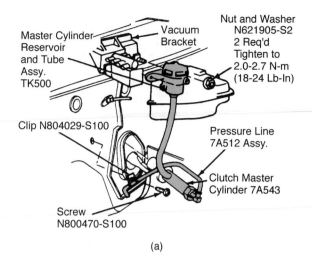

(a)

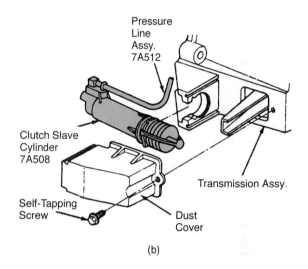

(b)

FIGURE 5-43   On some cars, faulty clutch master (a) or slave (b) cylinders are removed and replaced with new units. (Courtesy of Ford Motor Company)

◀   **SERVICE TIP**   ▶

A good tool for pumping fluid into the bleed value is a common squirt-type oil can that has never had oil in it.

clutch pedal in a smooth, slow manner. Air bubbles coming from the bleed valve indicate that the system needed bleeding. After the air bubbles stop and a constant flow of fluid occurs, close the bleed valve and wipe up any spilled fluid. An alternative method is reverse, or back, bleeding. This is done by forcing fluid through the slave cylinder bleed valve and upward to the reservoir (Figure 5-46).

REAL-WORLD FIX   The clutch of a 1992 2.2-L Cavalier (45,000 mi) slips at high rpm upshifts and downshifts. It was replaced 14,000 miles ago for the same problem. The clutch was disassembled, but there was no sign of anything wrong.

FIX

Close inspection of the clutch master cylinder revealed a snap ring cocked in the bore that prevented the piston from returning completely. Proper installation of this snap ring fixed this problem.

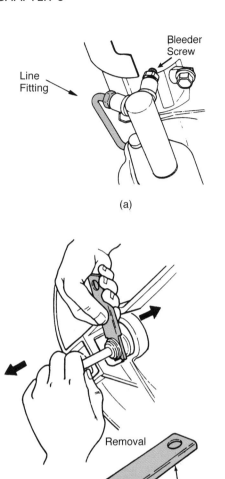

(a)

Removal

Disconnect Tool
T88T-70522-A

(b)

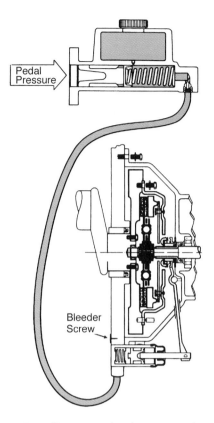

FIGURE 5-45   On many clutch systems, loosening the bleeder screw at the slave cylinder allows gravity to push the air out of the slave cylinder. Sometimes, it is necessary to have an assistant apply pressure at the pedal as the bleeder screw is opened. (Courtesy of LUK Clutches)

FIGURE 5-44   (a) Most older cars used threaded line connections to the clutch master and slave cylinders. (b) This vehicle uses a snap-in connector that requires a special tool for disassembly. (a: Portions of materials contained herein have been reprinted with permission of General Motors Corporation, Service and Parts Operations, License Agreement #0310807; b is courtesy of Ford Motor Company)

AUTHOR'S NOTE

The incomplete return of the master cylinder piston caused a pressure on the release bearing, which held the clutch in a partially released condition.

REAL-WORLD FIX The 1997 Chevrolet Cavalier (35,000 miles) worked fine in city driving but after about 30 miles of driving, the pedal became mushy and it was hard to shift gears. The clutch system had been bled and the master cylinder had been replaced, with no positive result.

FIX

While the transaxle was being removed, the slave cylinder came apart, revealing a faulty unit. Replacement of the slave cylinder fixed this problem.

3. Check the fluid level and correct it, if necessary.

REAL-WORLD FIX The clutch on a 1989 Ford Ranger (122,000 mi) was replaced, but the clutch did not disengage. The pedal went to the floor. The hydraulic system was bled several times, even with the back end and each side lifted.

FIX

This master cylinder is mounted at a rather steep angle. Disconnecting the master cylinder mounting so it could be held level allowed the air to be bled out, and this fixed this problem.

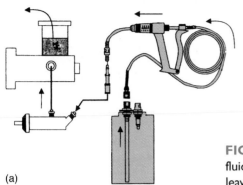

(a)

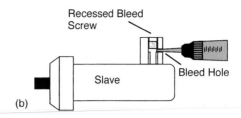

Recessed Bleed Screw

Slave

Bleed Hole

(b)

FIGURE 5-46 A clutch hydraulic system can be reverse bled by pumping fluid through the bleeder valve or hole and up to the reservoir; the air will leave the fluid at the reservoir. (Courtesy of Phoenix Systems)

◄ **PROBLEM SOLVING** ►

Imagine that you are working in a general automotive repair shop and this problem was brought to you.

Case 1

The 3-year-old FWD car has a complaint of gear clash on shifting into first or reverse gear. When you start the car, your check confirms the problem, and you also notice a slightly mushy pedal operation. With the engine off, your pedal check shows no free travel and the pedal going completely to the floor with fairly normal resistance. Your underhood check shows that the fluid level in the clutch reservoir is okay and no signs of leakage. What is probably wrong? What should you do next?

◄ **SERVICE TIP** ►

Some master and slave cylinders are mounted so that the cylinder portion is above the line connection, and this makes it extremely difficult to bleed air out of them. In some cases, it is possible to **bench bleed** them to remove all the air before installing them on the vehicle (Figure 5-47). If you need to bleed one of these difficult systems, an alternative bleeding method is to have a helper partially apply the clutch while reverse bleeding using pressure surges from the fluid injector (Figure 5-48).

◄ **SERVICE TIP** ►

Some clutch hydraulic systems will partially self-bleed if the clutch pedal is held completely depressed overnight using a brake pedal jack. Another bleeding method is to construct an adapter to the fluid reservoir so you can apply a vacuum to the fluid using a hand, electric, or air-powered vacuum pump. Reducing the air pressure on the fluid will cause the air bubble to expand and possibly move upward to the reservoir.

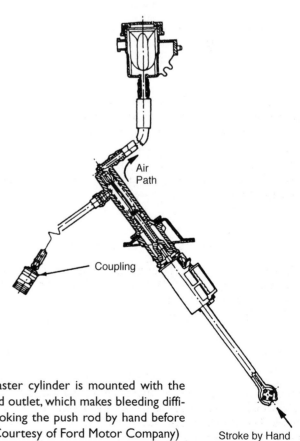

Air Path

Coupling

Stroke by Hand

FIGURE 5-47 This clutch master cylinder is mounted with the push-rod end above the inlet and outlet, which makes bleeding difficult. It can be bench bled by stroking the push rod by hand before mounting the master cylinder. (Courtesy of Ford Motor Company)

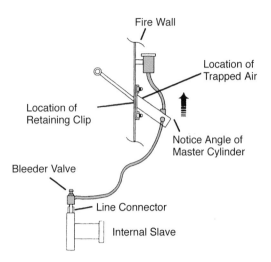

Fire Wall

Location of
Trapped Air

Location of
Retaining Clip

Notice Angle of
Master Cylinder

Bleeder Valve

Line Connector

Internal Slave

FIGURE 5-48 Another way of bleeding a difficult clutch master cylinder is to have an assistant depress the clutch pedal, build a pressure in the system using a fluid injector at the bleeder valve, and slowly release the pedal. The pressure surge will force the trapped air upward. This operation should be repeated several times. (Courtesy of Phoenix Systems)

REVIEW QUESTIONS

The following questions are provided to help you study as you read the chapter.

1. The clutch pedal free travel will _____ as the clutch disc facing wears.

2. Clutch pedal free _____ is the light resistance of the clutch pedal return spring as the clutch pedal is first depressed.

3. When checking for clutch slipping in the shop, the technician should have the _____ firmly applied.

4. When checking for a slipping clutch while on a road test, a clutch that is slipping will be most noticeable when driving _____.

5. Clutch drag will cause _____ when shifting.

6. When checking for a clutch noise, if the noise is noticed just beyond pedal free travel, the probable cause is the _____.

7. When checking for a clutch noise, if the noise is noticed when the clutch is completely disengaged the probable cause is the _____.

8. Clutch replacement normally involves replacing four components. What are they?

   a. _____   c. _____

   b. _____   d. _____

9. When removing a clutch _____, always remove the fasteners evenly.

10. The recommended method of surfacing the flywheel is _____.

11. Oil or grease on the clutch disc facing may cause it to _____ or _____.

12. An old transmission _____ shaft can be used as a clutch disc alignment tool.

13. Never let the transmission _____ on the clutch disc splines.

14. A drop in fluid level in the clutch master cylinder _____ indicates a fluid leak.

15. After a clutch master cylinder is replaced, it must be _____.

CHAPTER QUIZ

The following questions will help you check the facts you have learned. Select the answer that completes each statement correctly.

1. While discussing clutch adjustments, Student A says that free travel is always measured at the clutch pedal and should be between 3/4 and 1 in. (19 and 25 mm). Student B says that free travel should be more than this in most newer vehicles. Who is correct?

   a. Student A

   b. Student B

   c. Both Student A and Student B

   d. Neither Student A nor Student B

2. A vehicle has a slipping clutch. Student A says slippage is most noticeable when accelerating in first gear. Student B says a clutch slip test can be performed in the shop. Who is correct?

   a. Student A   c. Both A and B

   b. Student B   d. Neither A nor B

3. Clutch chatter can be caused by A. grease or oil on the clutch facing or B. broken motor mounts. Which is correct?

a. A only   **c.** Both A and B

b. B only   **d.** Neither A nor B

4. Student A says that a long clutch spin down is also called drag. Student B says that this can be caused by letting the transmission hang on the clutch shaft during installation. Who is correct?

   a. Student A

   b. Student B

   c. Both Student A and Student B

   d. Neither Student A nor Student B

5. Student A says that clutch slipping can be caused by a warped clutch disc. Student B says that slippage is the result of too much free travel. Who is correct?

   a. Student A

   b. Student B

   c. Both Student A and Student B

   d. Neither Student A nor Student B

6. A squeal begins as the clutch pedal is depressed about 1 in. (25 mm). This is probably caused by A. a faulty transmission bearing or B. a bad pilot bearing. Which is correct?

   a. A only   **c.** Both A and B

   b. B only   **d.** Neither A nor B

7. Student A says that you should replace at least four parts when you do a clutch job: the pressure plate, disc, release bearing, and pilot bearing. Student B says that breathing the dust around a worn pressure plate or disc can cause lung cancer. Who is correct?

   a. Student A

   b. Student B

   c. Both Student A and Student B

   d. Neither Student A nor Student B

8. Of the following, which is not a normal problem with worn discs?

   a. facing worn down to the rivets.

   b. broken damper springs.

   c. expanded Marcel.

   d. worn splines.

9. While discussing the installation of a clutch disc, Student A says that the damper assembly is normally positioned next to the flywheel. Student B says that some discs are aligned by their outer edge. Who is correct?

   a. Student A

   b. Student B

   c. Both Student A and Student B

   d. Neither Student A nor Student B

10. Student A says that a pilot bearing can usually be removed using chassis grease and a round rod of the correct size. Student B says that all pilot bearings need a thin coating of grease after installation. Who is correct?

    a. Student A

    b. Student B

    c. Both Student A and Student B

    d. Neither Student A nor Student B

11. Improper clutch disc alignment can cause A. difficulty and possible damage as the transmission is installed, B. early failure of the pressure plate. Which is correct?

    a. A only   **c.** Both A and B

    b. B only   **d.** Neither A nor B

12. During clutch installation, the clutch disc can be aligned to the pilot bearing using

    a. a commercial clutch disc alignment tool.

    b. an old transmission shaft.

    c. a plastic dummy transmission shaft.

    d. any of these.

13. While discussing the installation of a pressure plate, Student A says that grade 2 or better bolts can be used for the mounting bolts. Student B says that you need to move from bolt to bolt at least a dozen times while tightening the bolts. Who is correct?

    a. Student A

    b. Student B

    c. Both Student A and Student B

    d. Neither Student A nor Student B

14. Student A says that the groove in the bore of the release bearing should be filled with grease before it is installed. Student B says that too much grease in and around a clutch can lead to grab and chatter. Who is correct?

    a. Student A

    b. Student B

    c. Both Student A and Student B

    d. Neither Student A nor Student B

15. Student A says that clutch hydraulic cylinders can be rebuilt in the same manner as brake system cylinders. Student B says that a special brake bleeder is needed to get the air out of the hydraulic system. Who is correct?

    a. Student A

    b. Student B

    c. Both Student A and Student B

    d. Neither Student A nor Student B

◀ Chapter 6 ▶

TRANSMISSION THEORY

LEARNING OBJECTIVES

After completing this chapter, you should be able to:

1. Identify the parts of a standard transmission.
2. Know the purpose of each standard transmission part.
3. Trace the power flow for the various speeds.
4. Calculate the gear ratio for each gear speed.
5. Understand synchronizer operation.
6. Understand the requirements for good transmission operation.

TERMS TO LEARN

auxiliary transmission
ball bearing
blocker rings
bushing
cam
closed case
cluster gear
clutch shaft
constant mesh
detent
dog clutch teeth
dogs
double cone
hub

idler gear (for reverse)
input shaft
insert plates
interlock
keys
main drive gear
mainshaft
manual transmission
    fluid (MTF)
mineral oil
needle bearing
oiling funnel
open case
output shaft

overdrive
paper-lined ring
pitch
rail
reverse idler gear
reverse idler shaft
scoop
shift fork
sleeve
speed gears

splines
split case
struts
synchronizer assemblies
synchronizer rings
synthetic oil
tapered roller bearing
trough
tunnel case
viscosity

6.1 INTRODUCTION

The purpose of the transmission or transaxle is to provide neutral, forward gear speeds or ranges and reverse. They must be able to provide a gear ratio that is low enough, when multiplied by the final drive ratio, to increase the engine's torque sufficiently to accelerate the vehicle at the desired rate. The highest gear ratio should allow the vehicle to cruise at an engine speed that is low enough to conserve fuel and decrease noise level. There also need to be intermediate ratios spaced so that the engine will not overrev before a shift or lug after a shift. Reverse must be roughly the same ratio as first since the vehicle will be starting from a stop in both cases.

A transmission or transaxle has several different paths through which power can flow (Figure 6-1). These paths provide the required forward gear ranges and a re-

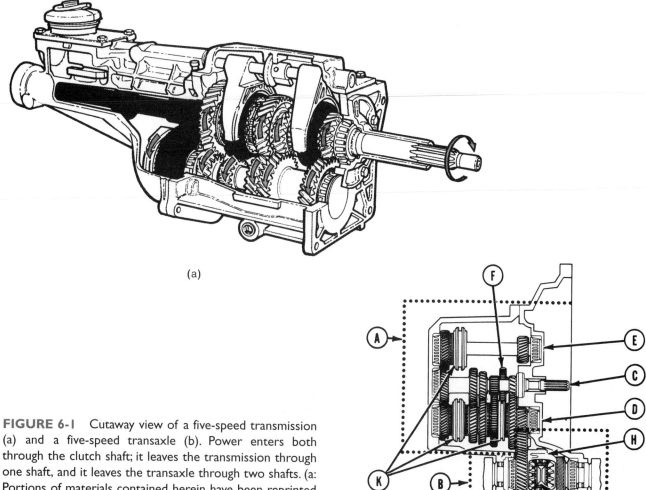

(a)

(b)

FIGURE 6-1 Cutaway view of a five-speed transmission (a) and a five-speed transaxle (b). Power enters both through the clutch shaft; it leaves the transmission through one shaft, and it leaves the transaxle through two shafts. (a: Portions of materials contained herein have been reprinted with permission of General Motors Corporation, Service and Parts Operations, License Agreement #0310807; b is courtesy of Ford Motor Company)

verse. A RWD transmission has the power entering the input shaft through at least two gear sets. The power will exit through the mainshaft and then on to the driveshaft. The transmission output shaft is directly in line with the input shaft.

The power enters the transaxle at the input shaft. It will pass through one gear set and then to the final drive gears. The power then will pass through the differential and out of the transaxle to the two axle shafts. Each of the available power paths through the transmission or transaxle represents a different gear ratio or transmission speed. Reverse is achieved in both the transmission and transaxle by having the power flow pass through an additional gear set.

Transaxles can be constructed in several ways, depending on whether the drivetrain is transverse or longitudinally mounted. Typically, the transaxle is mounted transverse. Transaxles have the input and output shafts parallel to one another. RWD drive transmissions will be discussed in this chapter, and transaxles in Chapter 7.

6.2 CONSTRUCTION

A RWD transmission has four shafts, one of which is nearly all gears and is commonly called a **cluster gear,** or countershaft gear. Besides the cluster gear, there is the **input shaft,** also called a **main drive gear** or **clutch shaft,** the **output shaft,** also called a **mainshaft,** and the **reverse idler shaft.** The mainshaft is

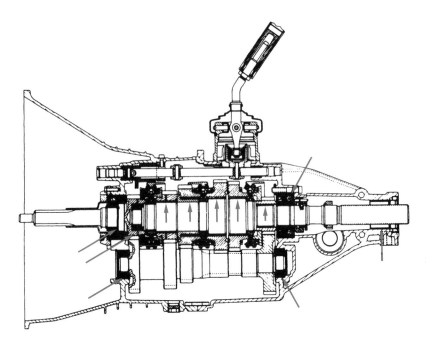

FIGURE 6-2 Bearings support the input shaft, countershaft, mainshaft, and speed gears (shaded). (Portions of materials contained herein have been reprinted with permission of General Motors Corporation, Service and Parts Operations, License Agreement #0310807)

piloted into the rear of the input shaft gear with a bearing. It is also supported at the rear of the transmission case by another large bearing, and by the universal joint spline, which in turn is supported by a bushing at the rear of the extension housing (Figure 6-2). The input shaft gear is supported by a bearing at the front of the transmission case and the pilot bearing in the end of the crankshaft. With most older transmissions, the cluster gear is supported by the countershaft with a bearing at each end. Many newer transmissions support the cluster gear directly by a bearing set; counter shafts are not used. Some transmissions with very long cluster gears and mainshaft gear groups use a support in the middle of the transmission with bearings for the cluster gear and mainshaft (see Figure 6-12).

There are two types of gear sets used in transmissions: Sliding gears and gears that are in constant mesh. Both types are used in modern transmissions. The forward gear ranges are all in constant mesh, with reverse typically being a sliding gear.

Sliding gears are engaged by sliding the gears into mesh. The gears have internal **splines** that match the external splines of the mainshaft (Figure 6-3). To shift gear, the sliding gear would be moved along the splines until it is meshed with its matching gear. The power would then be transfered from one gear to the other and then through the splines to the mainshaft. Sliding gears used for reverse do not use a splined shaft because they will be engaging two gears at the same time. The disadvantage of sliding gears is that it is difficult to shift gears with the vehicle moving.

Constant mesh gears are always engaged with their mating gear and are mounted so that one of them can freewheel on its shaft. The gears are shifted by connecting the freewheeling gear to its shaft. This is done through a synchronizer assembly. The synchronizer is splined to the shaft and has a sleeve that can be slid into place to engage the gear to the synchronizer. The power will then be able to flow from the gear to the synchronizer and then to the shaft. The advantage of constant mesh gears is that the synchronizer will allow shifts to be made while the vehicle is moving and without the driver needing to do any extra clutching (see Figure 6-6).

6.3 GEAR RATIOS

In all gear speeds but one, the power flows from the main drive gear (input) to the cluster gear and then from the cluster gear to the mainshaft (output) (Figure 6-3). The power passes through two gear sets. The exception is a 1:1 ratio, where the power flows directly from the main drive gear to the mainshaft. In older transmissions, this is high gear; in newer overdrive transmissions, this is third or fourth, one of the intermediate speeds.

All the forward gears are normally in **constant mesh** so they always rotate at their design speed relative to engine speed. The gears of the cluster gear rotate as an assembly. The output gears usually are mounted on the mainshaft so they float or rotate freely. These gears are called **speed gears;** they complete the ratio for each gear speed when they become coupled to the

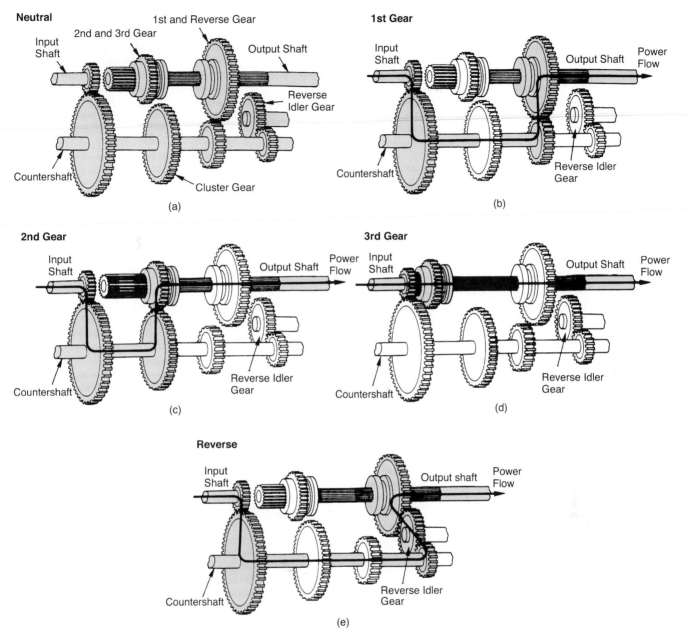

FIGURE 6-3   (a) Very simple transmission in neutral (no output gears in mesh); (b) first gear—the first–reverse gear is slid into mesh with the cluster gear; (c) second gear—the 2–3 sliding gear is in mesh with the cluster gear; (d) third gear—the 2–3 sliding gear is in mesh with the input shaft; and (e) reverse—the first–reverse gear is in mesh with the reverse idler gear.

mainshaft. The mainshaft includes synchronizer assemblies for each pair of gear speeds and can lock the individual speed gears to the mainshaft. This is done for each shift.

The gear set for a simple sliding gear three-speed transmission is shown in Figure 6-4. In this gear set, there are essentially six gear ratios to be concerned with: the main drive gear to cluster gear, cluster gear to first gear, cluster gear to second gear, cluster gear to reverse idler gear, reverse idler gear to reverse

gear, and main drive gear to output shaft. A four- or five-speed gear set is similar except that each additional speed requires a gear set consisting of one speed gear on the mainshaft and another on the cluster gear.

To calculate the ratios for the transmission shown in Figure 6-4, start with the input ratio.

- In this gear set, the main drive gear has 20 teeth, and it is meshed with a 48-tooth gear at the front

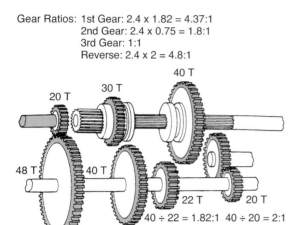

Gear Ratios: 1st Gear: 2.4 x 1.82 = 4.37:1
2nd Gear: 2.4 x 0.75 = 1.8:1
3rd Gear: 1:1
Reverse: 2.4 x 2 = 4.8:1

20 T
30 T
40 T
48 T
40 T
22 T
20 T
40 ÷ 22 = 1.82:1   40 ÷ 20 = 2:1
30 ÷ 40 = 0.75:1
48 ÷ 20 = 2.4:1

FIGURE 6-4 A transmission's gear ratios are computed by determining the ratios for each gear set and then multiplying the input gear set ratio by the ratio of the first, second, and reverse sets.

of the cluster. The ratio will be 48 (driven gear) ÷ 20 (driving gear), or 2.4:1. The engine will always rotate 2.4 times faster than the cluster gear (whenever the clutch is engaged).

- The cluster first gear has a 22-tooth gear that drives the 40-tooth first and reverse gear. This ratio is 40 ÷ 20, or 1.82:1. The first-gear ratio will be 2.4 times 1.82, or 4.37:1.

- The cluster second gear has a 40-tooth gear that drives the 30-tooth second gear; this ratio is 30 ÷ 40, or 0.75:1. The second-gear ratio will be 2.4 × 0.75, or 1.8:1.

- The third-gear power flow goes directly from the main drive gear to the output shaft, so the ratio is 1:1.

- The cluster reverse gear has a 20-tooth gear that drives the reverse idler gear which drives the 40-tooth first and reverse gear; this ratio is 40 ÷ 20, or 2:1. The reverse-gear ratio will be 2.4 × 2, or 4.8:1. A simple idler gear, as shown, will have no effect on the gear ratio.

Because the gears in modern transmissions are in constant mesh, they will always rotate at their gear ratio speed relative to the input shaft gear. In high gear, with a ratio of 1:1 (and first- and second-gear ratios of 2.07:1 and 1.46:1), you can drive down the road with an engine and mainshaft speed of 2000 rpm. The first-speed gear in this transmission will be turning at 966 rpm (2000 ÷ 2.07), and the second speed gear will be turning at 1370 rpm (2000 ÷ 1.46).

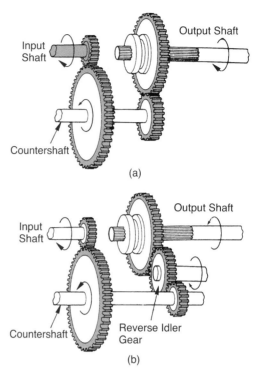

(a)

(b)

FIGURE 6-5 (a) The input shaft rotates in a clockwise direction; the countershaft rotates in a counterclockwise direction; and the first–reverse gear drives the output shaft in a clockwise direction. (b) When meshed with the idler gear, the first–reverse gear will be driven in a counterclockwise direction.

6.4 REVERSE

Reverse requires one more gear in the gear train. Remember that when one external gear drives another, they will rotate in opposite directions. In a transmission, the input shaft gear rotates in a clockwise direction (the same as the engine), the cluster gear rotates in a counterclockwise direction, the mainshaft rotates clockwise when driven either through the gear train or by the direct coupling (Figure 6-5a).

To make the vehicle back up, the mainshaft must rotate counterclockwise. To accomplish this, an **idler gear** is meshed between the cluster gear and the reverse gear on the mainshaft (Figure 6-5b). A simple idler will not change the ratio, but it will cause a reversal of rotation. The idler gears used in some transmissions are long, with a gear of one size meshed with the cluster gear and a different-sized gear to mesh with the reverse gear. This idler gear will affect the ratio such that the overall ratio becomes

main drive gear to cluster gear ratio × cluster gear to idler gear ratio × idler gear to reverse gear ratio

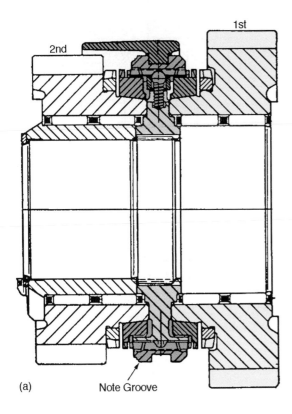

(a)   Note Groove

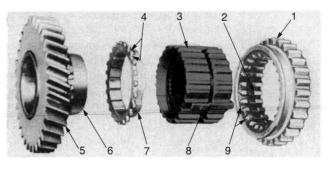

1. Sliding Sleeve	4. Wedge Angle on Teeth	7. Synchronizer (Blocker) Ring
2. Detent Groove	5. Gear	8. Key
3. Hub	6. Cone Surface	9. Wedge Angle on Spline

(b)

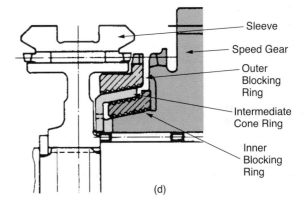

Speed Gear   Inner Blocking Ring   Intermediate Cone Ring   Outer Blocking Ring

(c)

Sleeve
Speed Gear
Outer Blocking Ring
Intermediate Cone Ring
Inner Blocking Ring

(d)

FIGURE 6-6 Cutaway (a) and exploded (b) view of a synchronizer assembly that uses brass blocker rings. Also shown is an exploded (c) and cutaway (d) view of an assembly that uses paper-lined blocking rings. (Portions of materials contained herein have been reprinted with permission of General Motors Corporation, Service and Parts Operations, License Agreement #0310807)

6.5 SYNCHRONIZERS

Most modern transmissions use synchronizer assemblies for all the shifts except reverse. A few transmissions, however, use a synchronizer for the reverse shift. A synchronizer assembly includes (Figure 6-6):

- A **hub,** which is secured to the mainshaft, has external splines to match the sleeve.
- A **sleeve** with internal splines, which is slid to one side or the other over the hub to make a shift.
- A pair of **blocker rings,** also called **synchronizer rings,** which have external teeth to match the sleeve and an internal cone clutch surface.

- A set of three spring-loaded **keys,** also called **struts, insert plates,** or **dogs.**
- A set of **dog clutch teeth** on each side of the speed gear on each side of the sleeve and a polished, external cone clutch surface.

It is the synchronizer's job to mesh two gears for a shift without gear clashing. To do this, it must block the shift motions until the synchronizer sleeve and the gear are rotating at the same speed. Normally, this entails slowing down the clutch disc, input shaft gear, and clutch shaft, cluster gear, and the gear being shifted into, as well as the other speed gears.

Follow what occurs through a 1–2 shift. Assume that the first-gear ratio is 2:1, the second-gear ratio is 1.5:1, and the engine speed before the shift is 4000 rpm. At the time of the shift, the mainshaft will be revolving at 2000 rpm, one-half of the engine speed, and the second gear will be revolving at 2667 rpm (4000 ÷ 1.5). The clutch disc speed will have to drop to 3000 rpm to bring the second gear to the same speed as the mainshaft (3000 ÷ 1.5 = 2000). When the clutch is released, the disc and related parts will begin slowing down, but not fast enough to avoid gear clash, especially if the shift is rushed.

To begin a shift with a synchronizer, the action follows this sequence (Figure 6-7):

1. When the shift lever begins moving, the sleeve moves toward the gear being engaged and the spring-loaded keys follow the sleeve and, in turn, push the synchronizer ring against the gear's cone clutch surface.
2. The synchronizer ring and gear cone clutches contact, the gear speed difference makes the synchronizer ring rotate, about one-half the width of a spline.
3. The rotation of the ring blocks further movement of the sleeve, but sleeve pressure causes the braking action of the cone clutch to slow the gear.
4. The engaging gear slows down and reaches the same speed as the hub and sleeve. It will rotate slightly backward relative to the sleeve to stop blocking the shift.
5. The sleeve moves sideways over the clutching teeth (dog clutch) of the engaging gear, and the shift is completed.

Synchronizer action occurs every time you make an upshift. A downshift is the same except that the synchronizing action must speed up the gear to be engaged. Occasionally, you can hear this occur when you make a downshift.

A synchronizer assembly has three positions: neutral in the middle plus two gear speeds. All three-speed transmissions have a 2–3 synchronizer; some also have a synchronized first gear. A four-speed transmission will normally have two synchronizer assemblies, a 1–2 and a 3–4. A five- or six-speed transmission will require an additional synchronizer. Other styles of synchronizers are used in a few transmissions, but they are uncommon and are not described in this book.

Traditionally, the synchronizer ring has been made from brass and has a series of sharp grooves on the internal cone surface (Figure 6-8a). These grooves break through the lubricating film on the mating gear's cone clutch surface. The grooves also hold lubricant so that they will break free and not wedge in place. Some trans-

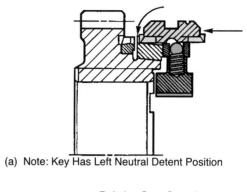

(a) Note: Key Has Left Neutral Detent Position

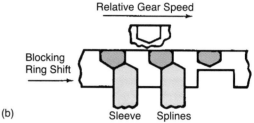

(b)

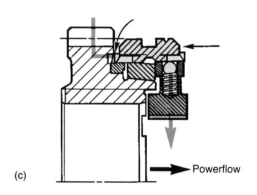

(c)

FIGURE 6-7   (a) A synchronized shift begins as the shift fork moves the sleeve toward the speed gear, and this action forces the blocker ring against the cone clutch surface of the speed gear (a). If they are rotating at different speeds, the blocker ring will rotate and block further motion of the sleeve (b). As the speed of the sleeve and speed gear become equal, the blocker ring will rotate back and allow the sleeve to slide into mesh with the dog clutch teeth on the speed gear (c). (Portions of materials contained herein have been reprinted with permission of General Motors Corporation, Service and Parts Operations, License Agreement #0310807)

missions use **paper-lined rings** (Figure 6-8B,C). The paper lining is essentially the same as that used to face automatic transmission clutch plates. Transmissions using paper-lined rings must use a special manual transmission fluid (MTF) or automatic transmission fluid (ATF) for lubricant. Some synchronizers use a **double cone,** with an outer cone and an inner cone along with the blocker ring (Figure 6-9). The multiple cones provide more surface area for better synchronization and longer service life.

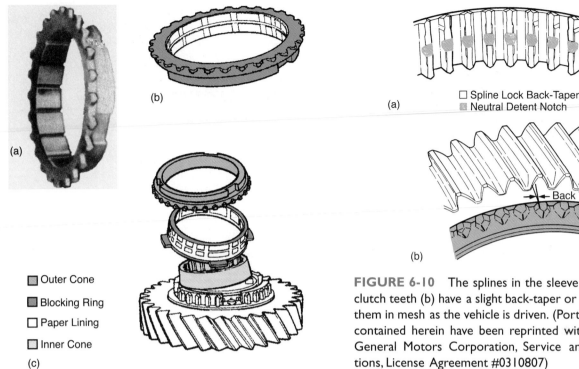

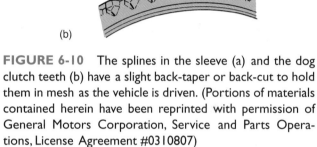

FIGURE 6-10 The splines in the sleeve (a) and the dog clutch teeth (b) have a slight back-taper or back-cut to hold them in mesh as the vehicle is driven. (Portions of materials contained herein have been reprinted with permission of General Motors Corporation, Service and Parts Operations, License Agreement #0310807)

FIGURE 6-8 (a) Older blocker rings are made from brass and have a series of fine grooves cut into the inner cone clutch surface. Paper-lined blocker rings are faced with paper and are either a single piece (b) or a two- or three-part assembly (c). (Portions of materials contained herein have been reprinted with permission of General Motors Corporation, Service and Parts Operations, License Agreement #0310807)

Many synchronizer sleeves have a slight back cut (taper) at the ends of the splines, which matches a similar back cut on the clutch teeth of the speed gears (Figure 6-10). This back cut tends to lock the gears in engagement to prevent the sleeve from jumping out of mesh. To slide out of mesh, the driven sleeve would have to speed up or the speed gear would have to slow down.

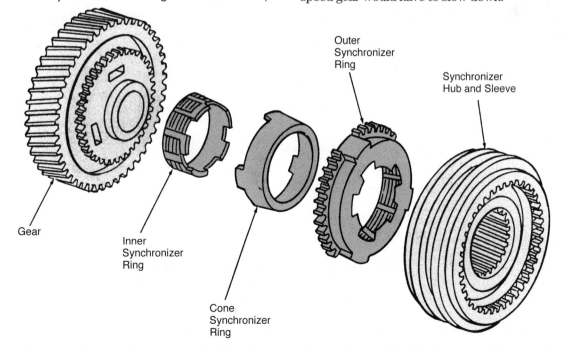

FIGURE 6-9 This double synchronizer assembly uses an inner ring that is splined to the outer ring and a cone with two surfaces that connects to the speed gear. (Courtesy of Ford Motor Company)

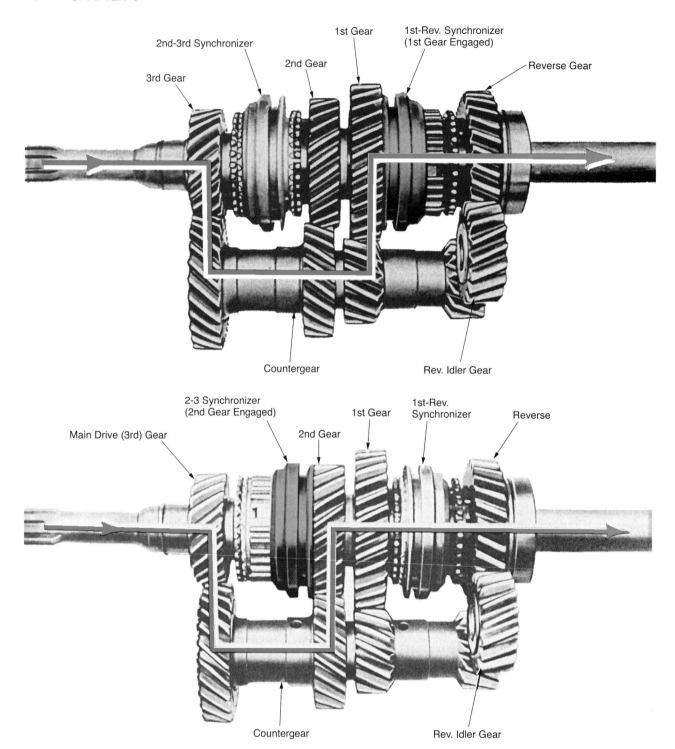

FIGURE 6-11   Different power flows through a modern three-speed transmission; note how the 2–3 or the 1–reverse sleeves are shifted to engage the various speeds. (Portions of materials contained herein have been reprinted with permission of General Motors Corporation, Service and Parts Operations, License Agreement #0310807)

6.6   POWER FLOW

Shifting into a particular gear involves moving a synchronizer sleeve or a gear into mesh to make a connection between the mainshaft and that particular speed gear. The three-speed transmission has four possible power paths, and they are first or low, second, third or high, and reverse (Figure 6-11). As the power flows through each of these paths, the amount of torque and speed or the direction of rotation is altered by each gear set.

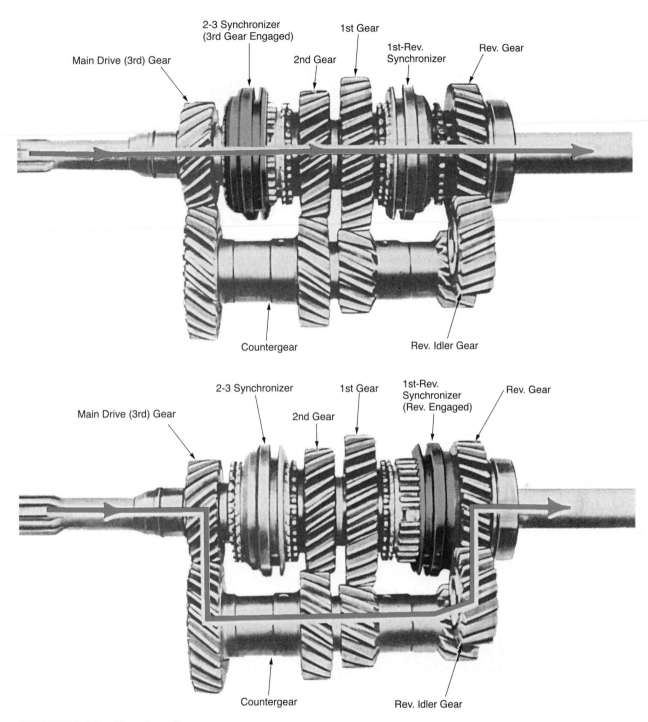

FIGURE 6-11   *(Continued)*

The major difference as we add gear speeds is the length and complexity of the transmission. Each new gear speed requires another driven speed gear, a driving gear on the cluster gear, and one-half of a synchronizer assembly. In some cases, the synchronizer assembly can be on the cluster gear to select which of the driving gears will transfer power (Figure 6-12). Another variation is the power flow for reverse. Some transmissions mount the reverse driven gear on the 1–2 synchronizer sleeve, and the shift into reverse is made by sliding the reverse idler into mesh with the reverse cluster gear and the reverse driven gear. Some transmissions mount the reverse driven gear as a speed gear on the mainshaft and use a sliding-sleeve shift. Other transmissions use a synchronizer, just like they do for a forward gear.

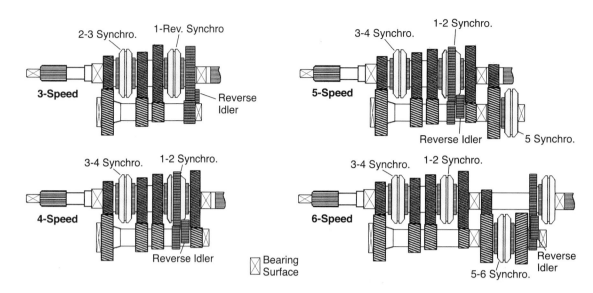

FIGURE 6-12   A comparison of three-, four-, five-, and six-speed transmissions shows the major differences to be the length of the unit and the number of synchronizer assemblies.

6.7 FOUR-SPEED TRANSMISSIONS

A four-speed transmission requires an additional gear on the cluster gear, an additional gear on the and a method of connecting this gear to the mainshaft. Note that on the transmission shown in Figure 6-13 the gear on the cluster gear in the second position is larger than the one in the first position, and the main drive gear is also larger than the gear on the other side of

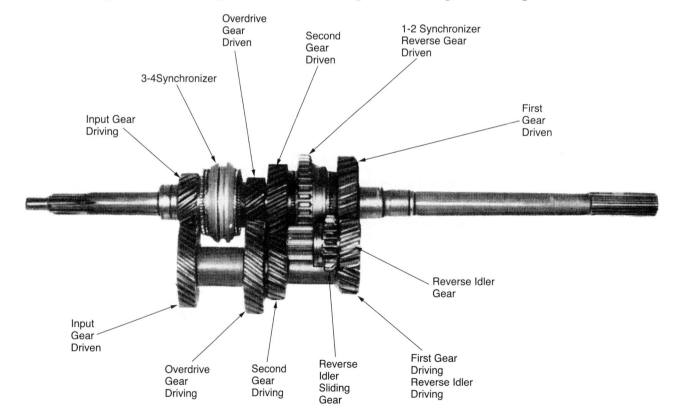

FIGURE 6-13   This four-speed transmission is similar to the three-speed unit in Figure 6-11. Note the additional gear on the cluster gear and the reverse gear teeth around the 1–2 sleeve and that the idler is shifted to engage reverse. (Courtesy of Ford Motor Company)

1st

1-2 Synchronizer
Shifted Rearward

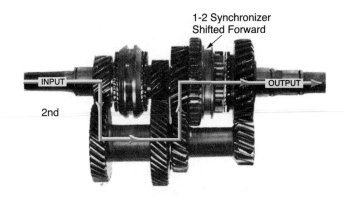

1-2 Synchronizer
Shifted Forward

2nd

3-4 Synchronizer
Shifted Forward

3rd

3-4 Synchronizer
Shifted Rearward

4th

Reverse

Reverse Idler Sliding
Gear Shifted Forward

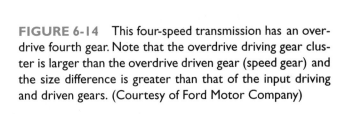

FIGURE 6-14 This four-speed transmission has an overdrive fourth gear. Note that the overdrive driving gear cluster is larger than the overdrive driven gear (speed gear) and the size difference is greater than that of the input driving and driven gears. (Courtesy of Ford Motor Company)

the 3–4 synchronizer. In this transmission, third gear will have a 1:1 ratio, and fourth gear will be an **overdrive** (Figure 6-14). This fourth gear will not be as efficient as third, even though it will reduce engine speed and improve fuel mileage. Sending the power flow through the cluster gear produces a small amount of load on the bearings, which causes a slight power loss, making the transmission about 85 percent efficient. In a 1:1 ratio with the input connected to the main shaft, a transmission is about 90 to 92 percent efficient.

To shift into reverse, many four-speeds place the reverse gear on the 1–2 synchronizer sleeve and slide the reverse idler into mesh with it and the cluster gear. Some early four-speed transmissions located the reverse gear in the extension housing.

The four-speed transmissions used in many pickups and older vehicles usually have a fourth-gear ratio of 1:1. The first-gear ratio in some pickups is very low, about 4 or 5:1, and this is often called a "granny gear." Some passenger vehicles have "close ratio" four-speeds, where the first-gear ratio is about 2.2:1, the fourth-gear ratio is 1:1, and the second- and third-gear ratios are between these. Close ratios allow a shift between gears with a minimal loss of engine rpm. The wide-ratio four-speed transmissions have a first-gear ratio of about 2.8:1. In many cases, the physical difference between the wide- and close-ratio versions of a particular transmission will be the size of the main drive gear and the number 1 gear on the cluster gear; all the other gears will be the same (Figure 6-15). Remember that the ratio of the main drive gear to the cluster gear affects all the other ratios except the direct drive.

Typical Ratios	Close Ratio	Wide Ratio
1st	3.50:1	4.03:1
2nd	2.14:1	2.37:1
3rd	1.89:1	1.49:1
4th	1.00:1	1.00:1
Reverse	3.39:1	3.76:1

FIGURE 6-15 The T4 transmission is available in two different ratios, as shown here. The close-ratio version has a 3.50:1 first-gear ratio, and the wide-ratio version has a 4.03:1 first-gear ratio. (Courtesy of BWD Automotive Corporation)

6.8   FIVE-SPEED TRANSMISSIONS

A five-speed transmission requires an additional gear on the cluster gear and on the mainshaft, plus another synchronizer (Figure 6-16). The synchronizer can be on the mainshaft with the other gears or on the cluster gear. In most cases, a five-speed transmission will have three forward reduction ratios (first, second, and third gears), a 1:1 fourth-gear ratio, and an overdrive fifth gear.

Most transmissions are built with a variety of ratios for each gear to suit the particular vehicle. Engine size

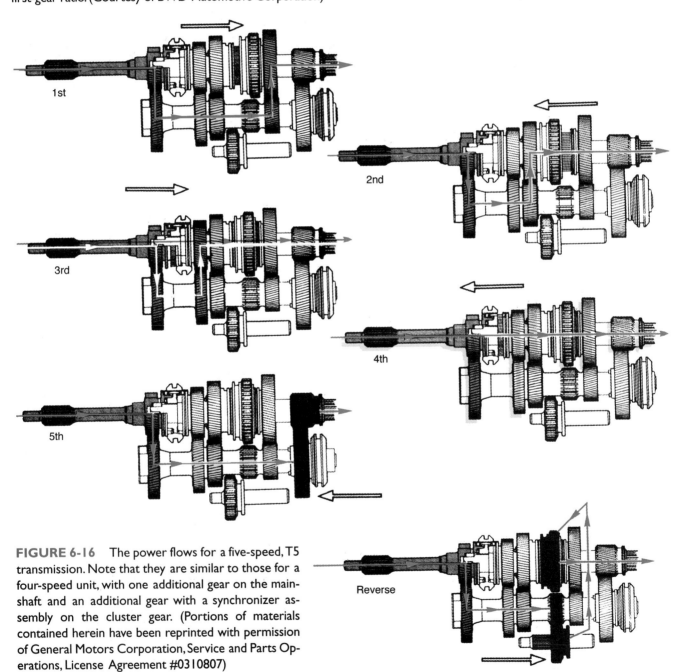

FIGURE 6-16 The power flows for a five-speed, T5 transmission. Note that they are similar to those for a four-speed unit, with one additional gear on the mainshaft and an additional gear with a synchronizer assembly on the cluster gear. (Portions of materials contained herein have been reprinted with permission of General Motors Corporation, Service and Parts Operations, License Agreement #0310807)

	Close Ratio		Wide Ratio
1st	2.95:1	3.35:1	3.97:1
2nd	1.94:1	1.99:1	2.34:1
3rd	1.34:1	1.33:1	1.46:1
4th	1.00:1	1.00:1	1.00:1
5th	.73:1	.68:1	.79:1
Rev.	2.76:1	3.15:1	3.70:1

FIGURE 6-17 Ratios for three versions of a T5 transmission. (Courtesy of BWD Automotive Group)

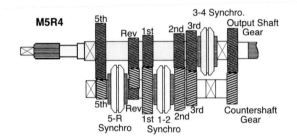

FIGURE 6-18 The M5R4 five-speed transmission has a long input shaft with four fixed gears, one speed gear, and the 3–4 synchronizer assembly. The countershaft has two fixed gears plus two synchronizer assemblies and four speed gears. The mainshaft has only one fixed gear and the clutch teeth for fourth gear (direct drive).

and vehicle weight are used to determine the best gear ratios for the vehicle (Figure 6-17). Heavy vehicles and small engines require lower first gears, with corresponding lower ratios in the other gear speeds.

6.8.1 Five-Speed Variation

The M5R4 transmission, used in later-model Ford Explorers, has a redesigned gear arrangement (Figure 6-18). The first, second, third, fifth, and reverse driving gears along with the 3–4 synchronizer are mounted on the longer-than-normal input shaft. The short mainshaft has the output shaft gear and the clutch teeth for fourth gear. The 1–2 and 5–R synchronizer assemblies are mounted on the countershaft.

6.9 SIX-SPEED TRANSMISSIONS

A six-speed transmission requires one more gear on the cluster, an additional speed gear, and one-half of a synchronizer assembly (Figure 6-19). This increases the weight, length, and cost of the unit. The additional gear

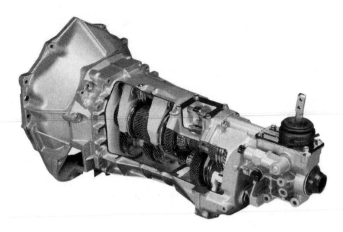

FIGURE 6-19 A T56, six-speed transmission. First through fourth gears are in the main case; fifth, sixth, and reverse gears are located in the extension. (Courtesy of Transmission Technologies Corporation, TTC)

is usually another overdrive ratio. Some six-speeds have low and high gear ratios similar to those of a five-speed, with the ratios closer together (see Figure 16-23). Six-speed transmissions are used in performance-oriented vehicles where the additional cost is less of a problem. Because these units have a limited market, they are manufactured by only a few companies.

6.10 TRANSMISSION TORQUE CAPACITY

A transmission is normally designed with enough strength to handle a certain amount of torque. High torque requires large input shafts, even larger output shafts, big wide gears, and large bearings. This increases the weight of the transmission and also increases the drag and power loss in the unit. Smaller transmissions improve fuel mileage, but they can break under load if they are too small. A transmission is designed to handle a particular amount of torque. This amount should not be exceeded. Exceeding the transmission's designed torque capacity will cause breakage and failure.

To get an idea of what higher torque load requires, compare the diameter of the input and output shafts of a transmission. The torque increase from first gear requires the larger output shaft.

6.11 SHIFT MECHANISMS

When the driver moves the gearshift lever, the shift mechanism moves one or two synchronizer sleeves or gears to engage the desired gear speed. Remember that

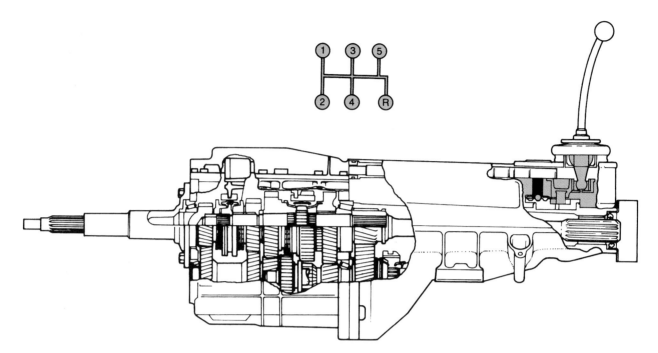

FIGURE 6-20 When the gearshift lever is moved, the internal linkage (shift rails) moves the shift fork and synchronizer sleeve to shift gear speeds. (Courtesy of BWD Automotive Corporation)

during an upshift or downshift, one sleeve is shifted to neutral before the desired gear is engaged. Most of you are familiar with the standard H gear-shift-lever pattern of a three-speed, the H pattern with an extension of a four-speed, and the double-H pattern of a five- or six-speed. As you move the lever across the H-pattern, you are selecting a shift lever or rail; as you move the lever from one of the legs toward the center of the H, you are moving a sleeve/gear out of mesh; as you move the lever outward to the end of one of the legs, you are moving a sleeve/gear into mesh (Figure 6-20).

With transmissions using external linkage, the motion is transmitted from the shift lever of the shifter assembly to the transmission by a group of two or three metal rods on the outside of the transmission (Figure 6-21). Many transmissions use internal linkage with everything mounted inside of the transmission case.

A shift mechanism must include two features, an **interlock** and a series of **detents.** Some transmissions also include a reverse lockout (Figure 6-22). The interlock prevents engagement of more than one gear at a time. It is impossible for the transmission to transmit power through two different ratios and have two different output shaft speeds at the same time. If two gears are engaged, the transmission will lock up, and both the input and output shafts will freeze and become stationary. A technician may do this intentionally at times during an overhaul if it is necessary to hold the input or output shaft from rotating.

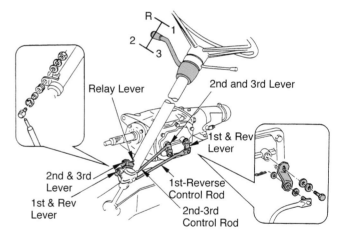

FIGURE 6-21 External linkage (shift rods) is used to transmit shift motions from the column levers to the transmission levers. (Portions of materials contained herein have been reprinted with permission of General Motors Corporation, Service and Parts Operations, License Agreement #0310807)

The detents are used to locate the internal **shift forks** in one of their three positions. A detent is usually a spring-loaded ball or bullet-shaped rod that is pushed into one of a series of three notches or a spring-loaded lever with three notches that drop over a cam (Figure 6-23). As you shift gears, you can feel the detents as they engage and disengage the shift rails or cams. Most synchronizers have three detent posi-

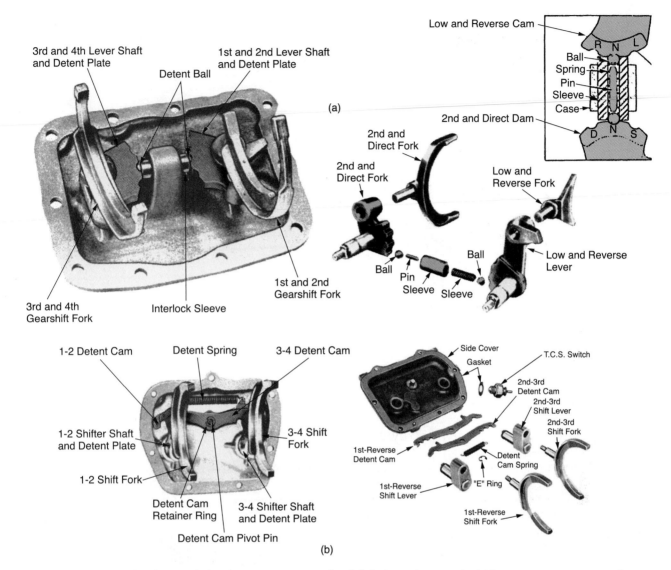

FIGURE 6-22 Every shift linkage includes detents to position the shift forks and an interlock(s) to prevent movement of more than one fork at a time. The styles shown in both an assembled and exploded form include cams and spring-loaded balls with an interlock sleeve (a), spring-loaded lever-type detent (and interlock) cams (b), rails with interlock pins and spring-loaded detent balls (c), and rail with interlock plate and spring-loaded detent ball (d). (a is courtesy of DaimlerChrysler Corporation; b: Portions of materials contained herein have been reprinted with permission of General Motors Corporation, Service and Parts Operations, License Agreement #0310807; c is courtesy of Ford Motor Company; d is courtesy of BWD Automotive Corporation)

tions—neutral plus a gear to each side. The synchronizer sleeve is moved by a shift fork that is mounted on either a rail or a cam. A **rail** is a metal rod that slides lengthwise; a **cam** usually pivots on its shaft, which extends out the side of the case or side cover. Since it must contact and move the spinning synchronizer sleeve, the contact surfaces of the fork will be either hardened steel, bronze, or a low-friction plastic or a nylon pad attached to the fork. After the sleeve/gear has been positioned, there should be little contact between the fork and the sleeve/gear. At this time, the fork is lo-cated by the detent. The sleeve is located by the synchronizer keys when in neutral and by the dog clutch teeth on the mating gear when it is shifted.

A reverse lockout mechanism is used to prevent accidental engagement of reverse while making an upshift. This mechanism requires the driver to perform an additional operation to shift into reverse. This might require that the shift lever by pushed downward or lifted up, or there may be an additional lever or button to be pushed. Some transmissions use a stronger spring so it takes extra effort to move the shifter to select the reverse shift rail.

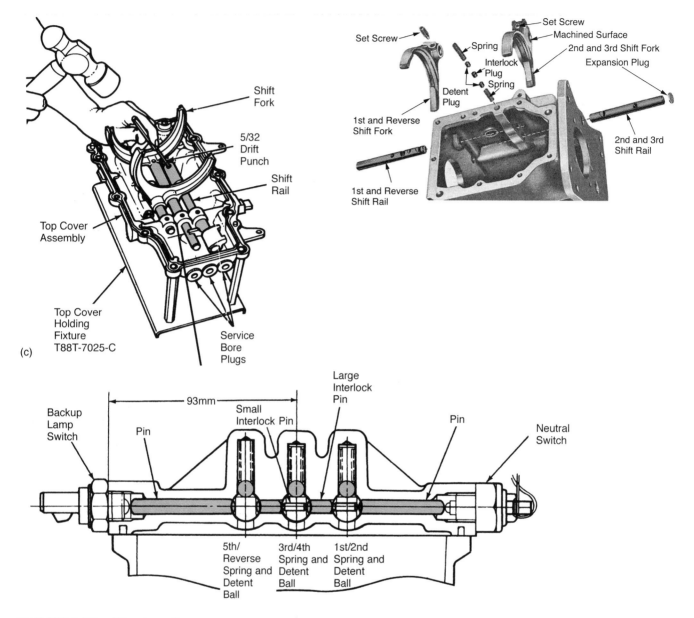

FIGURE 6-22   *(Continued)*

The detents, shift rails, and forks are not designed to hold the gear or sleeve into mesh, only to position it completely into mesh. The cut of the sleeve or gear is what actually keeps it into mesh during the different driving situations. Holding a gear into mesh with the fork will cause rather rapid wear of the fork and fork groove.

6.11.1   External Linkage

The gearshift assembly used with external linkage is normally bolted onto the transmission extension housing for floor shifts or is made as part of the steering column for column shifts. These assemblies have the gear selector arm mounted in such a way that it can swing and pivot through the necessary motions. The assemblies include a shift lever that is connected to each shift lever on the transmission by an adjustable rod. A four-speed transmission will have a 1–2 shift lever at both the shifter and the transmission connected by the 1–2 shift rod. There will also be a pair of 3–4 shift levers plus a 3–4 shift rod and a pair of reverse levers with a reverse shift rod (Figure 6-24).

When the gearshift/selector is moved laterally, across the car in a floor shift or parallel to the steering column in a column shift, a crossover blade at the end of the selector lever moves from one shift lever to the other to select a 1–2, 3–4, or reverse shift. Next, when

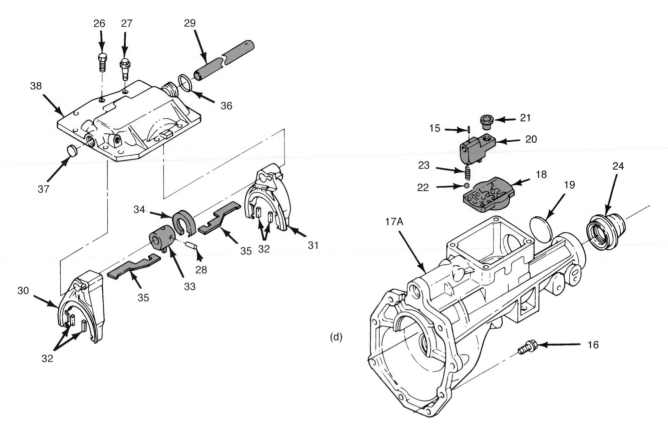

FIGURE 6-22 *(Continued)* *Key:* 15, roll pin; 16, bolt; 17, extension assy; 18, detent guide plate; 19, plug; 20, offset lever; 21, damper sleeve; 22, ball; 23, spring; 24, oil seal; 28, selector arm pin; 29, shifter shaft; 30, 3–4 shift fork; 31, 1–2 shift fork; 32, insert; 33, selector arm assy; 34, interlock plate; 35, selector plate; 36, O-ring; 37, plug; 38, case cover; 117, case assy.

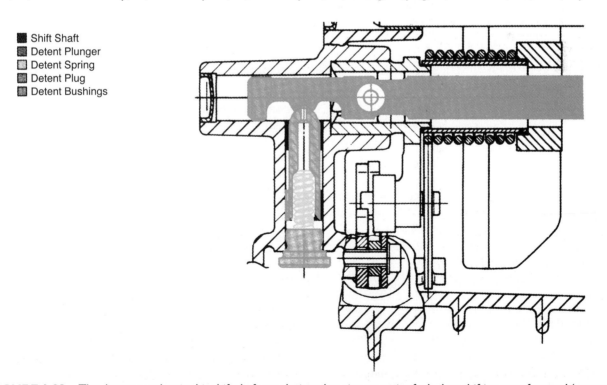

■ Shift Shaft
▨ Detent Plunger
□ Detent Spring
▨ Detent Plug
▨ Detent Bushings

FIGURE 6-23 The detent notches in this shift shaft are designed to give an easier feel when shifting out of neutral (center notch). The spring-loaded plunger will try to hold the shift shaft in one of the three positions. (Portions of materials contained herein have been reprinted with permission of General Motors Corporation, Service and Parts Operations, License Agreement #0310807)

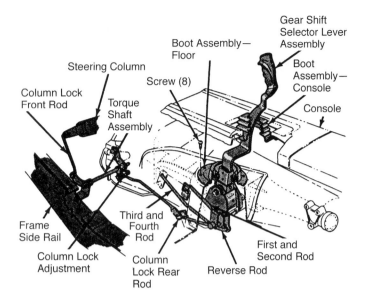

FIGURE 6-24 This floor-mounted gearshift assembly is attached to the transmission's extension housing. Note the column lock linkage used on some cars to allow ignition key removal only with certain gear positions. (Courtesy of DaimlerChrysler Corporation)

the selector lever is moved lengthwise to the car (floor shift) or up or down (column shift), that particular shift lever is moved and, in turn, moves the corresponding lever at the transmission and the desired sleeve/gear inside the transmission.

6.11.2 Internal Linkage

In a passenger vehicle transmission, the gearshift lever is normally mounted in the extension housing with one or more shift rails that transmit the shifting motions to the main case. In truck and many pickup transmissions, the shift assembly is built into the top cover of the transmission case (Figure 6-25). The selector lever with its pivot, the shift rails with the forks attached, and the detents and interlocks are all in this assembly.

A passenger vehicle transmission linkage is more complex, especially five-speeds and some four-speeds, where shift motions have to get to both the top and bottom areas of the transmission. There are quite a number of methods to do this, but they all work in essentially the same manner. Sideways motion of the selector lever will cause the selector lever either to engage one of the shift rails or to rotate a single rail to engage one of several shift forks, plates, or rails (Figure 6-26). As the selected fork, plate, or rail is engaged, the interlock moves to lock the remaining ones. Lengthwise motion of the shift lever will move

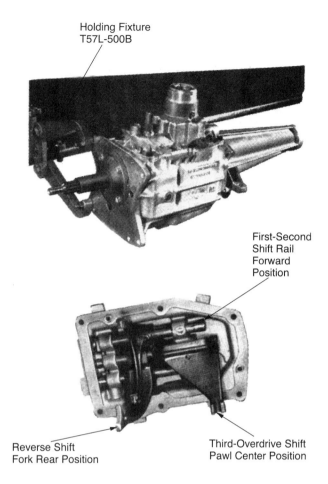

FIGURE 6-25 All of the shift linkage, including the shift forks, for this pickup or truck transmission is contained in the top cover. (Courtesy of Ford Motor Company)

the selected rail or plate, its fork, and the sleeve or gear into mesh.

Some modern six-speed transmissions include a reverse lockout to prevent shifting into reverse gear while the vehicle is moving forward. The six-speed shift pattern along with a synchronized reverse gear make a shift into reverse quite possible, and power train damage could easily occur. This mechanism uses an electric solenoid that is electronically controlled by the vehicle's electronic control module (ECM). The operation is described in Section 15.3.

6.12 GEAR LUBRICATION

Manual transmissions, transfer cases, and drive axles must be lubricated to reduce heat and friction. Lubricants can be either refined *petroleum* or *synthetic* products. Refined natural products, also called **mineral oils,** are usually less expensive. **Synthetic oils** are

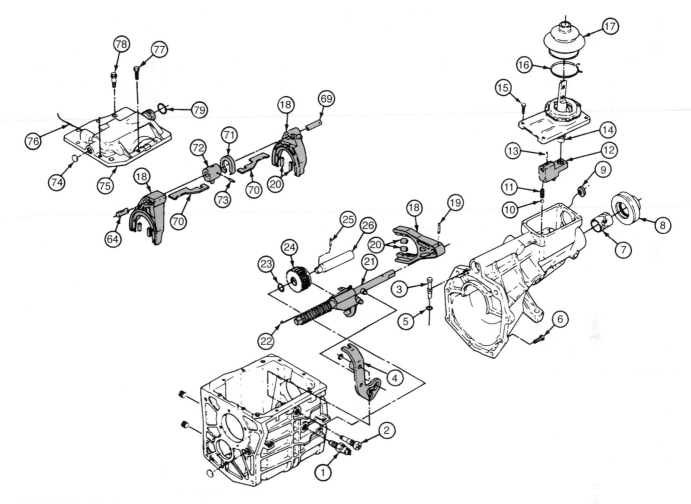

FIGURE 6-26 In this transmission, the shift lever is in the extension housing. A shift rail transmits motion to one of the four shift forks, and the detents and interlock plate are in the main case. (Courtesy of Ford Motor Company)

man-made from petroleum or vegetable-oil stock. The lubricant's job is to

- reduce friction so parts move easier,
- transfer heat away from the gears and bearings,
- reduce corrosion and rust, and
- move dirt and wear particles away from the moving parts.

Two rating systems help us select the proper lubricant for a particular usage. These are the Society of Automotive Engineers (SAE) viscosity rating and the American Petroleum Institute (API) Service Classification.

Viscosity is a measurement of fluid thickness. Viscosity is determined by how fast the fluid runs through a precisely sized orifice at a particular temperature. All oils are thicker and less fluid when cold and thinner, more fluid when hot. The viscosity index (VI) is an

indication of the amount of difference between hot and cold. In a gearbox, a lubricant that is too thick will deliver poor lubrication when cold because the thick fluid will not flow into smaller areas. A too thick gear oil might *channel*—i.e., flow in a ropelike pattern. It also increases drag between parts so they do not turn as easily, and shift collars will not slide as easily. Synchronizer cones will not work very well because they cannot break through the thick oil film. A too thin lubricant will not provide the lubricating film under hot conditions. Thin fluids also cause more gear noise. The viscosity numbers (60 to 140) used with gear oils are larger than those for engine oils (10 to 50), but the oil's actual viscosity is similar. Gear oils normally become thinner over time.

The API gear oil classifications are

GL-1: straight mineral oil; used in nonsynchromesh transmissions; might have some additives; not a satisfactory lubricant for modern passenger car transmissions.

GL-2: a designation for worm gear drives used mostly in industrial applications.

GL-3: contains mild EP additives; to be used in manual transmissions and transaxles with spiral bevel final drives.

GL-4: contains about half the additives used in GL-5; formulated to be used in manual transmissions and transaxles with hypoid final drives.

GL-5: enough EP additive to lubricate hypoid gears in drive axles.

GL-6: an obsolete designation.

An additional classification, GLS (Gear Lubricant Special), is sometimes used to indicate a proprietary set of specifications determined by the vehicle or gearbox manufacturer. **Manual transmission fluid (MTF)** usually is in this category. An MTF might contain a friction modifier to give proper synchronizer action and long life.

API classifications are an indication of the fluid's ability to maintain a lubricating film under the load between the gear teeth and prevent metal-to-metal contact. These classifications are also concerned with the oil's thermal stability, gear surface fatigue, and compatibility with oil seals, copper and brass, and other gear oils. Other concerns are foaming, corrosion resistance, and seal compatibility. Too much of one additive can have detrimental effects on other operating characteristics. For example, GL-5 can cause hard shifting problems in a transmission because the EP additive interferes with synchronizer operation.

Synthetic lubricants usually have a much better VI than conventional lubricants; the viscosity stays more stable with temperature changes. More stable viscosity provides better lubrication; this, in turn, allows more efficiency, less cold-operation drag, and better high-temperature lubrication. A synthetic lubricant also offers better resistance to oxidation, so the fluid will normally have a longer life span.

6.13   TRANSMISSION LUBRICATION

The lower transmission gears run in a bath of lubricant, and as they spin, their motion will throw the lubricant throughout the case. The lubricant used is gear oil, ATF, or manual transmission fluid, as determined by the manufacturer. The fluid level is normally at the bottom of the check/fill plug in the side of the case (Figure 6-27). This is usually at a level just below the rear bushing and seal.

The lubricant reduces friction so that the parts spin more easily and transfers heat away from the gear contact and rubbing parts. Poorly lubricated gears can get so hot that the metal becomes plastic and deforms (Figure 6-28). Floating gears on the mainshaft or cluster gear have special paths and provisions for getting the lubricant into their bearings, and some transmissions

Main Drive Gear

FIGURE 6-28   This transmission was operated without oil. Note the heat-darkened color and the lack of teeth on the main drive gear. The gear got so hot that the metal reached its plastic state, and the teeth were removed or reshaped.

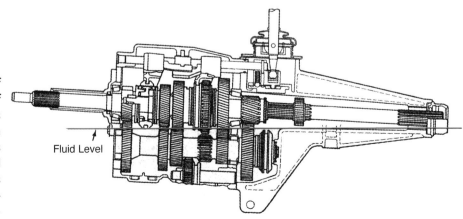

FIGURE 6-27   The fluid level of most transmissions is at the bottom of the fill plug opening, and the fluid is moved around inside the case when the gears rotate. (Portions of materials contained herein have been reprinted with permission of General Motors Corporation, Service and Parts Operations, License Agreement #0310807)

Fluid Level

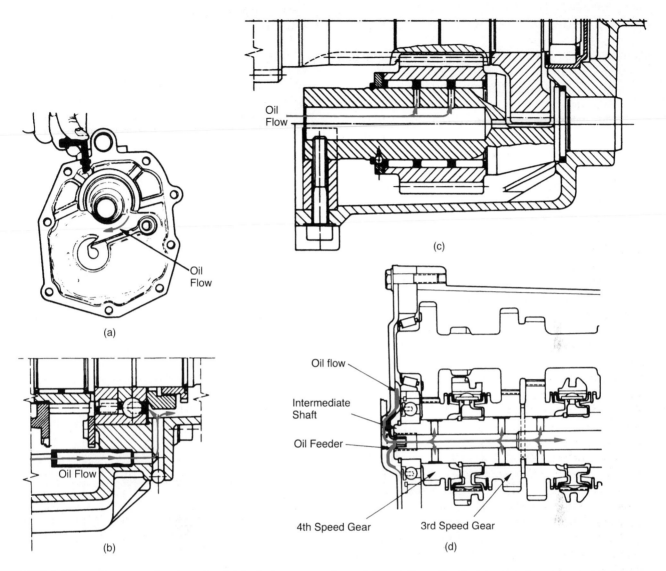

FIGURE 6-29   This extension housing (a) includes a trough to deliver oil to the cluster gear bearing; an oil delivery pipe (b) delivers oil to locations in the extension housing; shaft drillings (c) ensure lubrication to the reverse idler gear bearings; and an oil feeder (funnel) (d) delivers oil to the center of this shaft, where it will flow on to lubricate the speed gears. (a, b, and c: Portions of materials contained herein have been reprinted with permission of General Motors Corporation, Service and Parts Operations, License Agreement #0310807; d is courtesy of DaimlerChrysler Corporation)

have **scoops, troughs,** or **oiling funnels** to get lubricant into the critical areas (Figure 6-29).

Each transmission includes a vent, normally located at the top of the case. This relieves internal pressure that would occur as the gears and oil warm up while operating. If not relieved, the pressure would force the oil out past the input and output shaft seals. Many early transmissions used only a slinger—a large, flat washer—to stop the oil from flowing out at the front bearing.

A transmission's lubrication works from the oil being thrown off the cluster gear. If a vehicle is towed in neutral, the cluster gear does not rotate and wear can occur between the rotating mainshaft and the stationary gears that normally float on it. A transmission with the synchronizer on the cluster gear will receive some lubrication through its gear action.

6.14   DESIGN FEATURES

Knowledge of certain design features will increase your understanding of transmission operation, make problem diagnosis easier and more accurate, and improve service and overhaul techniques.

6.14.1 Gears

All forward gears in a modern transmission are helical gears; spur gears are often used for reverse. When you back up, you can often hear the difference between these gears as a whine or light growl from the transmission. Spur gears are used for reverse because they are less expensive, will shift into mesh more easily where sliding gear shifts are used, and have no tendency to generate end thrust under load.

The end thrust created by a helical gear requires a thrust surface on the side of the gear. This is especially true at the side loaded during forward motion. During deceleration, the thrust direction will reverse, and a helical gear will thrust in the opposite direction. Gear side or end float should be limited to reduce noise or possible damage from the resulting gear motion, especially in the gears used at cruising speeds where throttle change is normal (Figure 6-30).

The **pitch,** which is the distance between teeth or the number of teeth for a particular gear diameter, is determined by the manufacturer. Finer pitch gears, which have more teeth for a particular diameter, operate qui-

etly, but because the teeth are thinner, tooth breakage may occur under heavy loads.

A helical gear can also be made with the helix cut at different angles. As the angle is increased, the gear will run more quietly, but a greater amount of end thrust will occur. Some modern five-speeds use fine-pitched gears with a greater helix angle for the fifth gear (Figure 6-31). This produces quiet operation at cruising speeds where low torque loading is encountered.

When a gear is used where it slides sideways into mesh, the contacting ends of its teeth and those of the gear(s) it will mesh with are beveled, or cut at an angle (Figure 6-32). This allows the gear teeth to slide into mesh with each other much more easily, especially if they are not aligned exactly.

6.14.2 Mainshaft

Close inspection of a mainshaft reveals specific areas that serve specific purposes. Also, the positioning of the snap ring grooves is very exacting to locate parts in precise locations (Figure 6-33). The snap rings may be avail-

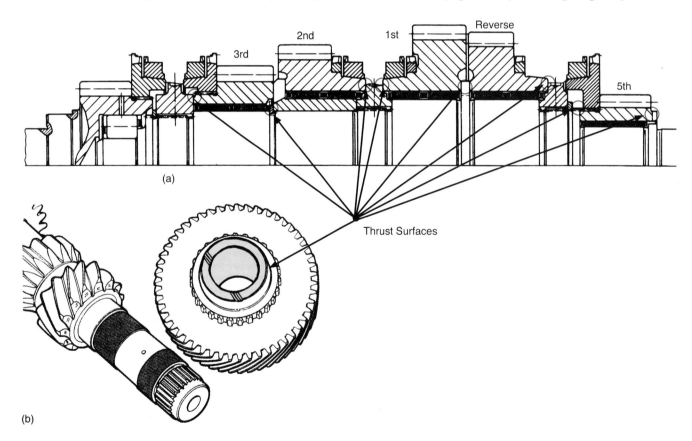

FIGURE 6-30 (a) Speed gears float on their journals on the mainshaft and have thrust surfaces at each side to keep them positioned. These surfaces are shaded in (b). (Portions of materials contained herein have been reprinted with permission of General Motors Corporation, Service and Parts Operations, License Agreement #0310807)

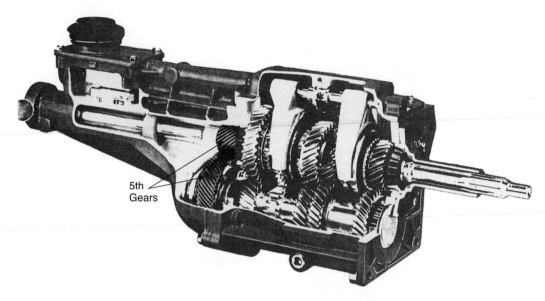

5th
Gears

FIGURE 6-31   Notice the gear teeth in this transmission; those on the fifth gears have a finer pitch and a greater helix angle, to produce quieter operation while cruising. (Portions of materials contained herein have been reprinted with permission of General Motors Corporation, Service and Parts Operations, License Agreement #0310807)

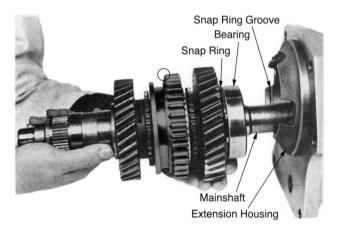

Snap Ring Groove
Bearing
Snap Ring
Mainshaft
Extension Housing

FIGURE 6-32   The left ends (circled) of the reverse gear teeth around this 1–2 synchronizer sleeve are beveled to allow easier engagement with the reverse idler during shifts into reverse. Constantmesh gears normally have teeth that are squared off. (Courtesy of Daimler-Chrysler Corporation)

able in different widths to adjust thrust clearance/gear end play. The mainshaft itself is located by the rear bearing, bearing surface, and retaining ring. Each synchronizer assembly has a set of splines so that torque can transfer to the shaft. Each gear location has a bearing surface, or journal, which often has special provision for lubricating the floating speed gear. A mainshaft will have a surface for the pilot bearing to the main drive gear at the front and the splines to match the U-joint splines at

the rear. Close to the rear of the shaft, there will be provision for mounting a speedometer drive gear or vehicle speed sensor (VSS) or the worm teeth for the speedometer drive gear will be cut into the shaft.

The mainshaft for older three-speed sliding gear transmissions has splines cut into the shaft so that first and reverse gears can slide into mesh with the first-gear portion of the cluster gear or the reverse idler gear (Figure 6-34). These splines are usually twisted to create a helix to counteract the side thrust of the helical first and reverse gears.

6.14.3   Countershaft and Cluster Gear

The cluster gear is supported by the rodlike countershaft with a set of needle bearings at each end in older transmissions (Figure 6-35). The countershaft has a press fit into the case. In units with a high amount of torque loading, a double set of needle bearings is used at each end to support the cluster gear. A thrust bushing is used between the gear and the case at each end to control end thrust. The thrust washer or a wear plate is keyed into the case so that it will not spin and wear into the case.

The fit between the countershaft and the case is tight enough to prevent lubricant leaks. At one end of the shaft, there is normally a locating device to prevent shaft rotation.

Some newer transmissions support the countershaft assembly, which includes the cluster gear, with a

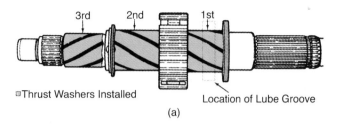

Thrust Washers Installed

Location of Lube Groove

(a)

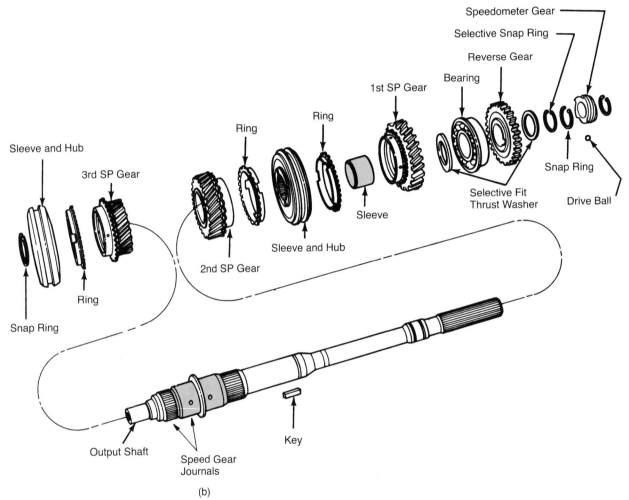

(b)

FIGURE 6-33   Most mainshafts have smooth journals for the speed gears and splined areas to connect to the synchronizer hubs. (a) Some include grooves for fluid flow. (b) Some include raised, washerlike thrust surfaces to keep the speed gears separated. (a: Portions of materials contained herein have been reprinted with permission of General Motors Corporation, Service and Parts Operations, License Agreement #0310807; b is courtesy of Ford Motor Company)

pair of tapered roller bearings (Figure 6-36). This bearing design is capable of absorbing thrust loads along with the normal side loads. Tapered roller bearings are normally adjusted during installation to obtain free running with a very slight clearance.

Most cluster gears are one-piece units, and if one of the gears is damaged, the entire unit must be replaced. The cluster gear used in the Tremec TR-3550 transmission is a three-piece unit (Figure 6-37). The two gears at the front of the cluster gear have a press fit onto the

main cluster gear. Woodruff keys help the assembly transfer torque. Another unusual cluster gear is used in the six-speed, T56 transmission. The cluster gear/countershaft fits in the main case and has the gears needed for first through fourth. A countershaft extension drives fifth, sixth, and reverse, and it fits in the extension housing. The back of the cluster gear and the front of the extension have matching splines to transfer torque (Figure 6-38).

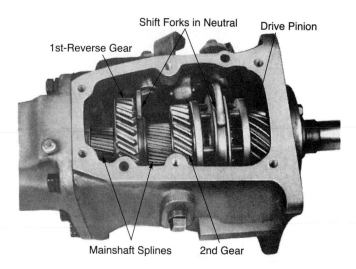

FIGURE 6-34 The mainshaft of this sliding gear transmission includes helical splines that allow the first–reverse gear to be slid into mesh and that offset the effect of that gear trying to thrust out of mesh under load. (Courtesy of DaimlerChrysler Corporation)

16. Lock Pin
18. Cluster Gear
19. Needle Bearings
20. Washer
79. Thrust Washer
84. Countershaft

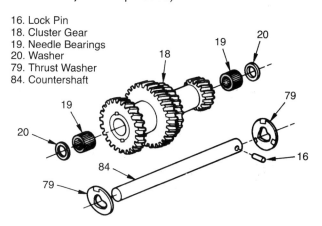

FIGURE 6-35 This cluster gear is mounted on two sets of needle bearings (19) on the countershaft (84) and uses two thrust washers (79) to absorb thrust loads. Note the lock pin (16), which keeps the countershaft in place and prevents rotation. (Courtesy of Ford Motor Company)

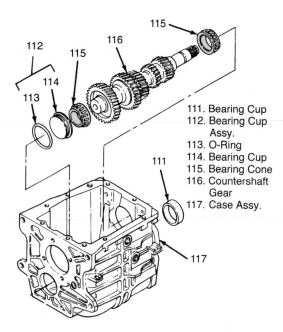

111. Bearing Cup
112. Bearing Cup Assy.
113. O-Ring
114. Bearing Cup
115. Bearing Cone
116. Countershaft Gear
117. Case Assy.

FIGURE 6-36 This countershaft gear is mounted on a pair of tapered roller bearings (115), which locate it in the case and allow it to rotate. (Courtesy of BWD Automotive Corporation)

6.14.4 Case

The main case and extension housing are usually made from aluminum castings. Older transmissions use cast iron cases. Most cases have openings for access to the gear train. The term **open case** is sometimes used for a case in which the side or top cover is removable and includes the shifting forks and other mechanisms (Figure 6-39a). A cover that includes the shift mechanism is normally located by dowel pins so that the shift motions do not cause movement of the cover, which could cause incomplete gear engagement. **Closed case** refers to a case that might have access openings, but the shift mechanism is located entirely within the case (Figure 6-39b). The Ford toploader is a closed case design. With a **tunnel**

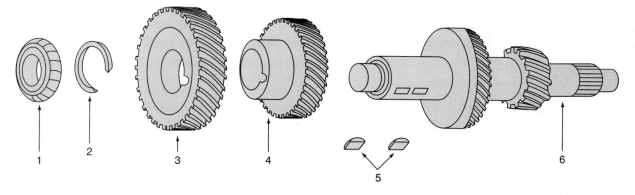

FIGURE 6-37 Two gears, the input (3) and third (4), are press fit onto the cluster gear for a TR-3550 transmission. (Courtesy of Transmission Technologies Corporation, TTC)

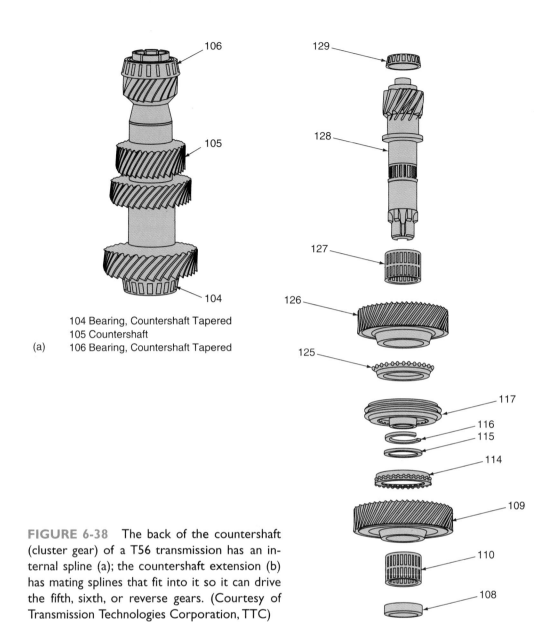

104 Bearing, Countershaft Tapered
105 Countershaft
(a)   106 Bearing, Countershaft Tapered

FIGURE 6-38   The back of the countershaft (cluster gear) of a T56 transmission has an internal spline (a); the countershaft extension (b) has mating splines that fit into it so it can drive the fifth, sixth, or reverse gears. (Courtesy of Transmission Technologies Corporation, TTC)

case, the gears and shafts are loaded from the end of the case (Figure 6-39c). In a split case design, the case has two halves that are bolted together (Figure 6-39d). Many five- and six-speed transmissions use a center plate design (see Figure 8-48). The center plate has bearings that support the mainshaft and cluster gear.

6.14.5   Bearings

Transmissions use a variety of bearings, depending on the particular design. The types used are **needle bearings, ball bearings, tapered roller bearings,** and plain **bushings** (Figure 6-40). To work properly, all types of bearings must have proper lubrication.

Needle bearings, either caged into a single unit or free, can carry large amounts of side loads but are unable to control end thrust loads. Free needle bearings are used to support the cluster gear in most older transmissions.

Ball bearings can carry moderate to high side loads and thrust loads. Thus they are commonly used for the main drive gear and mainshaft in many transmissions. A "maxi" version of the ball bearing can carry even greater side loads. A maxi bearing can be identified by the increased number of balls as well as loading notches at one side of the inner and outer races. The speed gears in many modern transmissions are mounted over needle bearings (see Figure 6-38).

Tapered roller bearings can carry large amounts of both side load and thrust load and are generally used in

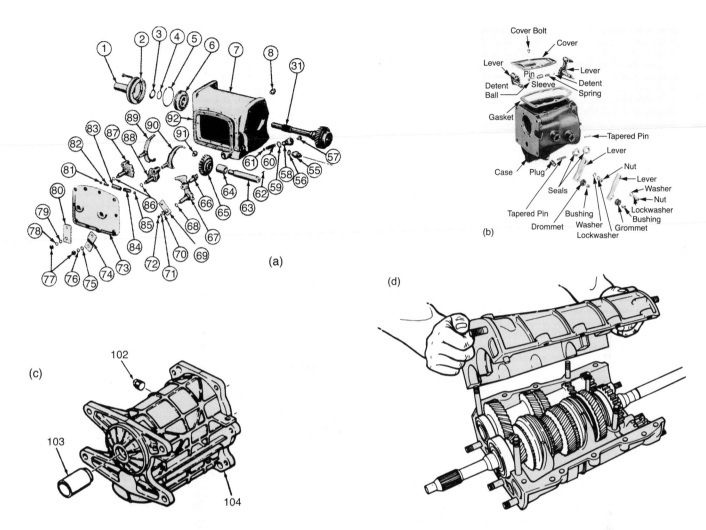

FIGURE 6-39 The major transmission case designs are the open case (a) with the shift linkage mounted in a cover; the closed case (b) the tunnel case (c), which is loaded from one end; and the split case (d). (a and b are courtesy of DiamlerChrysler Corporation; c: Portions of materials contained herein have been reprinted with permission of General Motors Corporation, Service and Parts Operations, License Agreement #0310807; d is courtesy of Ford Motor Company)

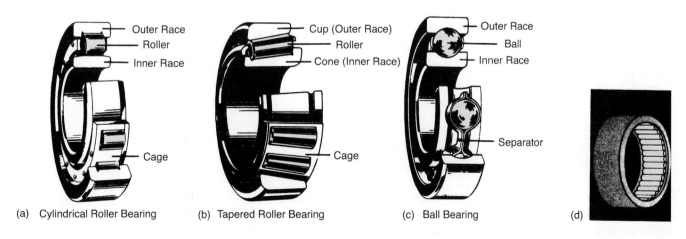

FIGURE 6-40 The major types of frictionless bearings are cylindrical or straight roller bearings (a), tapered roller bearings (b), ball bearings (c), and needle bearings (d). (Courtesy of CR Services)

pairs with the cones and cups facing in opposite directions. This bearing is normally installed with a method (usually shims) of adjusting end play or, in a few cases, preload. In some newer transmissions, tapered roller bearings are used to support the main drive gear, the mainshaft, and the countershaft.

A plain bushing is used to support the driveshaft slip yoke in the extension housing. A bushing can support a large side load and allows free in-and-out movement.

6.15   OVERDRIVE UNITS

Two approaches are used with a standard transmission to get an overdrive ratio. One approach, described in Section 6.7, is commonly used in newer transmissions. The other approach is to attach an overdrive unit in place of the extension housing on a RWD transmission. From the mid-1930s to the early 1960s, each domestic vehicle manufacturer offered a manual transmission with an overdrive of this type. In most cases, the unit was manufactured by Borg Warner (Figure 6-41). In England and Europe, several vehicle manufacturers used an overdrive unit known as the Laycock de Normanville. In the mid-1980s, an overdrive unit manufactured by Doug Nash Industries was used with a version of the Borg Warner T10 transmission and installed in Corvettes. Each of these units provides two ratios: a 1:1 direct drive, sometimes called *underdrive* or *passing gear*; and an overdrive with a ratio somewhere between 0.8:1 and 0.6:1.

The Borg Warner and de Normanville units use true planetary gear sets with a sun gear that can rotate or be held stationary. It uses a planet carrier that is driven by the transmission mainshaft, a ring gear

that is connected to the output shaft, and a one-way clutch assembly that allows the carrier to drive the output shaft. Overdrive occurs when the sun gear is held stationary. When the carrier is driven, the planet pinion gears will be forced to "walk" (rotate on their axis) around the sun gear. This motion causes the outer teeth of the planet gears, the ones in mesh with the ring, to move faster than the carrier; as a result, they will drive the ring gear at an overdrive ratio (Figure 6-42).

In the Borg Warner unit, sun gear motion is controlled by a mechanical cable actuated by the driver from the dash control and an electric solenoid. When the dash control is pulled outward, the sun gear is shifted to mesh with both the planet gears and the carrier; this locks the gear set into a 1:1 ratio. Pushing the control inward moves the sun gear so that it is in mesh with the planet gears and the sun gear control plate; now the sun gear and the control plate are free to rotate. Power can pass from the carrier to the output shaft through the one-way clutch in underdrive, and an electric solenoid can complete the shift into overdrive by engaging and locking the sun gear control plate stationary.

The Laycock de Normanville unit uses a similar gear arrangement and power flows but a different shifting procedure. It uses a large double-cone clutch that is attached to the sun gear and operated by a hydraulic piston. In underdrive (the 1:1 ratio), the cone clutch is moved rearward, locking the sun gear to the ring gear, and the gear set rotates as a single unit with no internal

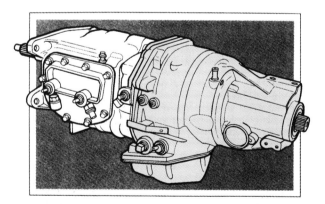

FIGURE 6-41   Four-speed transmission with an overdrive built into it to provide an overdrive, or fifth gear. (Portions of materials contained herein have been reprinted with permission of General Motors Corporation, Service and Parts Operations, License Agreement #0310807)

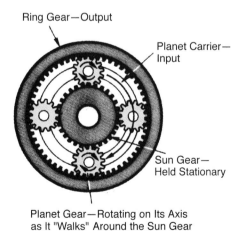

FIGURE 6-42   If the sun gear of a planetary gear set is held stationary while the planet carrier is rotated, the planet pinion gears will be forced to rotate on their axis and "walk" around the sun gear. This will force the ring gear to rotate at an overdrive ratio.

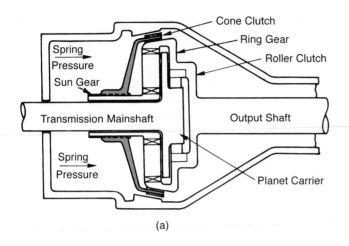

(a)

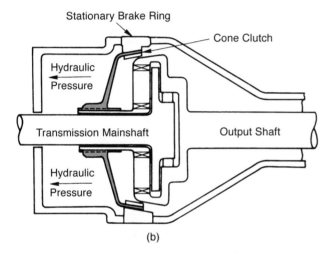

(b)

FIGURE 6-43   (a) Spring pressure forces the cone clutch to lock the sun gear and the ring gear together to provide a 1:1 ratio in this Laycock overdrive gear set. (b) Hydraulic pressure forces the cone clutch against the stationary brake ring, holding the sun gear stationary and causing an overdrive ratio.

motion (Figure 6-43). In overdrive, the cone clutch is moved forward, locking the sun gear to the case to produce the same planet gear operation described earlier. Hydraulic pressure to shift the cone clutch comes from a self-contained hydraulic system and is controlled by an electric solenoid.

The Doug Nash is not a true planetary gear set, but the operation is similar. In this unit, the transmission mainshaft is connected to one sun gear, another smaller sun gear is connected to the output shaft, and a carrier with a set of planet gears connects these two (Figure 6-44). Each of the planet gears has two sizes: The smaller end meshes with the front input sun gear, while the larger end meshes with the rear sun gear. Two clutch packs are used and arranged so that one is released

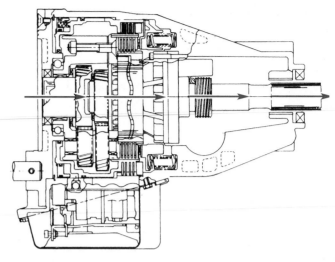

(a)

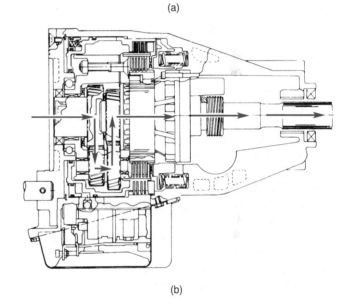

(b)

FIGURE 6-44   Application of this overdrive unit's direct clutch locks the carrier to the output shaft at a 1:1 ratio (a). When the overdrive clutch is applied, the carrier is held stationary and the power flow from the input sun gear to the planet gears to the output sun gear on the output shaft produces an overdrive ratio (b). (Portions of materials contained herein have been reprinted with permission of General Motors Corporation, Service and Parts Operations, License Agreement #0310807)

while the other is applied. In underdrive, one of the clutch packs locks the carrier to the output shaft, locking up the gear set. In overdrive, the other clutch locks the carrier to the case, and the large sun gear drives the set of smaller pinions; these, in turn, drive the other sun gear, producing the overdrive ratio. To make the shifts, this system also uses a self-contained hydraulic system controlled by an electric solenoid.

6.16 AUXILIARY TRANSMISSIONS

An auxiliary transmission, fitted between the main transmission and the drive axle, is used to provide an additional higher or lower gear or to reduce the size of the steps between the gear ratios of the main transmission. Heavy trucks commonly use auxiliary transmissions with "splitter" ratios. These provide a slight reduction, a 1:1 direct drive, and a slight overdrive (Figure 6-45). The gear changes go something like this: first–low, first–DD, first–OD, second–low, second–DD, second–OD, third–low, and so on. Note that between first–OD and second–low it is necessary to shift both the main and auxiliary transmissions.

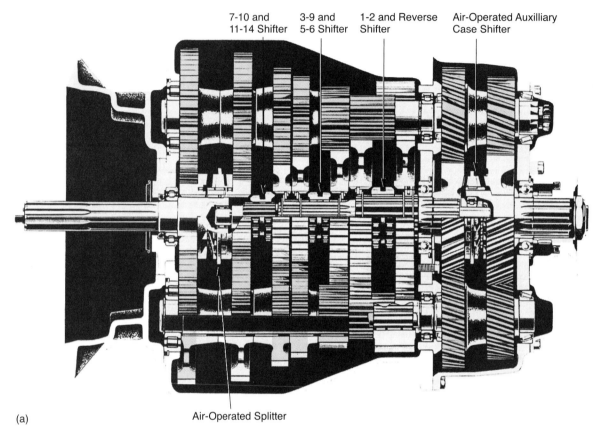

7-10 and 11-14 Shifter 3-9 and 5-6 Shifter 1-2 and Reverse Shifter Air-Operated Auxilliary Case Shifter

Air-Operated Splitter

(a)

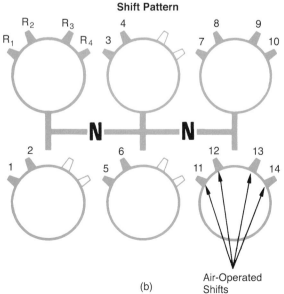

Shift Pattern

Air-Operated Shifts

(b)

FIGURE 6-45 This 14-speed heavy truck transmission has five forward gear ratios in the main gear section plus two "splitter" ratios, one at the main drive gear and one in the auxiliary section. The splitter shifts are air operated with the switch control on the shift lever. Twin cluster gears increase the torque capacity of this transmission. (Courtesy of Dana Corporation)

Auxiliary transmissions are popular in the recreational vehicle, (RV), and motor home (Figure 6-46). Aftermarket (produced for installation after the vehicle is constructed) units are available that are very similar to two-speed transmissions. These are usually two-speed units, one of the speeds being direct drive and the other speed being overdrive. But a unit may be constructed so it can be mounted either way. When mounted in the vehicle, it is positioned to produce the desired ratio. When positioned one way, it produces an overdrive, but if it is turned around and the input and output shafts are swapped, it produces an underdrive.

FIGURE 6-46   This auxiliary transmission is mounted between the transmission and drive axle. It provides a 1:1 ratio and either an overdrive or a reduction ratio.

REVIEW QUESTIONS

The following questions are provided to help you study as you read the chapter.

1. The are two types of gears sets used in standard transmissions. They are

    a. _____ _____

    b. _____ _____ _____

2. _____ _____ gears are shifted by the use of a synchronizer.

3. The vehicle needs to be at rest when shifting _____ _____

4. The synchronizer must be able to synchronize or match the _____ of the gears.

5. The purpose of the _____ on the inside of the synchronizer ring is to break through the lubricating film.

6. The power flow for second gear in a four-speed rear-wheel-drive transmission would be from the

    a. _____ drive gear to the

    b. _____ gear to the

    c. second _____ gear to the

    d. second _____ gear

7. The main difference between a four-, five-, or six-speed rear-wheel-drive transmission is the _____ of gears and the _____ of the transmission.

8. The _____ mechanism prevents the engagement of more than one gear at a time.

9. The _____ mechanisms are used to lock and hold the internal shift linkage in position.

10. All forward gears in modern transmissions use _____ gears; reverse typically uses _____ gears.

11. _____ are used to locate parts on the mainshaft.

12. The bearings that are best suited to handle both side and thrust loads are _____ bearings.

13. A bushing is used in the _____ housing to support the driveshaft slip yoke.

14. Name four types of bearings.

    a. _____ _____

    b. _____ _____ _____

    c. _____ _____

    d. _____ _____

15. _____ transmissions can be added to increase the number of gear ratios.

CHAPTER QUIZ

The following questions will help you check the facts you have learned. Select the answer that completes each statement correctly.

1. A four-speed transmission is in third gear. A. The 1–2 synchronizer is in neutral. B. The 3–4 synchronizer is moved to engage third gear. Which is correct?

    a. A only   **c.** Both A and B

    b. B only   **d.** Neither A nor B

2. A three-speed transmission is in third gear, so A. there is a 1:1 gear ratio; B. the 2–3 synchronizer has engaged the input shaft gear. Which is correct?

    a. A only   **c.** Both A and B

    b. B only   **d.** Neither A nor B

3. The cluster gear is supported by A. two sets of needle bearings around the countershaft; B. roller bearings between the countershaft and the case. Which is correct?

    a. A only   **c.** Both A and B

    b. B only   **d.** Neither A nor B

4. While discussing a four-speed cluster gear, Student A says that it is a combination of four or five gears. Student B says that it has six gears. Who is correct?

    a. Student A   **c.** Both A and B

    b. Student B   **d.** Neither A nor B

5. Two students are discussing synchronizer rings. Student A says they equalize the speeds of the synchronizer assembly and the speed gear being engaged. Student B says they block the synchronizer sleeve briefly during a shift. Who is correct?

    a. Student A   **c.** Both A and B

    b. Student B   **d.** Neither A nor B

6. During a normal upshift, the synchronizer must A. speed up the mainshaft assembly; B. slow down the clutch disc, main drive gear, cluster gear, and speed gears. Which is correct?

    a. A only   **c.** Both A and B

    b. B only   **d.** Neither A nor B

7. The idler gear is used for which gear?

    a. first gear.   **c.** third gear.

    b. second gear.   **d.** reverse.

8. A four-speed transmission is in second gear. A. the power flow is from the input shaft gear to the cluster gear and then to the second speed gear on the mainshaft assembly. B. The 1–2 synchronizer is moved so that the sleeve has engaged the clutching teeth of second gear. Which is correct?

    a. A only   **c.** Both A and B

    b. B only   **d.** Neither A nor B

9. When one synchronizer is shifted into gear, the movement of the other shift forks is blocked by the A. detents; B. interlocks. Which is correct?

    a. A only   **c.** Both A and B

    b. B only   **d.** Neither A nor B

10. The detent mechanism inside a transmission is used to

    a. locate the synchronizer sleeves in the correct position.

    b. prevent more than one shift fork from moving at one time.

    c. hold a gear into mesh.

    d. all of these.

11. A four-speed transmission with external linkage uses A. two shift rods to connect the shifter to the transmission; B. an interlock mechanism built into the shifter assembly. Which is correct?

    a. A only   **c.** Both A and B

    b. B only   **d.** Neither A nor B

12. The speedometer gear is driven off the

    a. main drive gear.   **c.** cluster gear.

    b. mainshaft.   **d.** driveshaft.

13. A transmission is lubricated A. by gear oil that is thrown around the case by gear rotation; B. to remove excess heat from the gears. Which is correct?

    a. A only   **c.** Both A and B

    b. B only   **d.** Neither A nor B

14. Two students are discussing a transmission that is noisy in first, second, third, and reverse but quiet in fourth gear. Student A says there is probably a bad input shaft gear. Student B says it probably has a faulty 1–2 synchronizer assembly because reverse is on the synchronizer sleeve. Who is correct?

    a. Student A   **c.** Both A and B

    b. Student B   **d.** Neither A nor B

15. A four-speed transmission makes a grinding noise only while shifting into second gear. This could be caused by a A. damaged main drive gear; B. faulty 1–2 synchronizer sleeve. Which is correct?

    a. A only   **c.** Both A and B

    b. B only   **d.** Neither A nor B

16. The main drive gear has 18 teeth that drive a 24-tooth gear at the front of the cluster gear. What is the ratio between these two?

17. Using the gear ratio from Question 16, how fast will the cluster gear be turning with an engine speed of 2000 rpm?

18. First gear on the cluster has 18 teeth, and the first speed gear has 28 teeth. What is the ratio?

19. If the input gear set is 18 and 24, what is the ratio for first gear?

20. Using the gear ratio from Question 19, how fast will the mainshaft be turning with an engine speed of 2000 rpm?

◀ Chapter 7 ▶

TRANSAXLE THEORY

LEARNING OBJECTIVES

After completing this chapter, you should be able to:

1. Identify the parts of a standard transaxle.
2. Know the purpose of each major part of a standard transaxle.
3. Trace the power flow for the different speeds.
4. Calculate the gear ratio for each gear.
5. Understand differential operation.
6. Understand the requirements for good transaxle operation.

TERMS TO LEARN

anaerobic sealants	intermediate shaft
axle gears	mainshaft
clutch shaft	pinion gears
countershaft	room-temperature
differential	vulcanizing (RTV)
drive pinion	spiral bevel pinion
extension rod	gear
final drive ring gear	spiral bevel ring gear
input shaft	stabilizer bar

7.1 INTRODUCTION

The development of the transaxle has, in part, made the modern, fuel-saving FWD vehicle possible. Other styles of FWD vehicles were built in the past, including the American Cord of the 1930s, the French Citroen, and the Oldsmobile Toronado and Cadillac Eldorado of the mid-1960s, but each of these designs had rather limited markets. A large majority of the vehicles sold today use a FWD transaxle that is transverse or longitudinally mounted.

Many features of the transmission portion of a transaxle are similar to those of a RWD transmission. There are differences, however, in the number of shafts and the power flow. There is also the addition of the final drive gears with the differential (Figure 7-1). This is the drive axle portion of a transaxle.

7.2 CONSTRUCTION

Most transaxles are made with four parallel shafts: the **input shaft,** the **mainshaft,** the **differential,** and the reverse idler shaft. Except for the reverse idler shaft, each of these shafts is supported by a pair of bearings at the sides of the case (Figure 7-2). The input shaft is sometimes called the **clutch shaft** because it extends out of the case where a splined section connects to the clutch disc. The driving gears are positioned on the input shaft, and there is one for each forward speed.

The mainshaft, also called a **countershaft** or an **intermediate shaft,** also includes a gear for each forward speed; these are the driven gears. The mainshaft also includes the **drive pinion.** The drive pinion gear is the transmission output and input for the

157

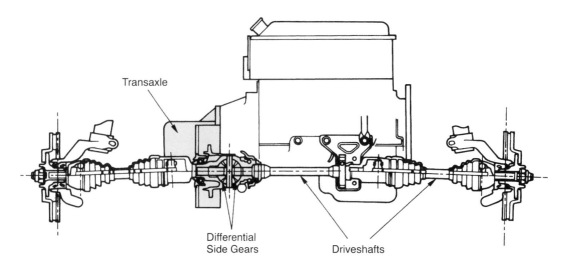

FIGURE 7-1 A transaxle is a transmission plus the final drive and differential, which are inside the rear axle of a RWD car. The inner CV joints of the front driveshafts connect to the side gears in the transaxle differential. (Courtesy of Ford Motor Company)

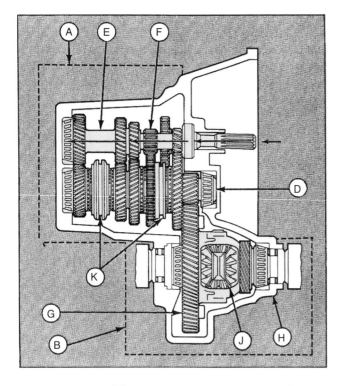

FIGURE 7-2 The transmission portion of many transaxles uses the top two shafts (A). The differential and ring gear are at the bottom shaft (B). (Courtesy of Ford Motor Company)

final drive. The **final drive ring gear** is mounted on the differential case.

The differential divides the power flow between the two CV joints coupled to the driveshafts and on to the

wheels. The **pinion gears** and **axle gears** in the differential allow for speed differences when the vehicle turns a corner.

All of the gears in a transaxle, with the exception of the reverse idler, are in constant mesh, and each of the gear pairs on the input shaft and mainshaft represents the power paths for a particular gear ratio. If you look closely at each gear pair, you can see that one gear is secured solidly to the shaft and the other floats on the shaft, right next to a synchronizer assembly (Figure 7-3). Some transaxles secure all the gears on the input shaft to form a cluster gear. These can be either a single cluster gear or a group of gears pressed onto a splined shaft. Other designs float all or some of the driving gears on the input shaft and secure the driven gears onto the mainshaft (Figure 7-4).

Most engines rotate in a clockwise direction (viewing the drive rotation from the right, or passenger, side of the car). As you view the transaxle, the input shaft rotates clockwise, the mainshaft rotates counterclockwise in forward gears, and the differential rotates clockwise to drive the wheels in a clockwise direction for forward motion (Figure 7-5).

In some transaxle designs, two mainshafts are used (Figure 7-6). If there is a space conflict in the car because of the length of the engine and transaxle, the transaxle can be shortened by placing some of the gears, such as fifth and an additional final drive pinion gear, on a separate shaft. This shaft becomes an alternate to the mainshaft for the power flow through these gears.

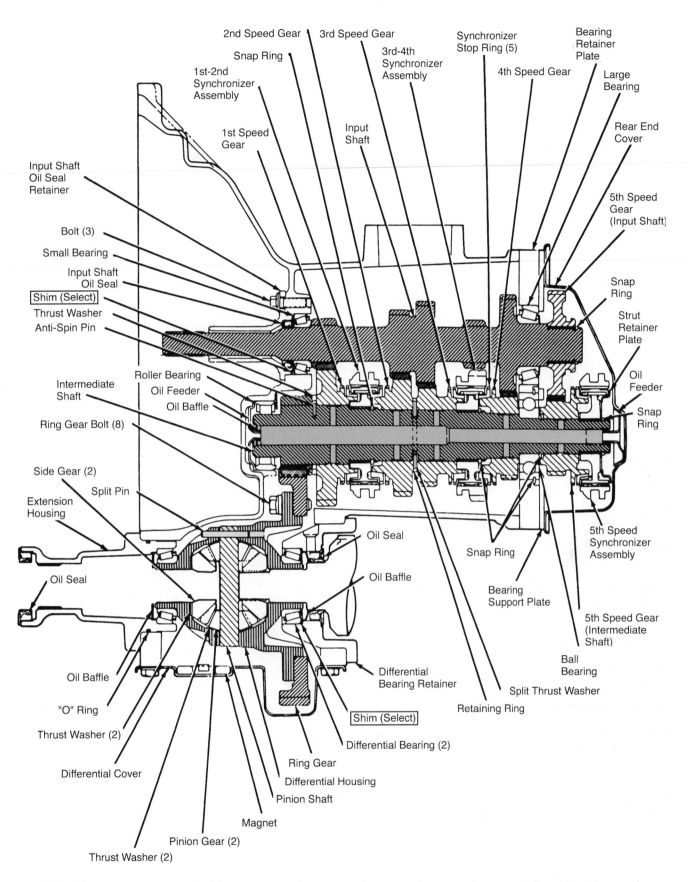

FIGURE 7-3 Five-speed transaxle. Note that all of the gears are fixed as a cluster to the input shaft and that the speed gears and synchronizer assemblies are on the intermediate shaft of this transaxle. (Courtesy of DaimlerChrysler Corporation)

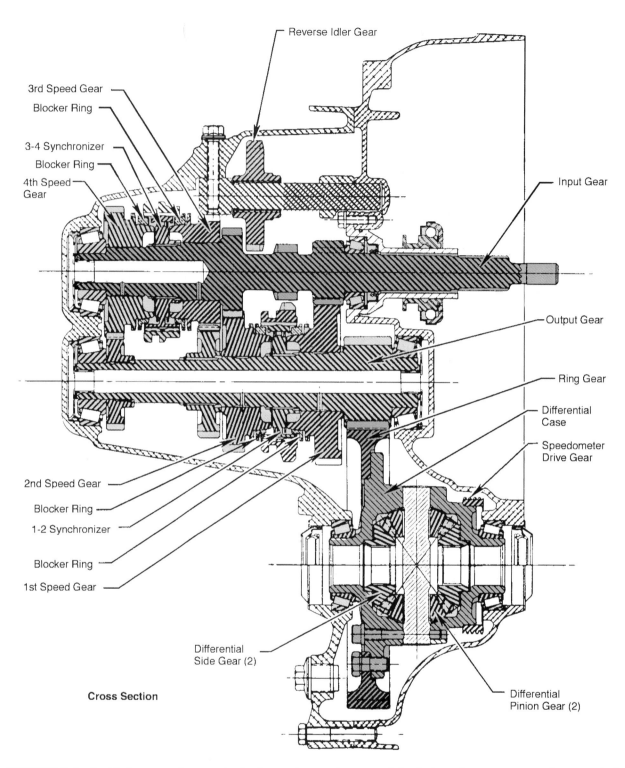

Reverse Idler Gear

3rd Speed Gear

Blocker Ring

3-4 Synchronizer

Blocker Ring

4th Speed Gear

Input Gear

Output Gear

Ring Gear

Differential Case

Speedometer Drive Gear

2nd Speed Gear

Blocker Ring

1-2 Synchronizer

Blocker Ring

1st Speed Gear

Differential Side Gear (2)

Differential Pinion Gear (2)

Cross Section

FIGURE 7-4 In this four-speed transaxle, the first and second gears and the 3–4 synchronizer are on the input shaft, while the 1–2 synchronizer and third and fourth gears are secured to the intermediate shaft along with the output gear (final drive pinion gear). (Portions of materials contained herein have been reprinted with permission of General Motors Corporation, Service and Parts Operations, License Agreement #0310807)

Engine Rotation
(Counter clockwise
when Viewed from
the Left Side)

FIGURE 7-5 In most FWD cars, the engine and the transaxle input shaft rotate in a clockwise direction (viewed from the right side). The intermediate shaft will rotate counterclockwise and drive the ring gear, differential, and driveshafts in a clockwise direction. (Courtesy of Ford Motor Company)

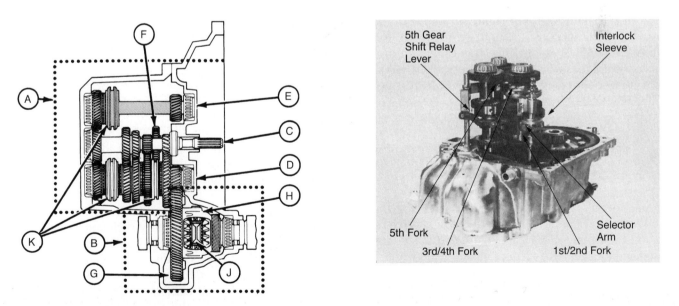

FIGURE 7-6 This transaxle mounts the fifth gear and synchronizer assembly on a separate shaft (E) along with a final drive pinion gear. (Courtesy of Ford Motor Company)

7.3 POWER FLOW

The power flow through the transmission portion of a transaxle is essentially the same in all the forward gears (Figure 7-7). The power passes from the driving gear on the input shaft to the driven gear on the mainshaft and then through the synchronizer assembly to the mainshaft itself. Because the power passes through only one set of gears, the ratio for that gear speed is determined by that pair of gears. The smallest gear on the input shaft drives the largest gear on the mainshaft for first gear, and the largest gear on the input shaft drives the smallest gear on the mainshaft for fourth gear. The synchronizers are the same as those used in a transmission; their parts and operation are identical (Figure 7-8).

The power flow for reverse gear is also similar to that of a RWD transmission. In most cases, the reverse idler is shifted into mesh with the reverse gear on the input shaft and the sleeve of the 1–2 synchronizer assembly, which has the spur gear teeth for reverse on the outer diameter. The idler gear will rotate in a counterclockwise direction viewed from the right side, the 1–2 synchronizer assembly will rotate clockwise, and the differential and drive wheels will rotate counterclockwise to drive the vehicle backward.

Also like a transmission, all of the gears, with the exception of the reverse idler and differential, will rotate whenever the input shaft rotates, and the speed gears on the mainshaft will rotate at a speed determined by their gear ratio (Figure 7-9). A 1:1 ratio requires a pair of gears like the other ratio, so transaxles do not necessarily use this ratio. The engineers are free to select the ratio that best fits the need of the vehicle.

7.4 FINAL DRIVE AND DIFFERENTIAL

As mentioned earlier, power leaves the mainshaft through the drive pinion that drives the final drive ring gear on the differential case (Figure 7-10). The drive pinion and ring gear are a pair of helical gears with a ratio, similar to a RWD rear axle, which determines engine rpm at cruise speeds. This gear set operates rather quietly and does not require critical adjustments like those necessary for the hypoid gear set used in a RWD rear axle.

The differential case has a differential pinion shaft running across it on which the two differential pinion gears float. These gears are not secured to the shaft. They are located between the differential case and the two side gears; side gears are also called *axle gears* (Figure 7-11). The axle gears also float in the case, but they have internal splines so they can drive the CV joints and driveshafts. All four of these gears are spur bevel gears. You can usually hear them operate by lifting both drive wheels and rotating one wheel by hand. At this time, note that the other wheel is rotating in the opposite direction; the pinion gears are acting like idlers between the two side gears.

The load of the side gears determines what the differential pinion gears do. If both side gears are loaded the same and offer the same resistance, the differential pinion gears remain motionless on their shaft and the entire differential assembly rotates as one mass with no internal gear movement. When a vehicle goes around a corner, the side gears are equally loaded, but the one connected to the outer wheel will rotate faster (Figure 7-12). At this time, the differential pinion gears will rotate on their shafts to compensate for this change in speed. The outer wheel will speed up relative to the car and differential, and the inner wheel will slow down the same amount. For example, if the outer wheel speeds up 20 percent from 100 rpm to 120 rpm, the inner wheel will slow down 20 percent to 80 rpm. Some people think of the differential as kind of a balance scale; it pivots when a change in load occurs.

The major drawback of a differential occurs when one wheel does not have traction. To demonstrate this, set the parking brake, raise one drive wheel off the ground, start the engine, release the parking brake, and carefully let out the clutch with the transmission in first gear. You should see the vehicle stand still with one wheel spinning. Be careful doing this because a vehicle with a limited slip differential or with excessive drag in the differential can drive both wheels enough to move the vehicle. Remember that the differential splits torque equally. Assume that it takes 10 ft-lb of torque to spin the raised wheel. When torque arrives at the differential, it will exert a force equal to 10 ft-lb at each side axle gear (Figure 7-13). When the side gear with the least resistance begins to spin, the pinion gears will simply rotate on their shaft and "walk" around the stationary side gear with good traction. The 10 ft-lb of torque is not enough to rotate the stationary side gear with the wheel in contact with the ground. At this time, the raised wheel will increase speed 100 percent, or double; if the differential case is turning 100 rpm, the wheel will be turning 200 rpm. Don't run the raised wheel too fast, above 35 mph (40 kph) on the speedometer; the tire could explode from the centrifugal force.

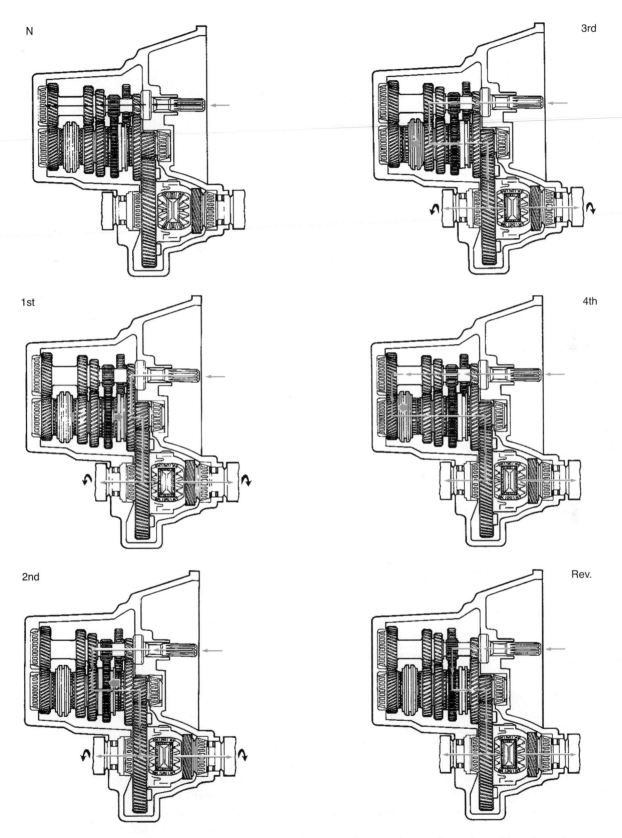

FIGURE 7-7 The power flows through the gear set of a four-speed transaxle are shown here. Note how they are similar except for the gear sizes and that, in reverse, an idler is used. (Courtesy of Ford Motor Company)

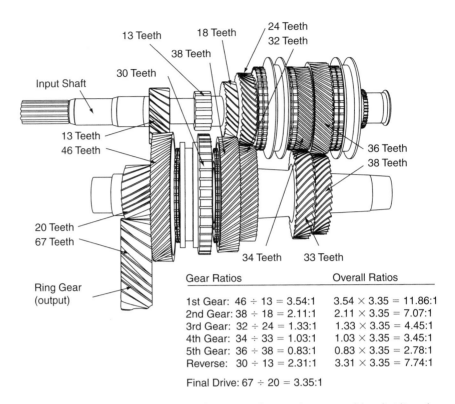

Gear Ratios | Overall Ratios

1st Gear: 46 ÷ 13 = 3.54:1   3.54 × 3.35 = 11.86:1
2nd Gear: 38 ÷ 18 = 2.11:1   2.11 × 3.35 = 7.07:1
3rd Gear: 32 ÷ 24 = 1.33:1   1.33 × 3.35 = 4.45:1
4th Gear: 34 ÷ 33 = 1.03:1   1.03 × 3.35 = 3.45:1
5th Gear: 36 ÷ 38 = 0.83:1   0.83 × 3.35 = 2.78:1
Reverse: 30 ÷ 13 = 2.31:1   3.31 × 3.35 = 7.74:1

Final Drive: 67 ÷ 20 = 3.35:1

FIGURE 7-8 The gear ratios of a transaxle are determined by dividing the tooth count of the driven gear by that of the driving gear. Multiplying the transaxle gear ratio by the final drive ratio gives us the overall ratio.

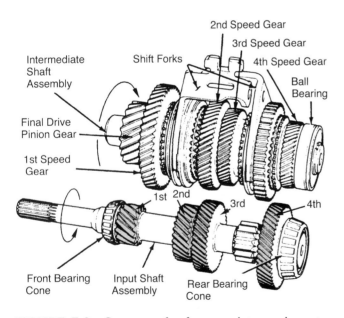

FIGURE 7-9 Gear set of a four-speed transaxle; note how first gear uses the smallest driving gear and the largest driven gear and how the gear sets change in size. (Courtesy of DaimlerChrysler Corporation)

Lack of one-wheel traction as just described is not a great problem in FWD vehicles because engine weight is close to the drive wheels. Rear-wheel traction is a larger problem with RWD vehicles, and one-wheel tire spin is more common. Limited slip differentials were developed to solve this problem, and they are described in Chapter 11. Occasionally, with RWD vehicles that encounter one-wheel spinning problems, the driver can partially apply the parking brake and drive out of the problem. Parking brake application will increase the drag and torque loading of the spinning tire and force the differential to send more torque to the other tire.

The differential case is usually mounted on a pair of tapered roller bearings. A drive gear for the speedometer is usually mounted on the differential case.

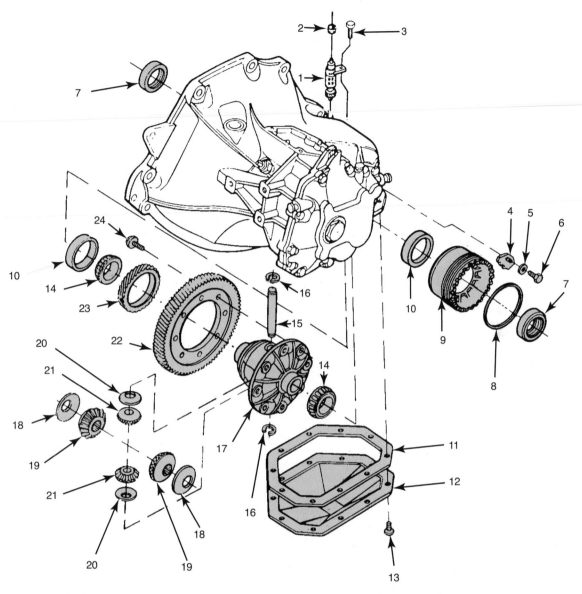

1. Speedometer Driven Gear
2. Seal
3. Hex Bolt
4. Lock Plate
5. Washer
6. Hex Bolt with Washer
7. Axle Shaft Seal
8. Bearing Ring Seal
9. Bearing Ring
10. Differential Side Bearing Cup
11. Differential Cover Gasket
12 . Differential Cover

13. Differential Cover Bolt
14. Differential Bearing Cone
15 . Differential Pinion Shaft
16. Pinion Shaft Retaining Ring
17. Differential Case
18. Differential Side Gear Thrust Washer
19. Differential Side Gear
20. Differential Pinion Thrust Washer
21. Differential Pinion Gear
22. Ring Gear
23. Speedometer Drive Gear
24. Ring Gear Bolt

FIGURE 7-10 The final drive pinion gear drives the ring gear mounted on the differential case. This is an exploded view of the differential and its parts. (Portions of materials contained herein have been reprinted with permission of General Motors Corporation, Service and Parts Operations, License Agreement #0310807)

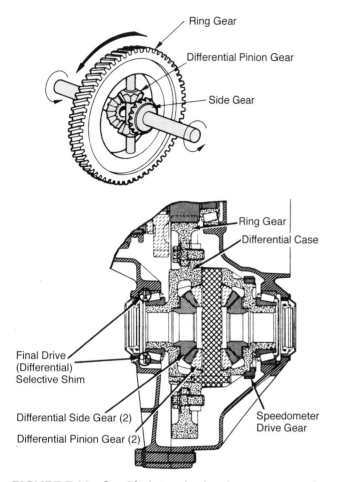

FIGURE 7-11 Simplified view (top) and cutaway view of a transaxle differential. The power flows from the ring gear to the differential case, through the differential shaft to the differential pinion and side gears, and on to the driveshafts. (Portions of materials contained herein have been reprinted with permission of General Motors Corporation, Service and Parts Operations, License Agreement #0310807)

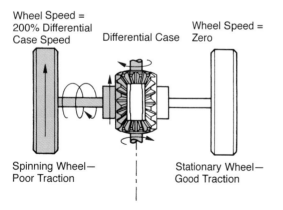

FIGURE 7-13 If one wheel has poor traction, it will rotate easily, so the differential pinion gears will rotate on their shaft and "walk" around the other side gear, which offers more resistance. The result is wheel spin on the side with poor traction.

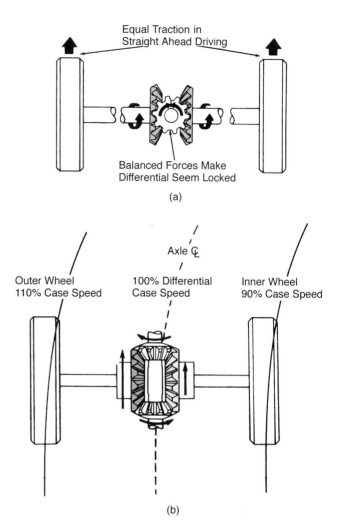

FIGURE 7-12 An equal load from each side gear will keep the differential pinion gears from rotating on their shaft, and both side gears will be driven at the same speed (a and b). If one wheel slows, the differential pinions will rotate on their shaft and drive the other side gear and wheel at an increased speed. (Portions of materials contained herein have been reprinted with permission of General Motors Corporation, Service and Parts Operations, License Agreement #0310807)

7.5 FIVE-SPEED TRANSAXLES

Adding an additional gear to the input shaft and an additional floating gear and synchronizer to the mainshaft is one way of making a five-speed version from a four-speed transaxle. On some units, the synchronizer and floating gear are placed on the input shaft, and the fixed gear is on the mainshaft (Figure 7-14). Because of space limitations in the case, the fifth-gear portion is often positioned under the cover at the left of the case or on a second mainshaft, as described earlier.

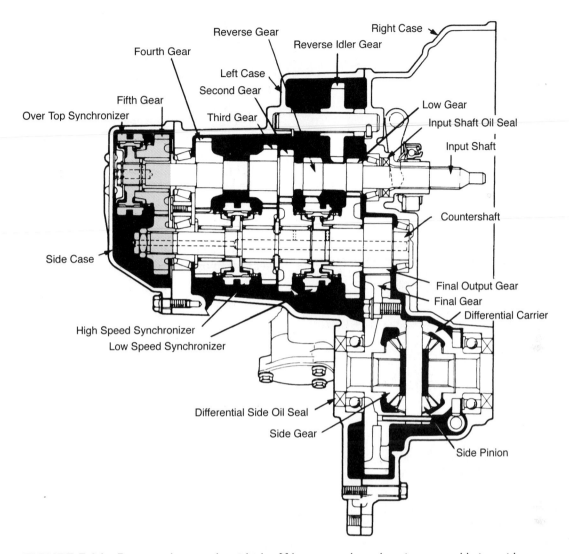

FIGURE 7-14   Five-speed transaxle with the fifth gears and synchronizer assembly in a side case. This unit is longer than the one shown in Figure 7-6. (Portions of materials contained herein have been reprinted with permission of General Motors Corporation, Service and Parts Operations, License Agreement #0310807)

7.5.1   Five-Speed, Four-Shaft Transaxle

The transaxle in some vehicles uses four shafts, with a synchronizer assembly and two driving gears on the input shaft (Figure 7-15). The driven gears are two of the driving gears fixed onto the intermediate shaft. The output shaft (mainshaft) has the floating speed gears and the 1–2 and 3–4 synchronizer assemblies. The lowest-ratio gear set between the input to intermediate shafts is used for first, the next lowest for second, and so on for third and fourth gears. Then the input shaft synchronizer is shifted for fifth gear. The higher-ratio gear on the input to intermediate shafts times fourth gear becomes the ratio for fifth gear.

7.6   LENGTHWISE TRANSAXLES

A few manufacturers place the engine in FWD cars longitudinally (lengthwise) instead of in a transverse position. This requires a major change in the transaxle. In these units the power must turn 90° to align with the front driveshafts (Figure 7-16). The transaxle portion of these units is basically the same as that just described except that the power leaves the mainshaft through a **spiral bevel pinion gear,** which is meshed with a mating **spiral bevel ring gear** mounted on the differential case. Some units use a hypoid gear set that mounts the drive pinion above or below the center of

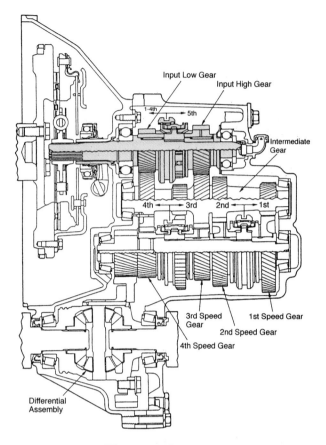

the ring gear (Figure 7-17). This gear set turns the power flow as it produces the necessary final drive reduction. The power flow from the ring gear through the differential to the CV joints is the same as described previously.

A spiral bevel gear set requires adjustments for proper ring and pinion gear positioning during assembly procedures. These adjustments are essentially the same as those for the hypoid gear set described in Chapter 11.

This transaxle lends itself to AWD or 4WD because of the lengthwise position of the mainshaft. It is a fairly simple matter for the manufacturer to install a dog clutch at the rear end of the mainshaft and extend an output shaft to connect to a driveshaft for the rear wheels. Transverse-mounted transaxles require a 90° gear set in order to drive a shaft for the rear wheels.

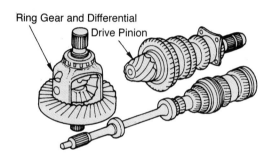

FIGURE 7-17   The gear sets from the transaxle illustrated in Figure 7-16 are shown here; the transmission section gear set and differential are very similar to those of other transaxles. (Courtesy of Subaru of America, Inc.)

FIGURE 7-15   This transaxle uses four major shafts; note how the uppermost synchronizer assembly can drive the intermediate gear set through either third or fourth gear. (Courtesy of Hyundai Motor America)

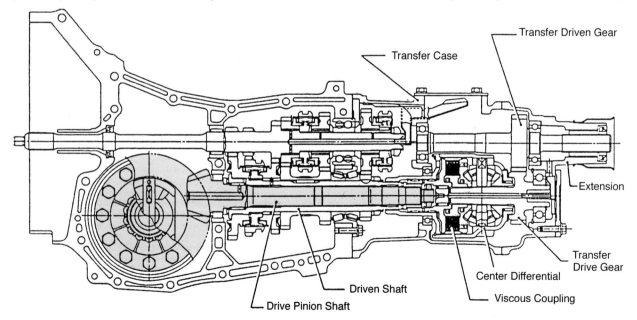

FIGURE 7-16   This FWD transaxle is used with an engine that is mounted lengthwise in the car. Note how the final drive is through a hypoid ring and pinion gear set. Also note the center differential and extension to drive the rear wheels of an all-wheel-drive vehicle. (Courtesy of Subaru of America, Inc.)

7.7 DUAL-CLUTCH TRANSMISSION

A dual-clutch transmission is essentially two transmissions built into one case. Each portion is driven by one of the clutches, and these clutches are applied, one at a time, to transfer power into the gear sets. The shifts can occur vary rapidly, being controlled by how fast each clutch can be applied. This transmission is presently available in some models of the Audi TT and Volkswagen Golf and is called a *direct shift gearbox (DSG)*.

The gear arrangement shown in Figure 7-18 illustrates how the 1–3 and 5 synchronizer assemblies are driven by clutch #1. The 2–4 and 6–reverse synchronizers are driven by clutch #2. Vehicle movement begins with the 1–3 synchronizer shifted to first gear and clutch #1 applied. The 2–4 synchronizer is then shifted into second gear by a hydraulic servo, and the 1–2 upshift will occur when clutch #1 is released and clutch #2 is applied. The remaining upshifts occur in the same manner, with the synchronizer shifted early and the actual shift occurring when the clutches are cycled.

The driver can control transmission using a floor-mounted shift lever or one of a pair of paddles mounted in front of the steering wheel. Clutch #1 and #2 are applied by hydraulic pressure, similar to automatic transmission clutches. As mentioned, the synchronizer sleeves are also shifted by hydraulic servos. The hydraulic flow to the clutches and servos is controlled electronically. Twelve sensors monitor operations like shift lever position, upshift and downshift paddles, engine rpm, and fluid temperatures, and the electronic control module uses information from these sensors to determine the proper clutch and shift servo operation.

7.8 SHIFT MECHANISM

The lengthwise transaxle can connect the shift linkage at the rear of the case and use internal linkage much like a RWD transmission. Transverse transaxles require external linkage to connect the shift lever to the transaxle, and this linkage is complicated by engine movement.

A transverse engine tries to rotate in a counterclockwise direction (viewed from the right) in reaction to its torque output. The engine mounts are made from rubber or are hydraulic to isolate engine vibrations. Heavy throttle acceleration will cause the top of the engine to move forward, while closed-throttle deceleration causes a light rearward motion. If the gearshift lever were secured to the vehicle body and connected to the transaxle by a solid rod, these engine motions could produce unwanted shifting in the transaxle.

Most transaxles mount the shift mechanism to the vehicle body through flexible mounts and connect to the transaxle by an **extension rod** or **stabilizer bar.** This bar maintains a constant distance between the

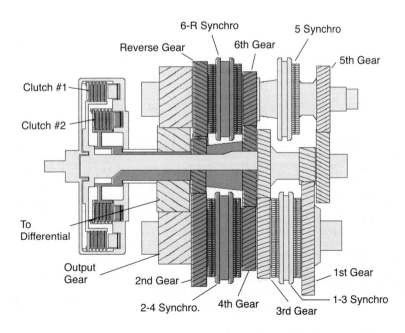

FIGURE 7-18 A dual clutch transmission has two clutches that can send power to the gear sets. The synchronizers are shifted by hydraulic servos for the selected gear, and applying one of the clutches completes the shift into that gear.

shifter and the transaxle (Figure 7-19). A single shift rod is used to connect the shift lever to the transaxle shift shaft, and both it and the extension rod connect to the transaxle through rubber isolaters to block vibrations.

Movement of the shift lever sideways, across the vehicle, will cause the shift rod and the shift shaft inside the transaxle to rotate. This motion will select the proper shift fork or rail (Figure 7-20). Lengthwise motion of the shift lever produces a lengthwise motion of the shift rod and an in-or-out motion of the shift shaft to move the selected fork or rail and its synchronizer sleeve or reverse idler gear in or out of mesh.

Some transaxles use a pair of cables to transfer the shift motion. By their nature, the cables' flexibility makes for easy alignment as well as absorption of engine vibrations and rocking motions (Figure 7-21). One of these cables, the crossover cable, transfers the selecting motion to the shift shafts, while the other transfers the shifting motions to the synchronizer.

The internal shift mechanism varies with manufacturers and can appear rather complex (Figure 7-22). It includes shift forks to move the synchronizer sleeves or reverse idler gear, detents to position the shift forks properly, and interlocks to prevent movement of more than one fork at a time.

7.9 LUBRICATION

Like transmissions, transaxles use a supply of oil in the sump at the bottom of the case that is circulated by motion of the gears. The oil is directed to critical areas by troughs and oiling funnels. The fluid level is normally checked at a fill-level plug or with a dipstick (Figure 7-23). Many transaxles use MTF or ATF for the lubricant.

Most transaxles have a common case so the transmission and final drive share the same lubricant. Some units separate the two. With these, a different oil may be used for each gear set, and there will be two fluid-level plugs.

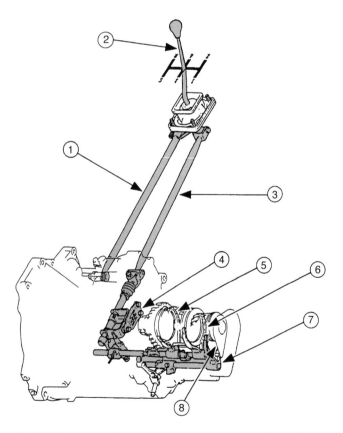

FIGURE 7-19 This shift linkage uses a stabilizer (1) to eliminate ill effects from engine motions. The shift rod (3) rotates for selection or moves fore or aft to complete shifting. (Courtesy of Ford Motor Company)

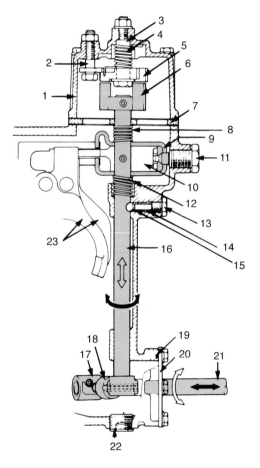

FIGURE 7-20 In this transaxle, selection and shifting motions entering the shift shaft (21) are transferred to the shift/select shaft and on to the shift forks (23). (Portions of materials contained herein have been reprinted with permission of General Motors Corporation, Service and Parts Operations, License Agreement #0310807)

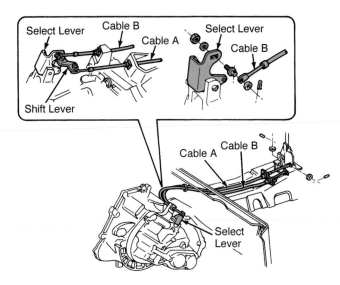

FIGURE 7-21   This transaxle uses one shift cable (A) to shift the gear and another (B) to select the gear to be shifted. (Portions of materials contained herein have been reprinted with permission of General Motors Corporation, Service and Parts Operations, License Agreement #0310807)

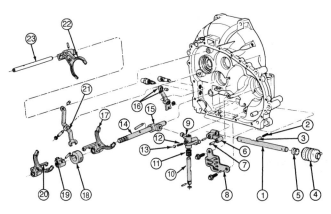

FIGURE 7-22   Exploded view of the internal shift linkage from a transaxle using a shift rod. (Courtesy of Ford Motor Company)

7.10   DESIGN FEATURES

As with transmissions, there are certain features that should improve your understanding of transaxle operation and service.

7.10.1   Case

Transaxle cases are made from cast aluminum. Most transverse units use a tunnel case design (Figure 7-24a). Some longitudinal transaxles use a split case (Figure 7-24b). Many cases use a two-part assembly with a

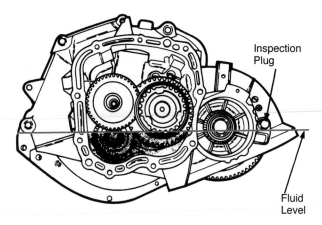

FIGURE 7-23   The fluid level of this transaxle is such that some of the gears run in the oil and throw oil onto the other gears and bearings. (Portions of materials contained herein have been reprinted with permission of General Motors Corporation, Service and Parts Operations, License Agreement #0310807)

right-hand case or cover that also forms the clutch housing and a left-hand or main case that contains the gears. Some units have a separate side case or side cover that encloses the fifth gear set and synchronizer or just the left side bearings. Some units have a bottom or differential cover that provides access to the differential assembly.

7.10.2   Case Sealants

Most modern units use formed-in-place gaskets. These are usually **room-temperature vulcanizing (RTV)** or **anaerobic sealants** (Figure 7-25). RTV is sometimes called *silicone rubber*. It is thick and very viscous as it comes out of the tube. Depending on temperature and humidity, it will set up to a rubber-like material in about 15 minutes. Anaerobic sealants are quite fluid and set up after the parts are assembled. Anaerobic sealants cure in the absence of air. RTV sealants are commonly used on covers that are less than perfectly flat, or on slightly flexible materials that do not necessarily make perfect joints. To make a good seal, an anaerobic sealant requires a wider, flatter, more perfect surface because it cures to a much thinner thickness than that of RTV. To make a good seal, both types of sealants require surfaces that are clean and oil-free when they are applied.

The proper gasket or formed-in-place gasket should always be used because in many cases the thickness of the gasket can affect transmission operation. These gasket materials have different assembled thicknesses that can determine the spacing between the parts.

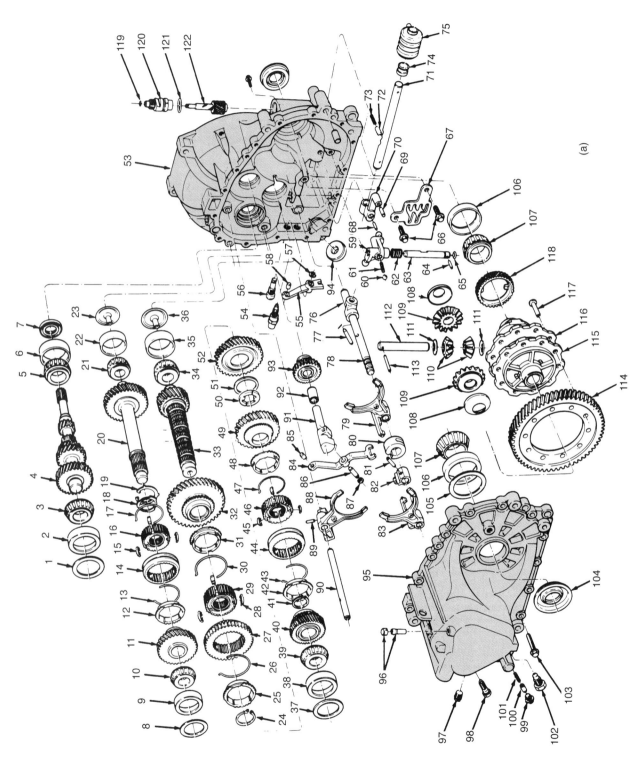

FIGURE 7-24 (a) Most transaxles locate the gear assemblies in the case (95) and the case/clutch housing (53). (b) A few designs use a split case. (a is courtesy of Ford Motor Company; b is courtesy of Subaru of America, Inc.)

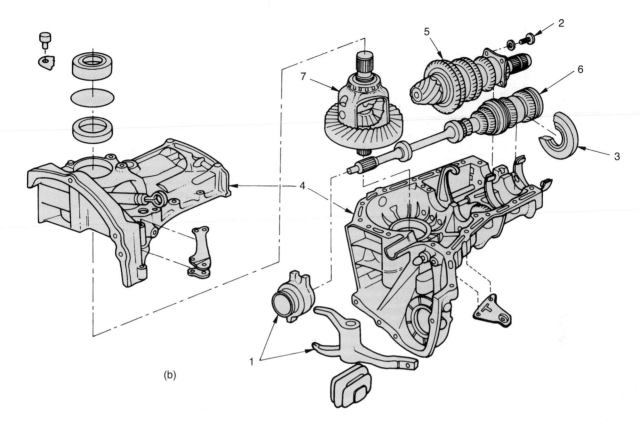

(b)

FIGURE 7-24 (Continued)

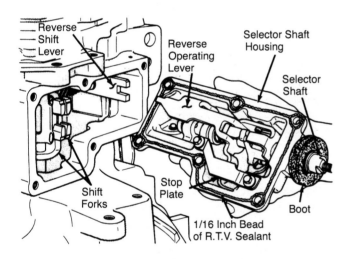

FIGURE 7-25 Most transaxles use formed-in-place gaskets between the case parts and covers, like the RTV sealant used here. (Courtesy of DaimlerChrysler Corporation)

7.10.3   Gears

Like transmissions, transaxles use helical gears for all the forward speeds and spur gears for reverse. To allow for engine length in the cramped width of the engine compartment, the speed gears, synchro-nizer assemblies, and bearings are kept as narrow and compact as practical. This design factor is much more critical with transaxles than with transmissions.

The journal area surfaces on many transaxles are made with lubrication slots to compensate for the reduced gear width; on other units, the speed gears are mounted on roller bearings. These features also improve the efficiency of the transaxle and fuel mileage.

7.10.4   Bearings

Some transaxles use a roller bearing at the engine end of the input shaft and mainshaft and a ball bearing at the other end of the shaft (Figure 7-26). The ball bearing supports one end and also positions the shaft to the case as the roller bearing supports the end with the greater side loading from the final drive. This feature makes for easy servicing, as the roller bearing can slide through the openings when the cover is removed or installed.

On transaxles that use tapered roller bearings, bearing clearance or preload is adjusted by selecting the correct size of shim to place at the bearing or

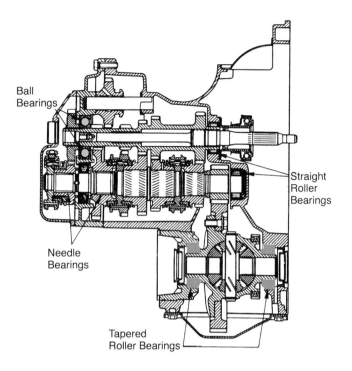

Ball
Bearings

Needle
Bearings

Straight
Roller
Bearings

Tapered
Roller Bearings

bearing cup (Figure 7-27). This selective shim is usu-ally positioned under the bearing cup in the case. Bearings are usually adjusted to a very slight clear-ance to ensure free rotation. In loaded areas where shaft movement can create a problem, such as the dif-ferential assembly, the bearings are adjusted to a slight preload.

FIGURE 7-26   This transaxle uses a roller bearing at one end of the upper shafts and locates the shafts with a ball bearing at the other end. (Portions of materials contained herein have been reprinted with permission of General Mo-tors Corporation, Service and Parts Operations, License Agreement #0310807)

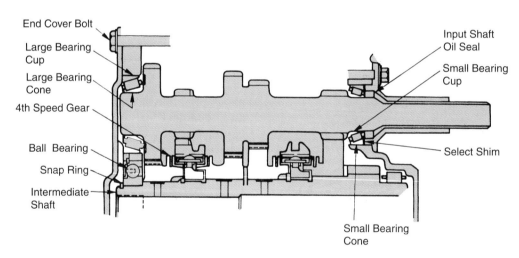

End Cover Bolt

Large Bearing
Cup

Large Bearing
Cone

4th Speed Gear

Ball Bearing

Snap Ring

Intermediate
Shaft

Input Shaft
Oil Seal

Small Bearing
Cup

Select Shim

Small Bearing
Cone

FIGURE 7-27   This transaxle uses tapered roller bearings at the input shaft. To adjust these bearings, the select shim is located at each bearing set. (Courtesy of DaimlerChrysler Corporation)

REVIEW QUESTIONS

The following questions are provided to help you study as you read the chapter.

1. A transaxle differs from a transmission in that it has _____ major shafts and it contains the _____.

2. The power flows from the mainshaft _____ gear to the final drive _____ gear.

3. The final drive gears of a typical transaxle are _____ gears.

4. Which gear range uses the largest driven gear and the smallest driving gear? _____

5. True or false: A 1:1 ratio is always used in transaxles. _____

6. The power flow for second gear in a four-speed transaxle from the input to the differential case would be from the
   a. _____ input shaft gear to the
   b. _____ gear to the
   c. _____ gear to the
   d. _____ gear.

7. If the input shaft is turning clockwise, what direction is the output shaft turning? _____

8. If the input shaft is turning clockwise, what direction is the differential case turning? _____

9. What determines engine rpm at cruising speeds? _____ _____ _____

10. A longitudinal transaxle must turn the power flow _____ _____.

11. A cable-operated shifter uses one cable to _____ the gear and the other to _____ the gear.

12. Transaxle cases are made out of cast _____.

13. When using a sealant to seal the transmission, the sealing surfaces must be _____ and _____ free.

14. _____ sealers dry in the absence of air.

15. In transaxles that use tapered roller bearings, the bearing clearance or preload is adjusted by selecting the correct size of _____.

CHAPTER QUIZ

The following questions will help you check the facts you have learned. Select the answer that completes each statement correctly.

1. Most four-speed transaxles have _____ gears on the input shaft.
   a. three   c. five
   b. four   d. six

2. Two students are discussing four-speed transaxles. Student A says they have three shift forks. Student B says they probably have two synchronizer assemblies. Who is correct?
   a. Student A   c. Both A and B
   b. Student B   d. Neither A nor B

3. When shifting into reverse, the reverse idler gear is moved into mesh with the A. reverse gear on the input shaft; B. 1–2 synchronizer sleeve gear. Which is correct?
   a. A only   c. Both A and B
   b. B only   d. Neither A nor B

4. The correct fluid level for a transaxle is at the A. bottom of the filler hole in the case; B. indicated area of the dipstick. Which is correct?
   a. A only   c. Both A and B
   b. B only   d. Neither A nor B

5. The ring gear on the differential is driven by a pinion gear on the A. mainshaft; B. countershaft. Which is correct?
   a. A only   c. Both A and B
   b. B only   d. Neither A nor B

6. The inboard CV joints on the driveshaft are splined to the A. differential pinion gears; B. differential case. Which is correct?
   a. A only   c. Both A and B
   b. B only   d. Neither A nor B

7. Two students are discussing four-speed transaxles. Student A says the differential pinion gears are turning on the differential pinion shaft when the car is going straight down the road. Student B says the axle gears are rotating at the same speed as the differential case. Who is correct?
   a. Student A   c. Both A and B
   b. Student B   d. Neither A nor B

8. On a five-speed transaxle, the fifth-gear synchronizer is mounted on
   a. the input shaft.   c. a separate fifth-gear shaft.
   b. the mainshaft.   d. any of these.

9. For lubricant, most transaxles use A. ATF; B. gear oil. Which is correct?
   a. A only   c. Either A or B
   b. B only   d. Neither A nor B

10. In a transaxle, the synchronizer assemblies are mounted on the A. input shaft; B. mainshaft. Which is correct?
   a. A only   c. Both A and B
   b. B only   d. Neither A nor B

11. Two students are discussing a four-speed transaxle with a 3.4:1 first-gear ratio. Student A says the mainshaft gear has 3.4 times as many teeth as the input shaft gear. Student B says the input shaft gear is about one-third the size as the mainshaft gear. Who is correct?
   a. Student A   c. Both A and B
   b. Student B   d. Neither A nor B

12. When a transaxle is shifted into third gear, a(n) A. shift fork slides the 3–4 synchronizer sleeve into mesh with third gear; B. interlock moves to lock the 1–2 shift fork stationary. Which is correct?
   a. A only   c. Both A and B
   b. B only   d. Neither A nor B

13. The final drive ring and pinion gears are
    a. hypoid gears.
    c. spiral bevel gears.
    b. helical gears.
    d. Both b and c.

14. When a transaxle shift shaft is A. rotated—a fork slides a sleeve or gear into mesh; B. slid in or out—a particular shift fork is selected. Which is correct?
    a. A only
    c. Both A and B
    b. B only
    d. Neither A nor B

15. Shift motions are transferred from the shifter assembly to the transaxle by A. either two or three shift rods; B. a pair of cables. Which is correct?
    a. A only
    c. Both A and B
    b. B only
    d. Neither A nor B

16. First gear on the clutch shaft has 11 teeth, and the first speed gear on the mainshaft has 39 teeth. What is the ratio between these two?

17. Using the gear ratio from Question 16, if the engine is running at 2000 rpm, how fast will the mainshaft be turning?

18. If the mainshaft final drive pinion has 19 teeth and the ring gear on the differential has 71 teeth, what is the final drive ratio?

19. Using the gear ratio from Question 18, if the manishaft is turning 1000 rpm, how fast will the differential be turning?

20. If we combine the gear ratios from Questions 16 and 18 in the same transaxle, what is the overall ratio for first gear?

21. Using the gear ratio from Question 20, if the engine is running at 2000 rpm, how fast will the wheels be turning?

Chapter 8

TRANSAXLE/ TRANSMISSION SERVICE

LEARNING OBJECTIVES

After completing this chapter, you should be able to:

1. Perform the maintenance operations needed to keep a transaxle or transmission operating properly.
2. Diagnose the cause of common transaxle/transmission problems.
3. Recommend the proper transaxle/transmission repair method.
4. Remove and replace a transaxle or transmission.
5. Overhaul a transaxle or transmission.
6. Inspect used transaxle/transmission components to determine their condition and usability.
7. Complete the ASE tasks for transmission and transaxle diagnosis and repair.

TERMS TO LEARN

blocker ring clearance	engine support
brinelling	excessive wear
burr	fretting
chip	galling
contamination	gear clash
crack	gear rattle
differential clearance	hard shift
dynamic shift test	indentation
electric arcing	jumps out of gear
end float	leak
end play	linkage adjustment
locked into gear	selective fit
lubricant checks	shift blockout
misalignment	shift effort test
neutral rollover	shim
nick	spalling
noisy transmission	static shift test
peeling	step wear
preload	uneven wear
scoring	visual check
seizing	

8.1 INTRODUCTION

Transaxle/transmission service includes preventive maintenance, problem diagnosis, and transaxle/transmission repair and overhaul. On most transmissions, the rear extension housing bushing and seal, backup light switch, and speedometer gear can be serviced with the transmission still in the vehicle. On some transmissions, the side cover with the shift mechanism can also be removed for service and inspection of the gears.

In-car service for most transaxles includes replacement of the output shaft seals, the backup light switch, and the speedometer gear. The left-side bearings and portions of the gear set can be removed, checked, and replaced with some transaxles.

These service operations vary depending on vehicle manufacturer and the transmission model. Service information should be consulted to determine what operations are required and how they should be performed.

8.2 TRANSAXLE/ TRANSMISSION IN-VEHICLE SERVICE

In-vehicle service, also called on-vehicle service, in most cases is a normal maintenance operation. It includes a periodic check of the lubricant level, linkage adjustment, mount replacement, and visual inspection for leaks and other abnormal conditions. Other repair operations are done on an as-needed basis. When a problem such as hard shifting occurs, the shift linkage is also checked and readjusted, if necessary. If possible, service and repair operations are done with the transaxle/transmission in the vehicle. Transmission removal and replacement (R&R) takes about $2\frac{1}{2}$ hours; transaxle removal and replacement may take up to 4 to $4\frac{1}{2}$ hours. This varies greatly depending on the vehicle and the experience of the technician, but in any case, transmission/transaxle removal and replacement costs time and money.

8.2.1 Lubricant Check

Often, the **lubricant check** is a neglected operation in our modern, fast-paced world. It is recommended to check the lubricant level at each engine oil change and is normally performed together with the other routine fluid checks. With the correct fluid level, most transaxle/ transmissions can operate for the life of the vehicle, but the gears and bearings can cook in a few minutes if operated while low on lubricant. A transmission usually requires that the vehicle be raised to gain access to the filler/level plug. While checking fluid level, you should also note the condition of the fluid.

◀ SERVICE TIP ▶

Manual transmission fluids should remain in like-new color and smell. Dirty fluid should be changed. Fluid with silver or gold metallic flakes indicates severe wear inside the transaxle/transmission.

To check the fluid level in a transmission/ transaxle:

1. Park the vehicle on a level surface. Raise and securely support a transmission-equipped vehicle on a hoist or jack stands.

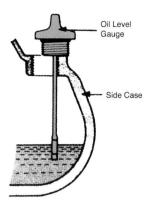

FIGURE 8-1   Some transaxles and transmissions use a dipstick to check the oil level. (Portions of materials contained herein have been reprinted with permission of General Motors Corporation, Service and Parts Operations, License Agreement #0310807)

◀ SERVICE CAUTION ▶

When working under a vehicle that is raised, make sure that it is supported securely in the proper manner.

2. If equipped with a dipstick, remove the dipstick, wipe it clean, reinsert it making sure it goes completely into the opening, remove it again, and read both sides (Figure 8-1).

◀ SERVICE TIP ▶

If there is a difference in the readings, believe the lower one. The fluid level should be between the "full" and "low" marks.

If equipped with a level plug, remove the plug, being prepared for a fluid spill due to a possible high fluid level. The fluid level should be even with the bottom of the opening (Figure 8-2a).

◀ SERVICE TIP ▶

If you cannot see any fluid, carefully insert a finger straight into the opening, and then bend it downward to serve as a level indicator (Figure 8-2a). Remove your finger, and check the fluid level on it.

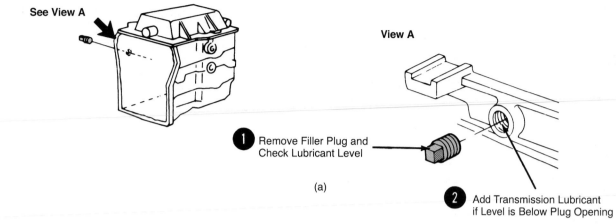

See View A

View A

1 Remove Filler Plug and
Check Lubricant Level

(a)

2 Add Transmission Lubricant
if Level is Below Plug Opening

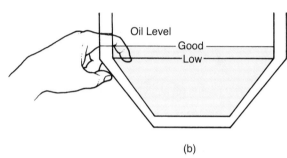

Oil Level
——— Good ———
——Low——

(b)

FIGURE 8-2   (a) With most transmissions, the oil level should be even with the bottom of the filler plug opening in the side of the case. (b) To judge the fluid level, insert your finger into the opening. (a is courtesy of Ford Motor Company)

3. If the fluid level is low, add the proper fluid to bring it to the correct level. Also, check for leaks or the reason for the low fluid level. If the level is high, drain out the excess fluid.

8.2.1.1 Lubricant Change. Some manufacturers recommend changing the lubricant after the first 5,000 miles (8,000 km) and then every 30,000 miles (48,000 km) after that. This removes any metal contaminants that can increase wear and helps ensure good lubrication. Draining the lubricant when it is hot, after driving the vehicle, helps the fluid drain and speeds up the operation.

◀ SERVICE TIP ▶

Gear oil breaks down at temperatures over 275°F (528°C). It should be changed immediately if subjected to these temperatures.

To change transaxle/transmission fluid, you should:

1. If possible, drive the vehicle to bring the lubricant up to operating temperature.

2. Raise and securely support the vehicle on a hoist or jack stands.

3. Locate the drain plug at the bottom of the transaxle/transmission, place a drain pan under it, and remove the drain plug.

◀ SERVICE TIP ▶

Some vehicles do not have a drain plug. The lower extension housing bolts are often drilled through to the inside of the case so these bolts can be removed to drain the case.

4. Allow the lubricant to drain out completely before replacing the plug.

◀ SERVICE TIP ▶

It is recommended to wrap Teflon tape around the threads of drain plugs using tapered pipe threads to prevent leaks.

5. Inspect the old lubricants for any contamination, and dispose of it in the proper manner.

6. Check the vehicle's owner's manual or shop information system to determine the correct lubricant type and refill quantity.

7. Refill the transaxle/transmission to the correct level.

◀ SERVICE TIP ▶

Most modern transmissions do not use the 90-weight gear oil of the past. If the wrong lubricant is put into a transmission, it can soak into the non-metallic blocker ring lining that is commonly used today. Even if drained immediately and refilled with the correct fluid, noise or erratic shifts can occur. One particular transmission will have failed blocker rings in a very short time period.

◀ SERVICE TIP ▶

It is normally recommended to use the manufacturer's recommendation for the fluid type and amount. If a unit is noisy or experiences hard shifting, a fluid replacement might cure the problem. A lubrication guide showing the recommendation of a leading rebuilder of manual transmissions and transfer cases is given in Appendix B.

REAL-WORLD FIX: A 1984 Porsche Carrera (68,000 mi.) had a slight grind when shifting up or down into second gear. The transmission was overhauled using new shift sleeves, synchronizers, 1–2 and 3–4 forks and brake bands, and a few bearings as needed. This did not cure the problem. The transmission was disassembled again, and the second gear set was replaced. The rest of the transmission appeared good, but the second gearshift grind was still there.

FIX

The 80–90, GL-5 gear oil was replaced with synthetic gear oil, and the shift coupler, that appeared good, was replaced. This fixed this shift problem.

8.2.2 Transaxle Linkage Adjustment

The exact method of adjusting transaxle shift linkage varies among manufacturers. Some provide no adjust-

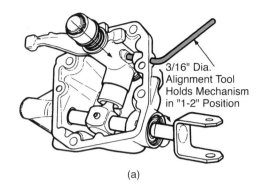

(a)

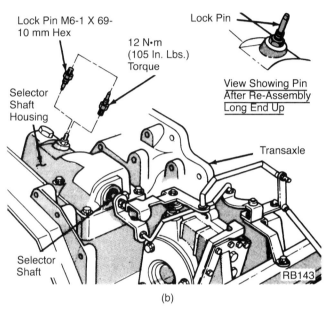

(b)

FIGURE 8-3   (a) An opening for an alignment tool to aid in the shift linkage adjustment is provided in some transaxles. (b) With some, the plug for the opening can be turned around and used for the gauge pin. (a: Portions of materials contained herein have been reprinted with permission of General Motors Corporation, Service and Parts Operations, License Agreement #0310807; b is courtesy of DaimlerChrysler Corporation)

ment; others provide adjustments with gauging methods to ensure accuracy. The description provided here is a composite of the procedure for two different domestic cars.

To adjust the shift linkage for a transaxle:

1. Shift the transaxle into neutral, and position the shift lever in the 1–2 neutral position.

2. Remove the lock pin or adjustment hole plug from the selector shaft housing (Figure 8-3a).

3. Depending on the vehicle, reverse the pin and replace it with the long end inward (Figure 8-3b) or install a gauge pin of the correct size into the open-

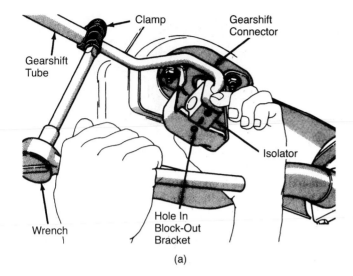

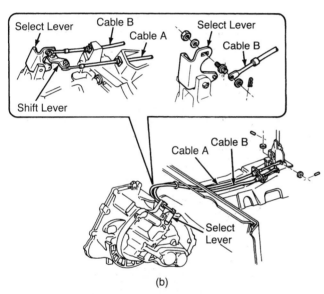

FIGURE 8-4 (a) Loosening the clamp on the gearshift tube allows adjustment of the tube length and positioning of the shift lever. (b) Some vehicles with cable linkage are adjusted as shown here. (a is courtesy of DaimlerChrysler Corporation; b: Portions of materials contained herein have been reprinted with permission of General Motors Corporation, Service and Parts Operations, License Agreement #0310807)

ing. This should lock the transaxle selector shaft in the 1–2 neutral position.

4. If the shift lever is not in the 1–2 neutral position, loosen the shift linkage clamp bolt, move the shift lever to the 1–2 neutral position, and retighten the clamp bolt to the correct torque (Figure 8-4).

5. Remove the gauge pin, reinstall the adjustment hole plug (or reverse the pin), and tighten it to the correct torque.

6. Move the gear selector to each gear position, checking for smooth operation and complete engagement into each gear. It might be necessary to start the engine and slip the clutch to align the gears to allow shifting.

8.2.3 Transmission Linkage Adjustment

Transmissions that use internal linkage usually do not have a linkage adjustment. Most transmissions with external shift mechanisms provide a gauge pin hole to lock the shift assembly levers in neutral.

◄ SERVICE TIP ►

Many technicians use the smooth end of the largest drill bit that will pass through the hole for a gauge pin.

To adjust the shift linkage on a transmission:

1. Raise and support the vehicle securely on a hoist or jack stands.

2. Place the linkage in neutral. Locate the gauge pin hole, and install a pin of the correct size into the hole (Figure 8-5). This should lock all of the shift levers into neutral.

3. Disconnect one end of a shift rod, move the shift rod or shift lever to locate the neutral detent in the transmission, and check to see if the rod is the exact length to reconnect. If the rod is the wrong length, adjust it as necessary. Reconnect the first rod, and repeat this operation on the remaining shift rods.

4. Remove the gauge pin, and move the shift lever to each gear position, checking for smooth operation and complete engagement into each gear.

REAL-WORLD FIX: A 2001 Mazda Tribute ES (20,000 mi.) had a vibration problem. It occurred while driving uphill just before the 4–3 downshift, and it lasted for a few seconds. The vibration seemed to be coming from the left front. A visual inspection of the transmission and driveshaft showed nothing wrong.

FIX

Replacement of the transmission mounts cured this problem.

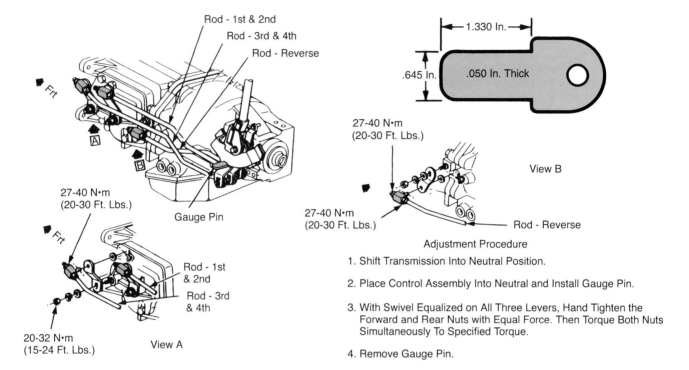

FIGURE 8-5   This transmission-mounted floor shifter has an elongated hole that can be used to pin all of the shift levers in neutral position using a shop-made pin. The procedure to adjust the linkage is shown. (Portions of materials contained herein have been reprinted with permission of General Motors Corporation, Service and Parts Operations, License Agreement #0310807)

8.2.4   Align Transaxle Mounts

The mount for a RWD transmission is aligned by the mounting bolts, so there are few problems with the mount or its replacement. A FWD transaxle must be aligned to the two front driveshafts. The alignment check is accomplished by completely compressing both inboard CV joints and measuring the distance between the joint and the transaxle (Figure 8-6). The position of the transaxle is then adjusted so that both distances are equal. Adjustment is accomplished by loosening the mounts and sliding the engine and transaxle sideways.

8.3   PROBLEM DIAGNOSIS

Most transaxle/transmission problems fall into one of these categories:

- **Leak:** fluid escapes from the transaxle/transmission
- **Hard shift:** requires an abnormally high amount of force to shift into gear
- **Shift blockout:** will not shift into one or more gears
- **Locked into gear:** will not shift out of a gear

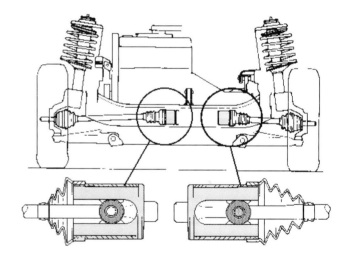

FIGURE 8-6   The enlarged views of the inner CV joints show that the engine and transaxle are misaligned; they should be moved toward the right.

- **Jumps out of gear:** will shift into neutral on its own
- **Clash/grinding during shift:** gear clash/grinding noise and vibration occur as shift is made

◀ SERVICE TIP ▶

An experienced technician completely diagnoses transmission concerns before removing the transmission. Once the transmission is out of the vehicle, it is too late to run further tests, so guessing begins as to what caused the problem.

REAL-WORLD FIX: The clutch was replaced in a 1990 Honda Civic (150,000 mi). The customer came back with a complaint of noise, so the release bearing was replaced, but the noise was still there.

FIX

Further tests showed the noise to be the input shaft bearings. Replacement of these bearings cured this noise complaint.

AUTHOR'S NOTE

A thorough diagnosis before replacing the clutch would have caught these other two problems and would have saved pulling the transaxle three times.

- **Noisy in neutral:** a grinding, growling noise while in neutral
- **Noisy in one gear:** a grinding, growling bearing noise or rough growling, buzzing gear noise in only one gear
- **Noisy in all gears:** same as above but in all gears
- **Noisy in all reduction gear ranges:** same as above, but quiet in the 1:1 gear range.

◀ SERVICE TIP ▶

A noise concern that occurs with the vehicle at idle speed in neutral can be caused by harmonic vibrations. Slowly increase engine speed to about 2,500 rpm; if the noise goes away, it is engine harmonics. The problem is not in the transmission; it could be caused by a faulty clutch disc damper, bad dual-mass flywheel, or out-of-tune engine.

Many of these conditions result from internal problems and will require transaxle/transmission removal for repair, rebuilding, or replacement. A few problems can be cured while the unit is in the vehicle (Figure 8-7).

An experienced technician will usually follow a test procedure that varies depending on the nature of the customer's concern and the technician's experience with the particular transaxle/transmission. Visual inspection for leaks or exterior damage, clutch pedal free play, engine-off shift tests, engine-running shift tests, and a road test are checks that can be made during problem diagnosis.

REAL-WORLD FIX A 1997 Mitsubishi Mirage (53,000 mi) would always grind on the 1–2 shift when it was cold. There was also difficulty shifting into first. Inspection of the internal parts showed no abnormal wear or abuse. The transmission had been rebuilt three times by the dealer and had updated synchronizers installed.

FIX

Replacement of the gear oil with 30-weight nondetergent engine oil cured this shift problem.

AUTHOR'S NOTE

This repair is not recommended by most vehicle manufacturers. A better choice would have been to use a synthetic gear oil.

◀ SERVICE TIP ▶

A **noisy transmission** usually has gear or bearing damage and probably needs repair. One rebuilder recommends draining the fluid from a noisy transmission, inspecting the drained fluid for metal particles, and if there is any doubt of its condition, refilling it with ATF and repeating the road test. If the unit is still noisy, it has internal damage. If the unit is filled with 90-weight gear oil, the heavy oil could cushion the worn parts and muffle the noise. This gives the impression that the problem is fixed, but it really only puts it off for a while. After the test drive, refill the transmission with the lubricant recommended by the manufacturer or in Appendix B.

◀ SERVICE TIP ▶

Don't forget that a bearing noise problem while in neutral with the clutch disengaged is related to clutch bearing noises. See Section 5.3.5.

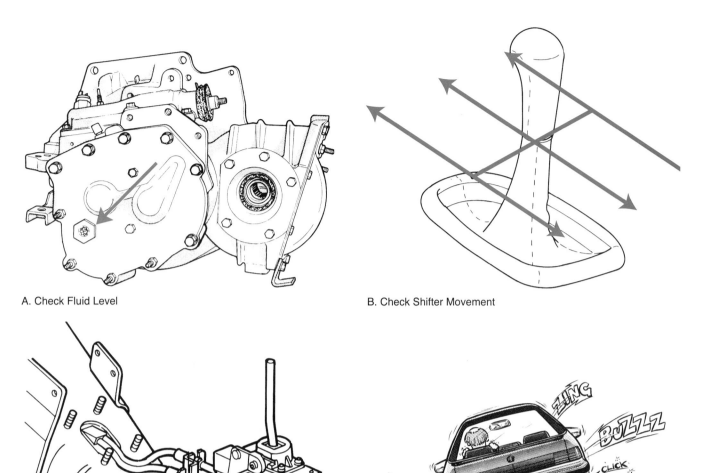

A. Check Fluid Level

B. Check Shifter Movement

C. Adjust Shifter Linkage

D. Road Test

FIGURE 8-7   When diagnosing transmission problems, begin by making sure that the lubricant is at the proper level (a); next, operate the shift levers through all of the gears with the engine off and running (b). If necessary, adjust the shift linkage (c). When making a road test, listen for unusual noises and check for proper operation (d).

◀ SERVICE TIP ▶

Don't forget that noises travel. For example, the drive shaft can transmit rear drive axle noises so they seem to be coming from the transmission. An NVH diagnostic tool, Chassis Ear, consists of a headset and six sensors that can be attached to various locations under the vehicle (See Figure 10-5). The vehicle is then driven on a road test while the technician listens to each of the six different locations. This should help locate the exact source of the noise.

Two noise conditions, **gear rattle** and **neutral rollover,** are normal in most manual transaxle/transmissions. They are the result of uneven power flow through a pair of gears. This causes the driving gear to change speed and slap the driven gear as the lash moves from the coast side to the drive side of the gear teeth. Both are metallic rapping noises. Gear rattle normally occurs as the vehicle is driven, and neutral rollover occurs with the engine running while the transaxle/transmission is in neutral with the clutch engaged. These problems fall into the noise, vibration, and harshness (NVH) category.

◀ **SERVICE TIP** ▶

Noisy operation along with fourth-gear jump-out can be caused by a misaligned clutch housing. If transmission disassembly reveals no internal problem, check clutch housing alignment as described in Section 5.4.2.4.

REAL-WORLD FIX: A 1996 GMC Sonoma pickup (37,000 mi) had a noisy transmission. The noise stopped as the clutch pedal was depressed. The gear oil was drained and inspected; there were no signs of metal. It was refilled using the correct GM fluid, and the noise was still there. The transmission was disassembled, and new bearings and seals were installed. This did not help.

FIX

The addition of an aftermarket, high-viscosity gearbox additive quieted this unit somewhat.

AUTHOR'S NOTE

At least the customer had the satisfaction of knowing the noise was caused by the transmission design.

8.3.1 Visual Check

Visual checks are made both under the hood and under the vehicle. The under-the-hood checks are for:

- Clutch master cylinder fluid level or mechanical linkage
- Broken or damaged engine motor mounts
- Transaxle/transmission and bell housing bolt tightness

The under-the-vehicle checks are for:

- Damage to the transaxle/transmission case, mounts, and support
- Worn, bent, or sloppy shift linkage
- Loose or missing transaxle/transmission or clutch housing mounting bolts
- Fluid leaks from the transaxle/transmission or clutch area

◀ **SERVICE TIP** ▶

If a leak is noted and you are trying to locate its source, remember that a fluid normally runs downward and that the wind under the vehicle will move the fluid to the rear, so the point of leakage is normally above and forward of the fluid drips.

8.3.2 Engine-Off Shift Test

The engine-off shift test, also called a **static shift test** or a **shift effort test,** measures the amount of effort it takes to move the synchronizer sleeve or gear, fork, and shift rail past the neutral detent and into mesh with the other detent engaged.

On transmissions with exterior linkage, you can disconnect the shift rod and make the shift using a torque wrench and a socket on the shift lever bolt. This enables you to measure the actual amount of torque needed to make a shift (Figure 8-8). Some manufacturers publish the torque for a normal shift.

FIGURE 8-8 An inch-pound torque wrench is being used to measure the amount of torque effort required to shift this transmission.

◀ **SERVICE TIP** ▶

> If no specifications are available, shifting a synchronizer sleeve should take about 40 to 60 in.-lb ($4\frac{1}{2}$ to 7 N-m) of torque. Over 72 in.-lb (8 N-m) of torque indicates a hard shift and internal problems.

On vehicles with internal linkage, the amount of effort is subjective and is checked by the amount of force needed to move the shift lever. You can compare the effort to shift into one gear with the effort for shifts into the gears on a similar transaxle/transmission. As the test is made, listen for any unusual noises that might occur in the transaxle/transmission or linkage.

To make an engine-off shift test:

1. Depress the clutch pedal to release the clutch.
2. Shift the transaxle/transmission into a gear to align the parts and then shift back to neutral.
3. Shift back into the same gear, carefully noting the amount of effort required.
4. Repeat this check on the remaining gears, noting any shift that requires a greater amount of effort.

REAL-WORLD FIX: A 1992 Honda Civic (65,000 mi) gearshift lever locked up and the transaxle wouldn't shift. The problem was very intermittent, occurring only once in a while. Fluid level was good, and shift lever and bushings appeared good.

FIX

Disassembly revealed badly worn synchronizer assemblies. The customer did not want to spend the money needed to rebuild the transaxle, so a used one was installed. This fixed the problem.

REAL-WORLD FIX: The 5-speed transmission in a 1989 Mustang (255,000 km) blocked 4–3 and 5–3 downshifts. There was no gear clash, and all upshifts were normal.

FIX

On inspection, a faulty third gear blocker ring was found; replacement of this blocker ring fixed this shift problem.

8.3.3 Engine-Running Shift Test

The engine-running test, also called a **dynamic shift test,** is almost a repeat of the engine-off check except that it checks for clutch drag as well as transaxle/transmission problems. Remember that a dragging clutch will cause the gears to rotate, and the synchronizer action will block shifts until equal speeds occur.

To make an engine-running shift test:

1. Check clutch pedal free play.
2. Apply the parking brake securely, and start the engine.
3. Let the engine idle in neutral, and note any unusual noises.
4. Depress the clutch, and shift into first gear. Note and compare the effort required to do this during the engine-off test; a greater effort indicates a dragging clutch. Also note any unusual noises as the shift occurs.
5. Release the parking brake and engage the clutch to cause the vehicle to move slightly while you check for unusual noises or movement.
6. Repeat this process for the remaining gears.

◀ **SERVICE TIP** ▶

> A problem of "hard shifting when cold" can often be cured by draining out the old lubricant and replacing it with synthetic gear oil.

REAL-WORLD FIX: A 1996 Ranger 4 × 4 (60,000 miles) was difficult to shift into first gear at a stop unless the shifter was first moved in the direction of second gear. All of the other shifts and the rest of the transmission operation were good. The fluid was clean.

FIX

The transmission was disassembled, and the blocker rings and shift forks that had wear grooves 1/8″ deep were replaced. The worn clutch was also replaced while the transmission was out, but the transmission repairs probably were what fixed this problem.

8.3.4 Road Test

If the customer's problem has not been located by the previous checks, the vehicle should be driven on the road. At this time, the technician checks the quality of the upshifts and downshifts between gears, listens for any unusual noises in each gear, and feels for any unusual movements or vibrations as he or she accelerates or decelerates in each gear. In cases where there is doubt about proper operation, the operation can be compared with that of a similar vehicle.

◄ **SERVICE TIP** ►

While on a road test it is possible to isolate a mainshaft bearing noise from the other noises by depressing the clutch and shifting to neutral and coasting. At this time, the mainshaft will be the only thing turning in a transmission; in a transaxle, the differential, final drive gear, and output shaft will be turning.

One vehicle manufacturer recommends a test-drive procedure similar to the following:

1. Check clutch pedal free play.
2. Check transmission oil level.
3. Warm up transmission before testing (drive aluminum case units for about 20 minutes).
4. With vehicle stationary, engine idling, clutch depressed, and in neutral:
   a. Release clutch and listen for noise, depress pedal; repeat 10 times, noting any noises.
   b. Release clutch, depress pedal, wait 3 seconds, and shift into reverse, then first, and then back to reverse. Repeat, but wait 20 seconds. Note any differences in noise or shifting ability.
   c. Note pedal movement, position point at which clutch engages, and any noises.
   d. Shift into reverse, release pedal, and while backing up carefully increase engine speed to 2,500 rpm, and note any noises.
5. Drive vehicle on road with little traffic:
   a. Start in first, accelerate, and upshift at 4,000 rpm (1–2, 2–3, and 3–4). Upshift 3–4 and 4–5 as possible depending on speed limits and driving conditions. Note shifts quality and any noises.

   b. Decelerate using engine braking, downshifting in each gear at about 3,000 rpm. Note shifts quality and any noises.
   c. Drive in fourth gear at speed limit or 60 mph, accelerate (if speed limit allows), and shift to fifth gear.
   d. Drive in fifth gear for a moment, and downshift to fourth gear. Repeat six times and note any problems.

◄ **SERVICE TIP** ►

During a shift, the synchronizer ring must cut through the lubricant to contact the speed gear cone. Hard shifts can result from a lubricant that is too thick or from worn synchronizer rings (the threadlike grooves are no longer sharp).

◄ **SERVICE TIP** ►

Downshifts are normally harder to execute than upshifts. During an upshift, the synchronizer must slow down the gear being shifted into, which the gear is doing naturally as soon as the clutch is depressed. During a downshift, the synchronizer must speed up those gears, and this normally requires a little more time and effort.

8.3.5 Transaxle/Transmission Diagnosis Charts

A technician may consult a chart like the one in Figure 8-9 to help locate the possible cause of a transaxle/transmission concern. It should be noted that some of the problems can be the cause of a faulty clutch. Others can be corrected by adjusting the shift linkage or tightening mounting bolts. Some problems can be corrected with the transaxle/transmission in the car. Internal transaxle/transmission problems, however, usually require removal of the unit.

Problem	Possible Cause
Leak	• Excessive lubricant • Wrong lubricant • Slight mist from trans. vent • Faulty seal • Faulty gasket
Hard shift	• Dragging clutch • Binding shift linkage • Faulty synchronizer assembly • Damaged shift rail, detent, or interlock • Improper lubricant
Shift blockout	• Damaged shift linkage • Interference with shift linkage or lever • Damaged synchronizer • Restricted travel of shift fork
Locked into gear	• Damaged shift linkage • Damaged synchronizer • Worn or damaged internal shift linkage
Jumps out of gear	• Improper linkage adjustment • Worn or damaged shift linkage • Interference with shift linkage movement • Broken or loose engine/trans. mounts • Worn pilot or main drive gear bearing • Worn shift fork • Worn synchronizer
Clash during shift	• Clutch drag • Worn or damaged shift fork • Worn synchronizer parts
Noisy in neutral	• Low lubricant level • Worn or damaged input shaft bearings • Worn countershaft bearings
Noisy in one gear	• Damaged teeth on that particular gear set
Noisy in all gears	• Low lubricant level • Contact between trans. and car body or exhaust • Loose mounting bolts • Worn or damaged gear teeth

FIGURE 8-9 Nine most common transaxle/transmission problems and their possible causes.

8.4 TRANSAXLE/TRANSMISSION REMOVAL

Removal and replacement of a transaxle/transmission is required to repair internal transaxle/transmission problems or gain access to the clutch assembly. The exact operation varies somewhat between vehicle models, so it is highly recommended that a service manual covering the particular vehicle model be used when you remove and replace a transaxle/transmission. It should be noted that the transaxle/transmission in some vehicles can only be removed along with the engine. With most 4WDs, the transfer case is removed prior to or along with the transmission.

Removal and replacement of the driveshaft(s) are described in Chapter 10. Some transaxles/ transmissions are quite heavy and awkward to handle, so it is recommended that a transmission jack be used to support and move the unit in and out of the vehicle.

◀ **PROBLEM SOLVING** ▶

Imagine that you are working in a general automotive repair shop and these problems are brought to you.

Case 1

The customer's complaint is a gear clash as she shifts into first or reverse. During your road test, you confirm the problem and find the rest of the transmission's operation to be normal. What do you need to do to fix this problem?

Case 2

The transaxle is very noisy; running in neutral makes a definite worn-bearing noise. When you check the fluid level, you can't find any fluid on the dipstick. What is probably wrong in this unit?

◀ **SERVICE TIP** ▶

Another simple aid that helps greatly during removal and installation is the use of guide pins (Figure 8-10). These are common grade-2 bolts with the heads cut off. The bolts must be the same size and thread as the transaxle/transmission mounting bolts, about 2 to 4 in. (50 to 100 mm) long. When they replace one or two of the mounting bolts, they support the transaxle/transmission so it can be slid straight out or into place with the clutch and bell housing or engine block. In most cases, the transaxle/transmission must be slid straight away from the engine 1 or 2 in. (25 to 50 mm) as the clutch shaft leaves or enters the clutch disc. In very tight installations, 1 to 2 in. is the maximum length that the guide pins can be.

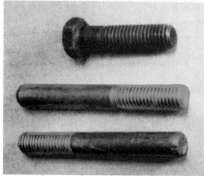

FIGURE 8-10   A pair of guide pins has been installed in place of two mounting bolts to support the transmission as it is slid out of or into the clutch and bell housing. The pins, about 3 in. long, were made by cutting the heads off of grade 2 bolts of the same size as the transmission mounting bolts.

8.4.1   Transaxle Removal and Replacement

To remove a transaxle:

1. From under the hood, disconnect the negative (−) battery cable.
2. Disconnect the following accessible parts: shift cables or rods, clutch linkage, backup light switch or wires, speedometer cable or speed sensor connections, and any hose or cable brackets with connections to the body or engine.

◀ **SERVICE TIP** ▶

Some switches are operated through a pin or a steel ball. After the removal of a switch, it is a good practice to probe into the hole using a small magnet to ensure that no small parts have been overlooked.

◀ **SERVICE TIP** ▶

In vehicles with the starter mounted to the clutch housing, it is necessary to disconnect and remove the starter.

◀ **SERVICE CAUTION** ▶

With the linkage disconnected, the clutch pedal can lower quite violently. Some manufacturers recommend placing a block of wood under the clutch pedal to keep it up.

3. Many vehicles require the installation of an **engine support** to keep the engine in the proper location as the transaxle and its mounts are removed (Figure 8-11).
4. Remove the upper clutch housing bolts and install a guide pin into one or two of the bolt holes.
5. Raise and securely support the vehicle on a hoist or on jack stands.
6. If a drain opening is provided, drain the transaxle oil, noting the condition and the amount that comes out.
7. Remove the left driveshaft as described in Section 10.4.1. Some vehicles require removal of the right driveshaft as well.
8. If necessary, remove portions of the body, suspension system, subframe, splash shield, and so on, or portions of the transaxle itself. Remove any items listed in step 2 that connect the transaxle to the body or engine.

FIGURE 8-11   With most FWD vehicles, it is necessary to install a fixture to support the engine before removing the transaxle. (Courtesy of DaimlerChrysler Corporation)

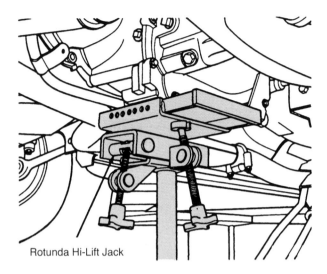

Rotunda Hi-Lift Jack

FIGURE 8-12 A transmission jack has been positioned to support this transaxle before removing the mounts and supports. (Courtesy of Ford Motor Company)

9. Position a transmission jack to support the transaxle, remove any transaxle mounts or supports, remove the remaining clutch housing bolts, and install the second guide pin (if not already installed). Slide the transaxle away from the engine to clear the clutch, and lower it out of the vehicle (Figure 8-12).

◄ **SERVICE TIP** ►

Do not depress the clutch pedal while the transaxle is removed.

Replacement of the transaxle usually follows the procedure just described, only in reverse. The following points should be observed during transaxle installation:

- Use guide pins and/or a transmission jack to support the unit to eliminate the possibility of hanging the transaxle on the clutch shaft.
- Be sure that wires, cables, and hoses are positioned correctly as the transaxle is slid into place.
- Install the mounts, mounting bolts, and supports before removing the transmission jack.
- Tighten all nuts and bolts to the correct torque.
- If the front suspension mounting points were disturbed, perform a wheel alignment to ensure proper vehicle operation.
- Fill the transaxle to the correct level with the correct lubricant before starting the engine.
- If necessary, check and adjust clutch pedal free travel and the shift linkage.

8.4.2   Transmission Removal and Replacement

To remove a transmission:

1. From under the hood, disconnect the negative (−) battery cable.
2. Raise and securely support the vehicle.
3. If a drain plug is provided, drain the fluid, noting the amount and condition of liquid that comes out. Remove the driveshaft as described in Section 10.4.2. If the fluid is not drained, install a stop-off tool into the rear seal. This can be a commercial tool, an old driveshaft spline, or a plastic bag secured by a rubber band (Figure 8-13).
4. Remove the backup light wires, speedometer cable or speed sensor connections, any hose or cable brackets attached to the vehicle, and the shift linkage. As with transaxles, check under any switches for removable operating pins or balls. On transmissions with internal linkage, it is usually necessary to remove the boot and shift lever from inside the vehicle before it is lifted (Figure 8-14). On some vehicles it is necessary to remove part of the exhaust system.
5. Position a transmission jack to support the transmission. Remove the transmission support bolts, raise the transmission slightly, and remove the transmission support. In some cases, it may also be necessary to remove the cross-member (Figure 8-15).
6. Remove the transmission-to-clutch housing or transmission-to-engine bolts, and install a pair of guide pins. On many vehicles you can lower the transmission enough to gain access to the upper mounting bolts.
7. Move the transmission and jack to the rear to clear the clutch shaft, and lower the unit out of the vehicle.

◄ **SERVICE TIP** ►

Do not depress the clutch pedal while the transmission is removed.

Transmission replacement usually follows the procedure just described, only in reverse. In addition, the installation points in Section 8.4.1 should be observed.

◄ **SERVICE TIP** ►

A film of high-temperature grease should be applied to the transmission output shaft splines before installing the driveshaft.

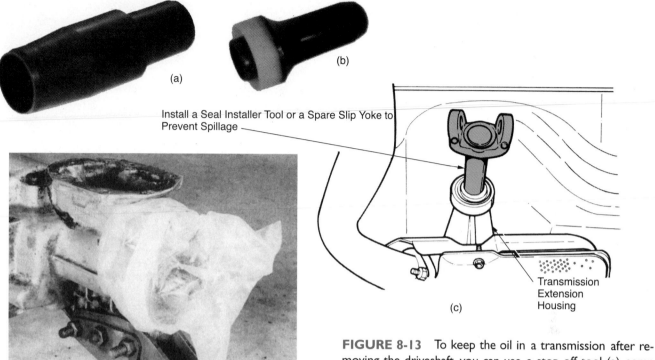

FIGURE 8-13 To keep the oil in a transmission after removing the driveshaft, you can use a stop-off tool (a), some types of seal installers (b), a spare slip yoke (c), or a plastic bag and rubber band (d). (a is courtesy of K-D Tools; b is courtesy of Kent-Moore; c is courtesy of Ford Motor Company)

◄ **SERVICE TIP** ►

The rear seal of some transmissions includes a dust boot that covers the driveshaft end and seal lip. Improper driveshaft installation can roll the seal lip inward and cause a future leak. When installing the driveshaft on these units, be sure to lubricate the driveshaft yoke and rotate the driveshaft as it slides under the seal lip.

◄ **SERVICE TIP** ►

An experienced technician realizes that when he or she rebuilds a transaxle/transmission, the average motorist will judge the repair by how the unit shifts and whether there are leaks or noise present. If the transaxle/transmission operates quietly and smoothly, without oil leaks and noise, it will be considered a good-quality rebuild. If not, there will probably be a comeback for the job to be done over at the technician's and shop's expense. It is a wise practice to note any noise or shifting problems during the diagnosis stages and make sure that these are cured in the rebuild.

8.5 TRANSAXLE/ TRANSMISSION OVERHAUL

The overhaul operations for most transaxles/transmissions are very similar. These include disassembly of the unit, gear inspection, bearing inspection, reconditioning of the subassemblies, and checking gear end float and adjusting bearing clearances as the unit is reassembled. The exact procedure for doing each of these will vary depending on the make and model. It is highly recommended that the service manual procedure be followed along with the clearances and torque specifications.

At one time, manual transmissions were rebuilt in the general automotive repair shop. The evolution of the transmission into a more complex unit and the development of the transaxle with its rather exacting repair procedures, along with the increasing amount of special tooling for both, has resulted in the emergence of shops that specialize in manual transaxle/ transmission repair.

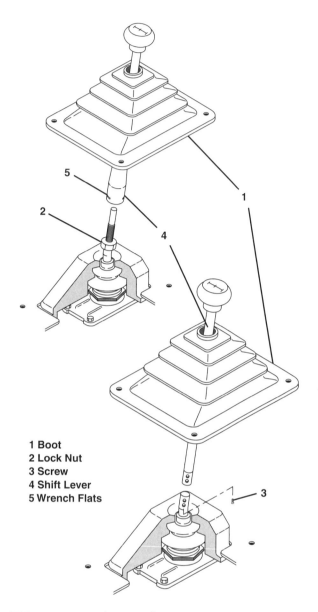

1 Boot
2 Lock Nut
3 Screw
4 Shift Lever
5 Wrench Flats

FIGURE 8-14   It is usually necessary to remove the shift lever (floor mounted) before removing the transmission. (Courtesy of Transmission Technologies Corporation, TTC)

◄ SERVICE TIP ►

The overhaul begins with the draining and inspection of the oil. Little or no oil, or oil that is burned or contaminated with metal particles, usually indicates an expensive rebuild because of the need to replace many damaged parts.

As the transaxle/transmission is disassembled, the experienced technician will look for the possible causes of the problem. For example, if a transaxle/transmission jumps out of fifth gear, the technician would check for a

FIGURE 8-15   A transmission jack has been positioned under this transmission before removing the mount/insulator and transmission support.

worn internal shift linkage, fork, or synchronizer sleeve; burred fifth-gear clutching teeth; or excessive fifth-gear end float. Experienced technicians know what the problem is and its probable cause before the transmission is removed from the vehicle. The following are normally checked during disassembly:

- The internal shift linkages for rough operation and wear
- Clearance between all shift forks and sleeves
- All shafts for excessive end play and rough operation
- All floating gears for excess end float or rough rotation
- All blocker rings for free motion and excessive or insufficient clearance
- All gears for chips or breakage

A large amount of force is required to remove and replace some parts. A press and special puller may be required. Many bearings, synchronizer assemblies, and some countershafts will slide out of and into the proper location using only light pressure. For example, when a shift rail will not slide out, it is usually held by a detent or interlock. Shafts, gears, shift rails, and most other parts must never be struck with a steel hammer. If struck with a steel hammer, a shaft will mushroom and a bearing or gear could chip. If it is necessary to hit these parts, you should use a "soft" hammer (plastic, brass, or lead) or a soft punch made from either brass or aluminum.

Worn parts are normally replaced with new ones, and the source for most new power train parts is the dealership for that vehicle make. There are also several aftermarket gear companies that specialize in replacement parts. When purchasing parts, sometimes upgraded parts, stronger than the original, are available to solve problems with particular units.

An experienced technician realizes that he or she is the final quality control check for all parts, new or used, and checks each new and used part thoroughly during and after assembly for proper operation.

8.5.1 Transaxle Disassembly

The procedure described in this text is very general and intended to provide you with an idea of what service operations are involved and how to perform them. Refer to a service manual for the exact procedure (Figure 8-16).

To disassemble a transaxle:

1. Clean all of the oil, dirt, and grease from the outside of the unit.

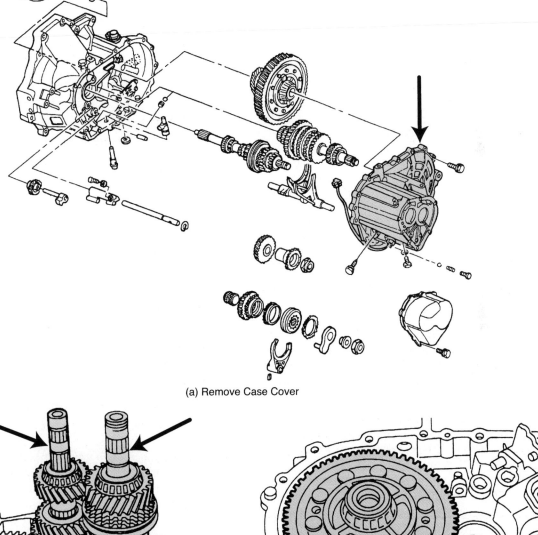

(a) Remove Case Cover

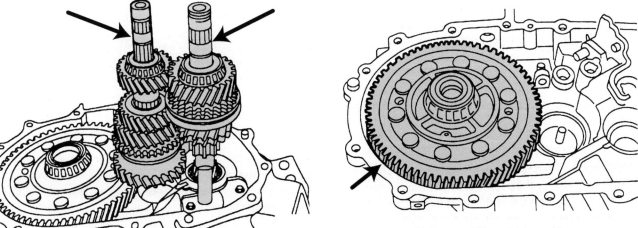

(b) Remove Input and Output Shaft Assemblies

(c) Remove Differential Assembly

FIGURE 8-16   The procedure to disassemble most transaxles is to remove the case cover (a), remove the transmission shafts (b), remove the differential assembly (c), and then disassemble the input (d) and output (e) shafts and differential (f).

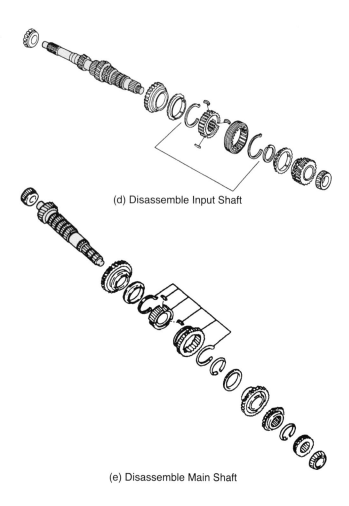

(d) Disassemble Input Shaft

(e) Disassemble Main Shaft

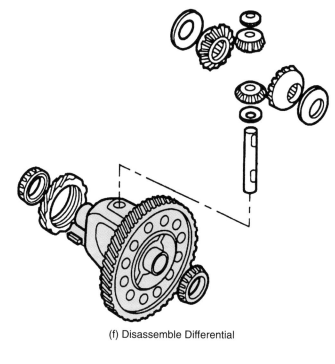

(f) Disassemble Differential

FIGURE 8-16   (Continued)

2. Remove the drain plug, and check the quantity and condition of the fluid. Also, remove the fill plug to ensure that it is not seized or has damaged threads.

3. On some transaxles, begin by removing the differential bearing retainer, extension housing, and differential (Figure 8-17). Disassembly of another transaxle may begin with the removal of the left-side case cover, fifth-gear synchronizer assembly, and the two fifth gears (Figure 8-18). Disassembly of a third transaxle may begin with the removal of the backup light switch, reverse idler shaft retaining bolt, detent plunger retaining screw, interlock sleeve retaining pin, and fill plug (Figure 8-19). During this step, you should remove all of the exterior parts that block or hinder removal of the case.

4. Remove the case-to-clutch housing or end-cover-to-case attachment bolts. As these bolts are removed, note their length so that they can be replaced in the proper hole. It will usually be necessary to tap the case with a plastic hammer or pry upward using a screwdriver to break the seal between the two parts (Figure 8-20). If you use a prying tool, try not to scratch the sealing surfaces.

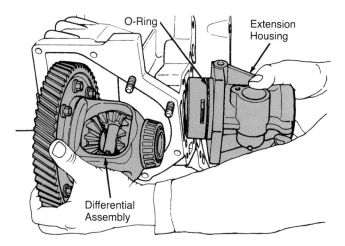

FIGURE 8-17   Disassembly of this Chrysler transaxle begins with the removal of the differential cover, extension housing, and differential assembly. (Courtesy of Daimler-Chrysler Corporation)

5. After removing the cover, remove portions of the shift mechanism, the reverse idler gear, and its shaft, if necessary (Figure 8-21).

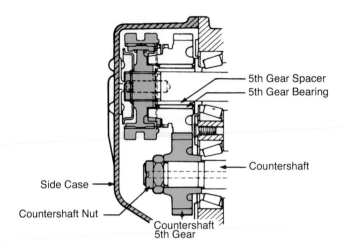

FIGURE 8-18 Disassembly of this General Motors transaxle begins with the removal of the side case, fifth-gear synchronizer assembly, and the countershaft fifth gear. (Portions of materials contained herein have been reprinted with permission of General Motors Corporation, Service and Parts Operations, License Agreement #0310807)

◄ SERVICE TIP ►

A good rule to follow during bolt replacement is that each bolt should thread in by hand (no tools) a distance that is equal to or greater than the diameter of the bolt.

6. Remove the input and mainshaft assemblies together, holding them so that the gears stay in mesh until the shafts leave their bearings (Figure 8-22).

7. If not done in step 1, remove the ring gear and differential assembly (Figure 8-23). The side gears of some differentials have rounded thrust faces so that they will rotate easily to the windows of the differential case and fall out (Figure 8-24). These gears are normally

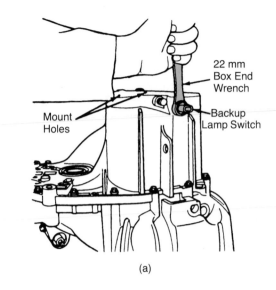

(a)

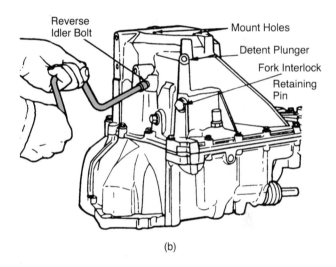

(b)

FIGURE 8-19 Disassembly of this Ford transaxle begins with the removal of the backup lamp switch (a), reverse idler bolt, detent plunger, fork interlock retainer pin, and filler plug (b). (Courtesy of Ford Motor Company)

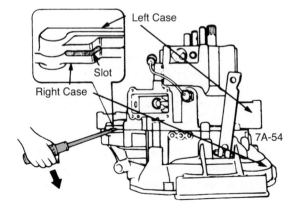

FIGURE 8-20 Most transaxles use formed-in-place gaskets that tend to glue the case and covers together. This unit has a slot (see inset) to allow prying without damaging the gasket surfaces. Once broken loose, one case can be lifted off the other. (Portions of materials contained herein have been reprinted with permission of General Motors Corporation, Service and Parts Operations, License Agreement #0310807)

held in place by a special tool or wooden or plastic plug inserted into them as the driveshafts are removed.

◄ SERVICE TIP ►

At this time, the unit should be disassembled, and the subassembly reconditioning steps can be performed. Most technicians will check or recondition each portion to ensure that with the exception of minor wear on the gears, the unit will perform like new when it is put back into operation.

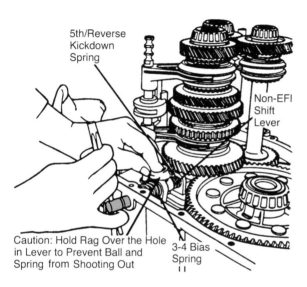

FIGURE 8-21   With some transaxles, the internal shift linkage is removed after the case cover has been removed. (Courtesy of Ford Motor Company)

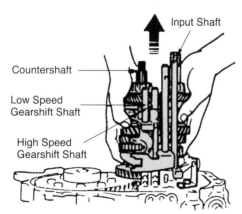

FIGURE 8-22   With the shift linkage disconnected, both shafts with gear assemblies can be removed. (Portions of materials contained herein have been reprinted with permission of General Motors Corporation, Service and Parts Operations, License Agreement #0310807)

8.5.2   Transmission Disassembly

As with a transaxle, the procedure given here is general and intended to familiarize you with the service procedures and how they are performed (Figure 8-25). The exact procedure for disassembling a specific transmission is printed in various service manuals (Figure 8-26). The order of the disassembly steps will be different from that given here for many transmissions.

Synchronizer assemblies are normally left assembled until it is time to inspect the parts. Most sleeves and hubs are factory-matched sets and should be kept in their same position relative to each other. An experienced technician will use a permanent marker or small grinder to place index marks on both the sleeve and hub to speed up

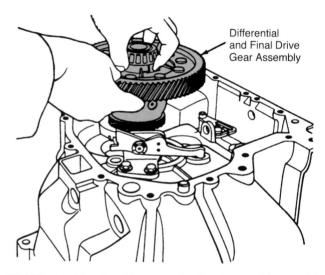

FIGURE 8-23   On this transaxle, the differential assembly is removed after the gear assemblies have been removed. (Courtesy of Ford Motor Company)

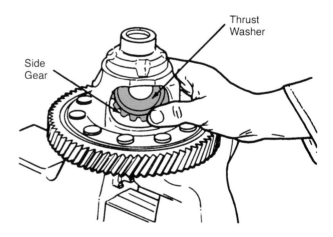

FIGURE 8-24   The side gears in some differentials have a rounded thrust surface and can roll out of position once the CV joints have been removed. (Courtesy of Ford Motor Company)

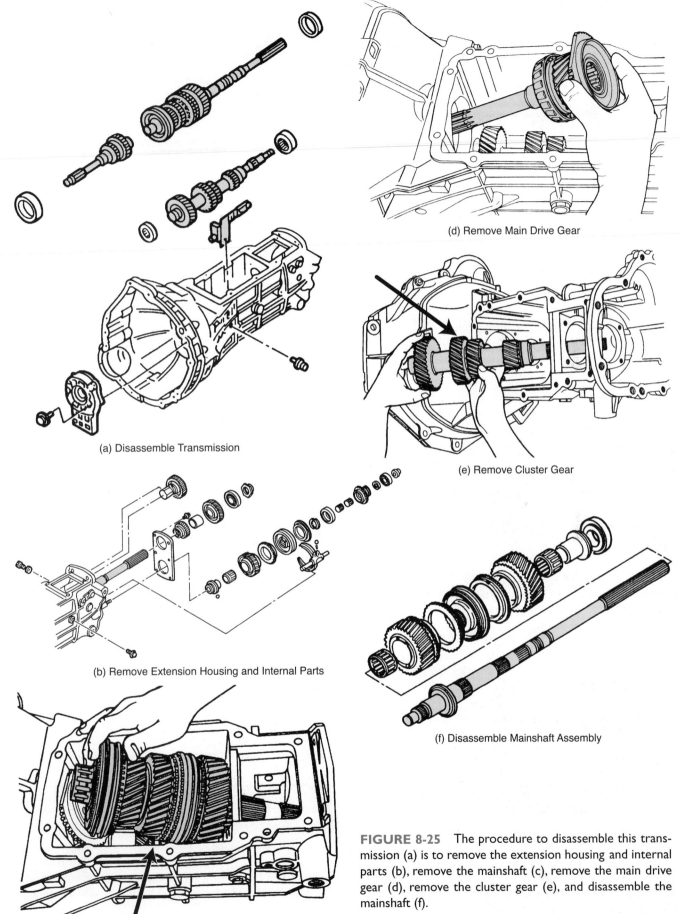

(a) Disassemble Transmission

(b) Remove Extension Housing and Internal Parts

(c) Remove Mainshaft Assembly

(d) Remove Main Drive Gear

(e) Remove Cluster Gear

(f) Disassemble Mainshaft Assembly

FIGURE 8-25 The procedure to disassemble this transmission (a) is to remove the extension housing and internal parts (b), remove the mainshaft (c), remove the main drive gear (d), remove the cluster gear (e), and disassemble the mainshaft (f).

197

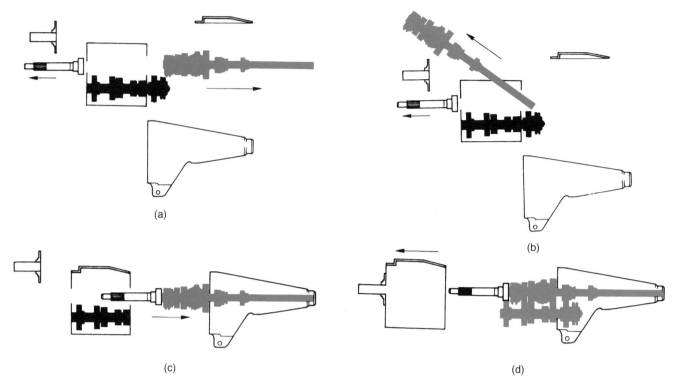

(a)

(b)

(c)

(d)

FIGURE 8-26 The disassembly procedure varies somewhat depending on the transmission. The clutch shaft and mainshaft may be removed from each end (a), the mainshaft may be removed through the top (b), the clutch shaft and mainshaft may be removed from the rear (c), or all the shafts may be removed from the rear (d).

Alignment Marks
(Single Set of Marks)

FIGURE 8-27 A synchronizer sleeve should never be removed from its hub without first checking for alignment marks or making alignment marks if there are none. A mispositioned sleeve can cause hard shifting. (Courtesy of Ford Motor Company)

reassembly and prevent future problems (Figure 8-27). In most cases, if any portion of this assembly is damaged, except for the blocker rings, replacement of the entire synchronizer assembly will be required.

To disassemble a transmission:

1. Clean all of the oil, dirt, and grease from the outside of the unit.

2. Remove the drain plug and check the quantity and condition of the fluid.

◄ SERVICE TIP ►

Also remove the fill plug to ensure that it is not seized and does not have damaged threads.

3. Remove the case cover on units with a plain case cover. On units with a case cover that includes a shift mechanism that is not attached to any other parts, remove the case cover and shift mechanism (Figure 8-28).

◄ SERVICE TIP ►

Some transmissions need to be shifted into a certain gear to allow removal of the shift forks.

On some units, it is necessary to disconnect the shift shaft in the extension housing, remove the ex-

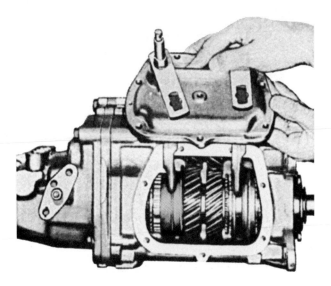

FIGURE 8-28 The disassembly of some transmissions begins with the removal of the side cover assembly; note that this transmission is shifted into second gear before removing the cover. (Portions of materials contained herein have been reprinted with permission of General Motors Corporation, Service and Parts Operations, License Agreement #0310807)

tension housing, and then remove the case cover and shift mechanism (Figure 8-29). Most tunnel-case transmissions do not have a case cover.

4. Remove the input bearing retainer, and note the top and bottom of this unit (Figure 8-30).

◄ **SERVICE TIP** ►

Some technicians will make index marks on the bearing retainer to expedite alignment during reassembly.

On units that use tapered roller bearings, remove the shims and bearing cup (Figure 8-31a). The input shaft/main drive gear can now be removed.

◄ **SERVICE TIP** ►

Some main drive gears have the teeth cut out from one section of the clutching teeth and must be aligned with the cluster gear to allow removal (Figure 8-31b).

◄ **SERVICE TIP** ►

On some transmissions, the shaft-to-bearing snap ring is removed, and the input shaft bearing is removed by prying forward on the outer snap ring. The gear is left in place (Figure 8-32).

◄ **SERVICE TIP** ►

A few transmissions use a special nut to lock the input shaft/main drive gear into the front bearing. This nut is removed by shifting the transmission into two gears—third and first, for example—to lock up and hold the gear set while the nut is removed using a special wrench (Figure 8-33).

◄ **SERVICE TIP** ►

Shifting into two gears is also used to lock up the output shaft when a nut is to be loosened or tightened.

5. Remove the extension housing (if not done in step 2); on some transmissions, the rear end of the mainshaft will be exposed (Figure 8-34).

   A puller is required on the T56 transmission to remove the speedometer rotor. After removing the reverse speed gear and synchronizer assembly, a puller is required to remove the 5–6 driven gear (Figure 8-35). The countershaft extension with the fifth and sixth drive gears and the synchronizer assembly along with the shift fork can be removed now (Figure 8-36).

◄ **SERVICE TIP** ►

On some units with internal shift linkage, portions of the shift linkage will need to be disconnected during extension housing removal (Figure 8-37).

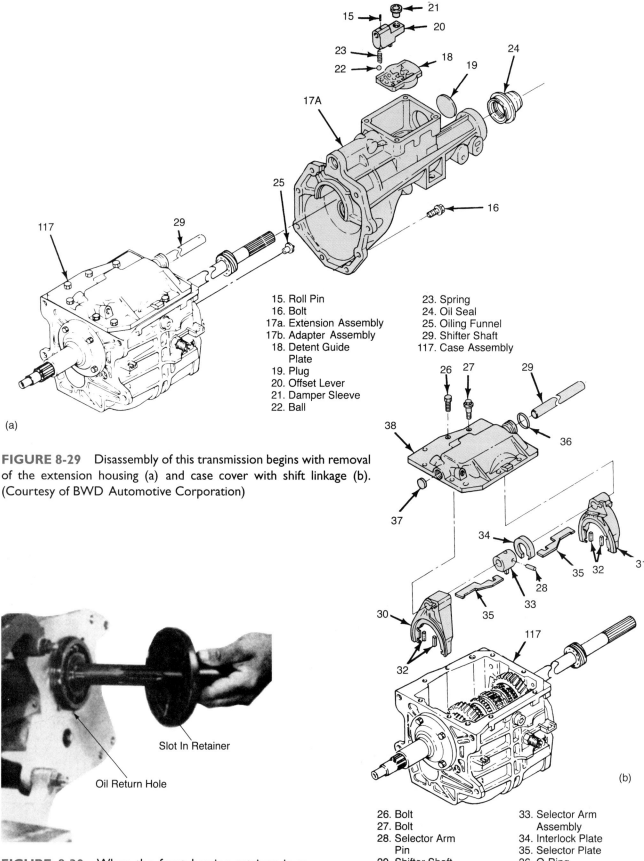

15. Roll Pin
16. Bolt
17a. Extension Assembly
17b. Adapter Assembly
18. Detent Guide Plate
19. Plug
20. Offset Lever
21. Damper Sleeve
22. Ball

23. Spring
24. Oil Seal
25. Oiling Funnel
29. Shifter Shaft
117. Case Assembly

(a)

FIGURE 8-29 Disassembly of this transmission begins with removal of the extension housing (a) and case cover with shift linkage (b). (Courtesy of BWD Automotive Corporation)

Slot In Retainer

Oil Return Hole

FIGURE 8-30 When the front bearing retainer is removed, it is a good practice to note the location of the oil return groove. (Courtesy of Ford Motor Company)

(b)

26. Bolt
27. Bolt
28. Selector Arm Pin
29. Shifter Shaft
30. 3-4 Shift Fork
31. 1-2 Shift Fork
32. Insert

33. Selector Arm Assembly
34. Interlock Plate
35. Selector Plate
36. O-Ring
37. Plug
38. Case Cover
117. Case Assembly

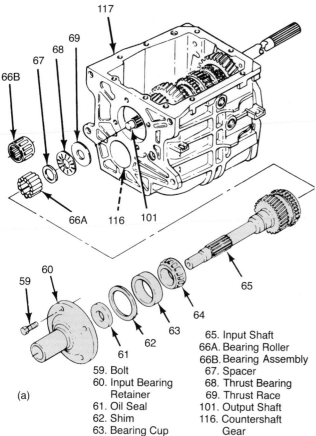

59. Bolt
60. Input Bearing Retainer
61. Oil Seal
62. Shim
63. Bearing Cup
64. Bearing Cone
65. Input Shaft
66A. Bearing Roller
66B. Bearing Assembly
67. Spacer
68. Thrust Bearing
69. Thrust Race
101. Output Shaft
116. Countershaft Gear
117. Case Assembly

(a)

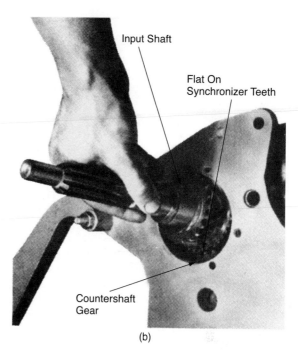

(b)

FIGURE 8-31 (a) This input shaft bearing includes a set of shims used to adjust transmission end play and an oil seal. (b) The synchronizer clutching teeth are cut away in one section of some input shafts to allow removal of the gear once the bearing retainer has been removed. (a is courtesy of BWD Automotive Corporation; b is courtesy of Ford Motor Company)

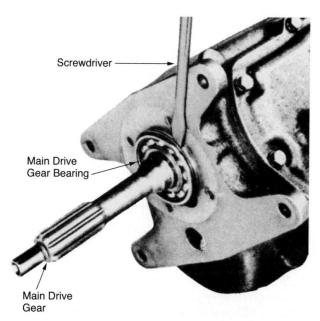

FIGURE 8-32 On this transmission, the bearing is pried off the main drive gear so that the gear, along with the main-shaft, can be removed through the rear of the case. (Portions of materials contained herein have been reprinted with permission of General Motors Corporation, Service and Parts Operations, License Agreement #0310807)

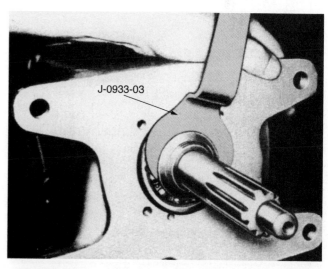

FIGURE 8-33 A special wrench is being used to remove the main drive gear bearing retainer nut. The transmission has been shifted into two different gears at the same time to lock it up and keep the main drive gear from rotating. (Portions of materials contained herein have been reprinted with permission of General Motors Corporation, Service and Parts Operations, License Agreement #0310807)

5/8 Inch Socket

Drain Pan

Shipping Seal

FIGURE 8-34 On many transmissions, the extension housing can be removed to gain access to the rear of the mainshaft. (Courtesy of Ford Motor Company)

◄ **SERVICE TIP** ►

On some units, the mainshaft assembly is removed along with the extension housing, and then the extension housing is removed from the mainshaft (Figure 8-38).

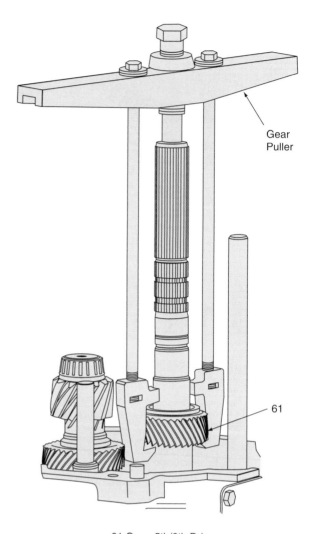

Gear Puller

61

61 Gear, 5th/6th Driven

FIGURE 8-35 A gear puller is used to remove the 5–6 driven gear. (Courtesy of Transmission Technologies Corporation, TTC)

◄ **SERVICE TIP** ►

On some tunnel-case transmissions, the extension housing and all of the internal gears are removed as a unit (Figure 8-39).

6. Remove the rear bearing, and then remove the mainshaft assembly (if not done in step 5) (Figure 8-40). This usually involves using a puller to remove a ball bearing or sliding the cup of a tapered roller bearing out of the case and then moving the mainshaft forward, upward, and out of the case.

7. Remove the cluster gear and countershaft (if not done in step 5). On one-piece tapered roller bearing

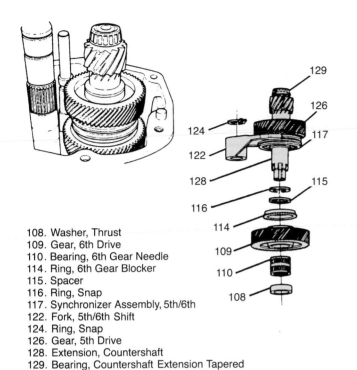

108. Washer, Thrust
109. Gear, 6th Drive
110. Bearing, 6th Gear Needle
114. Ring, 6th Gear Blocker
115. Spacer
116. Ring, Snap
117. Synchronizer Assembly, 5th/6th
122. Fork, 5th/6th Shift
124. Ring, Snap
126. Gear, 5th Drive
128. Extension, Countershaft
129. Bearing, Countershaft Extension Tapered

FIGURE 8-36 With the 5th/6th driven gear removed, the countershaft extension with the 5th and 6th drive gears and synchronizer assembly can be removed. (Courtesy of Transmission Technologies Corporation, TTC)

FIGURE 8-38 On this transmission, the extension housing is removed along with the mainshaft assembly. (Portions of materials contained herein have been reprinted with permission of General Motors Corporation, Service and Parts Operations, License Agreement #0310807)

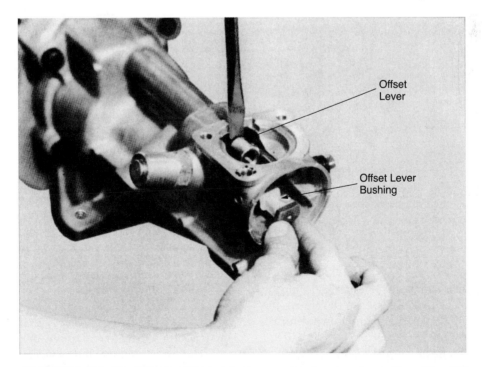

FIGURE 8-37 On this transmission, it is necessary to disconnect a portion of the shift linkage before removing the extension housing. (Courtesy of Ford Motor Company)

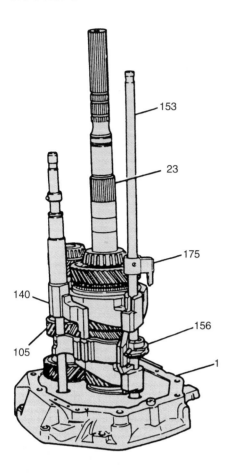

1. Transmission Front Adapter
10. Shaft, Input
23. Mainshaft
105. Countershaft
140. Rail Assembly, 5th/6th
    and Reverse Shift
153. Rail Assembly, 1st/2nd
    3rd/4th Shift
156. Plate, Interlock
175. Lever, Skip Shift

FIGURE 8-39 On tunnel-case transmissions, both the mainshaft and countershaft with their gear assemblies are removed from the case at the same time. The extension housing portions have been removed from this T56 during earlier steps. (Courtesy of Transmission Technologies Corporation, TTC)

units, remove the rear bearing retainer and slide the countershaft to the rear of the case to remove the rear bearing cup, then forward and upward for removal (Figure 8-41).

On two-piece needle-bearing units, locate the lock that keeps the countershaft from rotating; this is usually a key or pin. The pin will need to be removed; a key will fall out as the countershaft is re-

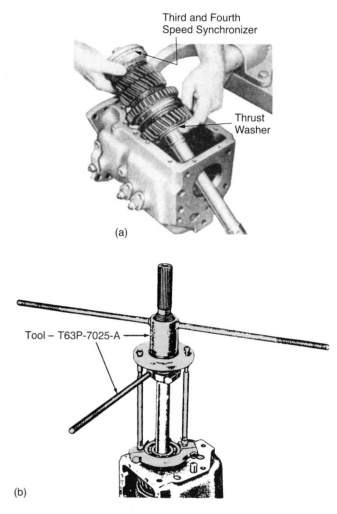

(a)

(b)

FIGURE 8-40 The mainshaft is removed through the top of the case (a) of this transmission after the output shaft bearing has been removed (b). (Courtesy of Ford Motor Company)

moved (Figure 8-42). Next, using a brass punch or commercial loading tool/dummy shaft, drive or press the countershaft out of the case; this will usually be toward the rear (Figure 8-43).

◄ SERVICE TIP ►

A loading tool is the preferred method of pushing out the countershaft because the needle bearings can be kept in place in the cluster gear. A loading tool can be made by cutting a piece of smooth plastic rod or tubing, metal tubing or pipe, or wooden dowel to a length slightly longer than the cluster gear. The diameter of the loading tool should be the same size or slightly smaller than the countershaft.

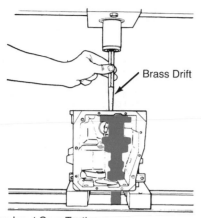
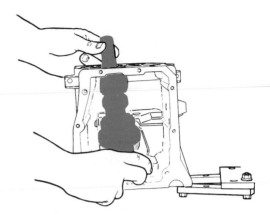

Note: Press on Input Gear Teeth

FIGURE 8-41 This T5 countershaft is removed from the case after tapping the rear bearing cone out. (Portions of materials contained herein have been reprinted with permission of General Motors Corporation, Service and Parts Operations, License Agreement #0310807)

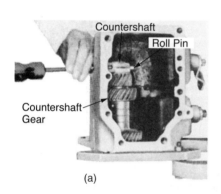

(a)

(b)

FIGURE 8-42 Transmissions with separate cluster gears and countershafts use a pin or key to locate the countershaft in the case. (a is courtesy of Ford Motor Company; b: Portions of materials contained herein have been reprinted with permission of General Motors Corporation, Service and Parts Operations, License Agreement #0310807)

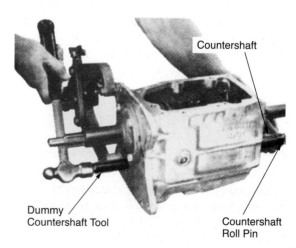

FIGURE 8-43 The dummy countershaft tool is being used to drive the countershaft out; it will stay in the cluster gear to hold the needle bearings in position until the gear is removed. (Courtesy of Ford Motor Company)

Remove the cluster gear and thrust washers from the top of the case (Figure 8-44).

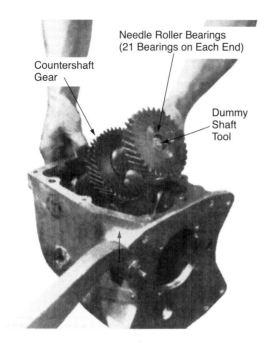

Countershaft Gear

Needle Roller Bearings (21 Bearings on Each End)

Dummy Shaft Tool

FIGURE 8-44 This cluster gear is being removed from the case along with the dummy shaft tool and needle bearings. (Courtesy of Ford Motor Company)

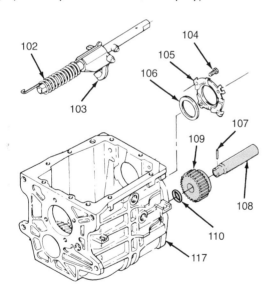

102. Spring	108. Reverse Idler
103. Fork, Pin and	Shaft
Roller Assembly	109. Reverse Idler
104. Bolt	Gear
105. Rear Retainer	110. O-Ring
106. Shim	117. Case Assembly
107. Roll Pin	

FIGURE 8-45 Reverse idler gear assembly showing the relationship of the various parts. (Courtesy of BWD Automotive Corporation)

8. Locate and remove the reverse idler gear shaft locking device, and remove the shaft, gear, and any thrust washers or O-rings (Figure 8-45).

On some units, the idler gear shaft must be driven out using a long tapered punch; the end of the shaft has a recess to keep the punch located properly (Figure 8-46).

On other units, the idler gear shaft must be pressed out (Figure 8-47).

At this time, the transmission should be disassembled and the subassembly reconditioning steps can be performed.

◄ PROBLEM SOLVING ►

Imagine that you are working in a transmission repair shop and you encounter these problems:

Case 1

The customer's concern was no second gear, and as you disassembled the transmission, you found the second-gear teeth stripped off the cluster gear. You should completely inspect the transmission to determine what new parts to install, but with this much information, what parts should be listed for replacement?

Case 2

The customer's concern is that the transaxle has no third or fourth gear. During your road test, you find a normal first, second, fifth, and reverse, but the shift is blocked for third and fourth. What do you think is causing this problem? What parts should you check carefully during the disassembly of this unit?

8.5.3   Parts Cleaning

The first step in cleaning is to check the debris attached to the magnet located in the bottom of the case (Figure 8-48). This will provide an important clue to the internal damage you may find. Large, irregular-shaped particles are probably chips from gear teeth. Small, fine, sandlike or powderlike particles indicate material worn off a bearing, gear, or synchronizer assembly.

The cleanup of most of the internal parts is done by dipping them in a safety solvent while scrubbing them with a parts-cleaning bristle brush or by running them through a hot-water washer. After cleaning, the parts are dried using compressed air and then rewashed and redried until they are clean.

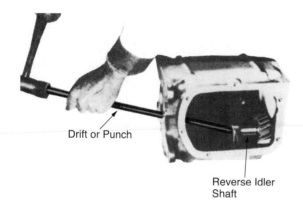

FIGURE 8-46   A recess is provided in the end of this reverse idler gear shaft so that a punch can be used to drive it out of the case. (Portions of materials contained herein have been reprinted with permission of General Motors Corporation, Service and Parts Operations, License Agreement #0310807)

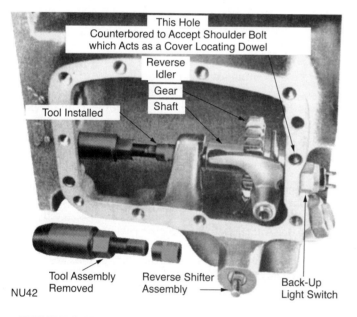

FIGURE 8-47   A special tool is being used to force this reverse idler gear shaft out of the case. For this purpose, a shop-made tool can be made from a nut, bolt, washer, and short piece of pipe. (Courtesy of DaimlerChrysler Corporation)

◀ SAFETY TIP ▶

Use care if cleaning with petroleum-based solvents. Some of these can cause skin or respiration problems and should not be breathed or allowed to remain in contact with your skin. There is also a fire hazard when the solvent is blown into the air as the parts are dried.

FIGURE 8-48   This case magnet has been removed from a badly worn transmission. Imagine where all this metal came from and the damage that occurred as it passed through the transmission.

When drying bearings, hold the bearing, or direct the air blast, so as not to spin and possibly damage the bearing. Thick deposits and caked-on debris can often be removed by scraping, using care not to damage the metal surfaces, especially the sealing surfaces.

◀ SERVICE TIP ▶

Parts should not be wiped dry with shop towels; this could leave lint, which later could block an oiling funnel or passage.

Old sealant is normally removed with an aerosol sealant-removing solvent or a small sealant-removing brush mounted in a drill motor.

8.5.4   Gear Inspection

In some cases, gear damage is quite obvious and easy to locate (Figure 8-49). There is no need to clean up some of the unusable gears shown in Figure 8-50. With other gears, however, a close inspection is necessary to determine if there is a problem with the teeth or thrust or bearing surfaces.

FIGURE 8-49   This transmission has been severely overheated; note the main drive gear and the blackened gear on the cluster that it was meshed with.

◄ SERVICE TIP ►

Burned-up cluster and main drive gears are caused by low lubricant level. Remember that the average motorist never checks standard transmission oil level unless there is a dipstick. The technician must make sure that all transmission seals are in good shape and educate the customer to have the gear oil checked at regular intervals.

◄ SERVICE TIP ►

If one gear of a set has a broken tooth, be aware that a tooth on the mating gear encountered the same load and is probably damaged. Normally, the broken gear and its mate are replaced together.

Each of the gears, along with their clutching teeth and their inner bore, should be inspected for wear or damage. Close inspection of a gear tooth will often show a smooth metallic sheen with a duller, cleaner area; this indicates the gear's contact pattern with its mating gear. Many gear teeth will also show underlying machine marks from when the gear was originally made; these marks are normal (Figure 8-51). The contact area should occur in the vertical center of the tooth and be almost as long as the tooth. Figure 8-52 shows acceptable contact patterns and patterns you should reject by replacing the gear(s). Improper contact patterns are especially important when checking for gear noise problems.

REAL-WORLD FIX: A 1992 Toyota MR2 (99,000 mi) had a problem of fifth-gear jump-out. After confirming the problem, the technician disassembled and inspected the transaxle. A loose fifth driven gear retaining nut and damaged fifth-gear clutch hub were found. The unit was reassembled, using a new fifth-gear hub, sleeve, keys, and springs. The transaxle worked fine for about 1500 miles, and then the problem returned.

FIX

The transaxle was disassembled again, and it was determined that a damaged fifth driven gear was overlooked during the original repair. Replacement of this gear fixed this transaxle.

AUTHOR'S NOTE

A thorough inspection during the first repair would have caught the other problem and would have saved pulling the transaxle a second time.

The late-design cluster gear used in the Tremec TR-3550 transmission is a three-piece unit (Figure 8-53). It can be disassembled to allow replacement of one or two of its parts.

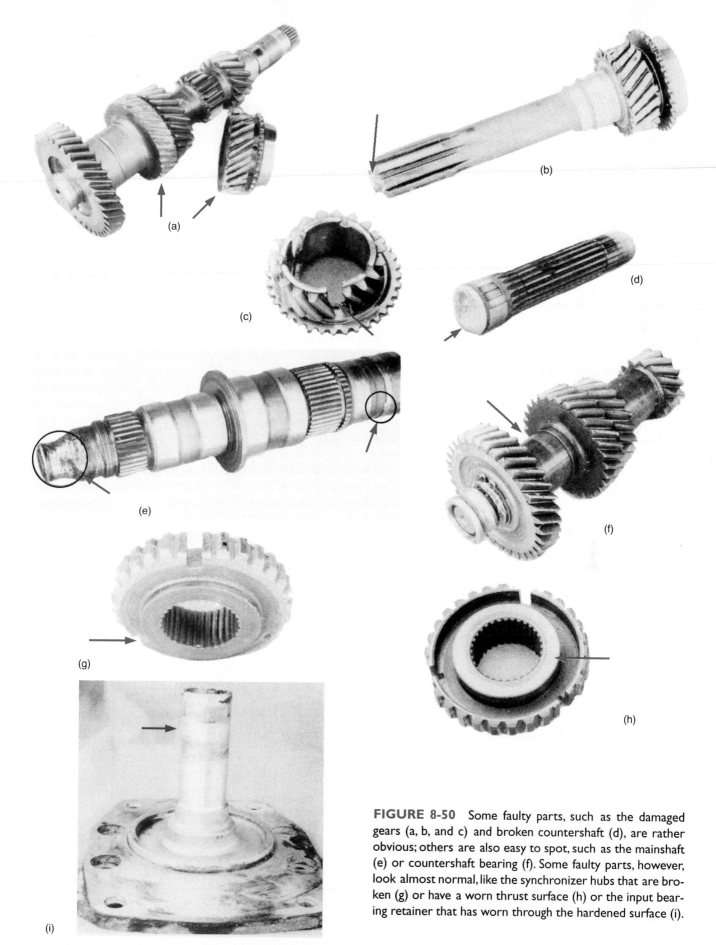

FIGURE 8-50 Some faulty parts, such as the damaged gears (a, b, and c) and broken countershaft (d), are rather obvious; others are also easy to spot, such as the mainshaft (e) or countershaft bearing (f). Some faulty parts, however, look almost normal, like the synchronizer hubs that are broken (g) or have a worn thrust surface (h) or the input bearing retainer that has worn through the hardened surface (i).

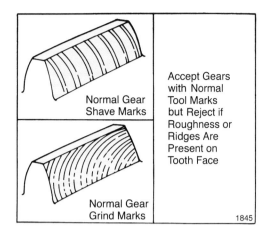

FIGURE 8-51   Normal machine marks on gear teeth are not cause for gear replacement. (Courtesy of BWD Automotive Corporation)

Gear damage occurs in many forms. The terms used by Borg Warner Automotive to describe damage are as follows:

- **Burr:** local rise of material forming a protruding sharp edge
- **Chip:** area from which a small fragment has been broken off or cut

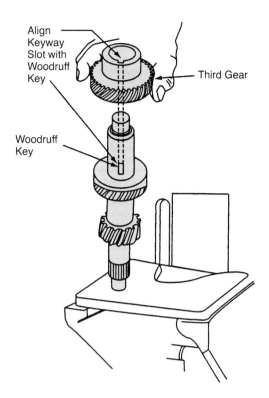

FIGURE 8-53   Third gear should be aligned with the key before pressing it onto the TR-3550 cluster gear. (Courtesy of Transmission Technologies Corporation, TTC)

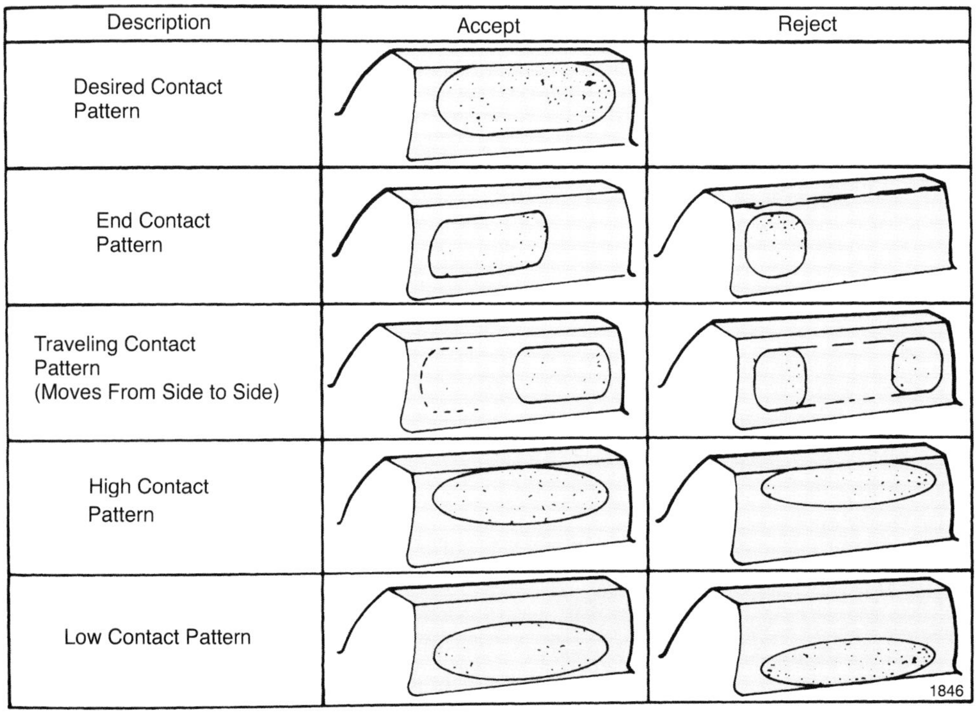

Description	Accept	Reject
Desired Contact Pattern		
End Contact Pattern		
Traveling Contact Pattern (Moves From Side to Side)		
High Contact Pattern		
Low Contact Pattern		

FIGURE 8-52   Worn gears will often show a contact pattern on close inspection. Good and bad patterns are shown here. (Courtesy of BWD Automotive Corporation)

- **Crack:** surface break in the nature of a line, indicating partial or complete separation of material
- **Excessive wear:** heavy or obvious wear beyond expectations, considering conditions of operation
- **Galling:** breakdown (or buildup) of metal surface due to excessive friction between parts; particles of the softer material are torn loose and welded to the harder material
- **Indentation:** displacement of material caused by localized heavy contact
- **Nick:** local break or notch; usually, displacement of material rather than loss
- **Scoring:** tear or break in a metal surface from contact under pressure; may show discoloration from heat produced by friction
- **Step wear:** heavy wear that produces a step that can be seen or felt between adjacent contact and noncontact surfaces
- **Uneven wear:** condition of localized, unevenly distributed wear; includes hollows, shiny spots, uneven polish, and other visual indications

◀ SERVICE TIP ▶

A technician often has to decide whether to reuse or replace slightly worn or damaged parts. Some cluster gears, for example are very expensive, and replacement can raise the cost of a rebuild significantly. Normally, chips that do not extend into the contact area do not require gear replacement (Figure 8-54). They can, however, cause a slight noise or be the base of a stress crack or further chipping. Small burrs and chips can be removed or blended into the gear surface using a high-speed grinder with a small abrasive stone (Figure 8-55). Worn, rounded, or burred clutching teeth can also be corrected by grinding.

8.5.5   Bearing Inspection and Service

Immediately after cleaning, an antifriction (ball, roller, or needle) bearing should be dipped in a clean, lightweight lubricant and covered to keep it clean and dust free. Inspection of a bearing is normally done by sight, feel, and

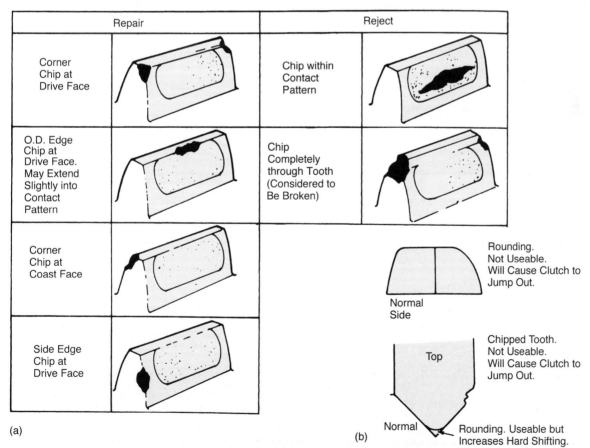

(a)

(b)

FIGURE 8-54   Some gear tooth (a) and clutch tooth (b) chipping is acceptable, and in these cases, the gear can be reused. If the chip extends into the contact pattern or is completely through the tooth, the gear should be replaced. (Courtesy of BWD Automotive Corporation)

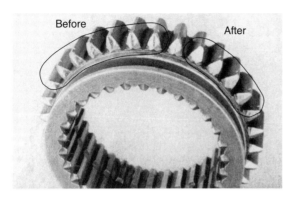

FIGURE 8-55   Teeth of a reverse gear before and after being touched up with a grinder.

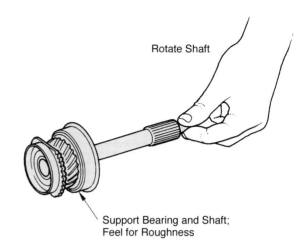

Rotate Shaft

Support Bearing and Shaft; Feel for Roughness

FIGURE 8-57   If you rotate the shaft while supporting it by the bearing race, you can feel any roughness that would indicate a faulty bearing.

sound. Visual inspection of a worn bearing can reveal a broken cage or pitted, spalled raceways (Figure 8-56).

◀ SERVICE TIP ▶

Holding the bearing in a vertical position by the outer race while spinning the inner race by hand allows you to feel and listen for damage not easily seen. Many technicians place the shaft inside the inner race, giving it a slight load and a much better turning handle (Figure 8-57). The weight of the shaft also makes any bearing problem more evident.

The cone of a tapered roller bearing should be pushed into its cup so that there is pressure between the two as they are rotated. If the bearing feels or sounds rough, rewash, air dry, lubricate with thin oil or ATF, and repeat this check. If it still feels rough, give it one more chance by re-

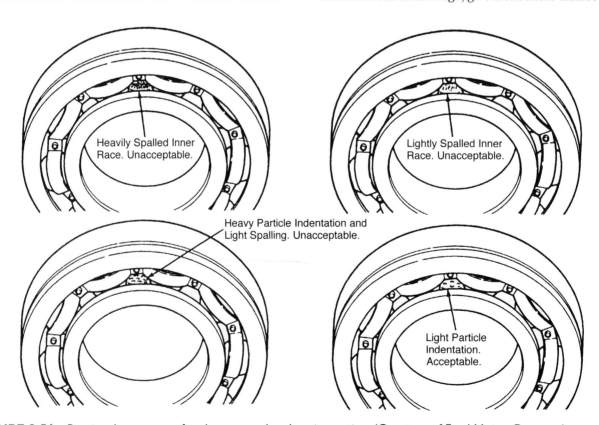

Heavily Spalled Inner Race. Unacceptable.

Lightly Spalled Inner Race. Unacceptable.

Heavy Particle Indentation and Light Spalling. Unacceptable.

Light Particle Indentation. Acceptable.

FIGURE 8-56   Bearing damage can often be seen under close inspection. (Courtesy of Ford Motor Company)

cleaning, lubricating, and rechecking it; replace it if it is still rough. If there is any doubt that the bearing is not in perfect condition, most technicians will replace it to prevent the possibility of noisy operation or comeback.

Bearing damage occurs in many forms. The terms commonly used to describe bearing damage are as follows:

- **Brinelling:** a series of indentations pressed or worn into a race
- **Contamination:** scratches, pitting, or scoring in a scattered pattern on the ball or roller surfaces
- **Electric arcing:** a series of small burn marks or grooves across the raceways
- **Fretting:** small particles that decay and break off the bearing races
- **Misalignment:** a diagonal polish of the stationary race while excess wear occurs all over the rotating raceway from a bore and shaft that are not correctly aligned
- **Peeling:** a light scraping away of the surface of the bearing race
- **Seizing:** caused when balls or rollers fail to roll; causes damage to cage and end of rollers with evidence of excessive heat
- **Spalling:** an advanced stage of decay with flaking away of particles from the bearing race

To protect themselves as well as the bearing, technicians should exercise care when removing or replacing bearings. A pressing force through or across a ball or roller bearing will ruin the bearing and could cause the bearing to explode. This is encountered, for example, when removing a front input shaft bearing or many rear axle bearings. Their inner races are pressed onto the shaft, and the gear or axle head often prevents you from gripping the inner race; thus you have to attach the pulling tool or press adapter to the outer race. The pressing force is then transmitted from the outer race through the balls to the inner race; a high amount of pressing force can damage (brinell) the balls and races and can cause explosive forces to build up in the outer race (Figure 8-58).

◀ SERVICE TIP ▶

When installing a tight-fitting bearing over a shaft, heat the bearing in an oven or hot oil. A temperature of 300 to 400°F will expand the bearing about 0.001″ per inch of bearing diameter. If you can't heat the external part, sometimes you can cool the internal part to make it smaller. Parts can be chilled by placing them in a freezer or immersing them in a container with dry ice and acetone. Either of these methods can change a press fit into a slip fit.

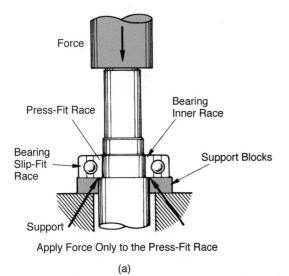

(a)

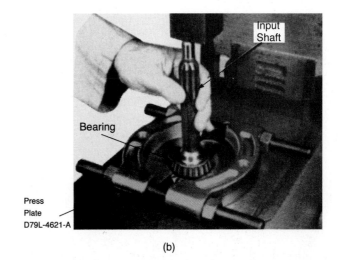

(b)

FIGURE 8-58   (a) When a ball bearing is pressed off a shaft, the bearing should be supported by the inner race (if possible) so that the force is not exerted on the outer race by the balls. (b) The bearing is often supported by a bearing separator, as shown here. (a is courtesy of CR Services; b is courtesy of Ford Motor Company)

◀ SERVICE TIP ▶

An experienced technician will always enclose the bearing in some form of shield to contain any possible flying parts and will always replace or carefully check any bearing that requires this type of removal. It is often possible to remove a bearing with a gear so that the gear will press against the bearing's inner race, saving the bearing. When installing a bearing that requires force, it is always a good rule to apply pressure on the race that is making contact at that time (Figure 8-59). Some shops make it a practice to heat any bearing that is pressed onto a shaft; the expansion makes installation easier, with less possibility of damage to the bearing.

8.5.6 Mainshaft Disassembly

Transaxle/transmission mainshafts are disassembled to allow a thorough inspection of the journals and bearings where the gears are mounted and for access to the synchronizer assemblies. In some cases, this is simply a matter of removing snap rings and sliding the various parts off the shaft; in most cases, the parts must be removed using a press or puller tool. All of these parts have a front and back; some technicians place a small index mark using a die grinder on the front of each part as it is removed. This mark will ensure that the part is positioned correctly during reassembly (Figure 8-60). Another aid is to place the parts in a holding fixture to keep the parts in the proper order.

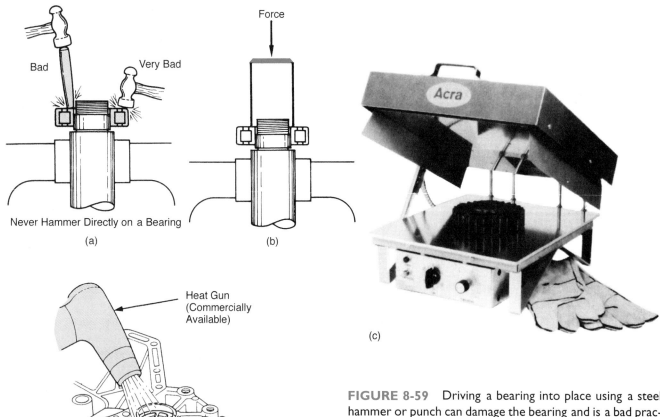

(a)

(b)

(c)

(d)

FIGURE 8-59 Driving a bearing into place using a steel hammer or punch can damage the bearing and is a bad practice (a). A tool, sometimes a piece of pipe, should be used so that an even force is exerted on the race (b). A heater, to expand the bearing (c) or the transmission case (d), can make installation easier. (a is courtesy of CR Services; b is courtesy of Ford Motor Company; c is courtesy of Acra Electric Corporation; d is courtesy of American Honda Motor Company)

FIGURE 8-60 The technician used a die grinder to place the V-shaped marks on these synchronizer sleeves. They are placed so that they show the front or to identify the particular unit.

◄ SERVICE TIP ►

Early bearing failure that results in a pitted bearing can be caused by poor electrical grounds. The pits are often completely around the bearing races. Current flow for the engine's electrical systems must return to battery ground and for the vehicle's electrical flow must return to the alternator. Weak engine ground straps will force this current flow to pass through the transmission and across the bearings and this can cause an arc at the bearing races. Adding an inexpensive ground strap to the transmission case eliminates this problem.

8.5.6.1 Bearing Lubrication. Some bearings, like those on a transmission cluster gear, are lubricated by being in an oil bath. Other bearings, like those of a mainshaft speed gear, must have oil brought to them; speed gear lubrication is often fed through passages in the mainshaft. Sometimes a trough or funnel is used to direct oil into a bearing or shaft (Figure 8-61). During a transmission rebuild, these oiling devices should be cleaned and checked to ensure that they will work properly.

◄ SERVICE TIP ►

An experienced technician will always check a parts blow-up illustration to locate the snap rings and to determine the direction in which the parts are removed. Some mainshafts are stepped with

reduced spline and journal diameters. Some have synchronizer hubs that are installed permanently on the shaft. Others have a thrust surface or flange that is part of the shaft (Figure 8-62). Any of these features will determine which way the parts are removed and replaced.

Remember that each gear next to a synchronizer assembly has a center bearing and a thrust surface on each side of it. The center bearing is either the smooth bore of the gear, a sleeve, or a set of needle bearings; and these operate on the mainshaft journals (Figure 8-63). The thrust surfaces are the smooth sides of the gears that can run against the smooth side of the synchronizer hub or a thrust washer. Each of these surfaces' possible wear areas are normally checked as the parts are disassembled.

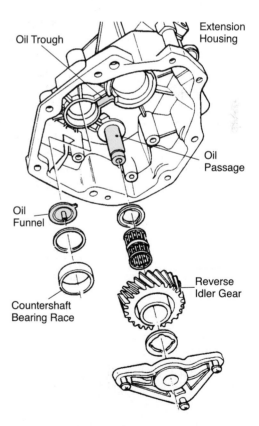

FIGURE 8-61 The oil trough feeds oil to the oil funnel and oil passage in the reverse idler shaft. The oil funnel feeds oil into the countershaft and sixth speed gear, and the oil passage feeds oil into the reverse idler gear bearing.

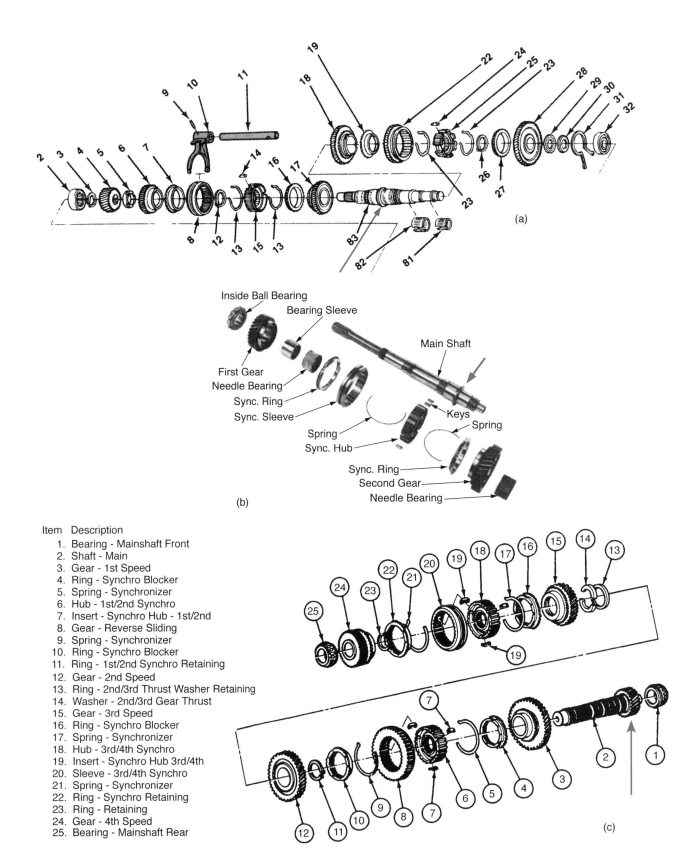

Item Description
1. Bearing - Mainshaft Front
2. Shaft - Main
3. Gear - 1st Speed
4. Ring - Synchro Blocker
5. Spring - Synchronizer
6. Hub - 1st/2nd Synchro
7. Insert - Synchro Hub - 1st/2nd
8. Gear - Reverse Sliding
9. Spring - Synchronizer
10. Ring - Synchro Blocker
11. Ring - 1st/2nd Synchro Retaining
12. Gear - 2nd Speed
13. Ring - 2nd/3rd Thrust Washer Retaining
14. Washer - 2nd/3rd Gear Thrust
15. Gear - 3rd Speed
16. Ring - Synchro Blocker
17. Spring - Synchronizer
18. Hub - 3rd/4th Synchro
19. Insert - Synchro Hub 3rd/4th
20. Sleeve - 3rd/4th Synchro
21. Spring - Synchronizer
22. Ring - Synchro Retaining
23. Ring - Retaining
24. Gear - 4th Speed
25. Bearing - Mainshaft Rear

FIGURE 8-62 (a and b) Some mainshafts have a thrust shoulder that requires disassembly from each end. (c) Some have a fixed gear at one end that requires disassembly from the other end. (d) Some have a synchronizer hub that must not be removed. (a: Portions of materials contained herein have been reprinted with permission of General Motors Corporation, Service and Parts Operations, License Agreement #0310807; b and c are courtesy of Ford Motor Company; d is courtesy of BWD Automotive Corporation)

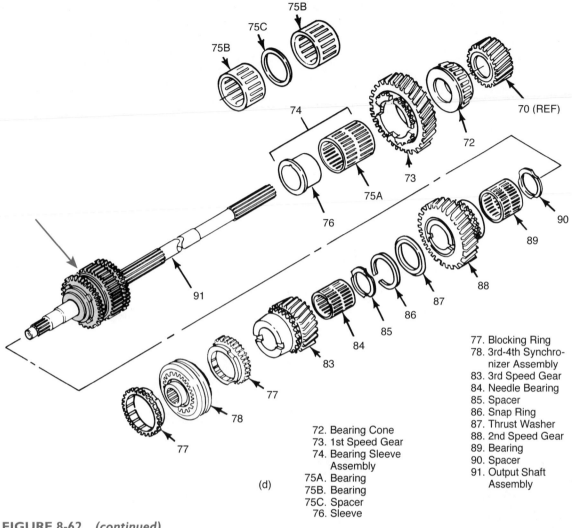

75B
75C
75B
74
75A
73
70 (REF)
72
76
90
89
91
88
87
86
85
84
83
77
78
77
(d)

72. Bearing Cone
73. 1st Speed Gear
74. Bearing Sleeve
    Assembly
75A. Bearing
75B. Bearing
75C. Spacer
76. Sleeve

77. Blocking Ring
78. 3rd-4th Synchro-
    nizer Assembly
83. 3rd Speed Gear
84. Needle Bearing
85. Spacer
86. Snap Ring
87. Thrust Washer
88. 2nd Speed Gear
89. Bearing
90. Spacer
91. Output Shaft
    Assembly

FIGURE 8-62   *(continued)*

◄ SERVICE TIP ►

Gears that are not secured to the shaft should rotate easily and smoothly on the shaft and have a few thousandths of an inch of end float. Rough or sloppy motion indicates a problem with the gear or shaft (Figure 8-64).

To disassemble a mainshaft:

1. In some cases, slide the end gear off the shaft. In other cases, the end gear will be held in place by a bearing that must be pressed off the shaft. Most shops will install a bearing separator onto the gear and press the shaft out of the gear and bearing (Figure 8-65). Since the gear will contact the inner bearing race, this should remove the bearing with no damage to it. A puller can also be used.

2. Remove the blocker ring and the synchronizer hub retaining ring, install a bearing separator onto the gear next to the synchronizer assembly, and press the shaft out of the gear, blocker ring, and synchronizer assembly (Figure 8-66).

3. Continue this disassembly procedure to remove any remaining gears, thrust washers, synchronizer assembly, and bearings.

8.5.7 Synchronizer Disassembly, Inspection, and Reassembly

Synchronizer assemblies are disassembled for cleaning, inspection, and occasionally for deburring the ends of the splines in the sleeve. As mentioned earlier, the sleeve and hub are factory matched so that index marks need to be placed on them before disassembly.

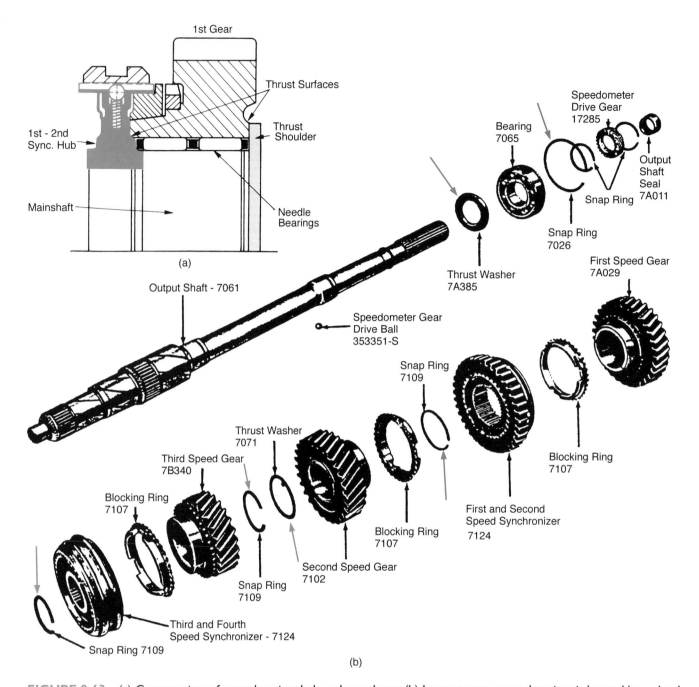

FIGURE 8-63 (a) Cutaway view of a synchronizer hub and speed gear. (b) In most cases, a synchronizer is located by a shoulder and a snap ring, and a speed gear is located by the synchronizer, a thrust washer or surface, and a snap ring. (a: Portions of materials contained herein have been reprinted with permission of General Motors Corporation, Service and Parts Operations, License Agreement #0310807; b is courtesy of Ford Motor Company)

Some synchronizer sleeves have notches for the inserts only in certain areas, and some assemblies include a detent ball and spring in addition to the inserts and energizer springs (Figures 8-67 and 8-68). Some assemblies use winged inserts or keys, which will remain in place as the sleeve is removed. Other inserts are plain with straight sides and will pop out of place as the sleeve is slid off.

To disassemble a synchronizer assembly, simply remove the energizer springs and slide the sleeve off the hub. Now the inserts will either fall or slide out of their grooves.

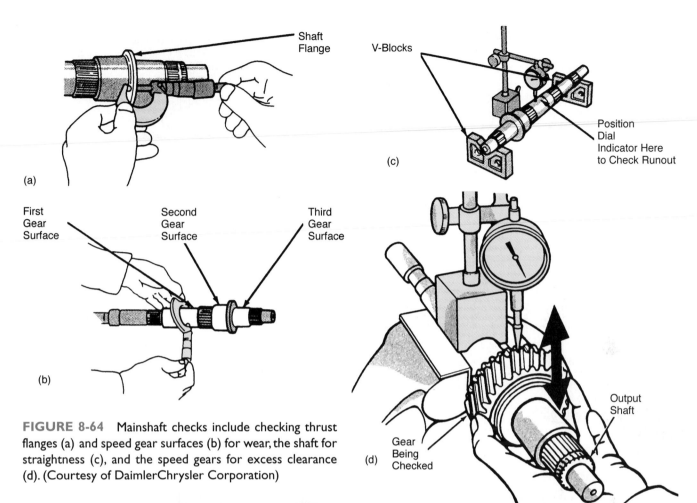

(a)

Shaft
Flange

V-Blocks

Position
Dial
Indicator Here
to Check Runout

(c)

First
Gear
Surface

Second
Gear
Surface

Third
Gear
Surface

(b)

Output
Shaft

Gear
Being
Checked

(d)

FIGURE 8-64 Mainshaft checks include checking thrust flanges (a) and speed gear surfaces (b) for wear, the shaft for straightness (c), and the speed gears for excess clearance (d). (Courtesy of DaimlerChrysler Corporation)

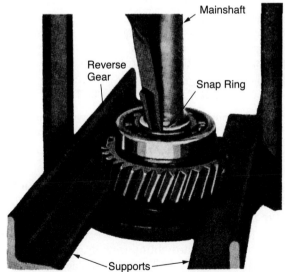

Mainshaft

Reverse
Gear

Snap Ring

Supports

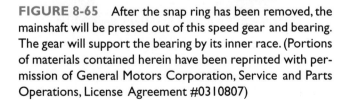

FIGURE 8-65 After the snap ring has been removed, the mainshaft will be pressed out of this speed gear and bearing. The gear will support the bearing by its inner race. (Portions of materials contained herein have been reprinted with permission of General Motors Corporation, Service and Parts Operations, License Agreement #0310807)

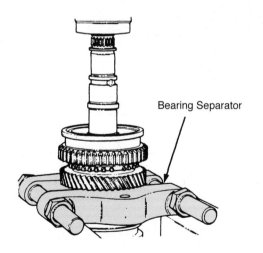

Bearing Separator

FIGURE 8-66 The bearing separator supports the speed gear, which, in turn, supports the synchronizer assembly as the mainshaft is pressed out of them. (Portions of materials contained herein have been reprinted with permission of General Motors Corporation, Service and Parts Operations, License Agreement #0310807)

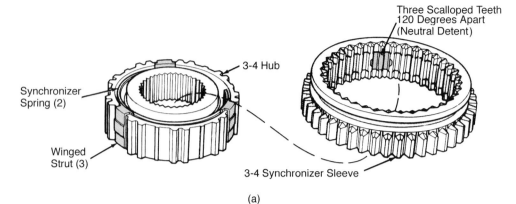

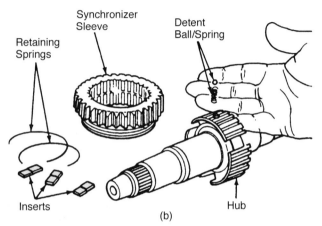

FIGURE 8-67 (a) The sleeve of this synchronizer has three scalloped teeth that must be indexed to the winged struts. (b) A detent ball and spring are included in this synchronizer assembly. (a is courtesy of DaimlerChrysler Corporation; b is courtesy of Ford Motor Company)

◄ SERVICE TIP ►

Some technicians prefer to disassemble synchronizer assemblies over a shop cloth or towel so that the small balls or springs won't roll away.

◄ SERVICE TIP ►

The parts should be washed in solvent and air dried. While cleaning and checking the hub, do not let it drop; many hubs are relatively soft and will bend fairly easily.

REAL-WORLD FIX: A Muncie four-speed was overhauled about 500 miles ago. Now there was gear clash on 4–3 downshifts. The transmission worked well except for this problem.

FIX

Close inspection of the keys/inserts from the 3–4 synchronizer showed them to be severely worn in the center, raised area. Replacement of these keys, two blocker rings, and energizer springs fixed this shift problem.

AUTHOR'S NOTE

A more thorough inspection of these synchronizer parts during the overhaul would have prevented this problem.

Inspection includes checking the inserts for wear or breakage, checking the sleeve for burrs, and checking the fit of the sleeve to the hub (Figure 8-69). A hub should fall freely through the sleeve. A tight-fitting sleeve will cause hard shifts. Usually, a fault with any part of the assembly will require replacement with a new synchronizer assembly.

To reassemble a synchronizer assembly:

1. Place the sleeve over the hub with the index marks aligned. If there are no index marks, locate the sleeve over the hub in a position where there

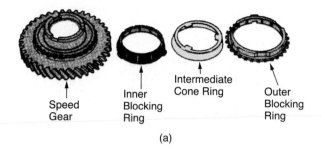

(a)

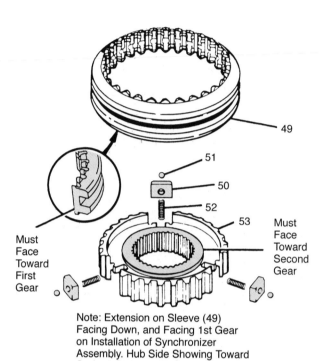

Note: Extension on Sleeve (49)
Facing Down, and Facing 1st Gear
on Installation of Synchronizer
Assembly. Hub Side Showing Toward
Second Gear.

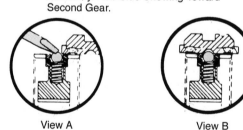

View A   View B

49. Sleeve, 1st/2nd Synchronizer
50. Key, 1/st2nd Synchronizer
51. Ball, 1st/2nd Synchronizer
52. Spring, 1st/2nd Synchronizer
53. Hub, 1st/2nd Synchronizer

(b)

FIGURE 8-68 Exploded views of a synchronizer assembly using three-part paper blocker rings and commonly found energizer springs (a) and one using coil detent springs (b). (Portions of materials contained herein have been reprinted with permission of General Motors Corporation, Service and Parts Operations, License Agreement #0310807)

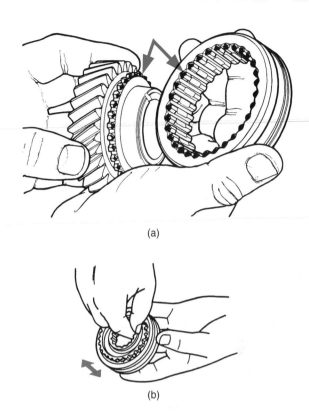

(a)

(b)

FIGURE 8-69 Common synchronizer wear points are the clutching teeth on the speed gear and sleeve (a). The sleeve should slide easily over the hub (b). (a: Portions of materials contained herein have been reprinted with permission of General Motors Corporation, Service and Parts Operations, License Agreement #0310807; b is courtesy of Ford Motor Company)

is free movement between them and in the correct front-to-rear position. Many technicians will set the sleeve and hub on a shop cloth placed on a benchtop with the front/engine ends upward. When aligned properly, the sleeve will free-fall over the hub.

2. Slide an insert into each of the grooves.

3. Set an energizer spring in place. A common spring style has a tang that enters one of the inserts and a tail that is placed under the other inserts in a clockwise direction (Figure 8-70). Other spring styles are positioned in a similar manner.

4. Turn the assembly over and place the tang of the second spring into the other end of the same insert, and place the tang under the other insert in a clockwise direction. In this way, the two springs are running in opposite directions. It should be noted that some manufacturers recommend placing the spring tangs into different inserts.

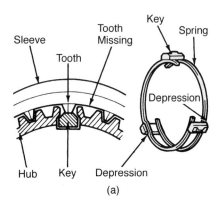

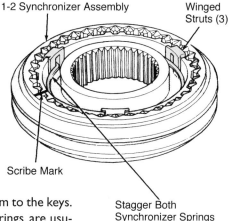

FIGURE 8-70 (a) Some energizer springs have a depression to locate them to the keys. (b) Other energizer springs have a tang to position them in a strut. The springs are usually staggered to different keys/struts and wrapped in opposite directions. (a is courtesy of Ford Motor Company; b is courtesy of DaimlerChrysler Corporation)

The purpose of the energizer spring placement is to obtain equal spring pressure under each of the inserts. When other spring styles are used, they are also positioned so as to distribute their force equally.

Although separate from the assembly, this is a good time to check the blocker rings and cone clutch area of the gear (Figure 8-71). Blocker ring problems commonly encountered are burred clutching teeth, broken rings, worn insert grooves, and wear on the inner cone surface.

◀ **SERVICE TIP** ▶

A good metal blocker ring will have a thread-like inner surface with the threads coming to a sharp point; the edges will not reflect light (Figure 8-72). A worn blocker ring will have flattened rings around the inner surface.

◀ **SERVICE TIP** ▶

After a quick visual check for visible damage, a technician will tap a metal ring with a metal object. A good blocker ring will make a bell-like ringing noise; a cracked or broken ring will make a dull, flat sound.

◀ **SERVICE TIP** ▶

Paper-lined blocker rings should be checked for glazing of the friction surface and discoloration, which often indicates glazing.

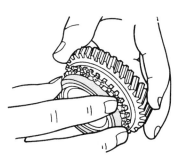

FIGURE 8-71 When pushed against its cone, a blocker ring should grab the speed gear but release cleanly and easily. (Courtesy of Ford Motor Company)

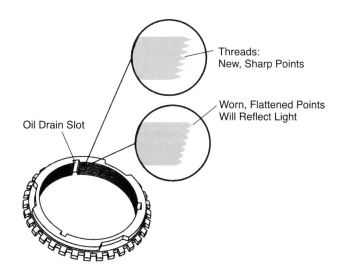

FIGURE 8-72 The threadlike grooves of a new blocker ring are sharp so they cut through the lubrication film. They become flattened as they wear, and the edges will reflect light.

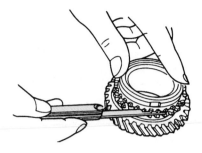

FIGURE 8-73   When the cone is pushed against the gear, there should be a minimum amount of clearance between the blocker ring and gear clutching teeth (feeler gauge). (Courtesy of Ford Motor Company)

The next check is to place the ring over the gear's cone and measure the clearance (Figure 8-73). Some manufacturers specify a minimum clearance of about 0.020 in. (0.5 mm). *Blocker ring clearance* is also called *ride height or synchronizer reserve.*

REAL-WORLD FIX: The five-speed, world-class transmission in a 1994 Mustang (75,000 mi) was rebuilt after a failure of the reverse gears. The cluster gear, second speed gear, and 1–2–reverse synchronizer were replaced. The vehicle came back with a complaint about second gear jumpout. There was also a nonrelated problem with the clutch, so the transmission needed to be removed.

FIX

The replacement 1–2–reverse synchronizer was designed for a non-world-class transmission. Replacement using parts for the correct version fixed this problem.

AUTHOR'S NOTE

Complete identification of the transmission when ordering the parts would have prevented this comeback.

◀ SERVICE TIP ▶

A world-class (WC) or non-world-class (NWC) T5 transmission can be identified by looking at the front of the case near the cluster gear bearing. On a WC unit, you will notice a bearing race, and you can read the part number. On a NWC unit, you will be looking at a flat, plain soft plug.

◀ SERVICE TIP ▶

If specifications are not available, you can measure the clearance using a new ring as a guide. The cone surface of the gear should be smooth and polished with no metal buildup (usually brass from the old ring). Metal buildup can be removed using fine emery cloth and polished using crocus cloth. Another check is to push the ring onto the cone as you rotate the gear. The ring should lock to the gear and rotate, but it should also pull right off the gear without sticking.

8.5.8 Mainshaft Reassembly

With the used parts cleaned and checked and any new parts needed available, the mainshaft is ready for reassembly.

◀ SERVICE TIP ▶

An experienced technician will check each part for proper operation as it is assembled, knowing that it is possible to get the wrong part and that some new parts are faulty.

A small parts kit may be obtained for reassembly. This usually includes new snap rings (old snap rings become weak, stretched, and should not be reused), thrust washers, and needle bearings; often, it also contains blocker rings, bearings, gaskets, and seals (Figure 8-74). During assembly, every moving part should be lubricated with gear oil, petroleum jelly, or transmission assembly lube.

To reassemble a mainshaft:

1. Place the first gear to be loaded (with its sleeve, bushing, or bearing, if used) onto the mainshaft along with its blocker ring. Set the synchronizer assembly in place, making sure that it is facing the proper direction. Turn the mainshaft so that the gear is above the synchronizer, align the blocker ring so that its notches engage the inserts, and shift the synchronizer sleeve to engage the gear's clutching teeth to keep the blocker ring aligned. Some synchronizer hubs have oiling grooves that must be aligned with an oil hole in the shaft (Figure 8-75).

2. Press the shaft into the synchronizer hub and install the snap ring to retain it (Figure 8-76). It is good practice to place wooden blocks or a shop

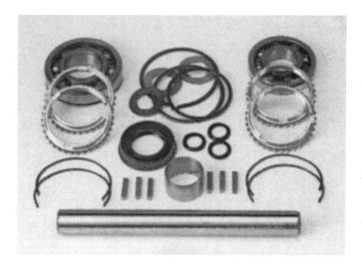

FIGURE 8-74   A transmission rebuild kit includes the parts that are normally replaced during a transmission rebuild.

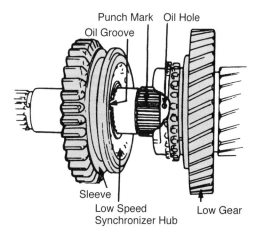

FIGURE 8-75   This synchronizer hub has an oil groove that must be aligned with the oil hole in the mainshaft during assembly. (Portions of materials contained herein have been reprinted with permission of General Motors Corporation, Service and Parts Operations, License Agreement #0310807)

cloth onto the press plates to protect the hub from becoming burred.

3. Shift the synchronizer sleeve to neutral, and check the gear and blocker ring for *end float* and free movement.

◄ SERVICE TIP ►

A blocker ring should move freely through a small amount of rotation. Each floating gear should have about 0.004 to 0.010 in. (0.1 to 0.25 mm) of end float (Figure 8-77).

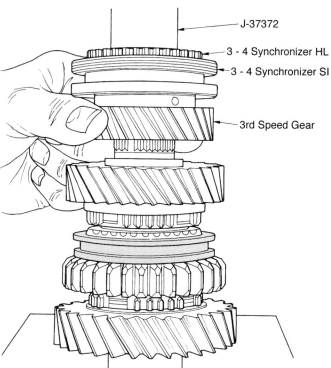

FIGURE 8-76   It is a good practice to install the blocker ring and speed gear and then shift the synchronizer sleeve; this will hold the blocker ring aligned with the synchronizer struts as the assembly is pressed onto the mainshaft. (Portions of materials contained herein have been reprinted with permission of General Motors Corporation, Service and Parts Operations, License Agreement #0310807)

In some cases, *selective-fit* snap rings or thrust washers are available to adjust the clearance, if necessary.

4. Place the next blocker ring and gear in place, making sure the blocker ring notches engage the inserts, and shift the sleeve to keep them aligned. Depending on the mainshaft, this will be followed by a thrust washer(s) and retaining ring or snap ring or a bearing and snap ring (Figure 8-78). The retaining/snap ring will often be the base for a thrust washer and another gear set, and this is usually a repeat of step 1. Pressing the shaft into a bearing normally completes the buildup of that end of the shaft.

5. After installing all the parts, check the assembly by shifting the synchronizer sleeves into neutral.

◄ SERVICE TIP ►

Each of the floating gears should rotate freely and smoothly with a slight end float. Each of the blocker rings should be loose and have a slight end float.

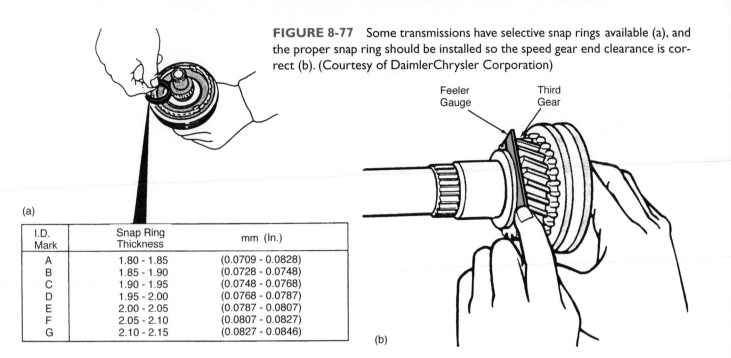

FIGURE 8-77 Some transmissions have selective snap rings available (a), and the proper snap ring should be installed so the speed gear end clearance is correct (b). (Courtesy of DaimlerChrysler Corporation)

(a)

I.D. Mark	Snap Ring Thickness	mm (In.)
A	1.80 - 1.85	(0.0709 - 0.0828)
B	1.85 - 1.90	(0.0728 - 0.0748)
C	1.90 - 1.95	(0.0748 - 0.0768)
D	1.95 - 2.00	(0.0768 - 0.0787)
E	2.00 - 2.05	(0.0787 - 0.0807)
F	2.05 - 2.10	(0.0807 - 0.0827)
G	2.10 - 2.15	(0.0827 - 0.0846)

(b)

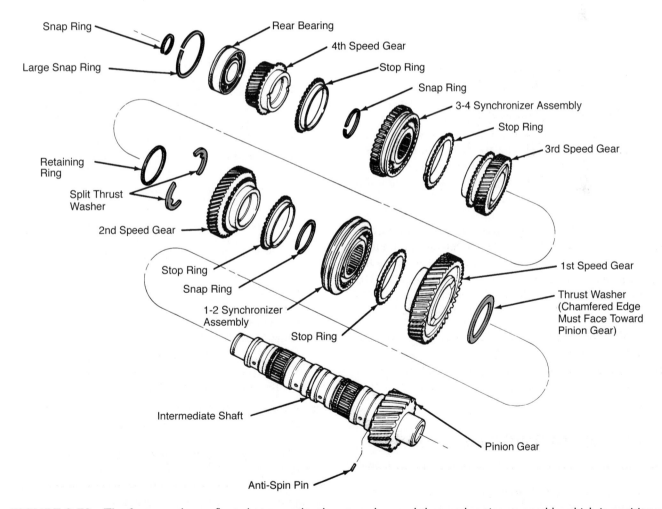

FIGURE 8-78 The first speed gear floats between the thrust washer and the synchronizer assembly, which is positioned by the snap ring. The second and third speed gears float between the split thrust washer and retaining ring and their synchronizer assemblies. The fourth speed gear floats between the rear bearing and the synchronizer assembly. (Courtesy of DaimlerChrysler Corporation)

8.5.9 Differential Disassembly, Inspection, and Reassembly

Transaxle differentials need to be partially or completely disassembled to replace the bearing cones, ring gear, or differential gears (Figure 8-79).

◀ SERVICE TIP ▶

Excessive clearance in the differential gear set can cause a clunk as the lash is taken up when the clutch is engaged. This is especially noticeable when changing direction, low to reverse or reverse to low.

Differential clearance can be checked using one of three methods; which method to use is determined by the access to the gears and how the specifications are given (Figure 8-80). The quickest and simplest method of checking differential clearance is to slide the largest feeler gauge that will fit between the axle side gear and case. On some differentials, this area is rounded, which prevents a feeler gauge check. Another method is to insert a strip of Plastigage between two of the gears as you rotate them and then measure the thickness of the crushed Plastigage. The third method is to set up a dial indicator with the stylus on a tooth of one of the side gears. Hold the other side gear stationary as you move the first gear back and forth against the lash. The amount of lash is shown by the amount of dial indicator needle movement. One manufacturer gives a specification of 0 to 0.009 in. (0 to 23 mm) for this check; some technicians use a judgment call. Too much clearance can be reduced in some differentials by using larger thrust washers behind the differential pinion and side gears. Other differentials do not use thrust washers, so the only way to reduce the clearance is to replace the differential.

To disassemble a differential:

1. Remove the pinion shaft lock pin (Figure 8-81).
2. Slide the pinion shaft out of the case and check it for step wear (Figure 8-82).
3. Roll the pinion gears to the case window(s) and remove the pinion gears and thrust washers and the side gears and their thrust washers (Figure 8-83).
4. Inspect the gears, thrust washers, and case surfaces for scoring and wear.

Reverse this procedure to reassemble the differential.

A puller is normally required to remove the side bearings. Some manufacturers recommend the use of a special puller; others use a sturdy two-jaw bearing puller

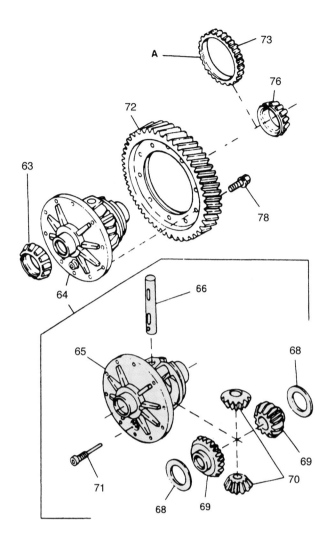

A. Electronic Speedo Gear (73) Required Heating Prior to Installation
63. Bearing, Differential
64. Carrier, Assembly Differential
65. Carrier, Differential
66. Pin, Cross Differential
68. Washer, Thrust Side Gear
69. Gear, Side Differential
70. Gear, Pinion Differential
71. Screw, 9 N•m (84 lb. in.)
72. Gear, Ring Differential
73. Gear, Speedo (Electronic)
76. Bearing, Differential
78. Bolt (Ten), 83 N•m (61 lb. ft.)

FIGURE 8-79 Exploded view of a differential from a transaxle. (Portions of materials contained herein have been reprinted with permission of General Motors Corporation, Service and Parts Operations, License Agreement #0310807)

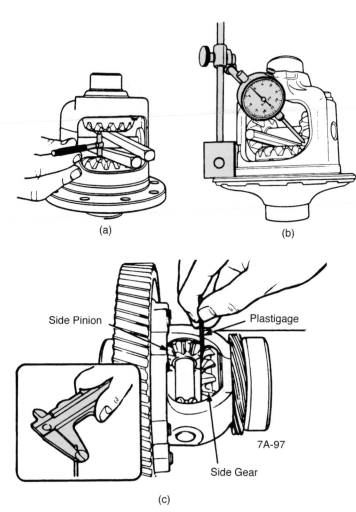

(a)   (b)

(c)

FIGURE 8-80 Differential wear can be checked by measuring the amount that the side gears can be spread apart (a), or by measuring the backlash of a side gear using a dial indicator (b), or Plastigage (c). (Portions of materials contained herein have been reprinted with permission of General Motors Corporation, Service and Parts Operations, License Agreement #0310807)

and a step-plate adapter (Figure 8-84). The new bearing is installed using a special bearing installer. Many shops will use a section of iron pipe of the correct diameter to fit the inner bearing race.

Ring gear replacement on most differentials is a matter of removing the bolts and then the gear. In some cases, heating the gear is required to seat it properly onto the case. The ring gear mounting bolts must be tightened to the correct torque. It is a good practice to tighten them in an alternating pattern, back and forth across the gear. In some differentials, the ring gear is installed using rivets. These are normally removed by drilling through the rivet head, cutting the remainder of

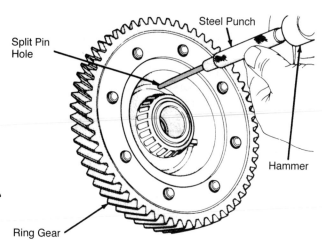

FIGURE 8-81 The first disassembly step for most differentials is to remove the pinion shaft lock pin or screw. (Courtesy of DaimlerChrysler Corporation)

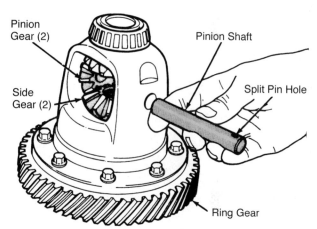

FIGURE 8-82 With the lock pin removed, the pinion shaft can be slid out of the differential case. (Courtesy of DaimlerChrysler Corporation)

the head off with a chisel, and driving the rest of the rivet out using a punch (Figure 8-85). Replacement ring gears have threaded holes and are furnished with bolts.

REAL-WORLD FIX: The differential in a five-speed transaxle blew apart and destroyed the transaxle in a 1998 Saturn SL (105,000 mi). An inspection showed a repaired portion of the engine block indicating this had happened before. The technician had located a low-mileage used transaxle but was concerned about possible failure in the future.

FIX

A check showed a TSB describing an updated differential pin and gears. Installation of these parts into the good, used transaxle ensured a long-lasting repair.

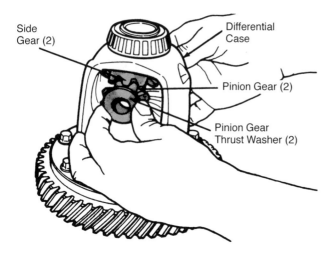

FIGURE 8-83   With the pinion shaft removed, the pinion gears can be rolled to the case windows and removed; then the side gears can be lifted out of the case. (Courtesy of DaimlerChrysler Corporation)

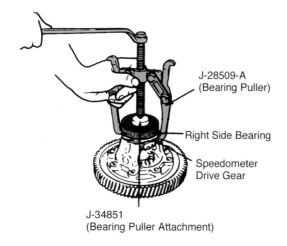

FIGURE 8-84   A faulty differential case bearing can be removed using a two-jaw bearing puller with an attachment for the puller to push against. (Portions of materials contained herein have been reprinted with permission of General Motors Corporation, Service and Parts Operations, License Agreement #0310807)

REAL-WORLD FIX: A 1992 Acura Legend (153,000 mi) would not move when put in gear and made a loud grinding noise. A visual inspection with the vehicle on a lift showed no obvious problem.

FIX

Disassembly of the transmission revealed that the shaft that transfers power to the front drive axle was stripped. Replacement of this shaft fixed this problem.

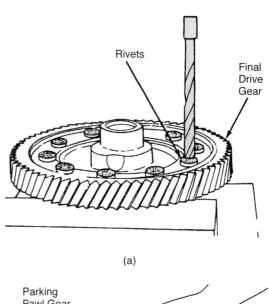

(a)

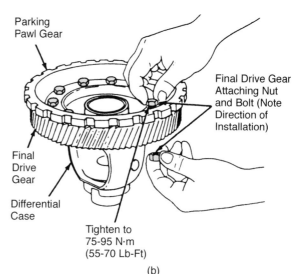

(b)

FIGURE 8-85   This final drive ring gear is riveted to the differential case. To replace it, the rivet heads are removed using a drill and chisel (a), and the new gear is installed using bolts and nuts (b). Note that b is for an automatic transaxle. (Courtesy of Ford Motor Company)

8.5.10   Shift Mechanism

There is a large variety of shift mechanisms. Some are contained in one assembly, such as the side cover of an open case transmission. Others are spread through several sections of the transmission. This spread-out shift mechanism is more common with transaxles (Figure 8-86). This wide variety often creates a problem when rebuilding a particular transaxle/transmission for the first time. It is easy to forget where and how each part goes for reassembly. Following service manual illustrations helps

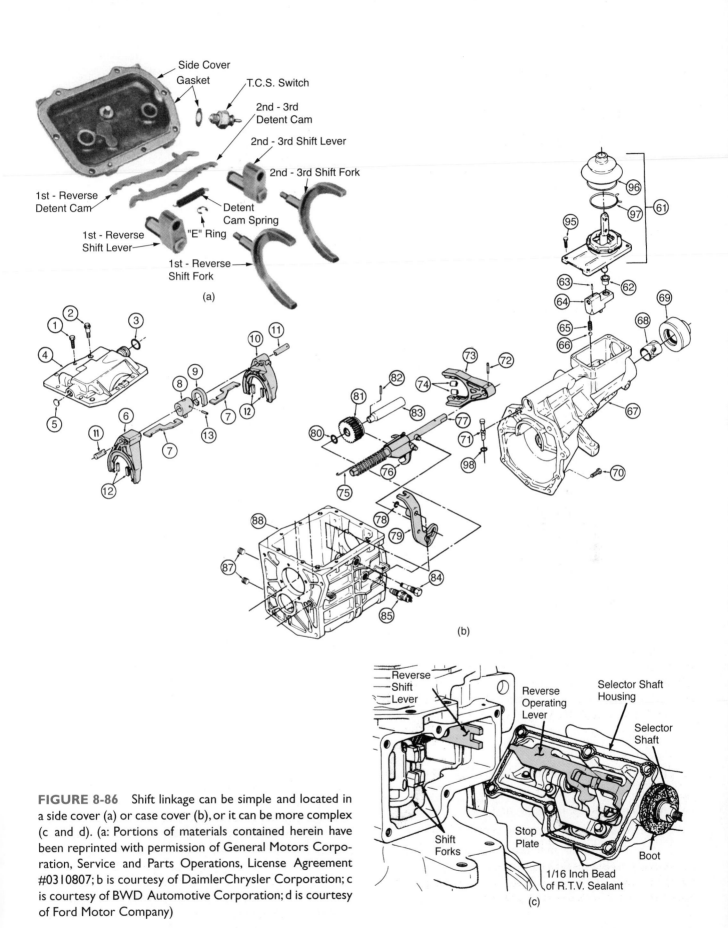

FIGURE 8-86 Shift linkage can be simple and located in a side cover (a) or case cover (b), or it can be more complex (c and d). (a: Portions of materials contained herein have been reprinted with permission of General Motors Corporation, Service and Parts Operations, License Agreement #0310807; b is courtesy of DaimlerChrysler Corporation; c is courtesy of BWD Automotive Corporation; d is courtesy of Ford Motor Company)

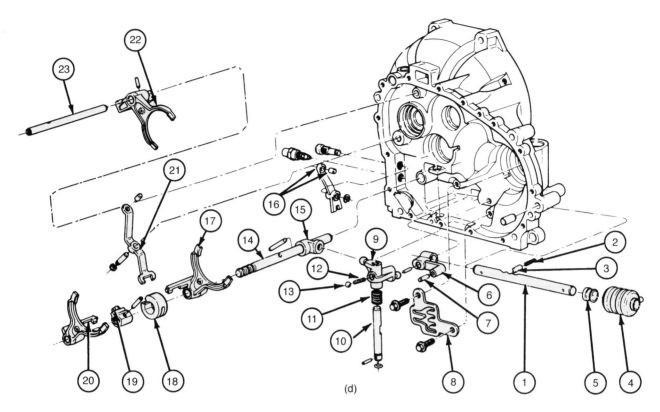

FIGURE 8-86   (Continued)

greatly, especially if the technician relates the part to its name and function. Understanding what each part is and what is does leads to a successful repair.

Each mechanism set contains a fork for each synchronizer sleeve or gear to be shifted, and each of these forks is mounted on a rail or lever that moves it through its travel. Each shifter includes one or more spring-loaded detent balls or cams and some form of interlock that allows only one shift fork to move at a time.

Each part should be checked as follows:

- **Shift fork:** distortion and bends, cracks, step wear at both the sleeve contact and cam contact areas, broken or worn inserts (Figures 8-87 and 8-88)
- **Shift rail:** distortion and bends, burrs, scores, grooves, elongated pinholes
- **Detent springs:** breakage
- **Detent cam (sometimes part of a rail):** wear, scoring
- **Interlock plates:** burrs, wear, scoring
- **Selector plates:** burrs, wear, scoring
- **Reverse lockout mechanism/solenoid:** proper operation (Figure 8-89)

As the transaxle/transmission is assembled, each of these parts should be checked for complete movement and smooth operation.

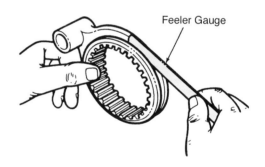

FIGURE 8-87   There should be a specified amount of clearance (about 0.030 in.) between the fork and the groove in the sleeve; excess clearance indicates a worn fork or groove. (Courtesy of Ford Motor Company)

REAL-WORLD FIX: A five-speed transaxle in a Pontiac Grand Am (35,000 mi) was rebuilt because of chipped teeth on the reverse gears. An upgraded gear set was installed. The transaxle now hung up in two gears.

FIX

Close inspection revealed a missing interlock pin, and the missing pin was blamed for the chipped reverse gear teeth. Installation of the interlock fixed this transaxle.

AUTHOR'S NOTE

As a unit is repaired for a problem, always look for a cause of that problem.

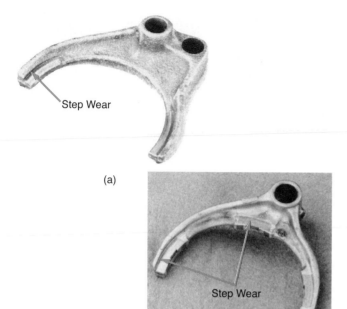

(a)

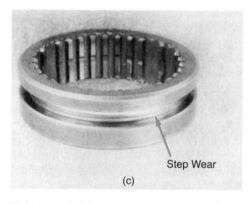

(b)

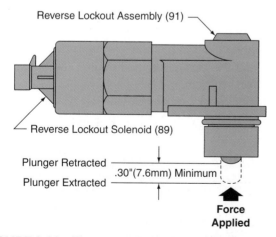

(c)

FIGURE 8-88 Close inspection of these shift forks shows a step caused by wear. Step wear and rubbing can also be seen in the synchronizer sleeve groove.

Reverse Lockout Assembly (91)

Reverse Lockout Solenoid (89)

Plunger Retracted

Plunger Extracted

.30"(7.6mm) Minimum

Force Applied

FIGURE 8-89 The reverse lockout plunger should move at least 0.300 in. when it is connected to a 12-V power source. (Courtesy of Transmission Technologies Corporation, TTC)

REAL-WORLD FIX: A 1995 BMW 318is (113,000 miles) had a problem of first gear jump-out. The transmission was removed and rebuilt, and a new 1–2 guide sleeve and first gear was installed along with new transmission mounts and rubber shifter mounts. But, this did not fix the problem.

FIX

Following advice, the shift fork was measured for wear as this fork tends to wear in a very smooth manner. The shift fork measured at 0.145 to 0.170 in., and the dimension of a new fork was 0.190 in. Replacement of this fork fixed this transmission.

REAL-WORLD FIX: A 1998 Camaro (92,000 miles) made a dry, grinding noise in fifth gear when it is cold that goes away after it warms up. The noise also occurred with the clutch depressed and the transmission in fifth gear.

FIX

Following advice, the transmission was disassembled, and inspection revealed that the plastic pads on the fifth gear shift fork had disintegrated. Replacement of the fifth gear shift fork and the plastic pads on all the shift forks fixed this problem.

8.5.11   Case and Covers

The case and all covers should be thoroughly cleaned and carefully checked for cracks, distortion or wear of bearing bores, and stripped bolt threads or worn throwout bearing supports. Damaged cases are normally replaced; however, they can be repaired, depending on the skill of the technician and the availability and cost of a replacement. Some rebuilders remachine the case and insert steel sleeves for worn bearing bores or throw-out bearing supports to return them to the original diameter and provide stronger-than-new material.

◄ SERVICE TIP ►

Many modern gear cases are cast from aluminum and, in a few cases, magnesium. Aluminum and magnesium have very similar properties except that magnesium burns. The metal will ignite at approximately 1,600°F (872°C) and burn with an intense white flame. Once combustion begins, it is extremely difficult to stop. Unpainted magnesium cases can be identified by a dull battleship-gray coating of magnesium oxide.

Stripped bolt threads are normally repaired by installing a thread insert (Figure 8-90).

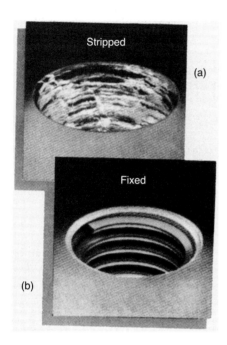

FIGURE 8-90 Stripped bolt hole (a) and one that has been repaired (b) by installing an insert (c). (Courtesy of HeliCoil)

To install a thread insert:

1. Using the correct tap, cut new threads in the damaged hole. It is often necessary to drill out the old threads using the tap drill sized to the special tap.
2. Place the insert onto the installing tool, and thread it into the hole until the outside end of the thread enters the case threads (Figure 8-91).
3. Break off the tang that is incorporated in some inserts, or stake or resize the insert to lock it in place.

Most cases include one or more seals, which are normally replaced during a rebuild. These seals include:

- Each shift shaft that passes through the case,
- One or two output shaft seals,
- Sometimes an input shaft seal.

Old seals are normally removed by prying them out using a seal puller or screwdriver, or by driving them out from behind. New seals are driven into place using

(a)   (b)   (c)

FIGURE 8-91 A damaged thread is repaired by drilling out the old threads to a specified size (a), cutting new threads using a special tap (b), and installing the insert using an installation tool (c). (Courtesy of HeliCoil)

a seal driver that fits against the entire outer surface to prevent seal distortion (Figure 8-92).

8.5.12 Transaxle/Transmission Reassembly

The procedure used to assemble a transmission or transaxle is normally the reverse of the procedure used to disassemble it; the last thing removed from the case is usually the first thing replaced. Unit assembly varies widely, and it is recommended that the manufacturer's information be reviewed for specifications and the specific procedure to follow. Each moving part should be lubricated as it is installed, and checked for free and smooth operation. Petroleum jelly, transmission assembly lube, or gear oil should be used for the lubricant.

A typical transaxle assembly follows this procedure:

1. Set the differential assembly into the case.
2. Place the input shaft and mainshaft together and set them in the case.
3. Install the shift forks and rails.
4. Install the reverse idler gear, shaft, and fork.
5. Apply sealant to the case mating surface.
6. Install the case cover and tighten the bolts to the correct torque.
7. Install the exterior parts.
8. Check the operation in neutral and all gears.

◀ **SERVICE TIP** ▶

After assembly, the input shaft should rotate smoothly and easily in neutral, with no drag when trying to turn the output shafts; each gear range should also rotate smoothly without excess drag.

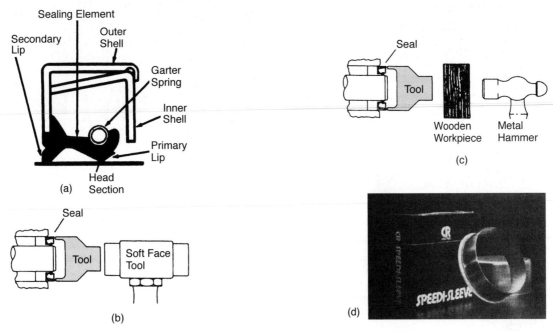

FIGURE 8-92   (a) Improper installation can damage the outer shell of a seal or dislodge the garter spring. (b and c) A new seal should be driven straight inward using a seal driver and a soft-face hammer or block of wood to cushion the impact of the driving tool. (d) If the sealing surface on the shaft is damaged, a thin sleeve can be installed over it. (Courtesy of CR Services)

Before the reassembly of a transaxle/transmission that uses tapered roller bearings, the **preload** or **end play** of each shaft should be checked. A selective **shim** is located at a bearing at one end of each shaft, and the thickness of this shim controls the amount of preload or end play (Figure 8-93). Preload causes a slight drag as a shaft is rotated; it is usually measured using a torque wrench or spring scale. End play is a free, lengthwise movement of the shaft; it is usually measured using a dial indicator or feeler gauge.

Gauging fixtures are available for some transaxles that allow for setting the clearance on all three of the shafts at one time (Figure 8-94). Without special fixtures, most shops will need to check the clearance on each shaft, one at a time. This must be done if a bearing, shaft, bearing retainer/case cover, or case has been replaced.

To check and adjust bearing clearance/preload on a transaxle:

1. Place the shaft to be checked with its bearings in the case. If new parts are used, adjustment is necessary. Use an adjusting shim that is too small, so there will be end play. A shim that is about 0.010 in. (0.25 mm) smaller than the one that was originally used, or the smallest one available, is normally used as a starter.

2. Install the bearing retainer or case cover, and tighten all bolts to the correct torque. Rotate the shaft several times as the bolts are tightened to seat the bearings.

3. Install a dial indicator with the indicating stylus at the end of and parallel to the shaft (Figure 8-95). Move the shaft up and down through its free travel several times while reading the amount of end play or clearance on the dial indicator.

◄ SERVICE TIP ►

Check end play at least three times or until you get consistent readings.

4. Compare the amount of travel to the specifications. If a clearance is specified and the travel is within the specifications, no adjustment is required. If a clearance is specified and the travel is more or less than the specifications, an adjustment is required.

◄ SERVICE TIP ►

If there is too much end play, the shim size usually needs to be increased. For example, 0.010 in. (0.25 mm) of travel with a specification of 0.001 to 0.003 in. (0.25 to 0.07 mm) is corrected with a shim that is 0.008 in. (0.2 mm) larger than the one used during the check. Too little travel is corrected in the same way but with a thinner shim.

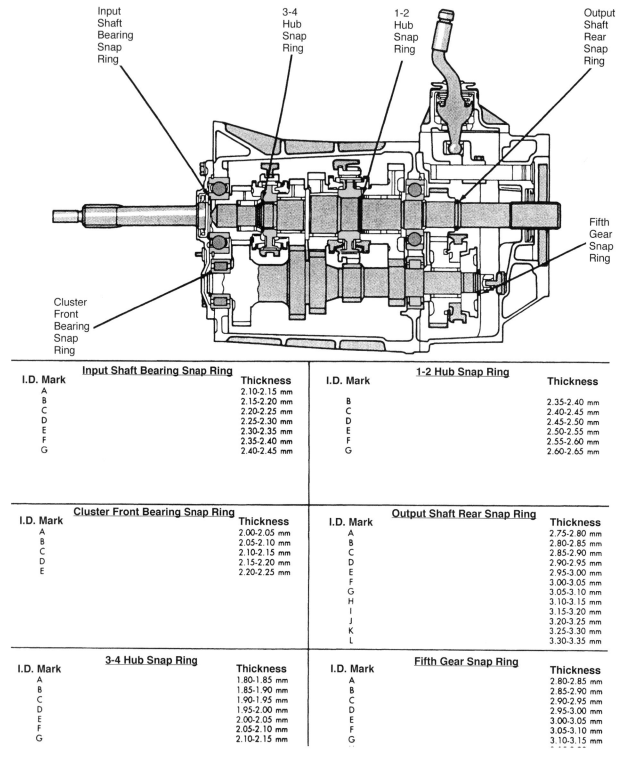

FIGURE 8-93 This transmission uses selective snap rings at six different locations to adjust end play or preload. (Courtesy of DaimlerChrysler Corporation)

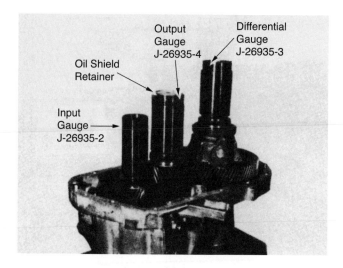

(a)

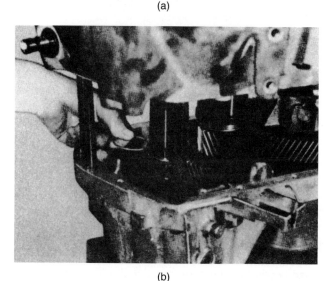

(b)

FIGURE 8-94 (a) The gauging procedure for shaft bearing clearance on this transaxle includes three tubular units placed over each shaft and a set of stands between the cases. (b) Then the technician selects the shim that fits at each bearing cup. (Portions of materials contained herein have been reprinted with permission of General Motors Corporation, Service and Parts Operations, License Agreement #0310807)

◄ **SERVICE TIP** ►

If a preload is specified, the shim size needs to be increased by the amount of clearance plus a preload factor of about 0.003 or 0.004 in. (0.07 to 0.1 mm), depending on the manufacturer. For example, 0.010 in. of travel is corrected with a shim that is 0.010 + 0.003 (or 0.013) in. (0.3 mm) larger that the one used during the check. If a preload is specified and there is no clearance, check the preload as described in step 6.

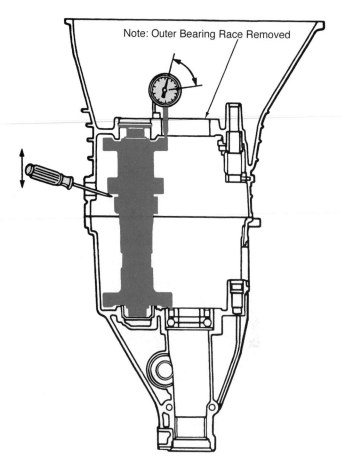

FIGURE 8-95 A dial indicator has been set up to measure the end play that occurs as the cluster gear is lifted and dropped. (Portions of materials contained herein have been reprinted with permission of General Motors Corporation, Service and Parts Operations, License Agreement #0310807)

◄ **SERVICE TIP** ►

An alternative method of measuring the distance between the case and the bearing cup is to place two very thin strips of solder in place of the shim between the case and the bearing cup, install the shaft and bearing, install the case cover and tighten the bolts to the correct torque. Disassemble the unit, and measure the thickness of the solder using a micrometer. This will be the shim size before adjusting for preload or end play.

5. If a shim change is required, remove the bearing retainer/case cover and remove the old shim. Measure the thickness of the shim. Add that size to the amount of change you measured in the last step (Figure 8-96). Select and install a shim of the correct size, replace the bearing retainer/case cover, tighten

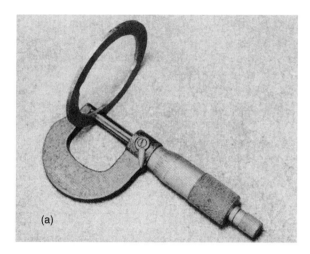

(a)

(b)

(c)

FIGURE 8-96 The size of a selective shim can be measured directly by using an outside micrometer (a) or indirectly by setting up a dial indicator to read zero on the case (b) and then sliding the shim under the indicator and reading the size (c).

the bolts, rotate the shaft to seat the bearings, and feel for end play. On preloaded shafts, there should not be any end play.

6. Using a torque wrench or spring scale and adapter, measure the torque required to keep the shaft rotating, not the breakaway or starting torque (Figure 8-97).

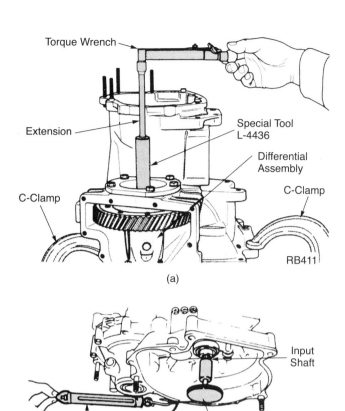

(a)

(b)

FIGURE 8-97 The preload or turning torque required to rotate a shaft can be measured using a torque wrench (a) or special tool and spring balance/scale (b). (a is courtesy of DaimlerChrysler Corporation; b: Portions of materials contained herein have been reprinted with permission of General Motors Corporation, Service and Parts Operations, License Agreement #0310807)

◀ **SERVICE TIP** ▶

An oversized socket can be used on splined shafts by placing cardboard or cloth over the shaft so that a pressure is required to slide the socket in place.

Compare the preload reading to the specifications; if they are within the specifications, you have the correct shim. Readings that are too high or too low indicate the wrong shim. In these cases, use the next larger or smaller shim, depending on the change needed.

7. When the clearance/preload is correct, remove this shaft, and repeat this check on the next shaft.

The assembly of a typical transmission follows this procedure:

1. Install the reverse idler gear and shaft.
2. Install the cluster gear and countershaft.
3. Install the mainshaft.
4. Install the input shaft and retainer.
5. Install the extension housing.
6. Install the side cover with shift mechanism.
7. Check the operation in neutral and all gears.

As the transmission is assembled, the end play of the cluster gear and the clearance or preload of the mainshaft and main drive gear should be checked and adjusted, if necessary.

To check the end play on two-piece cluster gear and countershaft assemblies:

1. Place a loading tool inside the cluster gear and load the needle bearings and thrust washers in place (Figure 8-98).

◄ **SERVICE TIP** ►

Petroleum jelly can be used to help stick the thrust washers in position.

◄ **SERVICE TIP** ►

If loading the needle bearings in a cluster gear and no loading tool is available, a common manila folder can be used. First put a layer of grease inside the cluster gear to help hold the needle bearings in place. Cut the folder to the same length as the cluster gear. Roll it into a tube so there is at least two or three thicknesses, and then cut off the excess. Slide the tube inside the cluster gear and use it to hold the bearings.

2. Place the gear assembly into the case and push the countershaft into place, pushing the loading tool out of the other end of the case (Figure 8-99).
3. Move the cluster gear to contact at the front, and using the largest feeler gauge that will enter, measure the clearance between the gear and thrust washer or case at the rear of the case (Figure 8-100a). Or, mount a dial indicator at the front of the case with the indicator stylus on the cluster gear and parallel to the countershaft (Figure 8-100b).

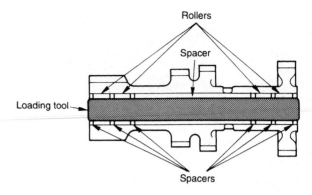

FIGURE 8-98 A loading tool should be used to hold the needle bearings and spacers in position while the cluster gear is installed in the transmission. The loading tool is a shaft that is the same diameter as the countershaft and the same length as the cluster gear.

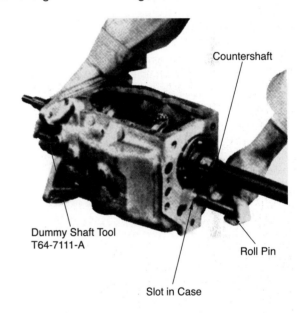

FIGURE 8-99 The loading tool/dummy shaft is pushed out as the countershaft is installed. Note that the roll pin is temporarily installed so that the hole in the countershaft can be aligned with the hole in the case. (Courtesy of Ford Motor Company)

Move the cluster gear up and down and read the amount of travel/clearance.

4. Compare the feeler gauge or dial indicator reading to the specifications. You can use 0.004 to 0.020 in. (0.1 to 0.5 mm) as a guide if specifications are not available. Excessive end play is an indication that the thrust washers are worn.

The procedure used to adjust the bearing preload/clearance on a one-piece cluster gear/countershaft using tapered roller bearings is the same as that used to

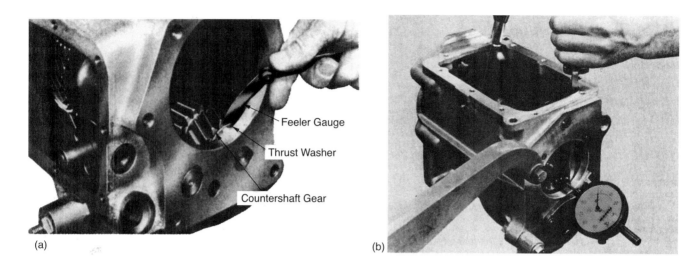

(a)   (b)

FIGURE 8-100   Cluster gear end play can be measured by prying the gear to one end and using a feeler gauge to measure the gap between the end of the gear and the thrust washer (a), using a dial indicator to measure the travel as the gear is pried from one end to the other (b). (a is courtesy of DaimlerChrysler Corporation; b is courtesy of Ford Motor Company)

adjust the shaft bearing clearance on a transaxle. For example, the countershaft gear of a T5 transmission should be adjusted to provide end play of 0.0005 to 0.004 in. (0.013 to 0.102 mm); the shim for this is at the rear bearing retainer (Figure 8-101).

The input shaft and mainshaft on the T5 transmission also use tapered roller bearings that are adjusted to provide zero free travel and preload during assembly. The selective shim for this is at the input bearing. Two different methods can be used to select the correct shim. One is to assemble the transmission, place it in a vertical position (output shaft up), rotate the shafts to seat the bearings, and measure the end play at the end of the mainshaft using a dial indicator (Figure 8-102). If there is more than zero end play, the shim thickness should be increased the same amount as the end play. For example, if there is 0.006 in. (0.15 mm) of end play, a 0.006-in.-larger shim needs to be installed.

The second method of adjustment is to assemble the transmission except for the input bearing retainer. With the transmission vertical (input shaft up), rotate the input and mainshaft to seat the bearings while pushing downward on the input bearing cup. Then measure the distance from the front of the bearing cup to the case using a depth micrometer (dimension A) and the depth of the bearing cup recess in the front bearing retainer (dimension B) (Figure 8-103). Subtract dimension A from dimension B, and add 0.003 in. (0.07 mm) for the overall thickness of the shim (B − A + 0.003 = shim thickness). After the proper shim is selected and installed along with the front bearing retainer, check the rotation of the input and mainshaft.

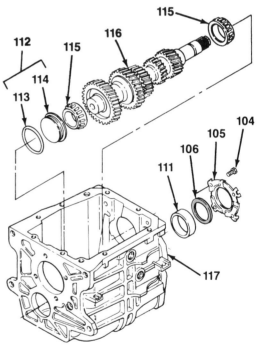

104. Bolt	113. O-Ring
105. Rear Retainer	114. Bearing Cup
106. Shim	115. Bearing Cone
111. Bearing Cup	116. Countershaft
112. Bearing Cup	Gear
Assembly	117. Case Assembly

FIGURE 8-101   This transmission uses a shim (106) to adjust countershaft gear end play to 0.0005 to 0.004 in. (0.013 to 0.102 mm). (Courtesy of BWD Automotive Corporation)

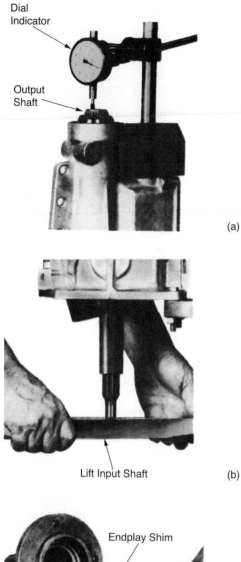

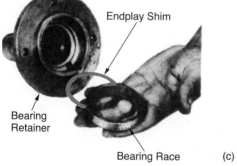

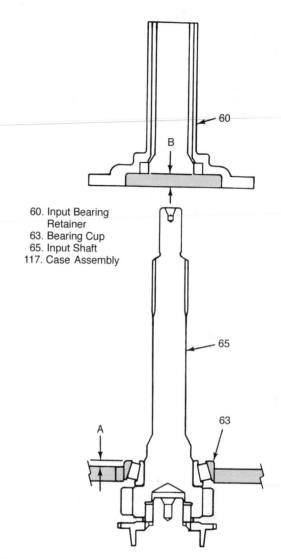

60. Input Bearing
    Retainer
63. Bearing Cup
65. Input Shaft
117. Case Assembly

FIGURE 8-103 A second method of adjusting input/output shaft bearing preload on a T5 transmission is to push the input bearing cup into the case and measure distance A; measure distance B in the bearing retainer; and subtract A from B. The shim should be this size + 0.003 in. (Courtesy of BWD Automotive Corporation)

FIGURE 8-102 One method of selecting the proper shim to get the correct amount of input/output shaft bearing preload on a T5 transmission is to assemble the transmission and mount and adjust a dial indicator at the output shaft (a) to read the end play as you lift the input shaft (b). Change the end play shim as needed to compensate for too much or too little end play (c). (Courtesy of Ford Motor Company)

They should turn with only a very slight drag and have no end play.

As the cover, extension housing, and front bearing retainer are installed, a gasket or sealant—usually RTV or anaerobic sealant—should be used to prevent lubricant leaks (Figure 8-104). Follow the manufacturer's recommendations the retaining bolts should be tightened in an alternating fashion, back and forth across the cover (Figure 8-105). Tighten each bolt to the proper torque.

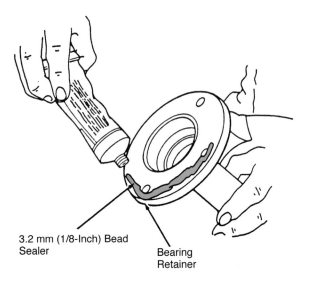

3.2 mm (1/8-Inch) Bead
Sealer

Bearing
Retainer

FIGURE 8-104 A bead of anaerobic sealant is used to prevent leaks between this front bearing retainer and the case. (Courtesy of Transmission Technologies Corporation, TTC)

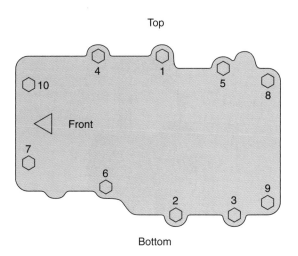

Top

Front

Bottom

FIGURE 8-105 The case-to-cover bolts of this TR-3550 transmission should be tightened to 18–22 lb-ft (24.4–29.8 N-m) using this sequence. Note that it starts with the center bolts and works to the ends. (Courtesy of Transmission Technologies Corporation, TTC)

REAL WORLD FIX: The transmission in a 1992 Explorer (150,000 mi) was rebuilt 5,000 miles ago. A damaged input shaft and all of the bearings were replaced using OEM parts. The end play was adjusted as shown in the Ford service manual. This transmission was repaired before for the same problem, a seized front bearing. It came back because of the same problem.

FIX

It was determined that the damage was caused by a fluid loss. The leak was through three loose rubber plugs at the back of the top cover. Replacement of the damaged input shaft bearing and the three rubber sealing plugs fixed this transmission.

AUTHOR'S NOTE

Experience teaches us that it is always a good practice when making a repair to determine what caused the problem. If you don't fix the cause, the problem can return.

After a transmission is assembled, the input shaft should turn freely in neutral with no drag when trying to turn the output shaft. Shifts into each gear should be smooth, and the shafts should rotate easily and smoothly in each gear.

◀ PROBLEM SOLVING ▶

Imagine that you are working in a transmission repair shop and you encounter these problems.

Case 1

You are fixing a problem of fourth-gear clash during shifts on a four-speed transaxle. The vehicle is an 8-year-old compact that is fairly worn. When checking the blocker ring-to-speed gear clearances, you find these clearances: first gear, 0.020 in.; second gear, 0.065 in.; third gear, 0.60 in.; and fourth gear, 0.0 in. You can't find any specs. So for this transaxle you measure a new blocker ring and find that its clearance is 0.085 in. With the cost of these blocker rings at $23.95 each and a limited budget of the customer, which should you replace?

Case 2

You've just about finished rebuilding a five-speed transmission by bolting the main drive gear bearing retainer in place, but when you turn the clutch shaft, you find that there is no neutral. The output shaft turns a little slower than the clutch shaft. What is probably wrong? What should you do next?

REVIEW QUESTIONS

The following questions are provided to help you study as you read the chapter.

1. To check the fluid level in a transmission or transaxle, a _____ plug or _____ stick is usually provided.

2. The fluid level should be at the bottom of the _____ plug hole.

3. A transmission or transaxle that shifts hard could be caused by a _____ clutch or binding in the _____ linkage.

4. A transmission that is noisy in neutral and all reduction gears could be caused by worn _____ bearings.

5. A pair of _____ _____ can be used to help support the weight of the transmission during removal and installation.

6. Transaxles removal may require the use of an engine _____ fixture.

7. The first thing that should be disconnected when removing a transmission is the _____ _____ _____.

8. _____ marks should be placed on the synchronizer sleeve and hub during disassembly.

9. Excessive friction between parts will cause _____.

10. Inspection of a bearing is done by _____, _____ and _____.

11. A _____ or special _____ may be required to dissemble the mainshaft.

12. _____ _____ snap rings or thrust washers are available to adjust bearings and gear clearances.

13. Old oil _____ can be removed by prying them out using a seal puller or screwdriver, or by driving them out from behind.

14. Bearing preload is measured using a _____ wrench or _____ scale.

15. After a transmission or transaxle is assembled, the input should turn freely in _____ with no drag when trying to _____ the output shaft.

CHAPTER QUIZ

The following questions will help you check the facts you have learned. Select the answer that completes each statement correctly.

1. While discussing transaxle gear lubricant, Student A says that the fluid level should be even with the bottom of the filler hole. Student B says that it should be in the hatch-marked area of the dipstick. Who is correct?
   a. Student A
   b. Student B
   c. Both Student A and Student B
   d. Neither Student A nor Student B

2. Student A says that an improperly adjusted shift linkage can cause a transmission to jump out of gear. Student B says that clutch drag can cause hard shifting. Who is correct?
   a. Student A
   b. Student B
   c. Both Student A and Student B
   d. Neither Student A nor Student B

3. A transaxle shifts easily through all the gear ranges with the engine shut off, but with the engine running, the shifts into all forward gears are hard and there is a clash when shifting into reverse. Student A says this problem could be caused by a worn shift fork. Student B says there could be worn countershaft bearings. Who is correct?
   a. Student A
   b. Student B
   c. Both Student A and Student B
   d. Neither Student A nor Student B

4. An engine support fixture is usually required when removing a A. transaxle or B. transmission. Which is correct?
   a. A only
   c. Both A and B
   b. B only
   d. Neither A nor B

5. Student A says that the shift linkage should be checked for proper adjustment after a transmission has been replaced. Student B says that you should be careful not to catch a wire or hose between the clutch housing and engine when replacing a transaxle. Who is correct?
   a. Student A
   b. Student B
   c. Both Student A and Student B
   d. Neither Student A nor Student B

6. Student A says that synchronizer sleeves can be replaced onto the hub in any position. Student B says that blocker rings should be snug and not wiggle around when installed. Who is correct?

   a. Student A

   b. Student B

   c. Both Student A and Student B

   d. Neither Student A nor Student B

7. While discussing a transaxle that makes a loud clunk as the clutch is engaged, Student A says that this could be caused by a worn differential pinion shaft. Student B says that it could be caused by a worn clutch disc. Who is correct?

   a. Student A

   b. Student B

   c. Both Student A and Student B

   d. Neither Student A nor Student B

8. When working with a cluster gear supported by a countershaft, a loading tool

   a. holds the needle bearings in place during installation.

   b. contains the needle bearings during teardown.

   c. is used to push the countershaft out of the case.

   d. all of these.

9. A faulty blocker ring A. makes a dull sound when tapped by a metal object, B. has less than 0.040 in. (1 mm) of clearance. Which is correct?

   a. A only   c. Both A and B

   b. B only   d. Neither A nor B

10. All of the following should be observed carefully when checking bearings except that

    a. bearings should be air dried by spinning them with compressed air.

    b. a rough bearing should be cleaned, dried, and rechecked.

    c. a bearing is checked by rotating it as you feel and listen for roughness.

    d. a bearing should be lightly oiled before checking.

11. Student A says that all gears with chips on their teeth should be replaced. Student B says that burrs on the clutching teeth can be cleaned up using a small grinder. Who is correct?

    a. Student A

    b. Student B

    c. Both Student A and Student B

    d. Neither Student A nor Student B

12. Student A says that blocker ring clearance can be checked using a feeler gauge. Student B says that synchronizer energizer springs are usually placed in the hub running in opposite directions. Who is correct?

    a. Student A

    b. Student B

    c. Both Student A and Student B

    d. Neither Student A nor Student B

13. Student A says that each gear next to a synchronizer hub should have a few thousandths of an inch of end float after it is installed. Student B says that new snap rings should always be used during transaxle reassembly. Who is correct?

    a. Student A

    b. Student B

    c. Both Student A and Student B

    d. Neither Student A nor Student B

14. Student A says that all cluster gears should have about 0.010 in. (0.25 mm) of end play after installation. Student B says there should be this same amount of end play on an input shaft. Who is correct?

    a. Student A

    b. Student B

    c. Both Student A and Student B

    d. Neither Student A nor Student B

15. The bearing on many transaxle input shafts and mainshafts is adjusted using A. selective shims, B. threaded adjusters. Which is correct?

    a. A only   c. Both A and B

    b. B only   d. Neither A nor B

16. You've replaced the third speed gear and the 3–4 synchronizer assembly on the clutch shaft of a five-speed transaxle and installed the retaining snap ring. The end float of the third speed gear is sloppy—0.35 mm of float (the specification is 0.06 to 0.21 mm). Seven retaining rings are available between the sizes of 1.80 and 2.10 mm; their size will increase 0.05 mm in each step. Remove the snap ring, measure it, and determine that its size is 1.85 mm. What size of retaining ring do you need to get the correct end float?

17. What are the largest and smallest shim sizes that you could use to correct the end float in Question 16?

18. The gear train is assembled in the five-speed transmission, and you need to replace the main drive gear bearing retainer. The distance from the front of the bearing to the case is 0.06 in., and the recess in the bearing retainer is 0.105 in. with the gasket in place. The specification is 0.0 to 0.004 in., and there are seven spacers available from 0.032 to 0.060 in. (0.004-in. increments). What size spacer do you need?

◀ Chapter 9 ▶

DRIVESHAFT AND UNIVERSAL JOINT THEORY

LEARNING OBJECTIVES

After completing this chapter, you should be able to:

1. Identify the parts of RWD and FWD driveshafts.
2. Name the purpose for each driveshaft part.
3. Understand the operation of a U-joint and CV joint.
4. Identify the different types of U-joints and CV joints.
5. Identify where each U-joint and CV joint style is used.
6. Understand the requirements for good driveshaft operation.

TERMS TO LEARN

ball and trunnion joint	Hotchkiss
brinelling	inboard joint
Cardan joint	outboard joint
circlip	phasing
cross and yoke joint	plunge joint
cross groove joint	Rzeppa joint
constant-velocity (CV) joint	slip joint
double-Cardan joint	slip yoke
double-offset joint	swage
driveline	tripod joint
fixed joint	tripod tulip joint
grease	tripod joint
halfshaft	torque tube
Hooke joint	universal joint (U-joint)

9.1 INTRODUCTION

A RWD vehicle has one driveshaft connecting the rear drive axle assembly to the transmission, and a FWD car has two driveshafts connecting the drive wheels to the transaxle (Figure 9-1). Most driveshafts are metal tubes or shafts with either a **universal joint (U-joint)** or **constant-velocity (CV) joint** at each end. RWD driveshafts are often called **drivelines** or propeller shafts. FWD driveshafts and the shafts connecting the rear drive wheel to the gear assembly of independent rear suspension (IRS) are often called **halfshafts.**

Most RWD driveshafts use a simple cross and yoke style of U-joint that allows the shaft angle to change while spinning and transmitting power. This angle change is necessary because of the rear axle's movement relative to the vehicle body each time a bump in the road is encountered (Figure 9-2). The vertical movement of the axle causes the transmission-to-drive axle distance to change. A **slip joint** compensates for this change. When the axle moves upward, the shaft must become shorter. In most cases, the slip joint is where the U-joint **slip yoke** enters the transmission; in a few cars and many trucks, a slip joint is built into the shaft.

FWD driveshafts encounter the same problems as a RWD driveshaft; in addition, they must allow the front wheels to steer sharply for turns. These sharp angles require CV joints at the outer, or outboard, end of the shaft (Figure 9-3). The inner, or **inboard, joint** can change length, or **plunge.** The outer, or **outboard, joint** is a

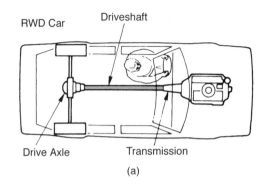

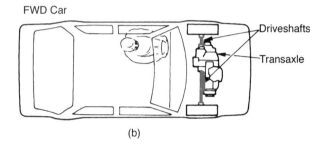

FIGURE 9-1   (a) A RWD vehicle uses a driveshaft to connect the transmission to the rear axle. (b) A FWD vehicle uses two driveshafts to connect the transaxle to the front wheels.

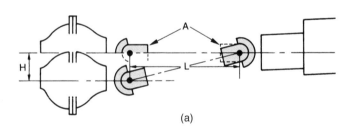

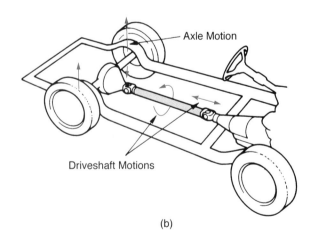

FIGURE 9-2   A driveshaft transfers power to an axle that moves up and down (a). To do this, the U-joints must change angle and the driveshaft must change length or move in or out of the transmission.

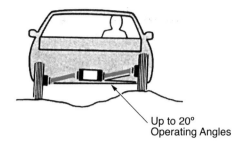

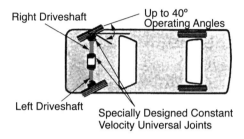

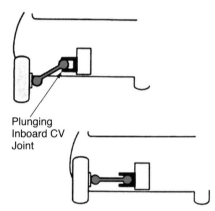

FIGURE 9-3   When the front wheels of a FWD vehicle move up or down, the CV joints must change angle and length; the outer CV joint must also change angle as the vehicle is steered. (Courtesy of Ford Motor Company)

fixed joint; it does not change length. The bending portion of this joint must stay in line with the vehicles steering axis.

9.2   UNIVERSAL JOINTS

The most common style of U-joint is the **Hooke** or **Cardan joint.** It is also called a **cross and yoke joint.** This joint uses two yokes that are connected by a cross, and the cross has a needle bearing assembly at each arm, or trunnion, where it connects to the yoke (Figure 9-4). This arrangement usually allows up to a 15° angle change. The cross, also called a spider, pivots in each yoke when the shaft runs at an angle. This pivoting action solves the problem of allowing the shaft to bend, but it creates another problem of speed fluctuation.

Driveshaft and Universal Joint Theory   **245**

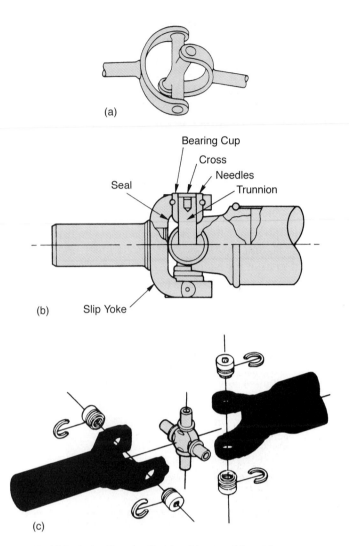

FIGURE 9-4   Simple Cardan U-joint (a), with a cutaway (b) and an exploded (c) view, used in most RWD driveshafts. (Portions of materials contained herein have been reprinted with permission of General Motors Corporation, Service and Parts Operations, License Agreement #0310807)

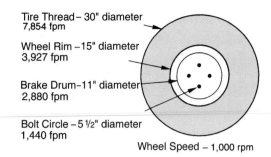

FIGURE 9-5   This wheel is spinning at 1000 rpm, so all the parts are rotating at the same speed; but because of their different diameters, the parts are traveling at different velocities.

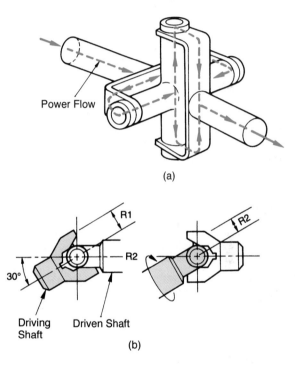

FIGURE 9-6   The power flow through a Cardan U-joint is from one yoke, through the cross, and out the other yoke (a). As the joint rotates, the radii of the driving and driven yokes change (b).

The speed of a spinning object varies with its diameter. Speed can be measured in two ways: by the revolutions per minute (rpm) and by the actual velocity of a given part. The actual velocity is determined by the rpm and the radius, or distance from the center of rotation. Figure 9-5 illustrates how a wheel spinning at 1000 rpm can have a brake drum surface moving at 2880 feet per minute (fpm) [878 meters per minute (mpm)], a wheel rim moving at 3927 fpm (1197 mpm), and a tire tread moving at 7854 fpm (2934 mpm)—all at the same time. This relates to a U-joint in that the driving plane of one yoke and the driven plane of the other yoke change radius twice per revolution (Figure 9-6). This results in two periods in which the driven yoke will speed up and

two periods in which it will slow down, or two speed fluctuations per revolution. This is an angle-related speed fluctuation; a greater angle will generate a greater amount of speed fluctuation (Figure 9-7).

These velocity changes usually do not create a problem because normally two joints are used on a shaft, so that one joint will cancel out the other. It just needs to generate an equal but opposite speed fluctuation. This is done by placing one joint's driving motion exactly 90° (one-quarter turn) behind the other, which is called **phasing.** Also, the operating angle of each joint

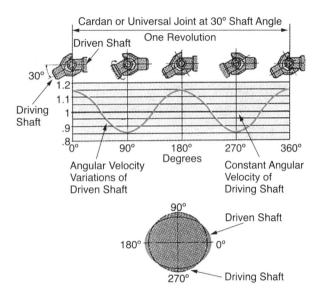

FIGURE 9-7 This chart illustrates the velocity variation through a Cardan U-joint operating at a 30° angle. (Courtesy of Ford Motor Company)

is kept equal (Figure 9-8). When done correctly, the leading joint causes the shaft to speed up. The trailing joint will slow the speed down by the same amount, so an even, steady spinning motion arrives at the rear axle drive pinion shaft. If the joints get out of phase or the operating angles become unequal, an annoying vibration usually results.

As the running angle of a U-joint increases, the efficiency will decrease, because of the power lost to friction in the joint. In contrast, a U-joint should never be run in a perfectly straight position. The needle bearings need to move so that they can wear evenly against the bearing journals of the cross and inside the cups. Lack

of needle movement on the cross will cause a wear pattern called **brinelling** (Figure 9-9).

9.2.1   Construction

The yokes of a Cardan U-joint are usually made of forged steel and are either welded onto the shaft, made as part of the slip yoke that slides over the transmission shaft, or made as part of the flange of the axle pinion shaft (Figure 9-10). The bearing cups are normally pressed into the bearing bosses of the first two styles, secured to the axle flange with U-bolts, or bolted directly to the flange using wing-style cups (Figure 9-11).

The U-joint cross is also forged steel and has a smooth journal for each of the bearing surfaces as well as a ground bearing surface at the very ends (Figure 9-12). The critical dimensions for a cross are also shown

FIGURE 9-9 This journal on a U-joint cross shows a brinelling type of wear pattern. Note the impression left by the bearing needles. (Courtesy of Dana Corporation)

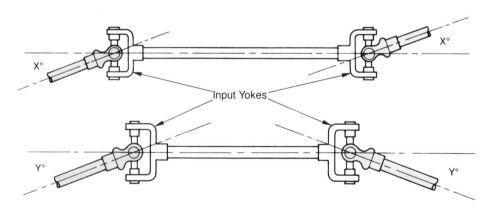

FIGURE 9-8 To eliminate vibrations, a driveshaft using Cardan U-joints must have the two joints operating at the same angles with the driving yokes of the two joints phased exactly 90° apart. In this example, joint angles X are equal to each other, as are angles Y. (Portions of materials contained herein have been reprinted with permission of General Motors Corporation, Service and Parts Operations, License Agreement #0310807)

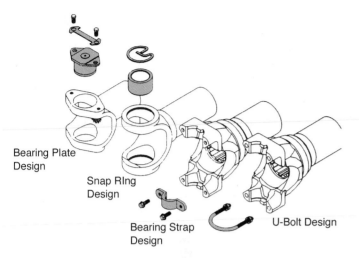

Bearing Plate
Design

Snap Ring
Design

Bearing Strap
Design

U-Bolt Design

FIGURE 9-10 Four styles of yokes used with Cardan U-joints. (Courtesy of Dana Corporation)

in the illustration. Note that the length of the cross is one of the critical dimensions. This distance provides a slight clearance at the inner ends of the bearing cups so that the cross will be centered to the yokes, which, in turn, center the two shafts to each other.

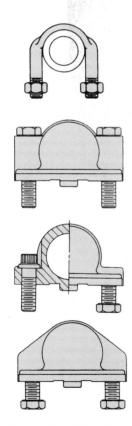

FIGURE 9-11 Four styles of bearing cups used with Cardan U-joints. The round bearing cup (at top with U-bolt) is the most common. (Courtesy of NEAPCO)

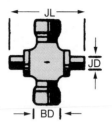

FIGURE 9-12 The critical dimensions of a cross with and without bearing cups. JL, joint length; JD, trunnion diameter; BD, bearing diameter. (Courtesy of NEAPCO)

The bearing cups are located in the yokes so that the cross and the two yokes will be centered to each other. They are held in this location by a retaining ring, a plastic intrusion, or swaging. The retaining ring is in a groove, either at the ends of the bores in the yoke for the outside lockup style of joint or in the bearing cup inside of the yoke for the inside lockup style of joint (Figure 9-13).

◀ SERVICE TIP ▶

U-joints with an outside retainer ring are sometimes referred to as Spicer-style joints, while inboard retainer joints are sometimes called Cleveland-, Detroit-, or mechanics-style U-joints. The critical dimensions of the joint vary in these different joint styles.

Removal of the retaining ring allows the joint to be disassembled. With a plastic intrusion, the plastic is sheared apart when the joint is disassembled, and the U-joint is replaced with one having an inside lockup style of bearing cups and retaining rings. A few manufacturers **swage** (upset or deform) the yokes to lock the bearing cups in place, and these joints normally cannot be rebuilt in the field. When a plastic intrusion or swaging is used to secure the bearing cups, the manufacturer can assemble the joint and correct any runout or off-center problems before locking the bearing cups in place.

The bearing cups are lubricated with grease and use a seal to keep the grease in and dirt and moisture out. Some crosses include a zerk (grease) fitting so that the joint can be lubricated periodically (Figure 9-14).

9.2.2 U-Joint Variations

Before the mid-1960s, Chrysler Corporation vehicles used a **ball and trunnion** style of U-joint at one or both ends of the driveshaft. This type of joint transmits

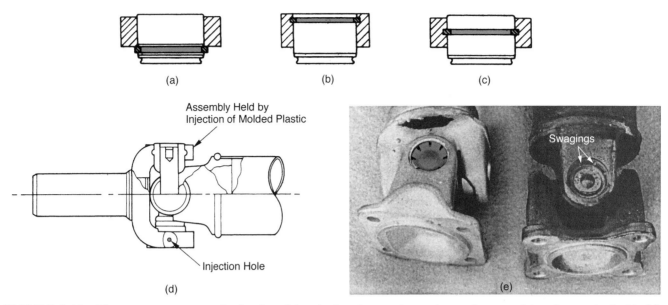

FIGURE 9-13 The most common methods of retaining the bearing cup in a yoke are by a retaining ring on the inside (a), a retaining ring on the outside (b), or plastic injection (c and d). In some joints, the cups are held in place by swaging the cup or retainer ring in place (e). (a, b, and c are courtesy of NEAPCO; d: Portions of materials contained herein have been reprinted with permission of General Motors Corporation, Service and Parts Operations, License Agreement #0310807)

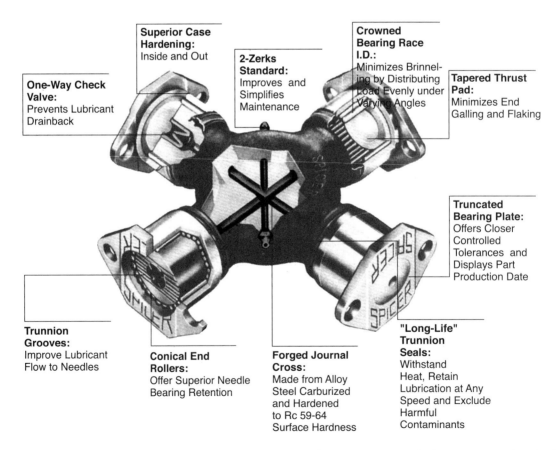

FIGURE 9-14 Some U-joint crosses are drilled and include a zerk fitting to lubricate the bearings; note that this heavy-duty joint uses two zerk fittings. Also note the seal between the bearing cup and cross to retain the grease in the bearing. (Courtesy of Dana Corporation)

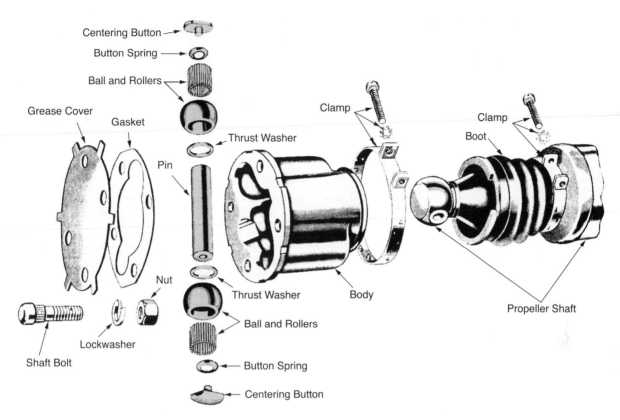

FIGURE 9-15   Ball and trunnion U-joint; the trunnion pin is pressed through the hole at the end of the propeller shaft. (Courtesy of DaimlerChrysler Corporation)

power through a trunnion pin that has a ball at each end; a set of needle bearings is used to allow easy ball rotation (Figure 9-15). The balls fit into two long grooves, or raceways, in the housing. This allows the housing to move lengthwise over the pin and balls and to pivot in the directions needed for U-joint action. In one plane, the housing is centered by the balls; in the other plane, it is centered by the centering buttons at the ends of the pin. This joint is packed with lubricant and sealed by the bellows-style boot.

Some driveshafts include a rubber coupling (Figure 9-16). This is a doughnut-shaped rubber ring that is

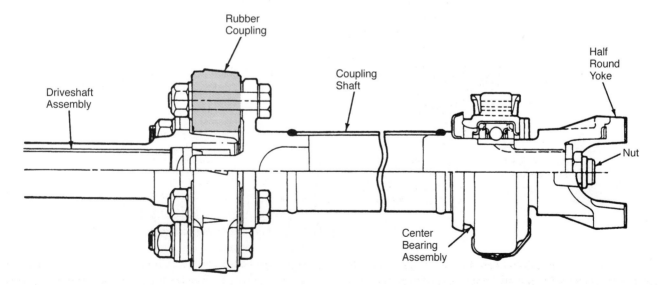

FIGURE 9-16   This driveshaft includes a rubber coupling to dampen torsional vibrations. (Courtesy of Ford Motor Company)

bolted to yokes on the driving and driven shafts. The coupling is used to dampen torsional vibrations and reduce noise, vibration, and driveline shock.

9.3   CONSTANT-VELOCITY JOINTS

There are several styles of CV joints used in power transmissions where constant velocity is necessary or desirable. In RWD vehicles they are used on the larger vehicles where comfort, quietness, and smoothness of ride are important. They can be found on some 4WD vehicles, where sharp operating angles result from short-wheelbase or high-ride height. They are also used on FWD vehicles because of the large amount of angle change required at the outboard joint. This joint must bend enough to allow for all steering motions. There is no way that the outboard and inboard operating angles can be kept equal.

There are several ways of obtaining constant velocity in a single joint. The double-Cardan joint is simply two Cardan joints built together in phase with a centering mechanism that keeps the joints at the same operating angles. The tripod joint uses three driving balls kept to a fairly tight radius. The Rzeppa joint uses six balls to produce a driving plane that bisects the operating angle.

Except for the double-Cardan joint, a CV joint must be kept in a clean, well-lubricated environment. These are expensive assemblies with very critical dimensions and tolerances, so they are enclosed in a bellows-type boot with a special lubricant (Figure 9-17). Originally, the boots were made from neoprene rubber. This material works well except that it will harden over time and begin to crack and break up. High temperatures will shorten its life considerably. Other rubber compounds,

such as silicone rubber, are used for extended, higher-temperature conditions; but with these harder compounds, it is more difficult to make a good seal with the housings. These materials can be identified by a more slippery feel or a color other than dull black. The boot is secured to the joint by either a pair of metal clamps or a clamp and a retaining ring.

9.3.1   Double-Cardan Joint

The **double-Cardan joint** is used in the driveshaft of larger RWD passenger vehicles, the rear shaft of short-wheelbase 4WD vehicles, and the front shaft of some 4WD pickups. It is simply two Cardan joints built as a single assembly (Figure 9-18). The center, connecting yoke transmits power from the leading cross to the trailing cross and phases these two 90° apart. There is a spring-loaded centering mechanism to ensure that the centerlines of the input and output shafts will intersect at the center of the center yoke. This ensures that the operating angles of the two halves will be equal.

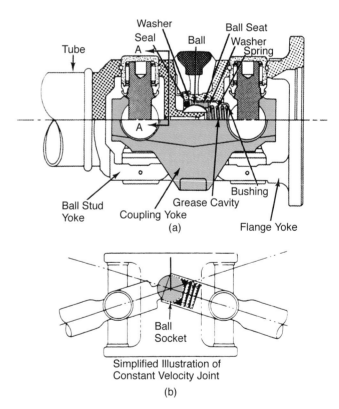

Simplified Illustration of Constant Velocity Joint

(b)

FIGURE 9-18   Double-Cardan CV joint (a); the coupling yoke with its centering ball keeps the two joint halves operating at equal angles (b). (Portions of materials contained herein have been reprinted with permission of General Motors Corporation, Service and Parts Operations, License Agreement #0310807)

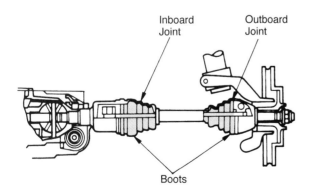

FIGURE 9-17   To keep it clean and full of grease, a CV joint uses a rubber boot held in place by a pair of clamps. (Courtesy of Ford Motor Company)

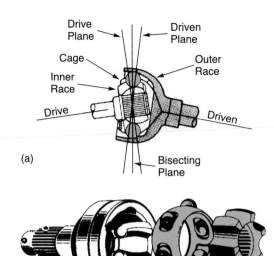

FIGURE 9-19   Cutaway (a) and exploded (b) view of a Rzeppa CV joint. This is the most common type of fixed, outboard joint. (a is courtesy of Ford Motor Company; b is courtesy of Moog Automotive)

9.3.2   Rzeppa Joint

This design is the most popular outboard CV joint used in FWD vehicles. It is a fixed joint, which means that it will not change length. The **Rzeppa** (pronounced "Sheppa") **joint** consists of an inner race, six steel balls, a cage, and an outer race (Figure 9-19). The inner and outer races have grooves or raceways in which the balls operate, and these grooves are curved to match the operating radius of the balls. The balls, all of which are aligned by the cage, transfer power between the two races, and when the vehicle turns, the balls will seek an operating plane that bisects the operating angle. This joint can operate through a range of about $45°$, $22\frac{1}{2}°$ to each side of the straight ahead.

9.3.3   Tripod Joint

The **tripod joint** is a fixed joint and has limited use as the outboard joint of some FWD vehicles manufactured in France. It drives through three steel balls fitted between the shaft, which has three raceways and an outer housing (Figure 9-20).

9.3.4   Cross Groove Joint

The **cross groove joint** is a plunge joint—the inner race can move sideways relative to the outer race to al-

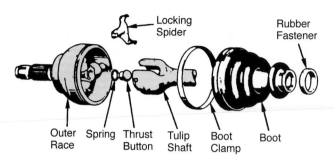

FIGURE 9-20   Tripod CV joint. This is also a fixed, outboard joint. (Courtesy of Ford Motor Company)

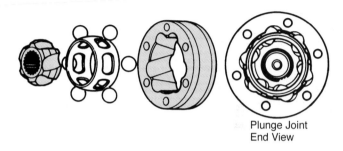

FIGURE 9-21   Cross groove CV joint; this is a plunging CV joint. (Courtesy of Moog Automotive)

low the shaft to change length as well as to make an angle change. It resembles a shortened Rzeppa joint except that the raceways are angled, not parallel. It consists of an inner race, six steel balls, a cage, and an outer race (Figure 9-21). This joint is used as an inner joint on FWD shafts and an inner or outer joint on rear halfshafts of rear-engine RWD vehicles.

9.3.5   Double-Offset Joint

The **double-offset joint** is another plunge joint commonly used as the inner joint on FWD shafts. It consists of an inner race, six steel balls, a cage, and an outer race (Figure 9-22). Except for the outer race, which is relatively long and straight, this joint resembles a Rzeppa joint.

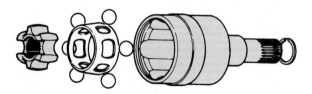

FIGURE 9-22   Double-offset CV joint; this is a plunging CV joint commonly used at the inboard end of the driveshaft. (Courtesy of Moog Automotive)

FIGURE 9-23 Tripod tulip joint; this is a common plunging, inboard CV joint. (Courtesy of Moog Automotive)

9.3.6 Tripod Tulip Joint

The **tripod tulip joint** is another popular plunge joint commonly used as the inner joint on FWD shafts. It resembles the older ball and trunnion joint except that it uses three driving balls. This joint consists of the trunnion assembly (also called a spider) and the tulip, which is the outer housing with three raceways (Figure 9-23). There are a variety of tulip housing shapes, depending on the manufacturer: cylindrical joints, cylindrical ones with open grooves, and several styles of elongated triangular shapes. The trunnion assembly has three trunnion pins, each with a set of needle bearings and a ball.

9.4 RWD DRIVESHAFTS

A RWD driveshaft is usually a thin steel tube between 2 and 3 in. (51 to 76 mm) in diameter with a wall thickness about 1/16 in. (1.6 mm). In cases where weight is critical, aluminum tubing or a composite of fiberglass or graphite fibers and plastic resin is used. A steel shaft is the least expensive and probably the most durable (Figure 9-24).

The U-joint yokes are welded in phase with each other at the ends of the tubing to form the driveshaft, and then this assembly is usually balanced. Balance weights appear as small metal tabs or washers that are welded to the shaft. Many driveshafts have a cardboard tube that is fitted snugly inside the tube (Figure 9-25a). This dampens the ringing noise if it is struck by a rock or other hard object. A few driveshafts include a rubber torsional damper (Figure 9-25b). It is constructed with two tubes that have a series of rubber rings pressed between them. The rubber rings are squeezed tightly enough to transmit torque and, at the same time, dampen torsional vibrations that might cause noise.

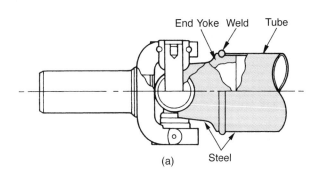

(a)

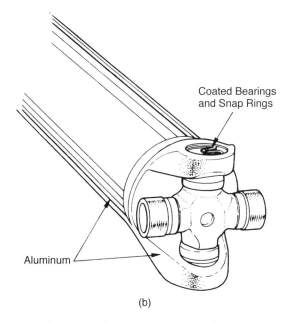

(b)

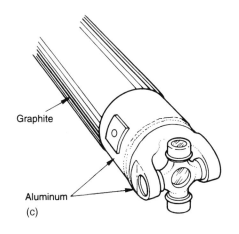

(c)

FIGURE 9-24 (a) Most RWD driveshafts are made by welding a steel yoke to the end of a steel tube. (b) Where weight is a critical factor, aluminum yokes are welded onto aluminum tubing. (c) Where weight, noise, or special environmental conditions warrant it, a carbon graphite replaces the aluminum of the center of the tube. (a: Portions of materials contained herein have been reprinted with permission of General Motors Corporation, Service and Parts Operations, License Agreement #0310807; b and c are courtesy of Dana Corporation)

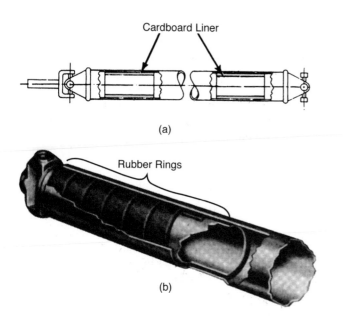

(a)

(b)

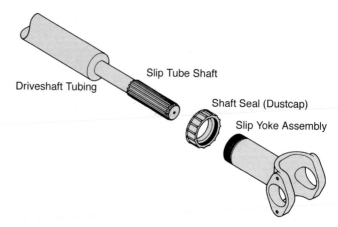

FIGURE 9-26   Some driveshafts include a slip joint to allow the shaft to change length. (Courtesy of Dana Corporation)

FIGURE 9-25   (a) Many driveshafts have a cardboard liner inside them to dampen noises. (b) Some driveshafts are two pieces with a series of rubber rings squeezed between them to reduce noise and torsional vibrations. (a: Portions of materials contained herein have been reprinted with permission of General Motors Corporation, Service and Parts Operations, License Agreement #0310807; b is courtesy of Ford Motor Company)

Some driveshafts include a slip joint in the shaft. The slip joint is normally an internal and external spline that is lubricated with grease and sealed to keep dirt out (Figure 9-26). Some slip joints use special coatings or bearings so that they can change length while loaded without binding.

9.4.1   Design Types

Almost every RWD vehicle uses a **Hotchkiss** style of driveshaft (Figure 9-27a). This is a traditional shaft that runs in the open and has a U-joint at each end. At one time, several manufacturers used a **torque tube** driveshaft to help control the position of the rear axle (Figure 9-27b). This driveshaft is a solid steel shaft, about 1 to $1\frac{1}{2}$ in. (25 to 38 mm) in diameter, which is enclosed inside the torque tube. The shaft couples directly to the rear axle drive pinion shaft and has a U-joint at the transmission. The torque tube is bolted solidly to the rear axle housing and has a rounded connection around the U-joint so that it can pivot where it connects to the transmission.

The purpose of a torque tube is to prevent the rear axle housing from revolving in reaction to the torque

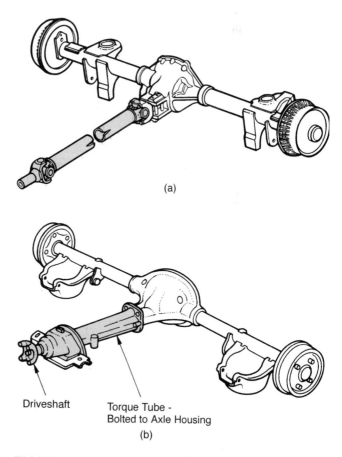

(a)

(b)

FIGURE 9-27   (a) Most driveshafts are of the Hotchkiss type and are open with two U-joints. (b) Some vehicles use torque tube driveshafts with only one U-joint and the shaft enclosed inside the torque tube. (a: Portions of materials contained herein have been reprinted with permission of General Motors Corporation, Service and Parts Operations, License Agreement #0310807)

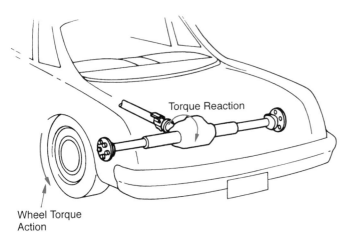

FIGURE 9-28 When axle torque rotates the tire to move the vehicle, an equal amount of torque tries to rotate the axle housing in the opposite direction.

needed to turn the drive wheels during acceleration or to retard them during braking (Figure 9-28). In a Hotchkiss design, these forces are controlled by leaf springs or rear axle control arms. The torque reaction can be seen by watching a short-wheelbase semitruck tractor pull a heavily loaded trailer from a standing start. As the clutch is engaged, the front end of the tractor will lift in reaction to the rear axle torque. At the same time, the left front will lift higher than the right in reaction to the driveshaft torque. Remember that for every physical action, there will be an equal and opposite reaction. To stop this rear axle wrap-up, some manufacturers bolt a long torque arm to the axle housing, with the forward end attached to the transmission through a rubber bushing.

Some vehicles use a two-piece driveshaft assembly that consists of two shafts, three U-joints, and a center bearing (Figure 9-29). The center bearing is needed to keep the shaft from whipping like a child's skipping rope. The front U-joint is positioned almost straight so that it does not generate a speed fluctuation, and the other two joints are phased to prevent vibration.

Halfshafts and the front driveshaft of 4WD vehicles are usually versions of a Hotchkiss shaft (Figure 9-30). In some cases, CV joints are used.

9.5 FWD DRIVESHAFTS

Most FWD driveshafts are mounted so that the splined end of the inboard joint connects with the axle gear inside the differential case and the splined end of the outboard joint connects with the drive hub of the front wheel (Figure 9-31). Some designs bolt the inboard joint to a flange extending from the differential axle gear. Re-

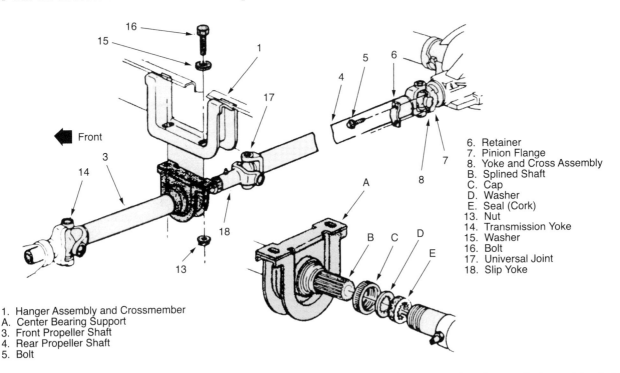

1. Hanger Assembly and Crossmember
A. Center Bearing Support
3. Front Propeller Shaft
4. Rear Propeller Shaft
5. Bolt

6. Retainer
7. Pinion Flange
8. Yoke and Cross Assembly
B. Splined Shaft
C. Cap
D. Washer
E. Seal (Cork)
13. Nut
14. Transmission Yoke
15. Washer
16. Bolt
17. Universal Joint
18. Slip Yoke

FIGURE 9-29 Some vehicles use a two-piece driveshaft. This design includes a center bearing to eliminate driveshaft whip. (Portions of materials contained herein have been reprinted with permission of General Motors Corporation, Service and Parts Operations, License Agreement #0310807)

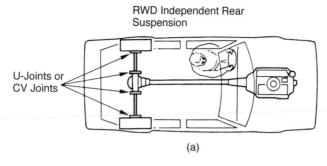

RWD Independent Rear
Suspension

U-Joints or
CV Joints

(a)

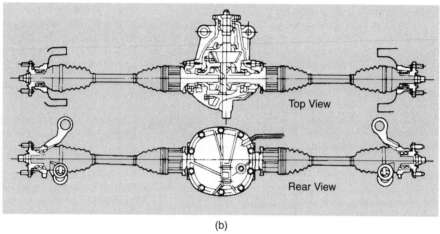

Top View

Rear View

(b)

FIGURE 9-30   (a) A RWD vehicle with IRS secures the center carrier section of the drive axle to the vehicle frame. (b) Two halfshafts are used to transmit the torque to the wheels. (b is courtesy of Ford Motor Company)

member that a FWD driveshaft turns slower (axle shaft speed) relative to a RWD driveshaft but carries three to four times the torque.

In most cases, the inboard joint is held in place by a **circlip** near the end of the splines, where it enters the axle gear. A circlip resembles a snap ring except that it has a rounded, wirelike cross section and that it remains in place on the shaft. A circlip is self-releasing when a strong side pull is exerted against it

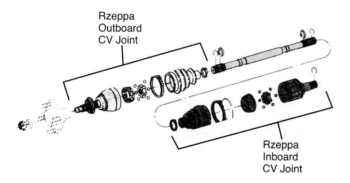

Rzeppa
Outboard
CV Joint

Rzeppa
Inboard
CV Joint

FIGURE 9-31   Most FWD driveshafts are solid steel and splined at each end to connect with the CV joints. (Courtesy of Ford Motor Company)

(Figure 9-32). The 1978 to 1981 Chrysler Corporation vehicles used a snap ring to secure the inner CV joint to the differential axle gear; this snap ring is removed and replaced from inside the differential.

The outboard CV joint is secured to the drive hub with a nut, which is normally torque-tightened securely and locked in place. If this nut were to come loose, there is a strong possibility that the drive hub and wheel would fall off. This is a fixed joint, so it does not change length. The bending point of the joint must stay in alignment with the steering axis. This is the plane where the steering knuckle pivots as the vehicle is steered.

The CV joints are secured to the splined ends of the driveshaft by either circlips, snap rings, or plastic clips, with circlips being the most common. The shaft itself is often a solid, round bar of steel. Most FWD driveshafts and CV joints can be disassembled to service the joints or boots.

Some driveshafts include a torsional damper. This unit consists of a split two-piece shaft with a rubber bushing that connects the two pieces (Figure 9-33). Torsional dampers are designed to absorb the impact that results from drivetrain lash when a vehicle with an automatic transmission is shifted into gear from neutral or when the clutch is let out in a manual transmission.

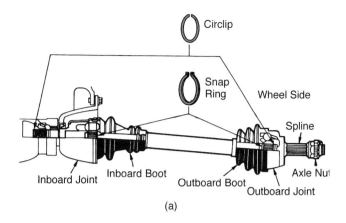

(a)

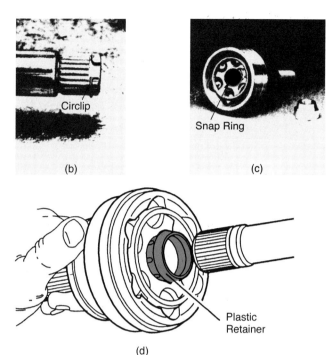

(b)

(c)

(d)

FIGURE 9-32   The CV joint is retained on the driveshaft by either a circlip or a snap ring (a). A circlip self-engages and self-releases (b); a snap ring requires a tool for removal (c); some newer CV joints use a plastic retainer (d). (a is courtesy of NEAPCO; b and c are courtesy of Perfect Circle; d is courtesy of Moog Automotive)

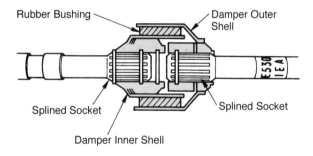

FIGURE 9-33   Some FWD driveshafts include a rubber damper to reduce torsional vibrations. (Courtesy of Perfect Circle)

Many vehicles with antilock braking systems (ABS) mount a toothed sensor ring around the outboard joint and position the wheel speed sensor in the steering knuckle right next to the sensor ring (Figure 9-34). The sensor ring is serviceable and can be removed and replaced, if necessary. If replacing a CV joint, the new joint must have a sensor ring that matches the old one in the correct location.

9.5.1   Torque Steer

Torque steer is a condition in which a FWD vehicle tends to pull to the right during hard acceleration. It is a throttle-sensitive condition in that the vehicle will drive

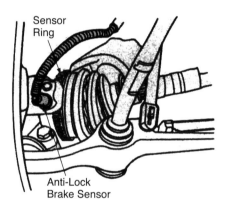

FIGURE 9-34   This CV joint includes a speed sensor ring for ABS. (Courtesy of Ford Motor Company)

normally under light throttle and produce the turning action only under heavy throttle. Because the differential is to the left of the vehicle's center, torque steer is caused by the right driveshaft being longer than the left one. When the torque reaches the two shafts, the longer one will have a greater tendency to twist. Any twisting will cause a slight lag in the time that it takes for the torque to reach that drive wheel, and this lag causes the steering action. Manufacturers can do two things to reduce torque steer. One method is to make the longer shaft in two pieces so that its longer part will be equal to the length of the left shaft (Figure 9-35a). A two-piece shaft requires an additional U-joint and a center bearing

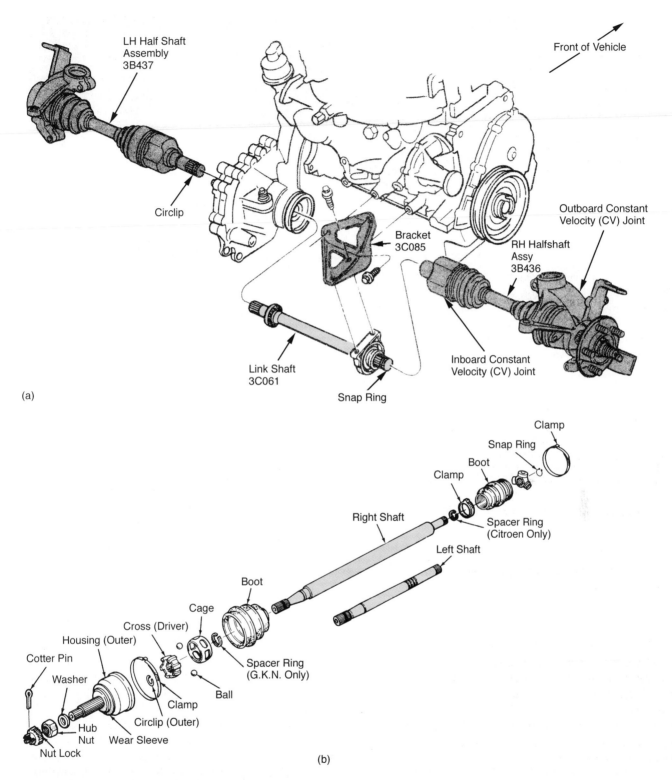

(a)

(b)

FIGURE 9-35 (a) One method of reducing torque steer is to use two equal-length driveshafts, requiring an additional shaft and support bearing. (b) A second method is to make the longer shaft from a larger-diameter material. (a is courtesy of Ford Motor Company; b is courtesy of DaimlerChrysler Corporation)

to prevent whipping. The other method is to make the longer shaft from larger-diameter tubing, which has a greater resistance to twisting (Figure 9-35b).

Torque steer can also be caused by the rolling diameter of the drive tires. Unequal diameter will cause the vehicle to steer toward the tire with the smallest diameter. Tire inflation pressure, internal construction, and tread wear can contribute to this problem. Swapping the tires side-to-side is the standard test for this; if the torque steer goes in the opposite direction after the swap, the tires are at fault. Another factor that can cause torque steer is the angle of the outboard CV joint. A greater operating angle will cause an increased tendency for the tire to toe-in—steer toward the center of the vehicle. Sharper angles are less efficient and absorb more torque within the joint. This effect is normally canceled out by the opposite side if the CV joint operating angles are equal. Sharper angles are less efficient and friction absorbs more torque within the joint. There will be less torque delivered to the wheel.

9.6 GREASE AND OTHER LUBRICANTS

CV and U-joints are lubricated by grease packed in the moving parts of the joints. **Grease** is about 90 percent oil—either natural mineral (petroleum) oil or synthetic oil. Similar to varieties of gear oils, mineral oil-based grease is less expensive, whereas synthetic oil-based grease has better oxidation resistance and high-to-low temperature characteristics. Grease gets its characteristic thickness from a thickener; lithium soap is commonly used as a thickener for automotive grease. Other compounds like complex calcium soap, complex lithium soap, and polyurea provide better high-temperature performance. Furthermore, additives can be included to further inhibit oxidation, prevent rust and corrosion, and improve the antiwear characteristics.

REVIEW QUESTIONS

The following questions are provided to help you study as you read the chapter.

1. A _____ _____ _____ vehicle typically has one driveshaft and a _____ _____ _____ vehicle has two driveshafts.

2. Most rear-wheel-drive vehicles use _____ _____ to allow the shaft angle to change.

3. Most front-wheel-drive vehicles use _____ _____ _____ to allow the shaft angle to change.

4. Lack of needle bearing movement in a universal joint will cause a wear pattern known as _____.

5. Three common methods for securing the universal cups in the driveshaft yoke are
   a. _____ _____
   b. _____ _____
   c. _____

6. Driveshafts can have _____ liners or _____ rings inserted into them to reduce noise.

7. A _____ _____ is used in a Hotchkiss-type driveshaft to reduce the shaft whipping like a child's skipping rope.

8. _____ _____ _____ are used on front-wheel-drive vehicles because of the extreme angles that the joint encounters.

9. Name six types of constant-velocity joints.
   a. _____
   b. _____
   c. _____ _____
   d. _____ _____
   e. _____ _____
   f. _____ _____

10. Of the six constant-velocity joints listed in Question 9, which is most commonly used as an outboard joint? _____

11. Of the six constant-velocity joints listed in Question 9, which is most commonly used as an inboard joint? _____ _____

12. In most cases, the inboard constant-velocity joint is held in place by a _____ near the end of the splines.

13. The outboard constant-velocity joint is secured to the drive hub with a _____.

14. The purpose of a _____ _____ is to prevent the rear axle from revolving in reaction to torque during acceleration and deceleration.

15. _____ _____ tends to pull a front-wheel-drive vehicle to the right during hard acceleration.

CHAPTER QUIZ

The following questions will help you check the facts you have learned. Select the answer that completes each statement correctly.

1. When the rear tires hit a bump that moves them upward, the A. driveshaft must become shorter, B. front U-joint operating angle changes. Which is correct?
   a. A only
   b. B only
   c. Both A and B
   d. Neither A nor B

2. The common U-joint used in RWD driveshafts is known as a
   a. Cardan joint.
   b. cross and yoke joint.
   c. Hooke joint.
   d. any of these.

3. Two students are discussing the common U-joint. Student A says it uses a cross with a set of needle bearings at each of the three journals. Student B says it normally has two yokes. Who is correct?
   a. Student A
   b. Student B
   c. Both A and B
   d. Neither A nor B

4. The bearing cups are held in place in the yokes by
   a. a snap ring positioned in a groove in the yoke.
   b. a snap ring positioned in a groove in the bearing cups.
   c. plastic that is injected through a hole in the yoke.
   d. any of these.

5. Two students are discussing how to prevent RWD driveshaft vibrations. Student A says that the rear U-joint must always be phased exactly one-half turn from the front joint. Student B says it should operate at the same angle as the front joint. Who is correct?
   a. Student A
   b. Student B
   c. Both A and B
   d. Neither A nor B

6. In a double-Cardan joint, the two portions operate at the same angle because of the A. centering ball, B. center yoke. Which is correct?
   a. A only
   b. B only
   c. Both A and B
   d. Neither A nor B

7. The CV joint that is most commonly used for the outboard joint on a FWD driveshaft is the
   a. double-Cardan joint.
   b. Rzeppa joint.
   c. double-offset joint.
   d. cross groove joint.

8. As the front wheels of a FWD vehicle move up and over a bump, the inboard joint must A. plunge to allow for a shorter or longer distance to the drive wheel, B. remain straight. Which is correct?
   a. A only
   b. B only
   c. Both A and B
   d. Neither A nor B

9. Which of the following is not a type of CV joint?
   a. Rzeppa
   b. triple tripod
   c. double-offset
   d. cross groove

10. A torque tube driveshaft gets its name A. from the torque it transfers to the rear axle, B. because it absorbs the torque reaction from the axles driving the wheels. Which is correct?
    a. A only
    b. B only
    c. Both A and B
    d. Neither A nor B

11. A Hotchkiss driveshaft has A. two U-joints, one at each end; B. a slip joint, so that it can change length. Which is correct?
    a. A only
    b. B only
    c. Both A and B
    d. Neither A nor B

12. Torque steer is A. caused because engine torque can more easily twist the longer, left shaft than the right shaft; B. a more common problem with RWD vehicles than with FWD vehicles. Which is correct?
    a. A only
    b. B only
    c. Both A and B
    d. Neither A nor B

13. A Rzeppa joint uses A. six balls to transfer power from the inner race to the outer race, B. a cage that keeps the balls aligned at a 90° angle to the inner race. Which is correct?
    a. A only
    b. B only
    c. Both A and B
    d. Neither A nor B

14. Many RWD driveshafts include a A. cardboard insert to keep them quieter, B. speed sensor for the braking system. Which is correct?
    a. A only
    b. B only
    c. Both A and B
    d. Neither A nor B

15. A center bearing is installed in A. two-piece RWD driveshafts, B. equal-length FWD driveshafts. Which is correct?
    a. A only
    b. B only
    c. Both A and B
    d. Neither A nor B

16. The pickup has a transmission shaft angle of 5° and a driveshaft angle of 8.5°. What is the operating angle of the U-joint?

17. This same pickup has a rear axle pinion shaft angle of 4°. What is the operating angle of the rear U-joint?

18. Are the two joints in Question 17 running at the same angle?

19. If the joints are not running as the same angle, how much difference is there?

◀ Chapter 10 ▶

DRIVESHAFT AND UNIVERSAL JOINT SERVICE

LEARNING OBJECTIVES

After completing this chapter, you should be able to:

1. Perform the maintenance operations needed to keep a driveshaft operating properly.
2. Diagnose the cause of common FWD driveshaft problems.
3. Recommend the proper driveshaft repair procedure.
4. Correct RWD U-joint angularity and driveshaft balance problems.
5. Remove and replace FWD and RWD driveshafts.
6. Disassemble, inspect, and reassemble the common U-joints.
7. Make normal U-joint and CV joint repairs.
8. Complete the ASE tasks for content area D, Driveshaft and Universal/Constant-Velocity Diagnosis and Repair.

TERMS TO LEARN

antilock braking system (ABS)
balancing
grease spray
inclinometer
level protractor
plug-in connection
phasing
reluctor
runout
speed sensitive
tone ring

torque sensitive
U-joint angle
visual inspection
wheel speed sensor (WSS)

10.1 INTRODUCTION

Driveshaft and U-joint service, also called driveline service, includes the maintenance operation of lubricating the cross assemblies of some Cardan and double-Cardan U-joints, the centering ball and socket of most double-Cardan U-joints, and the slip splines on some driveshafts. The driveshafts on most FWD vehicles and many modern RWD vehicles are maintenance free in that there are no lubrication fittings.

Drivelines should also be checked to find possible failure before it occurs. If a driveline problem occurs, the technician identifies its cause and repairs or replaces the faulty part(s). It should be remembered that the driveline is designed to be a weak link or "fuse" in the drivetrain (Figure 10-1). During severe operation, the driveshaft or U-joint should fail before the transmission or drive axle. Fortunately, it is much easier to service and less expensive to repair.

10.2 DRIVELINE LUBRICATION

Lubrication requirements vary greatly, depending on the manufacturer's requirement and the availability of

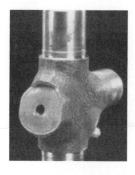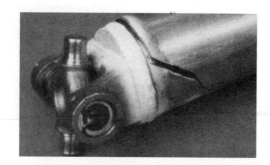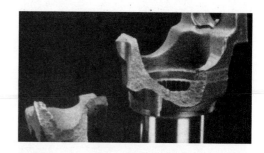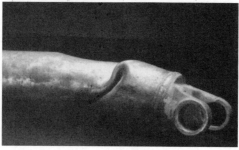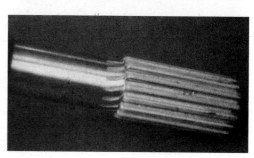

FIGURE 10-1 Many power train engineers consider the driveline to be the "fuse" for the power train. It is less expensive to replace these broken parts than to replace parts inside a transmission or drive axle. (Courtesy of Dana Corporation)

lubrication fittings. The fittings can be a zerk fitting or a flush-type fitting (Figure 10-2). Joints without fittings must be disassembled and repacked for lubrication. Recommended intervals for lubricating joints with fittings can be as short as every 2000 to 3000 miles (3218 to 4827 km) or every month for vehicles operating in severely dusty, dirty, wet, or muddy conditions.

The recommended lubricant for many U-joints is a good-quality lithium soap–based extreme pressure (EP) grease that meets NLGI (National Lubricating Grease Institute) grade 2 specifications. It is recommended that all the seals be purged so that the new grease can flush any dirt, moisture, or air out of the bearings.

To lubricate a U-joint:

1. Locate the zerk fitting, rotate the shaft for the best access, and wipe the fitting clean.
2. Attach a grease gun to the fitting, and add grease until you see clean grease flow from each seal (Figure 10-3).
3. If any seal fails to take grease and purge, move the driveshaft from side to side and reapply pressure from the grease gun.

To lubricate a double-Cardan U-joint:

1. Locate the fittings (there could be one, two, or three). Check each cross and the center socket.

The center socket fitting is often hard to get to and might require a special lube gun attachment (Figure 10-4).

2. Clean the fittings and lubricate them until clean grease leaves each seal.

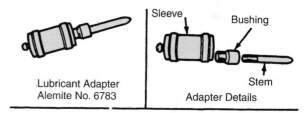

FIGURE 10-2 Some U-joint crosses include a standard zerk fitting to lubricate them; many double-Cardan U-joints use a flush-type fitting that requires a long, thin adapter. (Courtesy of Ford Motor Company)

FIGURE 10-3   When lubricating a modern U-joint, grease is pumped into the cross until it comes out of the seal at each bearing cup. (Courtesy of Dana Corporation)

FIGURE 10-4   The center socket fitting of a double-Cardan U-joint is often somewhat hidden (see arrow). (Courtesy of Dana Corporation)

To lubricate a slip spline:

1. Locate the lubrication fitting and clean it.
2. Attach a grease gun and add grease until clean grease escapes from the spline seal. Some units have a pressure relief hole that should be covered with your finger when grease starts escaping from it (Figure 10-5). This helps force grease completely through the joint.

10.3   PROBLEM DIAGNOSIS

Because of the type of joint used and the speed at which the joints operate, FWD and RWD driveline problems will show different symptoms and are diagnosed using different procedures. Most of the complaints will be noise or vibration oriented (Figure 10-6).

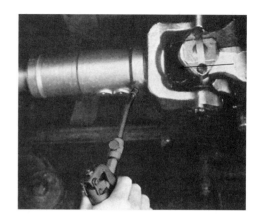

FIGURE 10-5   When grease comes out of the relief hole of this slip joint, the hole should be covered with a finger and grease pumped into the fitting until it comes out the yoke seal. (Courtesy of Dana Corporation)

10.3.1   FWD Problem Diagnosis

Unlike RWD, most FWD driveline problems are not speed related; noise or vibrations, which increase as vehicle speed increases, are more likely to be tire or wheel bearing problems than driveline problems. FWD driveline problems tend to fall into one of the following categories:

- A grease spray that is thrown from a torn boot
- Snapping, popping, or clicking noises while turning corners, which indicate a worn outboard joint

---

REAL-WORLD FIX A 1991 Mitsubishi Galant (63,000 mi) had a steering wheel oscillation at speeds below 35 mph. The front tires were rotated and balanced, but this did not help. The front suspension and steering parts were good. A visual inspection of the driveshafts and CV joints showed no problems.

FIX

Further checks revealed a faulty left-side, inner CV joint, and replacement of this shaft assembly solved the problem.

REAL-WORLD FIX A 1996 Dodge Avenger (40,000 mi) had a vibration between 55 and 60 mph that was torque sensitive. It did not occur while decelerating. A visual inspection of the driveshafts did not reveal a problem.

FIX

Removal of the CV joint boot allowed the technician to feel a wear groove inside of one of the inner CV joints. Replacement of this driveshaft fixed this problem.

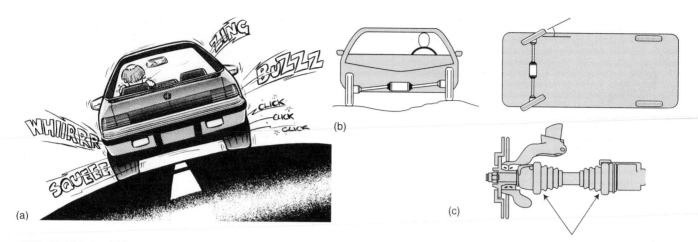

(b)

(a)   (c)

FIGURE 10-6   When diagnosing FWD CV-joint problems, road-test the vehicle, making turning maneuvers (a) so that the CV joints must change vertical as well as turning angles (b) along with throttle changes. Complete the checks with an inspection of the boots and the CV joint for looseness (c).

- Clunking noises during acceleration or deceleration, which indicate a worn inboard joint
- Vibration or shudder during acceleration, which indicates a worn inboard joint

If the complaint is **grease spray,** a visual inspection of the boots can confirm the cause of the problem. Parts suppliers say that a CV joint, once it begins to spray grease, will operate for 8 to 20 hours before failure.

To inspect CV joint boots:

1. Raise and securely support the vehicle on a hoist or jack stands.

2. Turn the front of one wheel outward, and rotate the tire so that all of the boot is visible (Figure 10-7). Many technicians will place their finger in a fold to feel for cracks or tears while rotating the tire. It is a good practice to pull apart the folds of the inboard boots for a complete inspection.

3. Repeat this process on the other driveshaft.

FIGURE 10-7   When checking a CV joint boot, run your finger around the boot in each of the pleats as you inspect for tears or cuts; the wheel can be turned outward on the outboard joint to get a better view of the boot. (Courtesy of Moog Automotive)

◀   **SERVICE TIP**   ▶

If a boot has a small cut or tear and there is still grease inside the joint, the joint is probably still good and should be repaired by installing a boot kit. If there is a large tear or portions of the boot are missing and the grease shows contamination, the joint will probably need to be replaced. A technician can check for grease contamination by rubbing some of the grease between his or her fingers (Figure 10-8). If the grease feels normal, the joint is probably good; if the grease has a gritty feel, the joint is probably damaged.

If the complaint is of noise or vibration, test drive the vehicle. Accelerate lightly with the wheels straight and then again with the wheels turned in one direction and then the other. If the noise gets louder when the wheels are turned, the problem is probably a worn outboard joint. A badly worn joint will snap, click, or vibrate when the wheels are straight. Next, accelerate hard while driving straight ahead or up a driveway ramp. A vibration or shudder indicates a sticking inboard joint; a clunking noise indicates a worn joint. Possible worn or sticking joints should be disassembled for visual inspection to confirm the problem and determine the proper repair procedure.

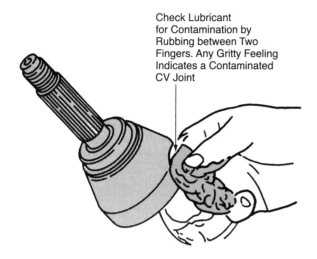

Check Lubricant for Contamination by Rubbing between Two Fingers. Any Gritty Feeling Indicates a Contaminated CV Joint

FIGURE 10-8   When checking a CV joint with a torn or suspicious boot, rub a grease sample from the joint between your fingers and feel for grit. Gritty grease indicates a joint that probably needs to be replaced. (Courtesy of Ford Motor Company)

REAL-WORLD FIX A 1992 Dodge Caravan (130,000 mi) was towed into the shop with the left inner CV joint popped out of the transaxle. The axle was replaced using an OEM part, and two weeks later it returned with the same problem. The motor mounts were inspected; one was found faulty and all were replaced. One week later, the van came back with the same problem.

FIX

Close inspection showed front subframe damage. Straightening the subframe and a wheel alignment fixed this problem.

REAL-WORLD FIX A 1987 Dodge Caravan (134,000 mi) had a noise when starting out, turning left, and accelerating. The driveshafts were removed and inspected. Each had a bad CV joint and the left hub bearings were worn. Both driveshafts and the left hub bearings were replaced, but this did not help.

FIX

A check of the shaft end-to-hub position showed a side-to-side difference of 5/8″. The motor mounts were loosened, and the engine was moved sideways to equalize the distances. This fixed the problem.

10.3.2   RWD Problem Diagnosis

Most RWD driveshaft problems also fall into the two categories of noise or vibration, with the vibrations tending to be **speed** and **torque sensitive**. Torque-sensitive vibrations will often increase with more torque; a full-throttle acceleration will have greater vibrations than a light-throttle acceleration. The vibrations will either increase as the speed increases or increase at certain speeds and decrease at others. For example, tire imbalance vibrations tend to be the greatest between 45 and 60 mph (72 and 97 kph) (Figure 10-9).

REAL-WORLD FIX A 1997 Jeep Grand Cherokee (9,000 km) had a vibration between 45 and 55 kph. The vibration went away when the front driveshaft was removed. A new front driveshaft was installed, but this did not help. The front drive and axle yoke were replaced, but this did not help. The U-joint angles on the front shaft were adjusted, but this did not help. The runout of the front shaft was checked, and it was fine: 0.001″ at the yokes and 0.005″ at the shaft.

FIX

The new front driveshaft was sent out to have the balance checked, and it was out of balance by 21 grams. Rebalancing this shaft fixed this vibration problem.

10.3.3   Driveshaft Checks

Five different checks are normally made to locate driveshaft problems. Most of the problems will be found in the first check, which is a **visual inspection** for wear and overall condition. The other four checks are for runout, angle, phasing, and balance.

REAL-WORLD FIX A 1998 Volvo AWD V70R (49,000 mi.) had a pop/clang noise coming from the front-to-rear driveshaft. The noise seemed to be coming from the front CV joint when the vehicle was operated on the lift rack.

FIX

It was determined that the grease in this joint failed because of heat from the catalytic converter next to it. It was also determined that the joint is available from the dealer so the entire driveshaft does not need to be replaced.

10.3.3.1 Visual Inspection. When a driveshaft problem is encountered, a technician normally will test drive the vehicle to confirm the symptoms. Then he or

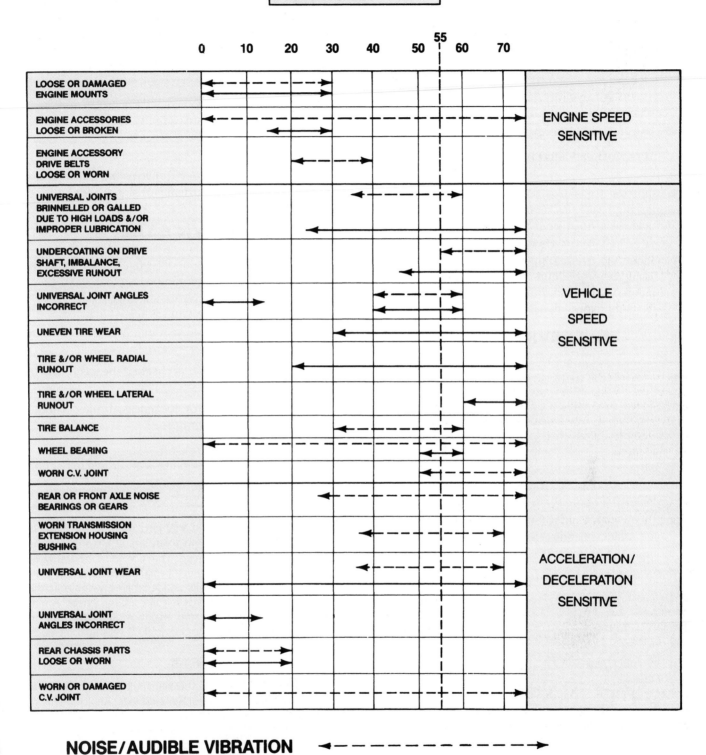

FIGURE 10-9 This chart indicates the speed at which the most commonly encountered vehicle vibrations occur and whether they show up as noise or a vibration that is felt. (Courtesy of Perfect Circle)

she will inspect the driveshaft for damage and looseness at the U-joints and slip splines.

◀ SERVICE TIP ▶

If a joint is disconnected, it should swing smoothly through its travel arc in each direction with no catches, roughness, or free play.

To perform a visual inspection:

1. Shift the transmission to neutral and release the parking brake. Raise and securely support the vehicle on a hoist or jack stands so that the drive wheels are free to rotate.
2. Check the overall appearance of the shaft. There should be no buildup of foreign material (such as undercoat), no major dents or damage to the tubing, and no missing balance weights.

◀ SERVICE TIP ▶

If the vehicle has been operated recently, carefully feel each joint; the joint should be warm, about the same temperature as the shaft. A hot joint is a sign of failure. Check for reddish dust from rust at each U-joint; that would indicate a dry, unlubricated joint.

3. Check each U-joint for looseness in both a rotary and a sideways direction (Figure 10-10). Grip the input and output yokes and try to twist them back

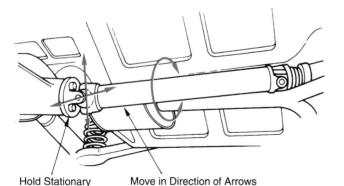

Hold Stationary   Move in Direction of Arrows

FIGURE 10-10   When checking a U-joint, hold one yoke so that it will not move and try to rotate the other yoke and move it in a direction that is parallel to the legs of the cross; any perceptible motion indicates a worn joint. (Courtesy of Ford Motor Company)

and forth in opposite directions; then hold one stationary as you try to move the other one vertically and side to side.

◀ SERVICE TIP ▶

Perceptible rotary motion of 0.006 in. (0.15 mm) in either direction indicates a faulty, loose joint.

4. Grip the slip yoke where it leaves the transmission and try to move it vertically or side to side.

◀ SERVICE TIP ▶

Slip yoke movement should be less than 0.007 in. (0.18 mm). Excessive clearance can be caused by a worn slip yoke or transmission bushing.

A slip joint in the shaft is checked the same way.

5. On shafts equipped with a center support bearing, check the bearing for looseness, broken rubber mounting, and temperature.

The repair of faulty U-joints is described in Section 10.5.2.

REAL-WORLD FIX A 1995 VW Jetta (88,000 mi.) came in for front-end work. The right front wheel bearing and the strut bearings were replaced. The CV joint boots were torn, so both driveshafts were replaced. The front wheels were aligned. But there was a side-to-side wobble at the front during acceleration that felt like a bent wheel. An inspection of the front end and engine mounts showed no problem.

FIX

A careful of inspection of the remanufactured driveshafts showed a problem on the driver-side axle. Replacement of this driveshaft fixed this problem.

10.3.3.2 Driveshaft Runout. **Runout** is caused by a bent shaft or one in which the cross or a yoke is not centered to the tube. It creates an imbalance, causing the vibration. Runout is usually checked using a dial indicator.

◄ SERVICE TIP ►

Runout can be confused with ovality, which occurs if a tube is slightly flattened (Figure 10-11). Runout will cause one high and one low reading per revolution, and ovality will cause two of each.

◄ SERVICE TIP ►

The maximum limits for runout or ovality for passenger cars and light trucks are 0.005 in. (0.12 mm) on a slip yoke, 0.020 in. (0.5 mm) on the tubing 3 in. (76 mm) from each end, and 0.010 in. (0.25 mm) in the center of the driveshaft (Figure 10-12).

To check driveshaft runout:

1. Shift the transmission to neutral and release the parking brake. Raise and securely support the vehicle on a hoist or jack stands so that the drive wheels are free to rotate.

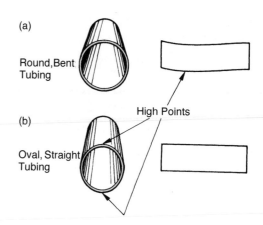

FIGURE 10-11 Driveshaft tubing problems show up as a round tube that is bent or off-center (a) and an oval tube that is flattened. (b) When checked with a dial indicator, a round tube will have one high point and an oval tube will have two. A bent tube will have more runout at the center than at the ends. (Courtesy of Dana Corporation)

2. Clean any dirt or rust from around the driveshaft at the center and 3 in. from each end.
3. Mount a dial indicator to the car's underbody, and position the stylus so that it points directly toward the center of the driveshaft (Figure 10-13).

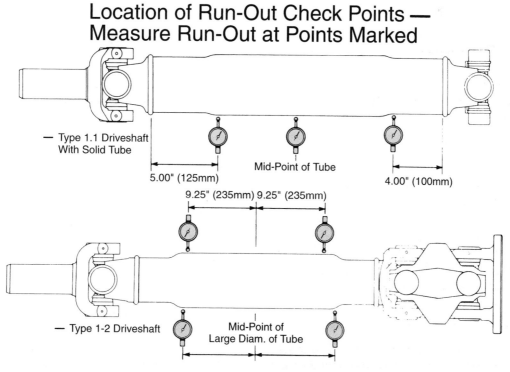

Location of Run-Out Check Points — Measure Run-Out at Points Marked

FIGURE 10-12 Driveshaft runout is checked at the center and near the ends of the tube section. (Portions of materials contained herein have been reprinted with permission of General Motors Corporation, Service and Parts Operations, License Agreement #0310807)

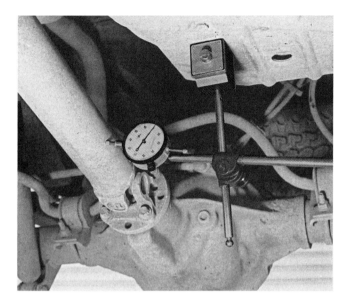

FIGURE 10-13   A magnetic-base dial indicator has been attached to the gas tank skid plate of this light truck with the indicator pointing directly toward the center of the drive-shaft. When the driveshaft is rotated, any runout will be shown on the dial indicator.

4. Rotate the driveshaft until the dial indicator needle is at its lowest reading; adjust the dial to zero and rotate the driveshaft to the highest reading.

5. Record the reading and location of the high point on the driveshaft, and repeat step 4 at the two or three other locations on the driveshaft.

◀   **SERVICE TIP**   ▶

Acceptable readings at the ends of the driveshaft with an excessively high reading at the center indicate a bent shaft. A bent driveshaft should be replaced or straightened, which is a job requiring specialized equipment and skills. An acceptable reading at the center with an excessively high reading at one end can be caused by a bad driveshaft or a faulty U-joint cross or end yoke.

◀   **SERVICE TIP**   ▶

If the high reading is at an end where the U-joint bolts to an end yoke or flange, disconnect the U-joint, rotate the driveshaft one-half turn to the alternate position, and repeat the check to determine if it is a faulty driveshaft or end yoke (Figure 10-14).

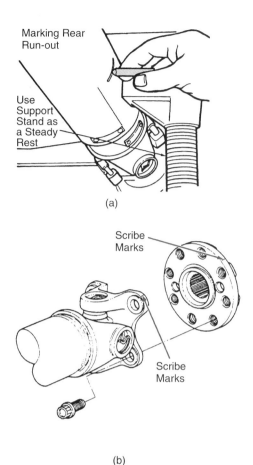

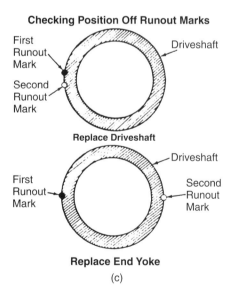

FIGURE 10-14   A quick runout check is made by holding a marking tool next to the shaft as it is rotated (a). If there is a high spot close to a U-joint, runout can sometimes be corrected by scribing index marks on the shaft, rotating the shaft one-half turn (b), and rechecking runout (c). The location of the second mark indicates the cause of any remaining problem. (Courtesy of Ford Motor Company)

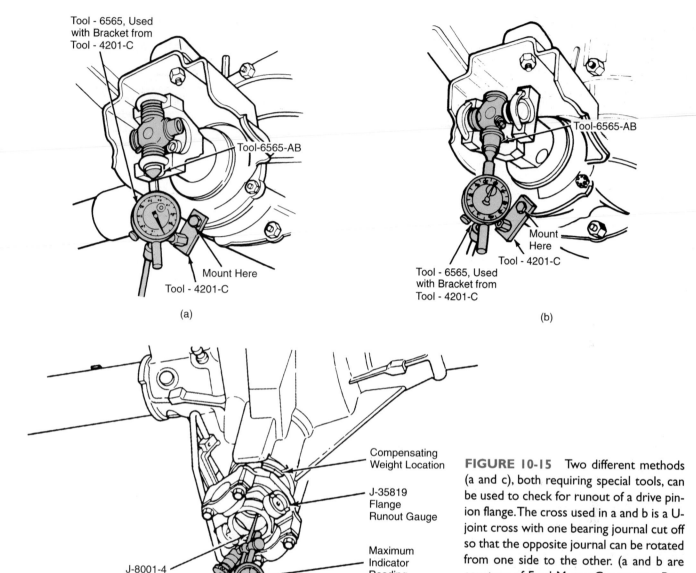

FIGURE 10-15 Two different methods (a and c), both requiring special tools, can be used to check for runout of a drive pinion flange. The cross used in a and b is a U-joint cross with one bearing journal cut off so that the opposite journal can be rotated from one side to the other. (a and b are courtesy of Ford Motor Company; c: Portions of materials contained herein have been reprinted with permission of General Motors Corporation, Service and Parts Operations, License Agreement #0310807)

◄ **SERVICE TIP** ►

A cross or yoke can be checked by positioning a dial indicator with the stylus positioned on the bearing cap. After ensuring that the stylus is centered on the bearing cap, adjust the dial to zero, carefully withdraw the stylus, rotate the shaft one-half turn, and read the position of the second bearing cap (Figure 10-15). The two readings should be within 0.010 in. (0.25 mm) of each other.

REAL-WORLD FIX A 1994 Lincoln (70,000 mi) had a vibration under acceleration at 48 mph. The vibration showed up at the same speed with the car on stands. Visual inspection of the driveshaft and rear axle showed no problems.

FIX

Checking driveshaft runout showed 0.038″. After disconnecting the driveshaft, rotating it one-half turn, and reinstalling it, the runout was reduced to 0.008. This fixed the vibration problem.

REAL-WORLD FIX A 1992 Ranger pickup (108,000 mi.) had a bad vibration during acceleration. The rear U-joints were replaced, but this did not help.

FIX

It was determined that the rear springs had sagged, and this changed the U-joint operating angles. Replacement of the springs fixed this vibration problem.

10.3.3.3 Phasing Checks

◀ SERVICE TIP ▶

Phasing is easy to check; the two yokes at the ends of a shaft should be in line with each other (Figure 10-16). Two straightedges laid across the yoke lugs should be parallel. You can also measure the crosswise angles of the yokes at each end of the shaft; both ends should be at the same angle when measuring across the vehicle.

10.3.3.4 Angle Checks

Checking **U-joint angles** requires a method of measuring angles relative to horizontal or vertical. To do this, technicians normally use a special gauge. A **level protractor** or a simple protractor, string, and weight can be used (Figure 10-17).

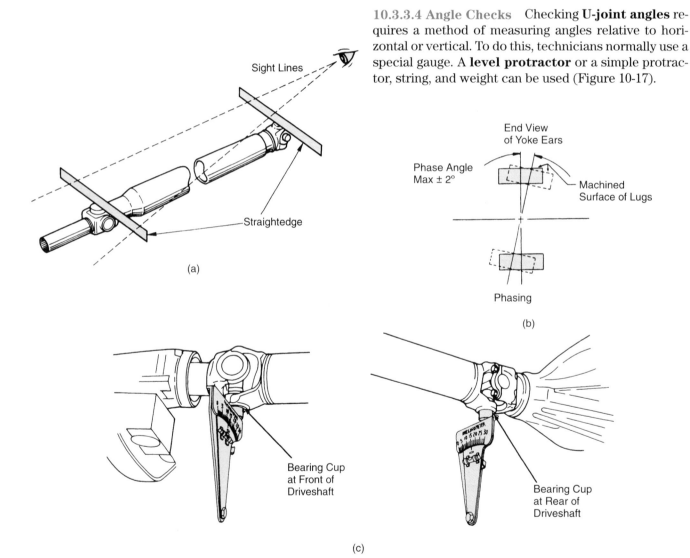

FIGURE 10-16 (a) Checking the phasing of the two U-joints can be done by placing a pair of straightedges across the bearing cups/cup bosses and sighting across them. (b) The straightedges should be within 2° of being parallel. (c) An alternative method is to place an angle gauge crosswise and measure the angle of both joints; they should be the same. (b is courtesy of NEAPCO; c: Portions of materials contained herein have been reprinted with permission of General Motors Corporation, Service and Parts Operations, License Agreement #0310807)

(a)

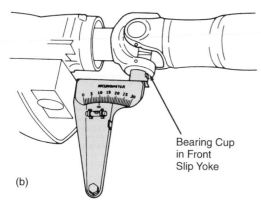

Bearing Cup
in Front
Slip Yoke

(b)

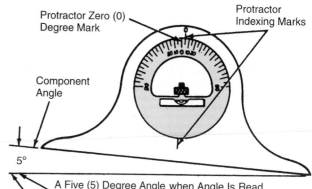

Protractor Zero (0)
Degree Mark

Protractor
Indexing Marks

Component
Angle

5°

Frame — A Five (5) Degree Angle when Angle Is Read
from the Zero (0) Degree Mark

Engine Angle

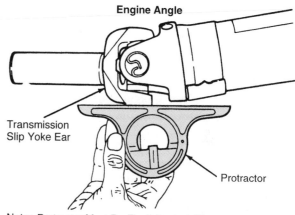

Transmission
Slip Yoke Ear

Protractor

Note: Protractor Must Be Flush Against Slip
Yoke Ear and Not Contact Driveshaft at
Any Point

(d)

Engine Angle

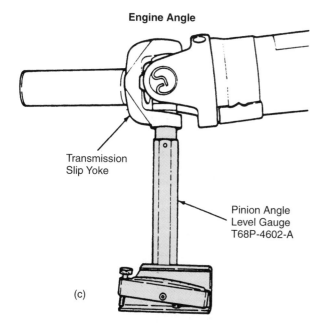

Transmission
Slip Yoke

Pinion Angle
Level Gauge
T68P-4602-A

(c)

(e)

FIGURE 10-17 U-joint angles can be measured using an
electronic angle gauge (a), a bubble-level U-joint angle gauge
(b and c), a machinist's protractor (with level) (d), a magnetic
protractor (e), or a simple protractor with string and weight
(f). (a is courtesy of Dana Corporation; b: Portions of materials contained herein have been reprinted with permission
of General Motors Corporation, Service and Parts Operations, License Agreement #0310807; c and d are courtesy of
Ford Motor Company)

(f)

Usually, the angles of the two shafts for a U-joint are measured, and one angle is subtracted from the other to determine the operating angle of the U-joint. The same is done for the second joint, and the two angles are compared to each other (Figure 10-18).

◀ SERVICE TIP ▶

Ideally, a single U-joint should operate at an angle between 1/2″ and 3″, and the operating angle of the two joints on a shaft should be within 1″.

◀ SERVICE TIP ▶

A quick and fairly accurate method of making this check is to measure the distance between the top and the bottom of the transmission and rear axle yokes (Figure 10-19). If the distances are equal, the angles are also equal.

To check U-joint angles using an inclinometer:

1. Raise and securely support the vehicle. Support the rear axle so it is in the normal position relative to the frame. The rear wheels must be free to turn.

Shift the transmission to neutral and release the parking brake.

2. Clean off the end of a U-joint bearing cup and rotate the driveshaft so that this bearing cup is downward.

3. Attach the inclinometer to the bearing cup, adjust it to center the bubble, and read and record the angle of this bearing cap and the driveshaft to which this yoke is attached (Figure 10-20).

4. Rotate the shaft one-fourth turn and repeat steps 2 and 3 to obtain the angle of the second shaft.

5. Subtract one measured angle from the other angle to get the operating angle for this joint.

6. Repeat steps 2, 3, 4, and 5 to get the operating angle for the second joint.

◀ SERVICE TIP ▶

An adjustment is necessary if the two angles are not within 1° of each other. Because the angle of the input or leading U-joint is determined primarily by the position of the transmission and engine, it is usually easier to change the operating angle of the rear U-joint, which is controlled primarily by the position of the rear axle (Figure 10-21).

To adjust the rear U-joint operating angle, the front of the rear-axle drive pinion shaft is usually raised or

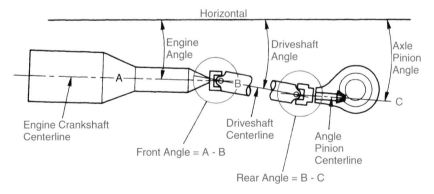

FIGURE 10-18 U-joint angles are normally determined by measuring the angle (with respect to horizontal) of the front yoke, engine crankshaft, or transmission shafts (A), the second and third yokes and driveshaft (B), and the rear yoke and axle driven pinion shaft (C). The difference between A and B is the angle of the front U-joint, and the difference between B and C is the angle of the rear U-joint.

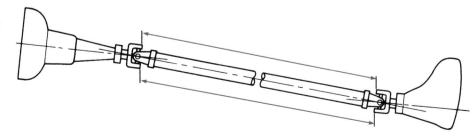

FIGURE 10-19 A quick way of checking U-joint angles is to measure the distance between the front and rear yokes at the top and bottom. If these distances are the same, the U-joints are at the same angle.

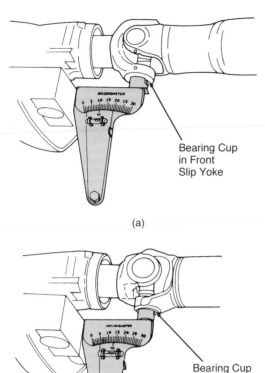

(a)

Bearing Cup
in Front
Slip Yoke

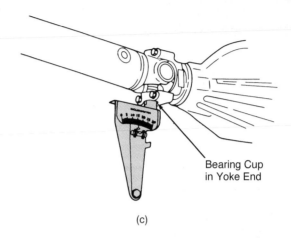

(c)

Bearing Cup
in Yoke End

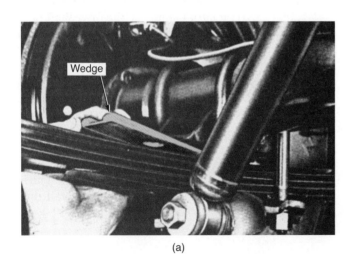

Bearing Cup
at Front of
Driveshaft

(b)

FIGURE 10-20 An accurate way to check U-joint angles is to measure the angle of the front yoke (a), either the second or third yoke (b), and the rear yoke (c). In this case, angle a is 10° and angle b is 13°, so the front joint angle is 3°. Angle b is 13° and angle c is 17°, so the rear joint angle is 4°. This gives a difference in angles of 1°, which is acceptable. (Portions of materials contained herein have been reprinted with permission of General Motors Corporation, Service and Parts Operations, License Agreement #0310807)

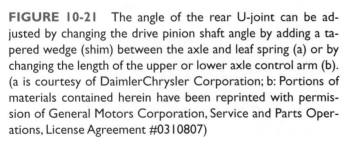

Wedge

(a)

FIGURE 10-21 The angle of the rear U-joint can be adjusted by changing the drive pinion shaft angle by adding a tapered wedge (shim) between the axle and leaf spring (a) or by changing the length of the upper or lower axle control arm (b). (a is courtesy of DaimlerChrysler Corporation; b: Portions of materials contained herein have been reprinted with permission of General Motors Corporation, Service and Parts Operations, License Agreement #0310807)

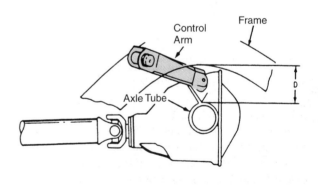

Control
Arm

Frame

Axle Tube

D

Rear Upper Control Arm (Cutlass, 88-98)

Service control arm	Rear axle nose angle change	Transmission angle change
Short Arm-Cutlass	$+1\frac{1}{2}$	$-1/2$
Long Arm-Cutlass	$-1\frac{1}{2}$	$+1/2$
Short Arm-88-98	$+2$	$-1/2$
Long Arm-88-98	-2	$+1/2$

(b)

lowered. Pinion shaft angle can be adjusted by using tapered shims between the axle housing and leaf springs on vehicles with leaf springs or by changing the length of the upper control arm(s). Shimming the control arm mounting points on vehicles with coil springs will adjust the operating angle.

REAL-WORLD FIX A 1999 Ford E-250 (9,000 mi) has a driveline vibration between 45 and 55 mph. The driveshaft was replaced using a new one, but this did not help. The engine and transmission mounts were isolated/neutralized, but this did not help either.

FIX

A check of the U-joint angles revealed the problem, and shimming the drive axle fixed it.

AUTHOR'S NOTE

The front and rear U-joint angles should be equal.

10.3.3.5 Balancing.   Driveshaft imbalance will cause a speed-sensitive, not torque-sensitive, vibration and thus will occur during coast-down as well as during acceleration or cruising. Usually, **balancing** a driveshaft is an off-vehicle operation, with each end being balanced separately.

◄ SERVICE TIP ►

A rather crude but fairly effective on-vehicle balancing can be done by a shop equipped with a strobe light, on-vehicle balance, and two or three screw-type radiator clamps. The head of the clamp is used for the balancing weight.

◄ SERVICE TIP ►

Shops that specialize in driveshaft repair have the ability to properly balance most driveshafts.

Caution: While doing this operation, you will be working close to a rapidly spinning shaft and a pair of brake drums with a running vehicle above you.

To balance a driveshaft:

1. Road-test the vehicle and record the speed at which the vibration is the greatest.

2. Raise and securely support the vehicle by the frame or body so that the drive axle is free to move up and down and the tires are free to turn. Remove both drive wheels and replace two lug nuts on each side to keep the brake drum in place.

3. Using chalk or crayon, mark the rear of the driveshaft with a line and number at four points, every one-fourth turn around the shaft (Figure 10-22).

4. Position the wheel balancer pickup probe under the rear-axle drive pinion shaft so that it is close to the driveshaft flange.

5. Carefully start the engine, shift into high gear, and operate the driveshaft to the speed that was recorded in step 1.

◄ SERVICE TIP ►

From under the vehicle, note the blur around the spinning shaft, which indicates the amount of runout being caused by the imbalance.

Point the strobe light at the spinning shaft. The effect of the light should make the shaft appear to be stopped; note the location of your marks.

6. Stop the engine and driveshaft, and by hand, rotate the shaft to the same position as it appeared in step 5. Place two radiator clamps on the driveshaft next to the end where you are checking. The heads of the clamps should be at the very top of the shaft; tighten the clamps (Figure 10-23).

7. Repeat step 5. If the vibration is gone, you are done; go on to step 8. If the vibration is still present and the strobe light makes the clamp heads appear at the bottom of the shaft, the clamps are too heavy. Stop the shaft and adjust the clamps by rotating them about one-quarter turn away from each other. Repeat this operation until the vibration is gone or the clamp heads are one-half turn from each other.

◄ SERVICE TIP ►

If the clamp heads move to positions opposite each other, they are too heavy. Remove one of the clamps, and position the other clamp in the original location.

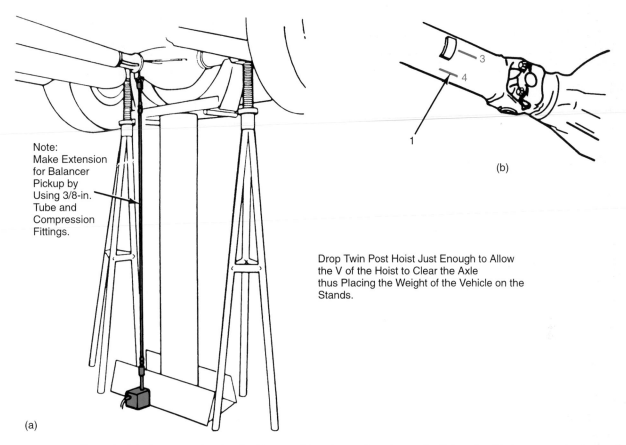

FIGURE 10-22 Driveshaft balance can be checked by attaching the probe of a strobe light wheel balancer to the front of the axle housing (a), placing reference marks on the rear of the shaft (b), and shining the strobe light on the shaft while it is running at the problem speed. (Portions of materials contained herein have been reprinted with permission of General Motors Corporation, Service and Parts Operations, License Agreement #0310807)

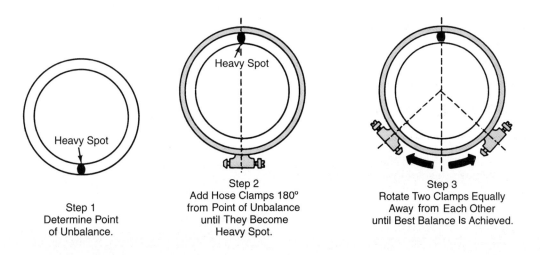

FIGURE 10-23 Once the heavy spot on the shaft has been determined, a hose clamp(s) can be placed on the shaft to serve as balance weight. (Portions of materials contained herein have been reprinted with permission of General Motors Corporation, Service and Parts Operations, License Agreement #0310807)

◄ **SERVICE TIP** ►

If the vibration is still present and the strobe light makes the clamp heads appear at the top of the shaft, the clamps are too light. Add a third clamp and repeat this step.

◄ **PROBLEM SOLVING** ►

Imagine that you are working in a general automotive repair shop and these problems are brought to you.

Case 1

The driver's complaint is a vibration between 15 and 30 mph. Your road test confirms the vibration, but when you lift the vehicle on a hoist, things appear good as far as the operating angles and clearance. You do notice that the rear U-joint is hotter than the driveshaft. What is probably wrong; what should you do next?

Case 2

The FWD compact car makes a definite clunk sound as you shift into drive or reverse. What is the probable cause? What should you do to locate it?

8. Replace the wheels and tighten the lug nuts to the correct torque.

10.4 DRIVESHAFT REMOVAL AND REPLACEMENT

As a driveshaft is removed, technicians are advised not to allow it to hang from one end, bending a still-connected U-joint or CV joint to its limit. If necessary, support the shaft using mechanic's wire or an old V-belt until both joints can be disconnected (Figure 10-24).

10.4.1 FWD Driveshaft Removal and Replacement

Most FWD driveshafts are held in place at the outer end by the nut securing the outboard CV joint to the front hub. After removing this nut, which is normally very

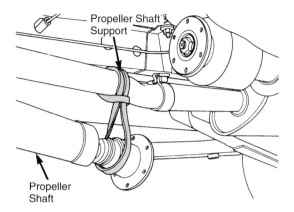

FIGURE 10-24 An old V-belt has been looped around the exhaust pipe and is being used to support the driveshaft. (Courtesy of DaimlerChrysler Corporation)

tight, the hub and steering knuckle must be moved outward and off the end of the splined section of the CV joint. This usually requires disassembling some portion of the suspension system (Figure 10-25). The driveshaft, along with the front hub and bearing, on General Motors W series vehicles (which include the Chevrolet Lumina) can be removed through the steering knuckle; the hub and bearing can then be removed from the outer CV joint (Figure 10-26).

Most inboard joints are held into the differential side gears by a circlip that usually pops free when enough outward pressure is exerted on it. This style is sometimes called a **plug-in** type of **connection**. Some inboard joints are bolted to a flange and shaft extending from the differential. Chrysler products from 1981 and earlier retained the CV joint in the differential using a snap ring that must be removed from inside the differential (Figure 10-27). A problem that can be encountered on some makes and models, such as Ford products using an ATX or MTX transaxle, is that the differential side gears can roll out of position when both CV joints are removed. Normally, the right driveshaft is removed first, then the left shaft is driven out through the differential using a special tool or 1/4-in. (6.3-mm) rod that is 12 in. (305 mm) long (Figure 10-28). This tool or rod is left in the differential to hold the gears in place until one of the driveshafts is replaced.

◄ **SERVICE TIP** ►

A FWD vehicle should not be moved by rolling the front wheels while the driveshaft is removed. Damage to the front wheel bearings can result. After the driveshaft is replaced, it may be necessary to check the alignment of the front end.

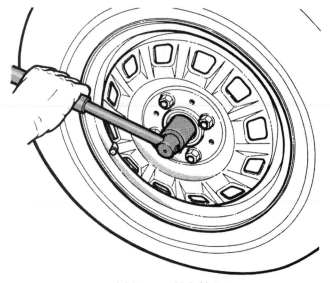

(a) Loosen Hub Nut

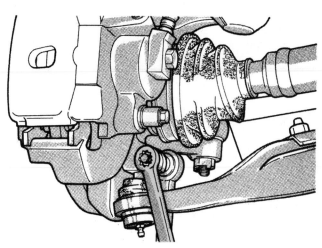

(b) Disconnect Ball Joint

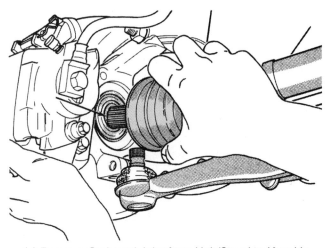

(c) Remove Outboard Joint from Hub/Steering Knuckle

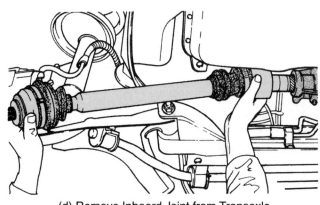

(d) Remove Inboard Joint from Transaxle

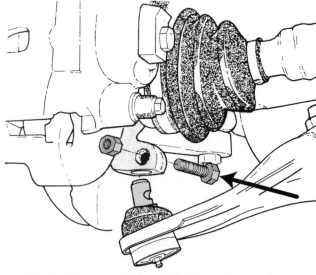

(e) Install Retaining Bolt and Tighten to Correct Torque

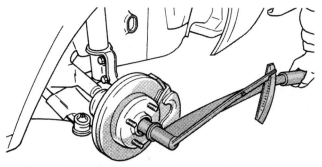

(f) Install New Hub Nut and Tighten to Correct Torque

FIGURE 10-25 Procedure to remove (a–d) and replace (e and f) a FWD driveshaft.

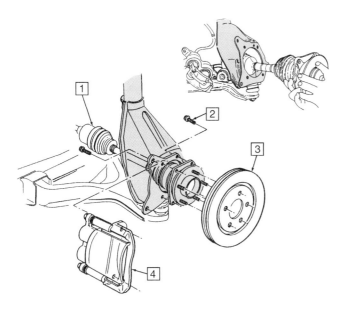

FIGURE 10-26 After the wheel bearing and inner CV joint have been disconnected from the steering knuckle, the hole in the steering knuckle on this FWD vehicle is large enough that the driveshaft with the hub and bearing can be removed through it. (Portions of materials contained herein have been reprinted with permission of General Motors Corporation, Service and Parts Operations, License Agreement #0310807)

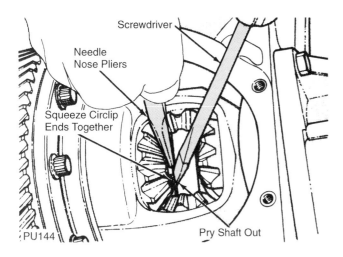

FIGURE 10-27 To remove the inner CV joint from the transaxle on this FWD vehicle, it is necessary to remove the transaxle differential cover and expand the circlip tangs. (Courtesy of DaimlerChrysler Corporation)

◀ SERVICE TIP ▶

Special dollies are available, that can be placed under the front of the vehicle to allow it to be rolled to another location (Figure 10-29).

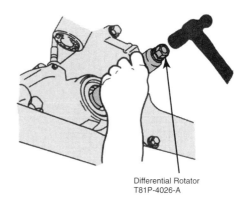

Differential Rotator
T81P-4026-A

FIGURE 10-28 After the right-side CV joint has been removed, a special tool should be used to drive the left-side inboard CV joint from this transaxle; the tool is then left in place to hold the differential pinion gears in alignment. (Courtesy of Ford Motor Company)

FIGURE 10-29 A special dolly can be placed under the front of the vehicle. This allows the vehicle to be moved while the front driveshafts are removed.

The following description is very general. It is recommended that you follow the procedure given in a service manual for the particular vehicle you are working on.

To remove a FWD driveshaft:

1. Remove the wheel cover and hub nut locking device, and loosen the front hub nut (Figure 10-30). For nuts that have been staked or bent to lock them in place, merely unscrew the nut. Most manufacturers recommend that you do not reuse this nut. Replace it with a new one during driveshaft replacement. Using an air impact wrench to loosen or remove this nut is not recommended.

2. Raise and securely support the vehicle, and remove the front wheel. Finish removing the hub nut (Figure 10-31). On vehicles with ventilated brake rotors, a pin can be placed into one of the ventilation slots to keep the driveshaft from turning as you remove the nut.

3. Remove the lower ball joint clamp bolt (Figure 10-32). Many manufacturers recommend replacing this nut and bolt with new ones.

FIGURE 10-30 Front driveshaft removal normally begins by loosening the front hub nuts. Because they are very tight, the wheel is left on the floor with the parking brake applied. (Courtesy of NEAPCO)

FIGURE 10-31 Once the hub nut has been loosened, the wheel can be removed to allow access for removing the hub nut and other parts. Note the pin to hold the rotor from turning (arrow). (Courtesy of NEAPCO)

FIGURE 10-32 On most vehicles, the lower control arm is disconnected from the ball joint by removing the clamp bolt and sliding the ball joint stud out of the steering knuckle. This allows for swinging the steering knuckle outward far enough to remove the outboard CV joint from the hub. (Courtesy of NEAPCO)

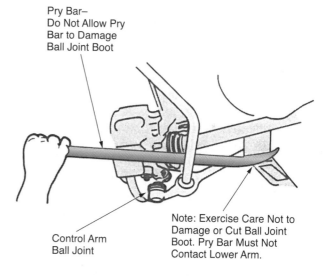

FIGURE 10-33 A pry bar is being used to force the lower control arm downward far enough to remove the ball joint stud from the steering knuckle. (Courtesy of Ford Motor Company)

◄ **SERVICE TIP** ►

In many FWD vehicles with an **antilock braking system (ABS)**, an ABS **reluctor/tone ring** is mounted on the outboard CV joint and a **wheel speed sensor (WSS)** right next to it. Be careful not to damage the speed sensor wire, WSS, or reluctor. Reluctor ring replacement is described in Section 10.5.1.3.

4. Pry the lower control downward to separate it from the steering knuckle as you pull the steering knuckle outward to separate the front hub from the CV joint (Figure 10-33). On some vehicles it is necessary to install a puller to push the CV joint inward (Figure 10-34). Never hammer on the end of the CV joint to drive it inward.

As you separate the hub and CV joint, be careful not to stretch the brake hose too far; on some vehicles it will be necessary to disconnect the brake caliper and hang it from the strut assembly using a hook or wire. Be ready to support the driveshaft so that it does not drop.

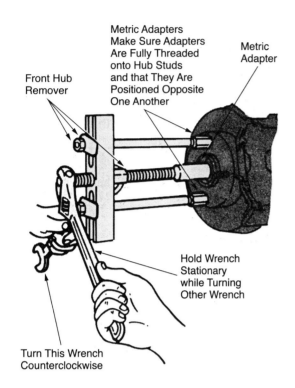

Front Hub Remover

Metric Adapters Make Sure Adapters Are Fully Threaded onto Hub Studs and that They Are Positioned Opposite One Another

Metric Adapter

Hold Wrench Stationary while Turning Other Wrench

Turn This Wrench Counterclockwise

FIGURE 10-34 This puller is being used to pull the hub outward and off the splines of the outboard CV joint. (Courtesy of Ford Motor Company)

5. On some vehicles the inner CV joint can be removed from the differential with a quick jerk on the prying tool, but do not put excessive force on the transaxle case (Figure 10-35).

◄ **SERVICE TIP** ►

An attachment for a slide hammer can be used to jerk the CV joint out of the differential. Do not use the outer CV joint and driveshaft as a slide hammer for this purpose.

6. Remove the driveshaft, being careful not to damage the CV joint boots. Keep the shaft horizontal so as not to stress the plunge joint (Figure 10-36).

To replace a FWD driveshaft (Figure 10-37):

1. Lubricate the seal area on the inboard CV joint, and being careful not to damage the seal, slide the CV joint completely into the transaxle.

◄ **SERVICE TIP** ►

When installing a front driveshaft that uses a circlip at the inner CV joint, sometimes the circlip hangs down and catches during the installation. Partially fill the circlip groove with enough grease so the grease will keep the circlip centered.

◄ **SERVICE TIP** ►

Test the installation by pulling outward on the CV joint housing; it should not pull free.

2. Pull the hub and steering knuckle outward as you insert the spline of the outboard CV joint through the hub. Rotate the hub, if necessary, to line up the splines.

3. Thread a new hub nut onto the CV joint and tighten the nut just enough to pull the CV joint into place.

◄ **SERVICE TIP** ►

A special tool is required to pull the CV joint into place on some domestic and imported vehicles; do not use the hub nut for this purpose.

4. Reinstall the lower ball joint using a new bolt where required, and tighten the nut to the correct torque.

◄ **SERVICE TIP** ►

Be sure to align the notch in the ball joint stud with the clamp hole on those studs that do not have a full groove around them.

5. Tighten the hub nut to about 50 ft-lb (70 N-m) of torque. Install the wheel and tire, and lower the vehicle. Set the parking brake and finish tightening the hub nut and lug nuts to the correct torque.

6. Install the hub nut locking device, raise the tire, and check to ensure that the tire rotates freely.

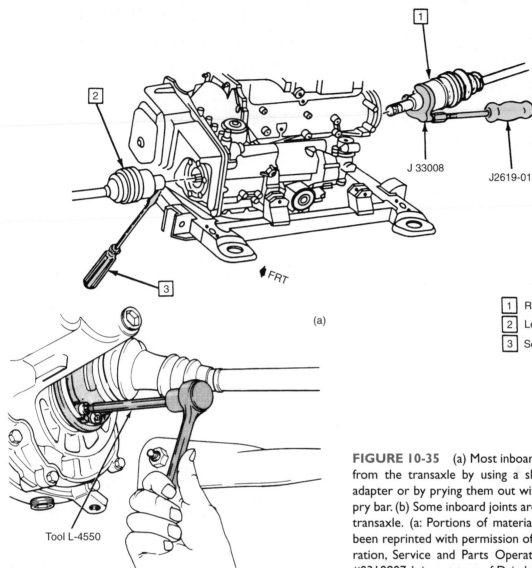

1	Right Axle Shaft
2	Left Axle Shaft
3	Screwdriver

(a)

FIGURE 10-35   (a) Most inboard CV joints can be pulled from the transaxle by using a slide hammer and special adapter or by prying them out with a large screwdriver or pry bar. (b) Some inboard joints are bolted to a flange at the transaxle. (a: Portions of materials contained herein have been reprinted with permission of General Motors Corporation, Service and Parts Operations, License Agreement #0310807; b is courtesy of DaimlerChrysler Corporation)

(b)

10.4.1.1 FWD Wheel Bearing Service.

Wheel bearing service is easier when the CV joint is removed from the steering knuckle. The bearing is usually a sealed bearing or modular assembly that allows the hub to rotate in the steering knuckle while holding the front wheel in proper alignment. A bearing is normally a press fit into the steering knuckle with the hub a press fit into the bearing. The hub is a part of the modular bearing and is bolted onto the steering knuckle; it is easily removed and replaced.

10.4.2 RWD Driveshaft Removal and Replacement

Most driveshaft slip joint splines float in the transmission mainshaft rear bushing. When the driveshaft is un-

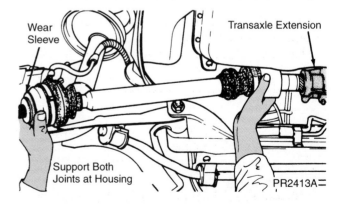

FIGURE 10-36   After a shaft has been disconnected, it should be removed carefully to prevent damaging the boots or CV joints; it should then be carried in a horizontal position. (Courtesy of DaimlerChrysler Corporation)

(a)

(b)

(c)

(d)

Steering
Knuckle

Groove in
Stud

Steering
Knuckle

Slot in
Stud

(e)

(f)

(g)

FIGURE 10-37 A FWD driveshaft is replaced by installing the inboard joint into the transaxle (a), swinging the steering knuckle outward so that the hub goes onto the splines of the outboard CV joint (b) [in some cases, the CV joint splines must be pulled into the hub (c)], installing the ball joint stud and retaining bolt correctly into the steering knuckle (d), tightening the ball joint nut (e), replacing the hub nut (f), and tightening the nut to the correct torque (g). (a, b, c, e, f, and g are courtesy of NEAPCO; d is courtesy of Moog Automotive)

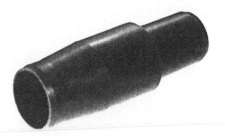

FIGURE 10-38 This stop-off tool is a quick, easy way to keep fluid in the transmission after the driveshaft has been removed. (Courtesy of K-D Tools)

bolted from the rear axle, it will slide right out of the transmission. This allows lubricant to run out of the unsealed opening.

◄ SERVICE TIP ►

To prevent leakage, many shops position a vehicle so that the back end is raised higher than the front. Many technicians use an old slip yoke or stop-off tool to plug the opening (Figure 10-38). A plastic bag and rubber band can also be used.

When replacing a driveshaft, be sure to put some grease or transmission oil on the slip yoke to lubricate the seal.

To remove a RWD driveshaft:

1. Raise and securely support the vehicle so that the driveshaft is free to turn.

2. Place index marks at the rear U-joint flange and rear of the shaft so that the shaft can be replaced in this same position (Figure 10-39).
3. Remove the bolts securing the rear U-joint to the flange. Do not let the two bearing cups fall off the U-joint cross.

◄ SERVICE TIP ►

Many technicians will wrap tape around the joint or slide an old sock over the U-joint and shaft to hold the bearing cups in place (Figure 10-40). Also, support the shaft so that it doesn't fall.

4. Slide the slip yoke out of the transmission, plug the back of the transmission, and remove the driveshaft from the vehicle.

Most RWD driveshafts are replaced by sliding the slip yoke into the transmission, aligning the index marks as the rear U-joint is connected to the rear-axle companion flange, and tightening the bolts to the correct torque.

◄ SERVICE TIP ►

When installing a driveshaft with the bearing caps held by a U-bolt or strap, make sure that the bearing cups are properly seated inside the locating lugs (Figure 10-41).

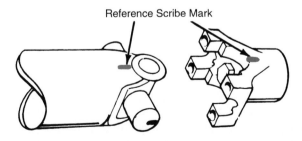

FIGURE 10-39 Before removal, make index marks at the rear U-joint so that the shaft can be replaced in its original position. (Courtesy of Ford Motor Company)

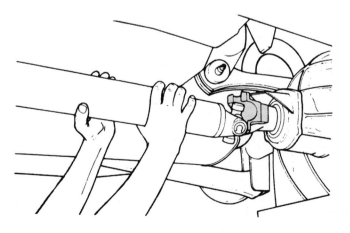

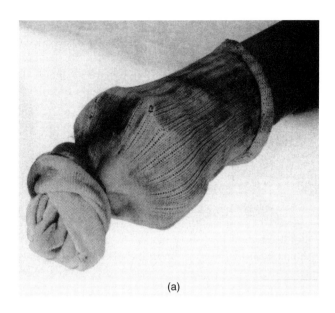

(a)

(b)

FIGURE 10-40 (a) An old sock has been slid over this driveshaft to hold the bearing cups onto the U-joint. (b) Tape can be used for the same purpose.

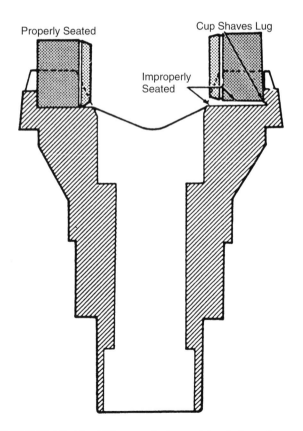

Properly Seated

Cup Shaves Lug

Improperly Seated

FIGURE 10-41 When replacing a driveshaft, make sure that the bearing cups are properly seated inside the lugs of the flange. (Courtesy of Ford Motor Company)

REAL-WORLD FIX A 1988 Chevrolet pickup had a clunk in the rear when it was accelerated from a stop. The noise was isolated to the driveshaft slip yoke. The transfer case and slip yoke splines were good, and when the splines were cleaned and regreased, the clunk disappeared. However, the clunk returned in a couple of months. The transfer case bushing was good.

FIX

A special lubricant, GM part number 12345789, was put on the splines, and this fixed the recurring problem.

10.5 DRIVESHAFT SERVICE

Driveshafts are removed for replacement with a new or rebuilt driveshaft assembly or, more commonly, for repair. U-joint and CV joint service requires only a few special tools and equipment. Major driveshaft operations such as balancing, straightening, or tube replacement are done by driveline specialty shops. When FWD CV joint problems are encountered, many repair shops will install new or rebuilt driveshafts that are available at most parts houses.

REAL-WORLD FIX A 1986 Suburban (144,000 mi) had a severe vibration from 15 to 30 mph, and the cause could not be found. The U-joints, carrier bearing, rear brake drums, and transmission mount had been replaced, and the driveshaft had been balanced at two different shops.

FIX

Many shops balance a driveshaft by single-plane balancing; each end is balanced by adding weight until the vibration smoothes out. The driveshaft was balanced once more, this time at a shop that had the ability to balance by two-plane balancing, which requires more sophisticated equipment. This more complex method solved the problem.

10.5.1 FWD Driveshaft Service

FWD driveshaft service includes CV joint removal for boot replacement; CV joint cleaning, rebuilding, or replacement; and service to the center bearing and U-joint. When used, most center U-joints are Cardan joints and can be serviced as described in Section 10.5.2.1. Replacement driveshafts are available in both new and rebuilt forms.

A universal-fit boot and quick installation process has been developed by Cosmos International; the Uni-Fit boot is designed so that four part numbers fit all CV joints. The large end of the boot will be too large for some joints, so the excess material is cut off. These boots can be installed in the normal manner by removing the CV joint or quickly by sliding the boot over the CV joint by using a special cone and lubricant.

CV joint boots with a split and locking seam are available to replace a damaged boot without removing the shaft or the joint from the shaft. Many technicians do not use these, however, because they feel it is necessary to remove the joint to clean out any debris that might have entered the joint. Also, to get a reliable seal with early designs, the seam must be perfectly clean and kept stationary for a fairly long period of time. Most technicians believe that the slightly longer period of time used to remove and replace the shaft and joint; to clean, check, and lubricate the joint properly; and to use a factory-approved boot is well worth the time and expense.

On some vehicles it is possible to remove the outboard CV joint with the driveshaft still connected to the transaxle. As a beginner, though, it is a wise practice to remove the entire assembly until you are skilled at the procedure used to remove and replace the joint on the shaft.

10.5.1.1 Boot Replacement. In most cases, boot replacement begins with the driveshaft removed and becomes part of the CV joint removal and replacement procedure. The old boot and clamps are cut off during CV joint removal, and a new boot and clamps are installed during the replacement. If using a Uni-Fit boot and installation cone, the CV joint can be left on the driveshaft. This process uses a cone-shaped device to stretch the boot over the CV joint.

To install a CV boot using the cone method:

1. Clean the driveshaft and CV joint to prevent dirt from entering the boot during installation.
2. Cut the old clamps and boot, and remove them from the shaft.
3. Warm the boot up to 78°F (25°C) (it can be rolled vigorously between your hands) and check the cone to ensure there are no cuts or nicks.
4. Spray the entire outer surface of the cone and boot with wax-type spray (Figure 10-42).
5. Turn the boot inside-out and place it over the waxed cone. Inner boots are installed right-side out, so the inside should be coated with spray and the boots are not turned inside-out.
6. Place the boot over the cone and install the cone onto the 1/2-in. bolt that is held either by the base plate or in a vise.
7. Place the CV joint into the cone, and quickly, with force, pull the boot up and over the cone.
8. Roll the boot right-side out, pack the CV joint with grease, and stretch the boot over the CV joint until a tight fit is formed.
9. Release any trapped air by inserting a blunt screwdriver under the boot.
10. Install a clamp at the large end of the boot in the original location. A special banding tool should be used to tighten the clamp.
11. With the boot at its natural length, install a clamp at the small end of the boot to secure it to the shaft.
12. If excess material extends past the clamp, cut it off using a sharp knife.

Another replacement boot is the Sisuner Quick Replacement Outer CV joint boot, a split-type boot using two unique springs at the closure (Figure 10-43). This boot can be installed over a CV joint with the driveshaft still in place, saving the removal and installation time. This particular boot has been approved by at least seven vehicle manufacturers. If using this style of boot, it is very important to check the condition of the CV joint and its grease to make sure that the grease is not contaminated and the joint is not worn.

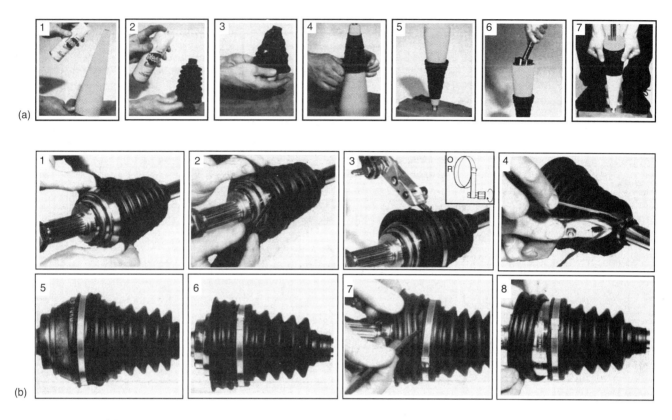

FIGURE 10-42   The procedure to install a new boot over a CV joint using a cone is shown in a, and the procedure used to connect a Uni-Fit boot is shown in b. (Courtesy of Cosmos International, Inc.)

To install a Quick Replacement boot:

1. Cut the old clamps and boot, and remove them.
2. Wipe away any grease remaining on the shaft and inspect the CV joint for damage or contamination (Figure 10-44).
3. Adequately lubricate the inner groove of the boot seam with the supplied sealant, and place the boot over the shaft.
4. Starting from the large end, insert the male side of the boot into the corresponding groove. Position the boot opening over the joint; and then complete joining the boot, working from the small end.
5. Install the small clamp, fill the boot with grease, and install the large clamp.
6. Check the joint to ensure that the seam is properly connected and that the boot has the proper shape.

10.5.1.2 CV Joint Removal.   Outboard CV joints are held onto the driveshaft by a snap ring, a plastic retainer, or a circlip. To determine which is used, a technician usually cuts and removes the boot and retaining rings, cleans the inner end of the joint, and looks for a snap ring. If a snap ring or plastic retainer is not visible, a circlip has been used (Figure 10-45).

It is a good practice to install a new circlip; the old one might be weakened and allow the CV joint to change position after installation. When replacing a circlip, use care not to overstretch it; this can prevent the circlip from releasing the next time.

A new boot and retainer clamps are always used when the CV joints are replaced. These are available in a kit, often with a packet of grease (Figure 10-46).

To remove a CV joint:

1. Mark the location of the boot on the shaft to ensure that the new boot and clamp are replaced in the same position (Figure 10-47a). Cut the boot and clamps using diagonal cutting pliers, and remove them from the shaft (Figure 10-47b).
2. Wipe the grease from the inner edge of the joint, and check for a snap ring.
3. If you can locate a snap ring or retainer, remove it from its groove and slide the joint off the shaft. If you locate a plastic retainer, expand it at the seam, and slide the joint off the shaft.

(a)

(b)

FIGURE 10-43   A Quick Replacement outer CV boot kit (a). This boot has a seam that is held together by two unique springs and the shape of the rubber (b). (Courtesy of Sisuner International)

If you cannot locate a snap ring, clamp the driveshaft in a vise equipped with soft jaws so as not to mark the shaft. Using a special driving tool or brass punch, strike a sharp, quick blow on the CV joint

(Figure 10-48). The joint should break loose and slide off the shaft; be ready to catch it. Leave the circlip in place on the shaft, unless it is to be replaced with a new one.

(a)

(b)

(c)

(d)

(e)

(f)

FIGURE 10-44   The installation steps for a Quick Replacement outer CV boot are to (a) cut away the old boot and clamps, (b) remove any excess grease and dirt, (c) check for wear and grit, (d) place the new boot over the shaft and lubricate the seam with sealant, then (e) start closing the seam from the big end and positioning it over the CV joint. The rest of the seam is closed (f) and the clamps are installed. (Courtesy of Sisuner International)

REAL-WORLD FIX During an oil change on a 1995 Nissan Quest, a torn boot was noticed on the outboard CV joint. The driveshaft was removed with the plan to remove the CV joint and replace the boot. No retaining ring was found, and a good hammer and brass punch blow did not pop the joint off the shaft. The technician sought advice.

FIX

The inner joint and boot were removed. A new boot was slid over the shaft, and installed over the outboard joint. The inboard joint with a new boot was then installed to fix this problem.

(a)

FIGURE 10-46 This CV joint boot replacement kit contains the boot, clamps, grease, and a new circlip. (Courtesy of Moog Automotive)

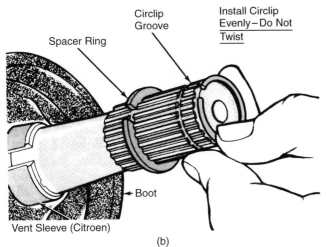

Spacer Ring

Circlip Groove

Install Circlip Evenly – Do Not Twist

Boot

Vent Sleeve (Citroen)

(b)

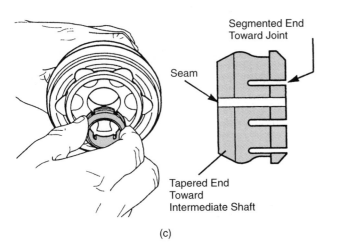

Segmented End Toward Joint

Seam

Tapered End Toward Intermediate Shaft

(c)

FIGURE 10-45 Some outboard CV joints are held in place by a snap ring (a). Most are retained by a circlip (b), sometimes with a spacer ring to help locate the joint. Some newer joints use a plastic retainer (c). (a is courtesy of NEAPCO; b is courtesy of DaimlerChrysler Corporation; c is courtesy of Moog Automotive)

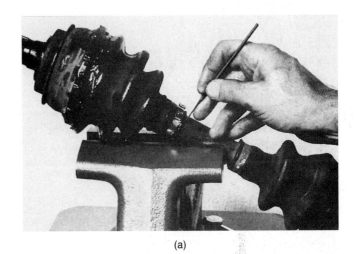

(a)

(b)

FIGURE 10-47 (a) Before the old boot is removed, the shaft should be marked so that the new boot can be clamped in the correct position. (b) Next, the clamps and the old boot are cut to allow easy removal. (Courtesy of NEAPCO)

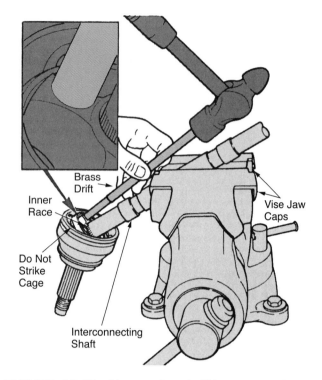

FIGURE 10-48 Most outboard CV joints can be removed from the shaft with a sharp tap from a brass drift punch. Be ready to catch the joint when it comes loose. (Courtesy of Ford Motor Company)

10.5.1.3 ABS Tone Ring Replacement. In most cases, a damaged speed sensor tone ring can be replaced. They are usually pressed onto the CV joint. Special tooling is often required when removing the old ring and installing the new one. Be sure that the replacement ring has the same number of teeth as the old one (Figure 10-49).

10.5.1.4 CV Joint Replacement. Once the joint has been cleaned in a solvent wash, it should be thoroughly dried.

◄ SERVICE TIP ►

Some technicians use a hot air gun for drying the washed joint and warming the boot.

The joint should then be packed with grease of the type and amount recommended by the manufacturer. The packet provided with the boot kit fills this requirement. Never use standard grease to pack a CV joint. Sealing the grease in and dirt and water out is critical.

Several types of retainer rings or clamps are used to lock the boot in place (Figure 10-50). Most boots use either a flat ring clamp or a flat band clamp. The ring clamp is placed onto the boot and then crimped to shorten and lock it in place. A band clamp is placed in position, pulled tight, and then crimped or bent to lock it in place. The boots on many GM vehicles use a preformed retaining ring that must be pressed in place along with the boot onto the CV joint. On newer, nonrubber boots, the clamps must be straight and tight for a good watertight seal.

To install a CV joint and boot:

1. Slide the boot and, if used, continuous ring retainers onto the shaft. Band retainers can sometimes be installed after the boot is in place.

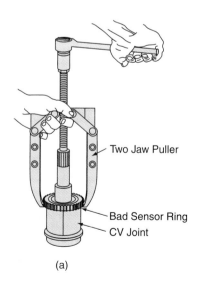

(a)

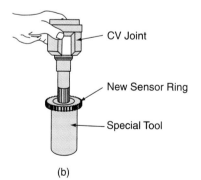

(b)

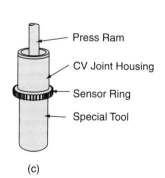

(c)

FIGURE 10-49 A damaged speed sensor tone ring can be removed using a puller (a) or special tools. The new ring is placed in position (b) and pressed into place (c) using a special tool.

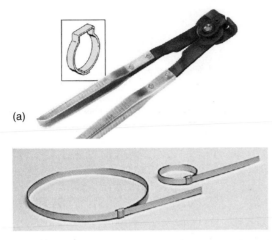

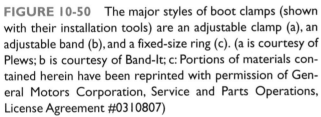

FIGURE 10-51   After the joint has been cleaned thoroughly, it is repacked with grease, working the grease into all parts of the joint. (Courtesy of NEAPCO)

FIGURE 10-50   The major styles of boot clamps (shown with their installation tools) are an adjustable clamp (a), an adjustable band (b), and a fixed-size ring (c). (a is courtesy of Plews; b is courtesy of Band-It; c: Portions of materials contained herein have been reprinted with permission of General Motors Corporation, Service and Parts Operations, License Agreement #0310807)

If a snap ring is used, slide the CV joint and snap ring onto the shaft, and replace the snap ring in its groove. If a plastic retainer is used, insert the segmented end into the joint, and slide the CV joint onto the shaft until you feel the retainer snap into its groove.

4. Place the small shaft end of the boot in the position marked on the shaft. Place the retainer in position, and lock the retainer and boot in place.

5. Place the large end of the boot in position on the CV joint. Work any abnormal folds or bulges out of the boot. Place the retainer in position, and lock the retainer in place (Figure 10-52).

Note: Steps 4 and 5 can be reversed on many joints.

2. Pack the CV joint with grease, moving the joint through all of its angles as you fill all the cavities of the joint (Figure 10-51).

3. If a circlip is used, slide the CV joint in place onto the shaft; you can often feel the circlip lock the joint in place.

◄   **SERVICE TIP**   ►

If a plastic retainer is used, insert the segmented end into the joint and slide the CV joint onto the shaft until you feel the retainer snap into its groove.

10.5.1.5 Outboard CV Joint Disassembly, Inspection, and Reassembly.   Most Rzeppa joints can be disassembled for cleaning and inspection rather easily and quickly. If the joint is usable, reassembly is also a fairly quick and easy operation. If the inspection reveals damage, the entire joint is normally replaced. A hammer and brass punch can be used to tilt the inner race. Special tools are available also.

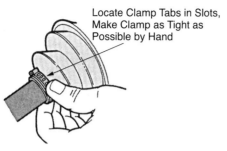

Locate Clamp Tabs in Slots,
Make Clamp as Tight as
Possible by Hand

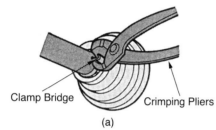

Clamp Bridge   Crimping Pliers

(a)

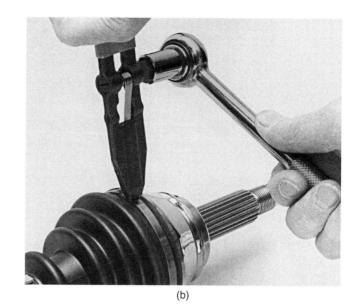

(b)

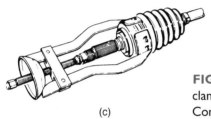

(c)

FIGURE 10-52 After the boot has been replaced and positioned properly, the clamps should be tightened using the correct tool. (a is courtesy of Ford Motor Company; b is courtesy of Band-It; c is courtesy of Plews)

To disassemble a Rzeppa joint (Figure 10-53):

1. Clean the visible portions of the joint, and check the inner race and cage for identifying features to help you position them correctly during reassembly.

◀ SERVICE TIP ▶

Index marks can be placed on the outer race and cage using a permanent marker.

2. Rock one side of the inner race inward as far as possible so that the ball at the opposite side is exposed. To aid disassembly and reassembly, check for slight differences around the CV joint outer race and cage. A wider slot or pair of wider windows allows you to take the joint apart or put it back together.

3. Remove the exposed ball and then rock this side of the race inward to allow removal of the opposite ball. Repeat these steps to remove the remaining balls.

4. Both the inner race and the cage can now be rotated completely.

The inner race and cage are removed together by rotating the cage 90° to the outer race and swinging it out.

5. The inner race can be removed from the cage by rotating it 90° to the cage and swinging it out.

6. Clean all the parts in solvent, and thoroughly air dry them.

After disassembly and cleaning, the balls, cage, and inner and outer races should be inspected for wear or damage (Figure 10-54). Normal damage can appear as chipped or pitted balls, a cracked or pitted cage, and worn grooves or channels in the inner and outer raceways.

To assemble a Rzeppa joint (Figure 10-55):

1. Swing the inner race into the cage and rotate it 90° until the inner race and case are aligned.

2. Swing the cage and inner race into the outer race and rotate them until they are aligned. Position the cage and inner race so that the windows and raceways are aligned with the outer raceways.

3. Rock one side of the cage and inner race upward, and place a ball into the cage window and inner raceway. This should be a tight fit.

Disassemble and Assemble Outer Joint assembly

Remove

1. Remove Parts as Shown.

Install

1. Put a Light Coat of Recommended Grease on Ball Grooves of Inner and Outer Races.
2. Install Parts as Shown.

NOTICE: Be Sure Retaining Ring Side of Inner Race Faces Axle Shaft.

3. Pack Joint with Recommended Grease.

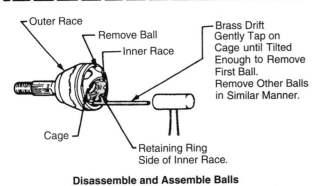

Balls (6) — Inner Race — Cage — Outer Race — Deflector Ring

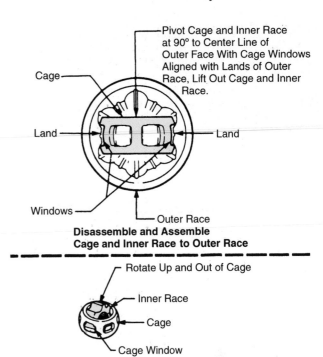

Pivot Cage and Inner Race at 90° to Center Line of Outer Face With Cage Windows Aligned with Lands of Outer Race, Lift Out Cage and Inner Race.

Cage — Land — Land — Windows — Outer Race

Disassemble and Assemble Cage and Inner Race to Outer Race

Rotate Up and Out of Cage — Inner Race — Cage — Cage Window

Disassemble and Assemble Inner Race and Cage

Outer Race — Remove Ball — Inner Race — Cage — Retaining Ring Side of Inner Race.

Brass Drift Gently Tap on Cage until Tilted Enough to Remove First Ball. Remove Other Balls in Similar Manner.

Disassemble and Assemble Balls

FIGURE 10-53 Procedure to disassemble a Rzeppa CV joint; special tools are available to swing the inner race for ball removal and installation. (Portions of materials contained herein have been reprinted with permission of General Motors Corporation, Service and Parts Operations, License Agreement #0310807)

4. Rock this ball downward, into the outer raceway, so that the window on the opposite side is exposed. Place a ball into this window and ball groove. Repeat this operation to install the remaining balls.

10.5.1.6 Inboard CV Joint Disassembly, Inspection, and Reassembly. Disassembly procedures vary somewhat between the commonly used double-offset and tripod joints. The following description is very general; it is wise to follow the procedure given in a service manual for the particular joint you are working on.

To disassemble a double-offset inboard joint (Figure 10-56):

1. Cut the clamps and boot, and remove them from the shaft.
2. Remove the retaining ring and the housing/outer race.
3. Remove the stop ring from its groove and slide it and the inner race assembly down the shaft so

that you can remove the circlip from the end of the shaft. Slide the inner race assembly off the shaft.

4. The balls can be pried out of the cage windows and the cage can be removed from the inner race.

To disassemble a tripod inboard joint (Figure 10-57):

1. Cut the clamps and boot, and remove them from the shaft.
2. Remove the retainer ring and slide the housing off the tripod assembly.

◄ **SERVICE TIP** ►

The roller and needle bearing assemblies are not retained on the trunnion in many tripod joints. Be ready to tape the rollers in place, if necessary.

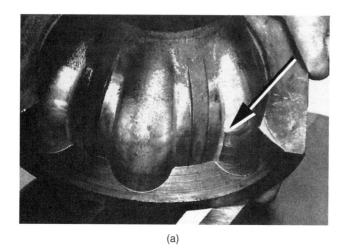

(a)

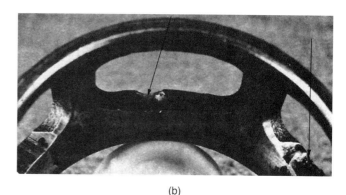

(b)

(c)

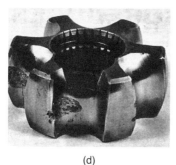

(d)

FIGURE 10-54 After the joint has been cleaned, it should be inspected for damage or wear to the outer race (a), cage (b and c), balls, and inner race (d). Wear problems such as those shown are reason to replace the joint. (Courtesy of NEAPCO)

◄ SERVICE TIP ►

Some Chrysler products use an internal spring in the joint that will force the housing off as soon as the retainer ring is removed.

Some joints have metal retainers that must be bent or slightly deformed to remove the housing.

3. Remove the snap ring and use a brass punch and hammer to remove the tripod assembly from the shaft.

After the joint has been disassembled, it should be thoroughly cleaned, air dried, and inspected for wear or damage. A joint with worn parts is normally replaced with a new one. Reassembly of these joints is simply the reverse of the disassembly procedure; be sure to install a new boot and clamps.

◄ PROBLEM SOLVING ►

Imagine that you are working in a general automotive repair shop and these problems are brought to you.

Case 1

The vehicle is an 8-year-old compact in OK condition with 85,000 miles on it. You pulled the driveshaft to replace a torn boot, but while cleaning out the old grease you notice that the cage windows are dimpled. There is no perceptible problems with the rest of the CV joint. What should you do next?

Case 2

The complaint for the 5-year-old Ford Taurus was a snapping noise while turning. When you lift the car, you find a torn boot on the right outboard CV joint. The grease spray indicates that this has been happening for some time. The joint appears dry. What should you do next? What will probably need to be done to fix this car?

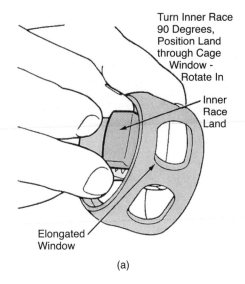

Turn Inner Race 90 Degrees, Position Land through Cage Window - Rotate In

Inner Race Land

Elongated Window

(a)

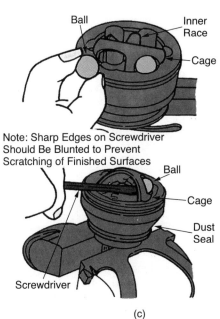

Ball

Inner Race

Cage

Note: Sharp Edges on Screwdriver Should Be Blunted to Prevent Scratching of Finished Surfaces

Ball

Cage

Dust Seal

Screwdriver

(c)

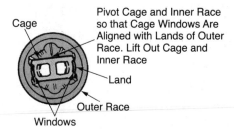

Pivot Cage and Inner Race so that Cage Windows Are Aligned with Lands of Outer Race. Lift Out Cage and Inner Race

Cage

Land

Outer Race

Windows

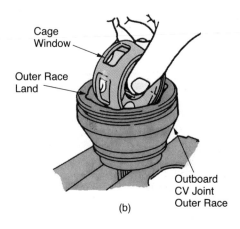

Cage Window

Outer Race Land

Outboard CV Joint Outer Race

(b)

FIGURE 10-55 A joint is reassembled by installing the inner race into the cage in the correct position (a), installing the cage into the outer race in the correct position (b), and replacing the balls into the cage windows (c). (Courtesy of Ford Motor Company)

10.5.2 RWD Driveshaft Service

Normal RWD driveshaft service includes U-joint rebuilding, CV-joint rebuilding, and the replacement of center bearings. Kits that normally include a new cross, bearing cups and seals, and retaining rings are used when rebuilding U-joints.

◄ **SERVICE TIP** ►

Never clamp a driveshaft in a vise by gripping the tube section.

10.5.2.1 Cardan U-Joint Disassembly, Inspection, and Reassembly. This operation is normally done to rebuild a worn or binding U-joint and usually includes the installation of a replacement kit. In some cases it is also done to repack a joint with lubricant.

◄ **SERVICE TIP** ►

Driveshafts with bearing cups located by swaging can be disassembled and remachined by some driveshaft specialty shops to accept standard U-joints using snap rings (Figure 10-58).

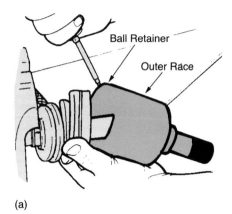

(a)

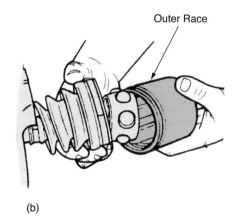

(b)

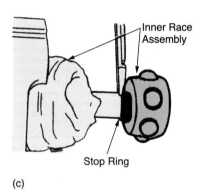

(c)

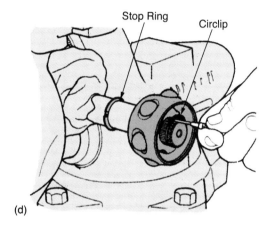

(d)

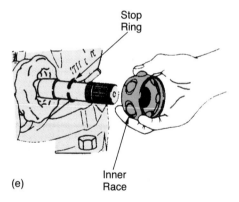

(e)

FIGURE 10-56 A double-offset CV joint is disassembled by removing the retainer (a) and the outer race (b) from the shaft, repositioning the stop ring (c), removing the circlip (d), and sliding the inner race off the shaft (e). (Courtesy of Ford Motor Company)

A variety of tools can be used to remove the bearing cups, which are pressed into the bosses in the yokes. These include a special U-joint press with adapters, special fixtures or adapters that are used with a shop press, two sockets and a vise, a specialized anvil and driving tool, and two blocks of wood and a hammer (Figure 10-59).

◀ SERVICE TIP ▶

The hammer methods are the quickest way to disassemble a joint but are rather crude for reassembly. The press methods are the most professional and will probably produce fewer errors during reassembly.

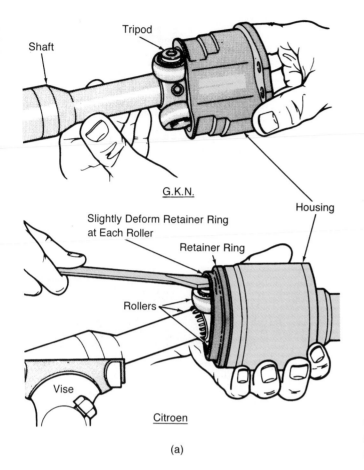

Shaft

Tripod

G.K.N.

Slightly Deform Retainer Ring
at Each Roller

Retainer Ring

Housing

Rollers

Vise

Citroen

(a)

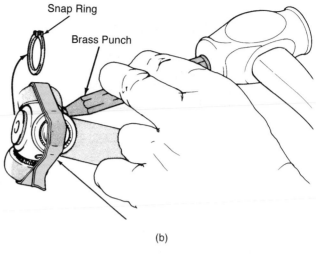

Snap Ring

Brass Punch

(b)

FIGURE 10-57 A tripod CV joint is disassembled by removing the retainer ring and housing (a) and removing the snap ring and driving the inner race from the shaft (b). (Courtesy of DaimlerChrysler Corporation)

(a)

(b)

FIGURE 10-58 These two U-joints (a) have been assembled and the bearing cups locked in place by swaging; normally, they cannot be rebuilt. This joint (b) has been machined to accept snap ring locks for the bearing cups; this saves the replacement cost of an entire driveshaft. (Photo by Tom Birch, courtesy of **Drive Line Service of Sacramento**)

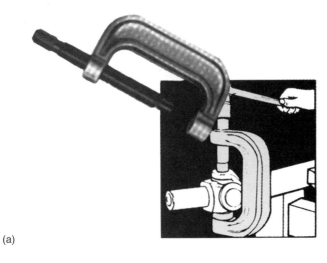

(a)

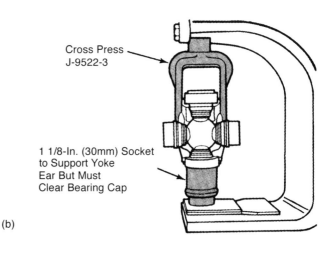

Cross Press
J-9522-3

1 1/8-In. (30mm) Socket
to Support Yoke
Ear But Must
Clear Bearing Cap

(b)

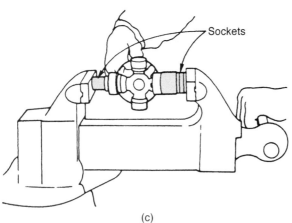

Sockets

(c)

(d)

FIGURE 10-59 A Cardan U-joint can be disassembled using a special tool set (a), a press with special adapters (b), a vise and two sockets (c), or a hammer and special tool set (d). (a is courtesy of OTC Tools; b, c: Portions of materials contained herein have been reprinted with permission of General Motors Corporation, Service and Parts Operations, License Agreement #0310807)

A bearing cup is pressed out of the yoke by either forcing the cross toward the yoke or the yoke toward the cross (Figure 10-60). Usually, the configuration of the yoke prevents complete removal of the bearing cup as you are pressing it. Cup removal usually requires gripping it with pliers or a vise and pulling it out with a twisting motion.

Driveshafts using plastic intrusion to secure the bearing cups allow some manufacturing flexibility. When they are assembled, the manufacturer has the ability to align the input and output yokes slightly off-center to compensate for any yoke runout. Injecting the plastic locks them in this position, and the driveshaft will run vibration free. This is also true with driveshafts using swaged bearing cups. A vibration can occur if a U-joint is replaced on these driveshafts because the two yokes will now be aligned by the new U-joint.

◀ SERVICE TIP ▶

The most common problems encountered during joint reassembly is the possibility of one or more needles of the bearing getting out of position and lodging between the end of the cross and the bearing cup.

◀ SERVICE TIP ▶

When joints using a plastic intrusion are rebuilt and replaced with bearing cups located by snap rings, runout and vibration can occur. Rebalancing the driveshaft will usually correct the vibration.

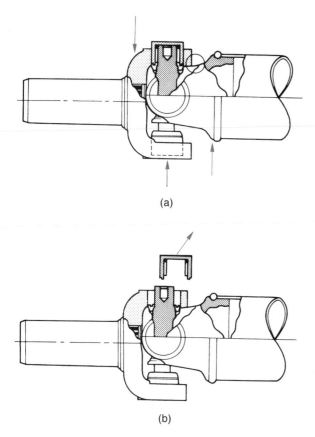

(a)

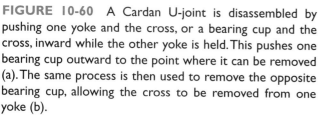

(b)

FIGURE 10-60 A Cardan U-joint is disassembled by pushing one yoke and the cross, or a bearing cup and the cross, inward while the other yoke is held. This pushes one bearing cup outward to the point where it can be removed (a). The same process is then used to remove the opposite bearing cup, allowing the cross to be removed from one yoke (b).

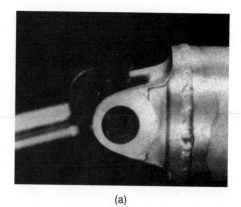

(a)

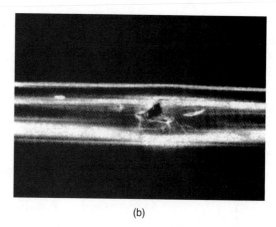

(b)

FIGURE 10-61 (a) Aluminum driveshafts should be inspected for any signs of cracks in the yokes, weld, or tubing. (b) Composite driveshafts should be checked at the aluminum yokes and for scratches in the graphite material and to make sure that there is no movement between the graphite and aluminum sections. (Courtesy of Dana Corporation)

Aluminum and composite driveshafts use aluminum U-joint yokes. Care should be exercised with these shafts because of the relative softness of the aluminum yokes and tubing. Composite tubes can also be easily damaged. These types of shafts should be checked for cracks where the yokes are attached to the tube and for damage to the tubing; scratches, gouges, or cracks greater than 0.008 in. (0.2 mm) require replacement of the shaft (Figure 10-61). Scratching a composite shaft creates a stress raiser that could cause failure. If the U-joints in an aluminum or composite driveshaft need to be replaced, you must use a kit designed specifically for aluminum. The bearing cups in these kits have a special coating that will prevent galvanic corrosion.

To disassemble a Cardan U-joint using a pressing tool (Figure 10-62):

1. Locate and remove the retaining rings. If you cannot locate any retainer rings, check the side of the yoke for a bit of plastic that will indicate a plastic intrusion or swaging marks. The plastic intrusion will be broken as the bearing cups are removed.

2. Check the cross for a zerk fitting. Remove it if there is one.

◄ **SERVICE TIP** ►

If you find a zerk fitting, note its position relative to the yoke before removing the fitting.

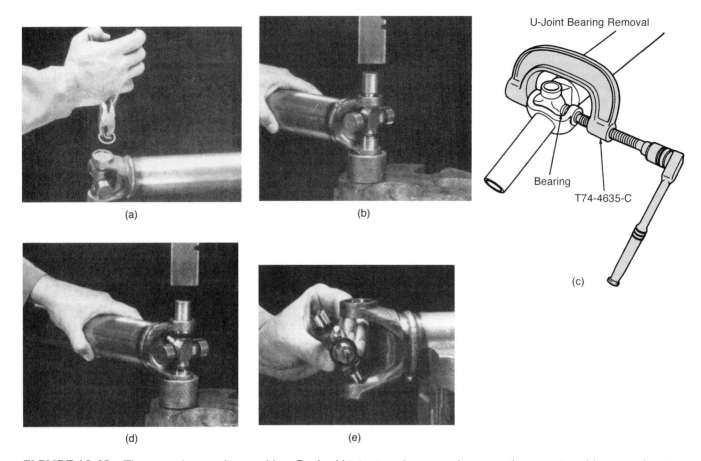

(a)

(b)

U-Joint Bearing Removal

Bearing

T74-4635-C

(c)

(d)

(e)

FIGURE 10-62   The procedure to disassemble a Cardan U-joint is to loosen and remove the snap rings (a), press a bearing cup inward until the cross is against the opposite bearing boss using either a press and adapters (b) or a U-joint press (c), remove the protruding bearing cup and repeat step b or c to remove the opposite bearing cup (d), and lift the cross out of the yoke (e). (a, b, d, and e are courtesy of Dana Corporation; c is courtesy of Ford Motor Company)

3. Select a press receiver adapter that has a hole larger than the bearing cup diameter. Some presses simply use the boss in the press. Select a pressing adapter that is smaller than the bearing cup diameter, and install it in the press.

◄ **SERVICE TIP** ►

When using sockets and a vise, one socket is sized to receive and the other to press.

4. Place the U-joint in the press so that one bearing cup is aligned with the receiver and the other with the pressing adapter, and tighten the press to force a bearing cup into the receiver adapter as far as possible.

◄ **SERVICE TIP** ►

Many technicians prefer to clamp the U-joint press in a vise so that the driveshaft can be placed on a benchtop.

5. Grip the bearing cup with pliers and rotate it as you pull it out of the yoke.

◄ **SERVICE TIP** ►

If the bearing is too tight to pull using pliers, grip it in the jaws of a vise and pull the driveshaft from the bearing using a rotating motion.

6. Reverse the U-joint in the press and push the opposite bearing cup out the other side. Repeat step 5 to remove the bearing cup.

7. With both cups out, remove the cross from the yoke. Repeat steps 4, 5, and 6 to remove the other two bearing cups and cross from the other yoke, if necessary.

The hammer and anvil method of U-joint disassembly simply supports the boss of one yoke as the top bearing cup or driveshaft yoke is driven downward to force the cross and bearing cup out of the lower yoke (Figure 10-63). This replaces steps 4 and 5 in the procedure just given.

Once the joint is apart, the technician should check the cross for wear or damage (Figure 10-64).

◄ SERVICE TIP ►

Besides doing a visual inspection, rotate the cross with your thumbnail against the bearing journals to feel for brinelling, the most common wear problems.

If the cross is good, check the seals in the bearing cups; if the seals are still good, the joint can probably be reused. Many technicians will install a U-joint kit with its new parts.

Caution: Using excessive force while following the steps described here can collapse the yoke.

FIGURE 10-63 In the hammer and anvil method, a U-joint is disassembled by driving the cupped driving tool against the side of one yoke while the anvil supports the other yoke, along with the cross.

◄ SERVICE TIP ►

When installing a joint with a cross that is drilled for a zerk fitting, many technicians prefer to place the zerk fitting in a compression-loaded position rather than a tension-loaded position (Figure 10-65). Visualize the torque transfer. As one yoke drives the other, two sectors of the cross are squeezed together under a compression load; the other two sectors are under a tension load, which is trying to pull them apart. Because the zerk fitting hole is a weak point where cross breakage can begin, the zerk fitting should be located in a sector that is under a compression load and on the side of the cross that is toward the driveshaft. If the cross does not include a zerk fitting, each bearing cup should be lubricated before assembly.

◄ SERVICE TIP ►

Bend the joint through its two different directions; it will often feel tight. Strike a quick, sharp hammer blow on the heavy part of the yoke near the bearing bosses and feel the joint's bending resistance again. Many joints will free up as the jar of the hammer blow realigns the needle bearings in a straight position. Lubricate the joint as described in Section 10.2.

To assemble a Cardan U-joint using a pressing tool (Figure 10-66):

1. Check the yoke bosses for burrs or raised metal in the bores and at the ends of the bores. Raised metal can be removed using a file; driveshafts with elongated yoke bosses should be replaced.

2. Place the cross in the yoke with the zerk fitting hole facing the driveshaft.

3. Move the cross so that one journal extends into the yoke boss as far as possible, and place a bearing cup over the journal. Be sure not to dislodge a needle bearing as you do this.

4. Keep the cross in position in the bearing as you press the bearing cup into the yoke, and install the snap ring.

5. Rotate the yoke one-half turn and start inserting the second bearing cup into the yoke.

FIGURE 10-64 Commonly encountered U-joint faults are a cross with a burned journal (a); broken cross (b); a cross journal with end galling (c), brinelling (d), or spalling (e); a fractured yoke (f); a yoke with a broken tang (g); and a bent yoke (h). A special checking gauge is being used to check the yoke (h) for distortion. (Courtesy of Dana Corporation)

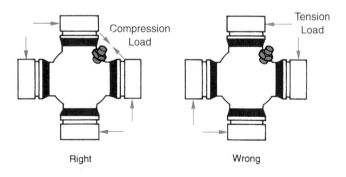

FIGURE 10-65 A U-joint should be assembled so that the cross is positioned with a compression load at the zerk fitting. The cross will fracture more easily if it is positioned with a tension load.

◀ **SERVICE TIP** ▶

As the bearing cup approaches the cross, slide the cross over so it is halfway into each of the bearings, being careful not to knock any of the needle bearings out of position.

Press this bearing cup into place and install the snap ring.

6. Make sure that the retaining rings are completely seated into their grooves.

7. Repeat steps 3, 4, 5, and 6 to install the second yoke and its bearing cups.

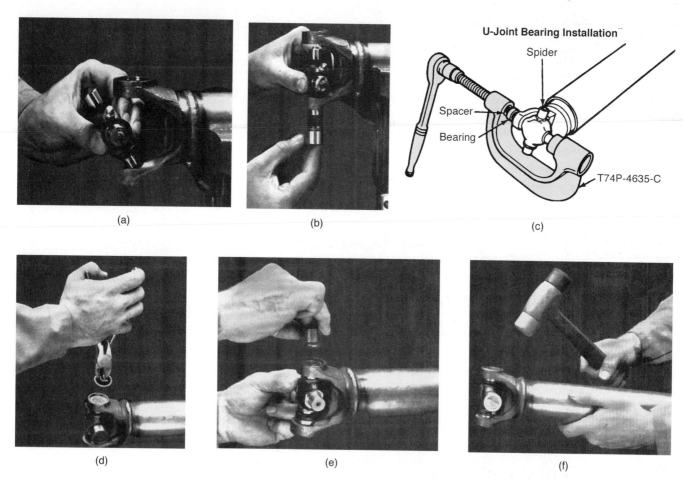

(a)   (b)   (c)

(d)   (e)   (f)

FIGURE 10-66   A Cardan U-joint is assembled by placing the cross in a yoke (a), starting a bearing cup onto a cross journal (b), and pressing that bearing cup into position using a U-joint press or press with adapters (c). Installing the snap ring (d), repeating steps b, c, and d to install the opposite bearing cup (e), and striking the yoke to seat the needle bearings (f). (a, b, d, e, and f are courtesy of Dana Corporation; c is courtesy of Ford Motor Company)

10.5.2.2 Double-Cardan CV Joint Disassembly, Inspection, and Reassembly.   This procedure is essentially the same as the one just described. The same tools are used (Figure 10-67).

To disassemble a double-Cardan CV joint (Figure 10-68):

1. Remove all of the snap rings and note the relative position of the various parts. Some technicians will place index marks on each of the yokes to aid in keeping each part in the same position during reassembly.
2. Select press adapters as described in Section 10.5.2.1, Cardan U-joint disassembly, step 3.
3. Press one of the bearing cups at the yoke end of the centering yoke inward until the bearing cup on the opposite side is moved outward far enough to be gripped.
4. Grip the bearing cup in a vise and tap the yoke off the bearing cup.

5. Rotate the yoke one-half turn and repeat steps 3 and 4 to remove the opposite bearing cup. Now remove the cross and the socket yoke.
6. Repeat steps 3, 4, and 5 to remove the other four bearing cups, cross, and coupling yoke.

A double-Cardan joint can be inspected as if it were a simple Cardan joint with an additional cross and centering assembly. Normally, a double-Cardan joint will show the most wear at the centering ball. Replacement kits include two crosses with bearing assemblies, snap rings, and a center kit.

To assemble a double-Cardan CV joint (Figure 10-69):

1. Check the yoke bosses for burrs or raised metal in the bores and at the ends of the bores. Raised metal can be removed using a file; driveshafts with elongated yoke bosses should be replaced.

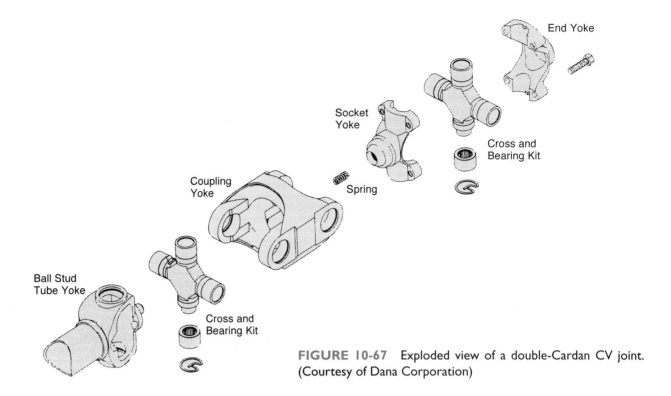

FIGURE 10-67 Exploded view of a double-Cardan CV joint. (Courtesy of Dana Corporation)

2. Place a cross in the tube yoke so that one journal extends into the yoke boss as far as possible, and place a bearing cup over the journal.

3. Keep the cross in position in the bearing as you press the bearing cup into the yoke, and install the snap ring.

4. Rotate the yoke one-half turn and start inserting the second bearing cup. Press this bearing cup into place and install the snap ring.

5. Repeat steps 2, 3, and 4 to install the center yoke onto the cross you just installed.

6. Install the centering kit and socket yoke, making sure that the spring is in place and that the lube fitting is aligned properly.

7. Repeat steps 2, 3, and 4 to install the remaining cross into the center yoke.

8. Make sure that every snap ring is installed completely into its groove, and tap each yoke near the bearing cups to align the needle bearings.

9. Test the joint by bending it in its two major directions. It should bend smoothly and snap over center because of the action of the centering mechanism. Lubricate the joint as described in Section 10.2.

◀ **SERVICE TIP** ▶

Be sure not to dislodge a needle bearing as you install the cross. Also, make sure that the zerk fitting in the cross will be in the proper position.

10.5.2.3 Center Support Bearing Removal and Replacement. Most center support bearings are mounted in rubber in a bracket bolted to the vehicle's frame and positioned on the driveshaft at a slip spline (Figure 10-70).

◀ **SERVICE TIP** ▶

As the bearing cup approaches the cross, slide the cross over so that it is halfway into each of the bearings. Be careful not to knock any of the needle bearings out of position.

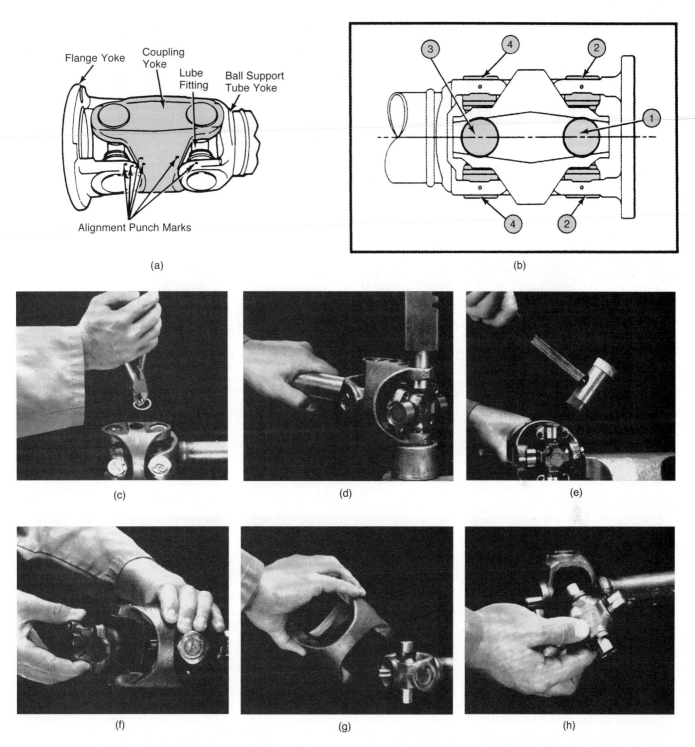

FIGURE 10-68 Disassembly of a double-Cardan CV joint begins with placing alignment marks on the coupling yoke and the two end yokes (a) and then removing the bearing cups in order (b). The snap rings are removed (c); the bearing cups are pressed out (d) and removed (e); one cross and the socket yoke are removed (f); steps c and d are repeated to remove the coupling yoke (g) and the second cross (h). (a, b: Portions of materials contained herein have been reprinted with permission of General Motors Corporation, Service and Parts Operations, License Agreement #0310807; c, d, e, f, g, and h are courtesy of Dana Corporation)

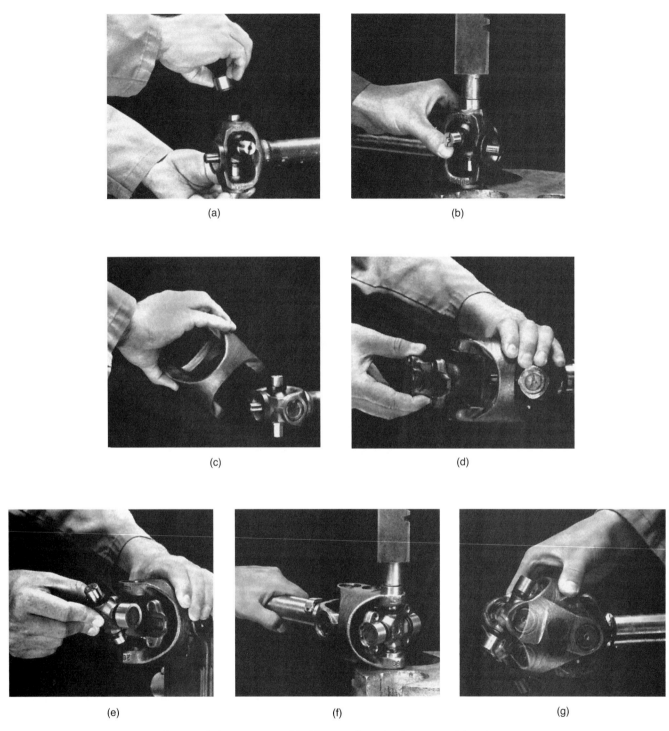

FIGURE 10-69 A double-Cardan CV joint is assembled by installing the first cross (a) and pressing the bearing cups in place (b), installing the coupling yoke onto the cross (c) along with its bearing cups, installing the centering kit and coupling yoke (d) and the second cross (e) and its bearings (f), and after installation of the snap rings, checking for proper operation (g). (Courtesy of Dana Corporation)

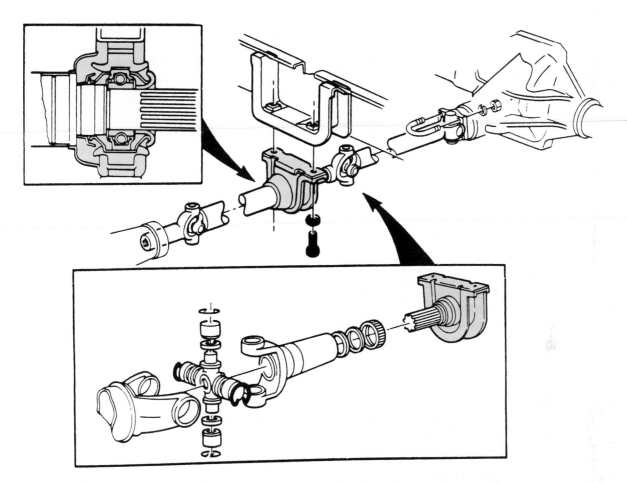

FIGURE 10-70 Two-piece driveshaft with center support bearing. (Portions of materials contained herein have been reprinted with permission of General Motors Corporation, Service and Parts Operations, License Agreement #0310807)

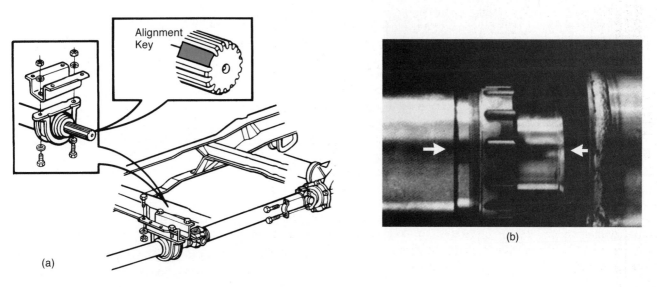

Alignment Key

(a)

(b)

FIGURE 10-71 Some slip yokes use an alignment key (missing spline) (a) or a pair of index marks (b) to aid in realignment so that the U-joints can be kept in phase. (a: Portions of materials contained herein have been reprinted with permission of General Motors Corporation, Service and Parts Operations, License Agreement #0310807; b is courtesy of Dana Corporation)

To remove a center support bearing:

1. Disconnect the bearing bracket from the frame cross member. Some bearing supports will have shims that must be replaced in the same position.
2. Remove the driveshaft as described in Section 10.4.2.
3. Check the slip joint for index marks. If there are none, mark both sides of the joint so that you can align them to keep the U-joints in phase when reassembling the shaft.

4. Unscrew the collar and seal, and slide the slip joint apart.
5. Pull the bearing off the shaft.

Before reassembly, the cavity alongside the bearing, inside the dust shields, should be filled with a waterproof lithium soap grease (Figure 10-72). Some grease should be put on the slip joint splines as well. The rest of the reassembly procedure is the reverse of the disassembly procedure.

◄ **SERVICE TIP** ►

Some slip joints will have a bind or master spline, which makes the index-mark step unnecessary (Figure 10-71).

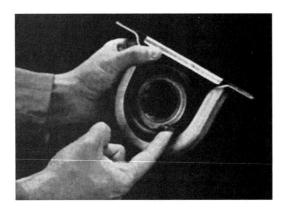

FIGURE 10-72 Before reassembling a center support bearing, waterproof grease should be packed into the cavity around the bearing to shield it from water and other contaminants. (Courtesy of Dana Corporation)

◄ **PROBLEM SOLVING** ►

Imagine that you are working in a general automotive repair shop and these problems are brought to you.

Case 1

You've just assembled a U-joint and installed the last retaining ring, and it was very tight. Now the joint has locked up and won't bend in one of the directions. What went wrong? What should you do to correct it?

Case 2

You rebuilt the U-joints on the compact pickup last week, and it seemed OK when you reinstalled it. But the customer brought it back with a complaint of a vibration at 50 mph that wasn't there before you repaired the driveshaft. What might have gone wrong? What should you do next?

REVIEW QUESTIONS

The following questions are provided to help you study as you read the chapter.

1. Most of the customer concerns relating to driveshaft problems are _____ or _____ oriented.
2. Front-wheel-drive driveshaft problems include _____ spray, _____ noise while turning, _____ noise on acceleration, or a _____ during acceleration.

3. The _____ spray from a constant-velocity joint is the result of a damaged _____.
4. A _____ noise while turning a vehicle equipped with constant-velocity joints indicates a damaged _____ joint.
5. A _____ or shudder indicates a sticking inboard joint and a _____ indicates a worn CV joint.

6. A quick way to check U-joint angles is to measure the distance between the _____ and _____ yokes at the top and bottom of the yokes. If the measurements are the same, the U-joint angles are the same.

7. A _____ _____ can be used as a weight to balance a driveshaft.

8. Most inboard CV joints are held into the transmission by a _____ that usually releases when enough outward pressure is placed on it.

9. When replacing a CV joint circlip, use care not to _____ it. This can prevent the circlip from releasing the next time the driveshaft needs to be removed.

10. The most common wear problem for Cardan U-joints is _____.

CHAPTER QUIZ

The following questions will help you check the facts you have learned. Select the answer that completes each statement correctly.

Two students are discussing FWD driveshaft removal.

1. While discussing driveshaft problems, student A says that the most common cause of vehicle vibrations at 50 mph is a faulty U-joint or CV joint. Student B says that all driveshaft-caused problems are torque sensitive. Who is correct?
   a. Student A
   b. Student B
   c. Both Student A and Student B
   d. Neither Student A nor Student B

2. A FWD vehicle makes a clicking noise while the vehicle is turning but not while going straight. This is probably caused by a faulty A. inboard CV joint, B. outboard CV joint. Which is correct?
   a. A only   c. Both A and B
   b. B only   d. Neither A nor B

3. A FWD vehicle has a spray of grease inside the front wheel well. This is probably caused by a A. torn CV joint boot, B. faulty wheel bearing seal. Which is correct?
   a. A only   c. Both A and B
   b. B only   d. Neither A nor B

4. Student A says that a vibration may result if the rear U-joint operating angle is more than 1° different from that of the front joint. Student B says that a tight, binding U-joint can cause vibration during acceleration. Who is correct?
   a. Student A
   b. Student B
   c. Both Student A and Student B
   d. Neither Student A nor Student B

5. Student A says that the removal of the driveshaft usually requires partial disassembly of the front suspension. Student B says that the first step in driveshaft removal is to loosen the front hub nut. Who is correct?
   a. Student A   c. Both Student A and Student B
   b. Student B   d. Neither Student A nor Student B

6. Student A says that the outer portion of the driveshaft can be used as a slide hammer to pop the inboard CV joint out of the transaxle. Student B says that you should not hammer on the outer end of the outboard CV joint to get it out of the hub. Who is correct?
   a. Student A
   b. Student B
   c. Both Student A and Student B
   d. Neither Student A nor Student B

7. Student A says that index marks should be placed at the rear of the driveshaft and rear-axle pinion shaft flange before disconnecting the U-joint. Student B says that a vibration might result if the front slip yoke is installed onto the transmission mainshaft in the wrong position. Who is correct?
   a. Student A
   b. Student B
   c. Both Student A and Student B
   d. Neither Student A nor Student B

8. When a driveshaft is removed from the transmission, the gear oil leak can be stopped by using a
   a. commercial stop-off tool.
   b. old slip yoke.
   c. plastic bag and rubber band.
   d. any of these.

9. Most outboard CV joints are held onto the driveshaft by a _____ at the end of the shaft.
   a. cap screw   c. circlip
   b. snap ring   d. any of these

10. While discussing CV joint boot clamps, Student A says that all clamps can be locked in place using ordinary combination pliers. Student B says that a plastic tie wrap can be used for a boot clamp. Who is correct?
   a. Student A
   b. Student B
   c. Both Student A and Student B
   d. Neither Student A nor Student B

11. Student A says that a Rzeppa joint is disassembled by tilting the inner race and removing the balls, one at a time. Student B says that the cage of a Rzeppa joint must be rotated to the correct position before it can be removed from the outer race and housing. Who is correct?

    a. Student A

    b. Student B

    c. Both Student A and Student B

    d. Neither Student A nor Student B

12. The inboard CV joint is usually held onto the shaft by an A. snap ring, B. circlip. Which is correct?

    a. A only   **c.** Both A and B

    b. B only   **d.** Neither A nor B

13. Striking the yokes of a Cardan joint with a hammer after assembly is done to A. align the needle bearings, B. free up the joint. Which is correct?

    a. A only   **c.** Both A and B

    b. B only   **d.** Neither A nor B

14. Student A says that the parallel wear marks along the bearing journals of a Cardan U-joint cross are called brinelling. Student B says that the cross can be used if the marks are not too deep. Who is correct?

    a. Student A

    b. Student B

    c. Both Student A and Student B

    d. Neither Student A nor Student B

◀ Chapter 11 ▶

DRIVE AXLES

LEARNING OBJECTIVES

After completing this chapter, you should be able to:

1. Identify the parts of a RWD drive axle assembly.
2. Tell the purpose for each of these parts.
3. Identify the parts of a gear tooth.
4. Understand the power flow through a hypoid gear.
5. Identify the different types of limited slip differentials.
6. Understand how the limited slip differentials operate.
7. Identify the different styles of axle shafts.
8. Understand how the different axle shafts are retained.
9. Understand the requirements for good drive axle operation.

TERMS TO LEARN

axle gears
backlash
bearing-retained axle
carrier bearings
C-clip-retained axle
coast side
dead axle
differential
drive side

electronic traction control (ETC)
extreme pressure (EP)
face
final drive
flank
float
friction modifier
full-floating axle

gear contact pattern
heel
hunting
Hydra-Lok
hypoid gear set
independent rear suspension (IRS)
integral carrier
lash
limited slip differential
live axle
locked differential
nonhunting
open differential
overhung pinion
partial nonhunting

pinion depth
pinion gear
pitch line
Positraction
removable carrier
ring gear
semifloating axle
side bearings
side gears
straddle mounting
three-quarter-floating axle
toe
torque bias ratio
Torsen®
Vari-Lock

11.1 INTRODUCTION

All RWD vehicles use a drive axle assembly to transfer power from the driveshaft to the drive wheels. Because it is powered, it is sometimes called a **live axle;** FWD cars use a **dead,** nonpowered rear axle. The major parts of a drive axle are the ring and pinion gears, differential, and axle shafts (Figure 11-1). Many 4WD vehicles use a similar axle at the front, the major difference being steerable drive wheels.

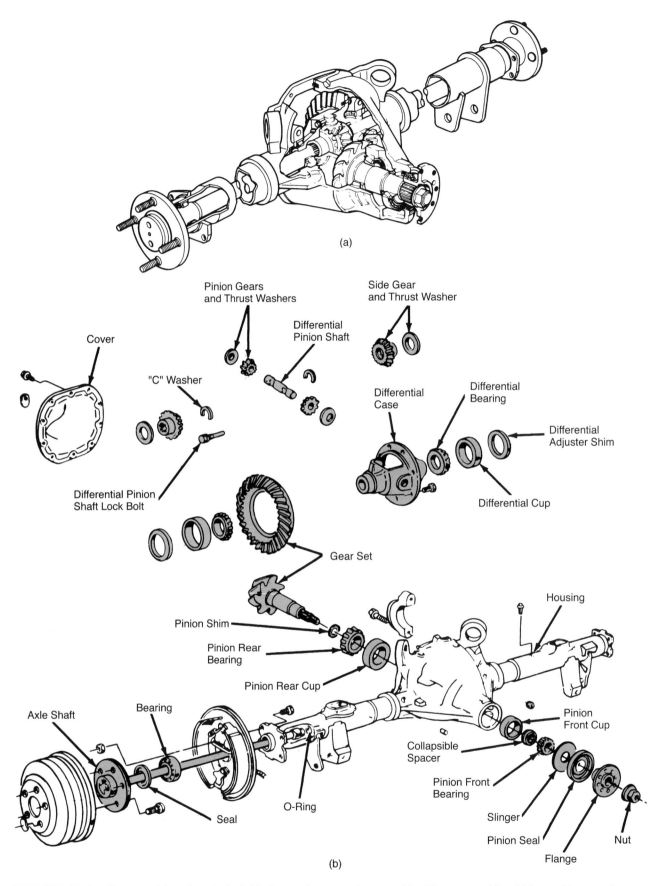

FIGURE 11-1 Cutaway (a) and exploded (b) views of a rear axle assembly. (Courtesy of Ford Motor Company)

11.2 RING AND PINION GEARS

The **ring** and **pinion** gears are the **final drive** reduction gears. Their ratio is normally selected to provide, along with the tire diameter, the proper engine rpm for cruise speed. Sometimes the ratio must be selected so that it, along with the transmission's first-gear ratio, will provide sufficient torque for low-speed operation. Many people consider the reduction for low-speed operation the transmission ratio's job, and the reduction for cruising speed the drive axle ratio's job. With today's fuel mileage and emission requirements, the axle ratio has come under federal control, and ratio changes are done only for off-road situations. With these requirements and today's lower-profile tires, the rear axle ratio of most 1990 cars is between 2.7:1 and 3:1. Fifty years ago, the driving situations were slightly different and taller tires were used; the average ratio for a 1950s vehicle was around 4:1.

Besides determining the gear ratio, the ring and pinion gear set must also turn the power flow from the driveshaft 90° to align with the axles. The ring and pinion gear set is a hypoid type. These are similar to spiral bevel gears except for the height position of the pinion gear (Figure 11-2). In a spiral bevel set, a line drawn through the pinion shaft will intersect the center of the ring gear. In a **hypoid gear set,** the pinion gear is lower, below center. This accomplishes two things: (1) to lower the driveshaft so that the tunnel or hump in the floor of the vehicle can be lower, and (2) to create a longer, larger, and stronger drive pinion gear in which the pinion gear teeth slide across the teeth of the ring gear. This also makes a hypoid gear set quieter. The sliding, wiping action of the gear teeth requires a special GL-4 or GL-5 lubricant. Most gear oils sold in the United States are of hypoid quality (Figure 11-3).

As a gear set is made, after the gears have been cut, hardened, and ground to shape, the ring and pinion are run against each other in a machine with abrasive compound on their teeth. This laps or wears them to match each other perfectly. At this point, they become a matched set, and damage to one will require replacement of both with another matched set. There is normally a mark etched on the head of the pinion gear and on the side of the ring gear to identify a particular set. There is often stamping that indicates the gear ratio or part number, and sometimes there will also be marking that indicates the pinion gear depth (Figure 11-4).

11.2.1 Gear Tooth Terminology

When a gear set is adjusted, reference is often made to particular parts of the gears and their teeth. The outer ends of the ring gear teeth are called the **heel** and the inner ends the **toe** (Figure 11-5). The **pitch line,** as with other gear sets, is the design center of contact between the two gears and is about halfway up the tooth. The **face** of the tooth is above the pitch line, and the **flank** is below it.

The **drive side** of the ring gear teeth is the more vertical, *convex* side of the tooth. This is the side of the tooth that contacts the pinion gear while the engine is driving the vehicle forward (Figure 11-6a). At this time there should be a clearance at the coast side of the tooth; this is called **backlash.** The **coast side** of ring gear teeth is the slanted, *concave* side of the tooth. This surface receives pressure while the vehicle is coasting; the vehicle is driving the engine (Figure 11-6b). While coasting, the backlash will be at the drive side of the tooth. The third tooth-load condition is called **float** (Figure 11-6c). At this time there is no load on the gear teeth so that backlash will be on both sides.

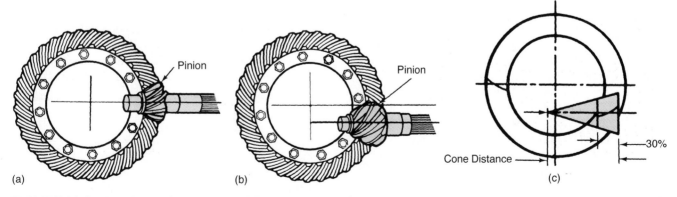

FIGURE 11-2 Spiral bevel (a) and hypoid (b) gear sets; most drive axles use a hypoid gear set for the ring and pinion gears. (c) The amount of offset and cone distance are gear design factors. (Portions of materials contained herein have been reprinted with permission of General Motors Corporation, Service and Parts Operations, License Agreement #0310807)

SAE 85W90 MULTI-PURPOSE HYPOID GEAR OIL

• A light duty gear off with extreme pressure additives perfect for auto, truck and bus standard transmissions and differentials requiring API/GL-3 and GL-4 oils
• Para transmisiones y diferenciales manuales
• Contains anti-wear and extreme pressure properties
• Protects against oxidation, rust, corrosion and foaming
• Not corrosive to copper, bronze or other non-ferrous alloy bearings and bushings

• Extends life of gear teeth
• Good high temperature properties

MEETS SPECIFICATION US STEEL 224 and AGMA 250.03

Contains: Solvent Dewaxed Residual Oil 64742-62-7, Naphthenic Lube Oil Blend 64742-18-3, Mineral Oil 64742-54-7, Alkyl Sulfide 800967-5492P, Naphthenic Lube Oil Blend 64742-52-5
This product contains chemicals known to the State of California to cause cancer, birth defects and other reproductive harm.

Fill to manufacturer recommendations.
DISPENSING PUMP (PRODUCT NO.SL4344) available at additional cost.

Sta-Lube® is a wholly-owned subsidiary of CRC Industries, Inc.
Technical Service: 1-800-521-3168
Customer Service: 1-800-272-8963
©1997 CRC Industries, Inc.   97A
Warminster, PA 18974

0 72213 24229 4
Product Part No. SL24229

FIGURE 11-3   Two gear oil containers (left); the container should indicate that the oil is suitable for hypoid use or GL-4 (right). (Courtesy of Sta-Lube, a division of CRC Industries)

FIGURE 11-4   Hypoid ring and pinion gear set; the 750 etched on each gear indicates a matched gear set. This pinion gear will operate properly only with this ring gear. (Courtesy of Dana Corporation)

Most hypoid gear sets are classified as **hunting** gears. This term refers to the pattern of tooth contact between the gears; think of it as a pinion gear tooth hunting for a mate. If the pinion gear has 11 teeth and the ring gear 24 teeth, the ratio will be 2.182:1. This gear set is identified as hunting, where a single pinion tooth will contact every tooth on the ring gear. If the drive pinion has 10 teeth and the ring gear 40 teeth, the gear set will be **nonhunting.** With a ratio of 4:1, 1 pinion tooth contacts 4 different ring gear teeth on one revolution and then the same 4 teeth on the next revolution. It will only mate with 4 other teeth. If the pinion gear has 10

teeth and the ring gear has 25 teeth, the ratio will be 2.5:1 and the gear set is classed as **partial nonhunting** (Figure 11-7a). In the first revolution a single pinion tooth will contact 2 ring gear teeth (or 3, depending on which one starts); during the second revolution, it will contact 3 (or 2) different ones; and the third revolution will be a repeat of the first. The 1 tooth of the pinion will always contact the same 5 teeth on the ring gear.

◀ SERVICE TIP ▶

Nonhunting and partial nonhunting gear sets normally have index marks that are called like timing marks (Figure 11-7b). These marks indicate the relationship of the two gears during the lapping stage of the manufacturing process. These marks must be aligned when a gear set is assembled.

11.2.2 Mounting

Because of the large torque load involved, the ring and pinion gears must be mounted securely. Gear separation forces try to move the gears away from each other. The ring gear is bolted or riveted to the differential case.

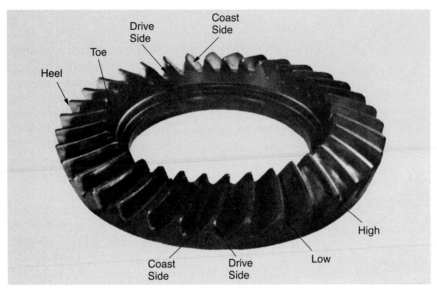

FIGURE 11-5 Ring gear showing the terms used to identify certain sections of the gear. (Courtesy of Ford Motor Company)

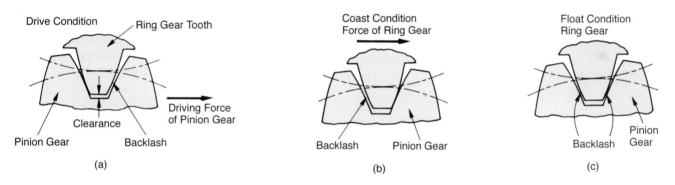

(a)   (b)   (c)

FIGURE 11-6 (a) During a drive condition, the pinion gear is driving the ring gear, and there is backlash at the coast side of the ring gear tooth. During a coast condition, this action is reversed (b); and during a float condition, lash is split between both sides of the tooth (c).

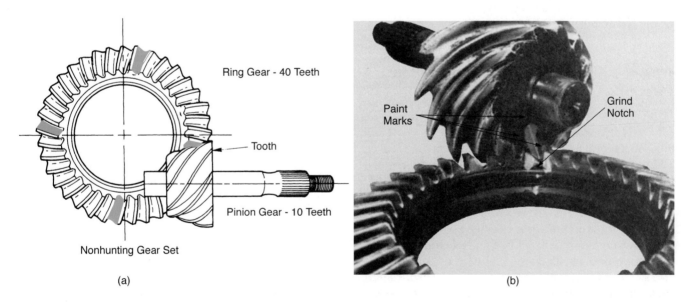

(a)   (b)

FIGURE 11-7 (a) In this nonhunting gear set (4:1 ratio), one pinion gear tooth will contact the same four teeth on the ring every revolution. (b) These gear sets have timing marks so that the gear teeth can be located correctly. (b is courtesy of Ford Motor Company)

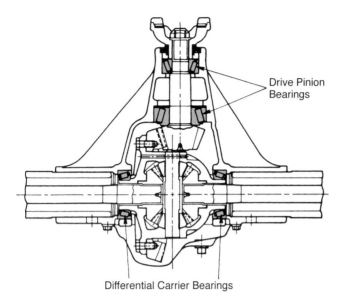

Drive Pinion
Bearings

Differential Carrier Bearings

FIGURE 11-8 A pair of tapered roller bearings called carrier bearings are used to locate the drive pinion gear and the differential case and ring gear. Another pair of bearings locates the drive pinion gear. (Courtesy of Dana Corporation)

Rivets provide a secure and permanent mounting, but they make it harder to remove the ring gear. The differential case is mounted on a pair of tapered roller bearings, which are commonly called **carrier bearings** or **side bearings** (Figure 11-8). The differential carrier is the heavy cast-iron portion of the rear axle assembly that provides mounting points for the drive pinion shaft bearings and the carrier bearings. Many carriers have special reinforcing webs to contain the gear separation forces of the ring and pinion gear set.

Many older axles had **removable carriers,** and the carrier (also called a *third member, drop-out,* or *pumpkin*) could be unbolted and removed from the housing for service (Figure 11-9). Most newer designs use **integral carriers,** and the axle tubes are welded to extensions of the carrier (see Figure 11-1). An integral carrier is stronger in the areas around the carrier bearings. An integral carrier axle assembly, sometimes called a *Salisbury* or *Spicer axle,* has a removable rear cover for access to the differential and other internal parts.

The pinion shaft is also mounted on a pair of tapered roller bearings. There are two common styles of mounting the shaft and gear (Figure 11-10). In the first and most common style, called an **overhung pinion,** the pinion gear hangs over from the rear bearing. The two tapered roller bearings are positioned as far apart as practical to hold the pinion shaft rigid and not allow any movement of the pinion gear as it tries to climb or move away from the ring gear. In the second style,

called **straddle mounted,** the pinion gear is straddled by two bearings: the rear tapered roller bearing in front of the gear and a pilot bearing behind the gear. The pilot bearing is usually a smaller roller bearing. Straddle mounting is the strongest, in that the pilot bearing prevents any bending of the pinion shaft between the gear and the rear bearing. It also eliminates any gear-to-bearing leverage effects and allows the two tapered roller bearings to be placed fairly close to each other.

The drive pinion gear bearings are located in the carrier. With an overhung pinion, they are mounted directly in the carrier. With a straddle-mounted pinion, they are mounted in a separate casting that is bolted to the front of the carrier.

11.2.3   Adjustments

A hypoid gear set must be aligned precisely if it is to operate correctly. Improper adjustments will produce a noisy gear set that might fail early. Four adjustments are normally made when an axle is serviced; two of them are for gear positioning and two for bearing preload (Figure 11-11). Each pair of bearings, carrier, and drive pinions must be adjusted to a light preload, which means slightly tighter than free running; the bearings have a load on them while at rest. *Drive pinion bearing preload* is normally adjusted by tightening the pinion nut to the point where it collapses or shortens a spacer between the bearings (Figure 11-12). Bearing preload becomes greater as this space becomes shorter. In some axles, fixed-length spacers and shims are used.

Depending on the axle, *carrier bearing preload* is adjusted by either threaded adjusters or shim packs alongside the bearings. Most integral carriers use shim packs (see Figure 11-1), while most removable carriers use threaded adjusters (see Figure 11-9). Turning the threaded adjuster inward or increasing the size of the shim packs increases carrier bearing preload.

With both sets of bearings, too little preload might allow the gears to move partly out of mesh during high-torque conditions, and this could cause noise or gear failure. Too much preload increases the drag and power loss and might lead to early bearing failure.

Drive pinion gear position, normally called **pinion depth,** is usually adjusted with selective shims (Figure 11-13). With an overhung pinion, the shims are normally positioned between the gear and the rear bearing; a thicker shim will move the gear deeper into mesh with the ring gear. With straddle-mounted pinions, the shim is normally positioned between the

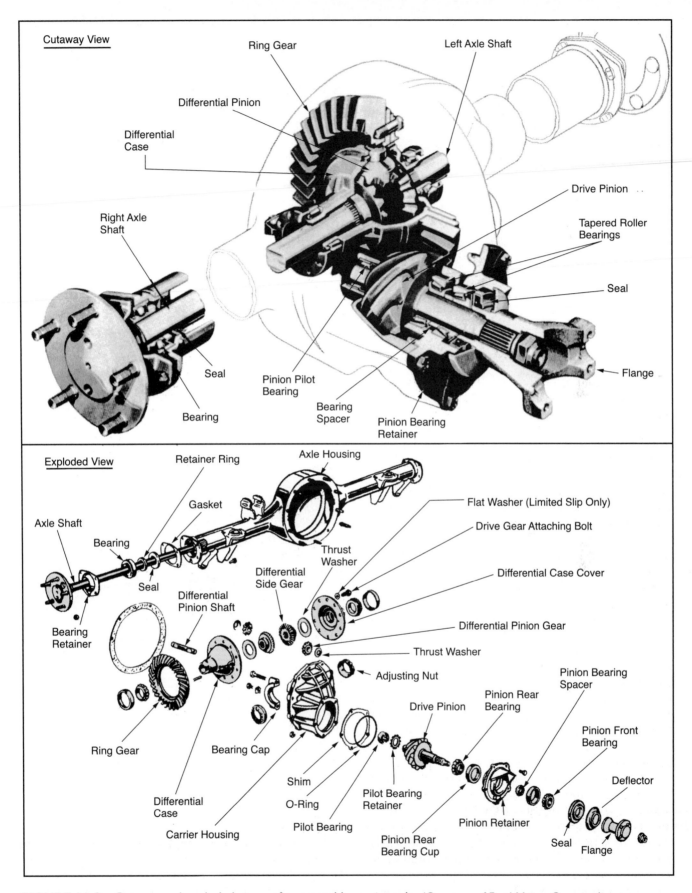

FIGURE 11-9 Cutaway and exploded views of a removable carrier axle. (Courtesy of Ford Motor Company)

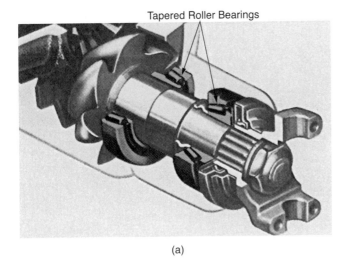

Tapered Roller Bearings

(a)

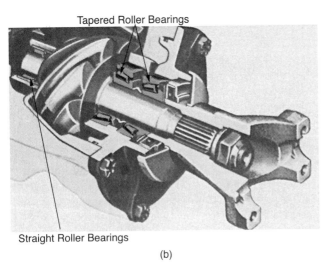

Tapered Roller Bearings

Straight Roller Bearings

(b)

FIGURE 11-10 (a) An overhung-mounted pinion gear uses a pair of tapered roller bearings and locates them several inches apart. (b) A straddle-mounted pinion gear uses a straight roller bearing in addition to the pair of tapered roller bearings. (Courtesy of Ford Motor Company)

bearing housing and the carrier; a thicker shim will move the pinion gear away from the ring gear for a shallower mesh.

Ring gear position, normally called **lash,** is adjusted at the carrier bearings. Loosening the left- or ring-gear-side bearing while tightening the right-side bearing moves the ring gear away from the pinion gear and will increase lash (Figure 11-14). Doing the opposite will move the ring gear into the pinion gear and reduce lash. Lash and carrier bearing preload are usually adjusted at the same time.

The manufacturer determines proper gear position as the gears are operated in a machine. A load is placed on the gears, and the operator listens to the gear noise

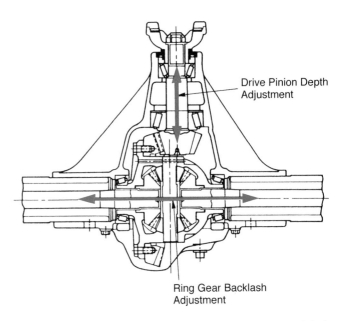

Drive Pinion Depth Adjustment

Ring Gear Backlash Adjustment

FIGURE 11-11 When a hypoid gear set is assembled, pinion depth and ring gear backlash, as well as bearing preload on each bearing set, must be adjusted.

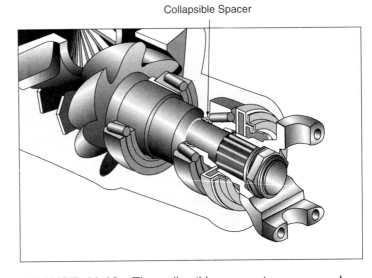

Collapsible Spacer

FIGURE 11-12 The collapsible spacer is compressed during the drive pinion bearing preload adjustment to get the correct amount of preload on the bearings. Some axles use solid spacers and shims for this adjustment. (Courtesy of Ford Motor Company)

and watches the contact pattern. Pinion depth and lash are adjusted to produce the quietest operation. This position is then marked on the gears.

During a drive axle repair, a technician will usually coat the ring gear with a marking compound so that a **gear contact pattern** can be made and then examined. A good pattern indicates proper ring and pinion gear po-

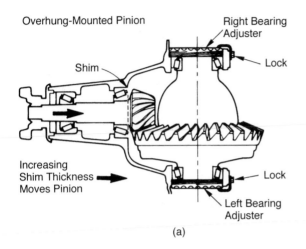

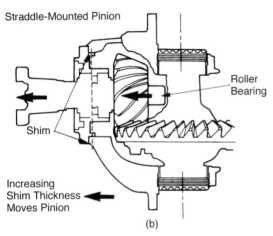

FIGURE 11-13   The shim used to adjust pinion depth is located between the pinion gear and rear bearing in most axles (a) and between the pinion retainer and carrier in some axles (b). (Courtesy of Ford Motor Company)

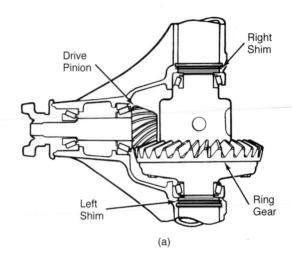

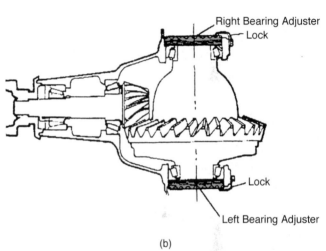

FIGURE 11-14   (a) Reducing the size of the left shim and increasing the size of the right shim will move the ring gear away from the pinion and increase backlash. (b) Turning the left adjuster outward and the right adjuster inward will do the same thing. (a: Portions of materials contained herein have been reprinted with permission of General Motors Corporation, Service and Parts Operations, License Agreement #0310807; b is courtesy of Ford Motor Company)

sitioning, which should result in a quiet gear set that will operate for a long time (Figure 11-15). Other patterns indicate a need for further adjustment. Complete adjustment of a gear set is described in Chapter 12.

11.2.4   ABS

Most RWD vehicles with ABS mount the rear wheel speed sensor(s) to the rear axle assembly. Some vehicles will use a single speed sensor mounted to the driveshaft flange, drive pinion shaft, or ring gear; others will use a pair of sensors near the end of the axle at each wheel hub (Figure 11-16). Since they include a magnetic core, sensors that are in the axle housing can be affected by metal particles worn from the gears or bearings. Sensors at the axle shafts can be affected by worn axle bearings.

11.3   DIFFERENTIAL

A drive axle assembly must include a **differential** to allow the drive wheels to rotate at different speeds on corners. The differential used in most drive axles is the same as that described in Section 7.4. When used with larger engines and heavier vehicles, some differentials use four pinion gears for increased strength (Figure 11-17).

As mentioned earlier, pickups and RWD vehicles encounter more single-wheel traction problems than FWD cars. They encounter more driving conditions in which the normal **open differential** action is not suitable.

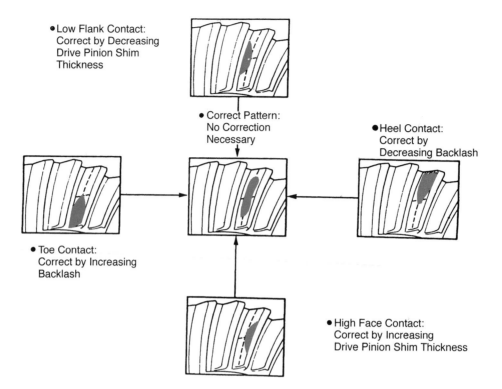

• Low Flank Contact:
Correct by Decreasing
Drive Pinion Shim
Thickness

• Correct Pattern:
No Correction
Necessary

• Heel Contact:
Correct by
Decreasing Backlash

• Toe Contact:
Correct by Increasing
Backlash

• High Face Contact:
Correct by Increasing
Drive Pinion Shim Thickness

FIGURE 11-15 Good ring gear contact pattern (center) and patterns that require further adjustment. The location of the gear contact shows the technician what adjustment is needed. (Portions of materials contained herein have been reprinted with permission of General Motors Corporation, Service and Parts Operations, License Agreement #0310807)

Remember that a differential splits torque equally to the drive wheels. The amount of torque that can be delivered is a product of tire traction as well as engine torque times gear multiplication. One tire cannot receive more torque than either tire can transmit to the ground. A **limited slip differential** is designed to deliver a minimum amount of torque to each drive wheel as well as to provide differential action on turns. A **locked differential** is one in which differential action cannot occur, and this is not suitable for driving around corners on pavement.

11.3.1 Differential Torque Bias Ratio

An open differential has a **torque bias ratio (TBR)** of 1:1 (Figure 11-18). A 1:1 TBR indicates that each wheel receives the same amount of torque. But this means that the amount of torque that can be sent to the two wheels is twice that of the tire with the least amount of traction. Any more torque than this will cause the tire with poor traction (loose tire) to spin, and the vehicle could be stuck. If the poor-traction, loose tire spins at 50 ft-lb of torque, only 50 ft-lb of torque can be sent to the tight, good-traction tire, which could transfer more torque.

Limited slip and Torsen® differentials can send as much as five times additional torque to the tire with good traction; this would be a TBR of 5:1. If the differential has a TBR of 2.5:1 and 50 ft-lb of torque can be sent to the loose tire, then 50×2.5 or 125 ft-lb of torque can be sent to the tight tire. A total of 175 ft-lb of torque can be sent to both tires. The limited slip differential designs that use preloaded clutches will tend to bind up on turns during normal driving because the clutches are forced to slip.

11.3.2 Limited Slip Differentials

Limited slip differential is a generic name for a group of specific vehicle line units. Many people use the term *Positraction* to refer to all limited slip differentials, but **Positraction** is the specific name of the limited slip differential used in Chevrolet vehicles. Other manufacturers have their specific names, such as Equa-lok or Traction-lok for a Ford unit and Sure-grip for a DaimlerChrysler unit.

Many modern vehicles use **electronic traction control (ETC)** to prevent single-wheel spin. ETC uses the wheel speed sensors, control module, and hydraulic modulator of the antilock brake system (ABS) to sense

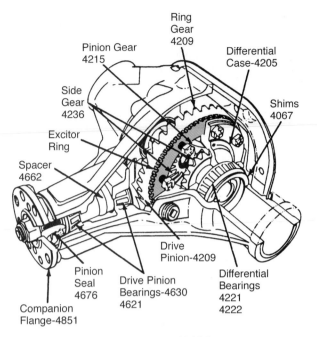

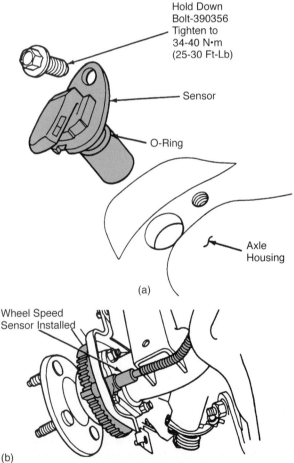

FIGURE 11-16 Vehicles with ABS will have a single rear wheel speed sensor at the ring gear (a) or a speed sensor at each axle shaft (b). Some will use a sensor similar to (a) at the drive pinion shaft. (Courtesy of Ford Motor Company)

wheel spin and, if spin occurs, to apply the brake on that wheel. This will transfer torque to the other drive wheel.

There are seven different styles of limited slip differentials (Figure 11-19): preloaded clutches, self-applying clutches, viscous couplings, Eaton locker differential, hydraulic applied clutches, mechanical ratcheting mechanism, and worm gears. Of these, only the first six are commonly used in passenger cars and pickups, so they will be described here. The others are intended more for racing and off-road use and are described in Chapter 16. Each style has different operating principles.

11.3.2.1 Preloaded Clutch Differential   Differentials with a preloaded clutch(es) provide two different paths for power to pass through the differential (Figure 11-20). One path is through the gears as in other differentials, and the other path is directly through the clutch pack(s). Most of these units use two clutch packs, one on each side, but a few designs use a single clutch pack. Operation is essentially the same.

Flat, hardened-steel plates with various-shaped oiling grooves are used for the clutch plates. Half of them are splined to the axle gear and the other half are splined to the differential case. To provide the preload pressure to apply the clutch, spring pressure forces the axle gear against the clutch pack. The spring can be a single coil spring, a group of coil springs, an S-shaped spring, or one or more Belleville springs.

Lubrication of the plates is critical because the plates have to slip across each other every time the vehicle turns a corner or rounds a curve. A special friction modifier additive is required in the gear oil to make it slippery enough for these differentials. Most filler openings or plugs will be marked to indicate the proper fluid (Figure 11-21). A common problem encountered with these differentials is a stick/slip condition in which the plates stick together, break apart, stick together, and so on, instead of sliding smoothly over each other. This problem shows up as a series of clunks or chuckle sounds as a car rounds a corner. It is very important to keep the drive tires the same diameter with these differentials. Having tires of different diameters will cause the clutch stacks to slip continuously, which, in turn, will cause early failure.

This style of differential has a tendency to lock up under high-torque conditions like hard acceleration because of the gear separation force between the differential pinions and the **side gears.** Applied torque will try to move the **axle gears** away from the differential pinion gears. The separation force, also called torque loading, will increase the applied pressure at the clutch packs. Some limited slip differentials use a pair of cone clutches in place of the clutch plates (Figure 11-22). A cone is splined to each axle shaft, and the differential case is machined to form the mating cone surface.

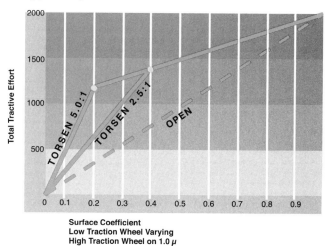

Typical Split Coefficient Performance Curve

FIGURE 11-18 This curve shows the torque bias ratio, the increased amount of torque that can be sent to the tire with good traction. (Courtesy of Zexel Torsen, Inc.)

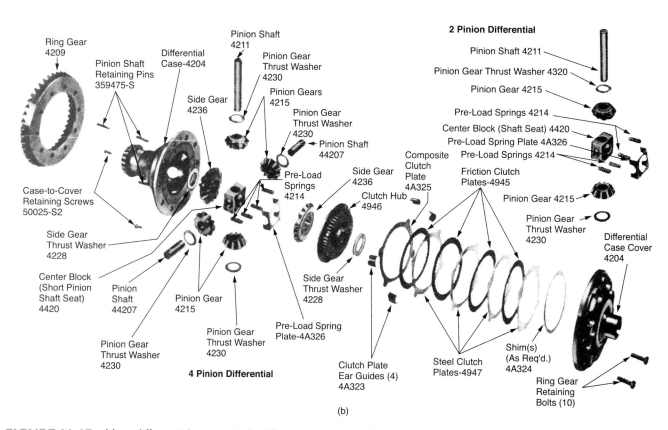

FIGURE 11-17 Most differentials use a single differential pinion shaft with two pinion gears (a). Some use four pinion gears for increased torque capacity (b); also note that this unit is a limited slip differential. (Courtesy of Ford Motor Company)

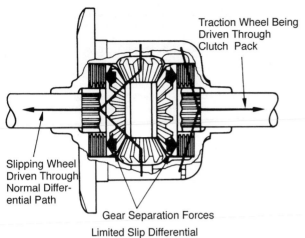

Traction Wheel Being
Driven Through
Clutch Pack

Slipping Wheel
Driven Through
Normal Differ-
ential Path

Gear Separation Forces

Limited Slip Differential

FIGURE 11-19 A limited slip differential transfers most of the torque through the pinion shaft and gears like a conventional differential. A certain amount of torque is also transferred through the clutch pack going from the case through the clutch to the side gear (right).

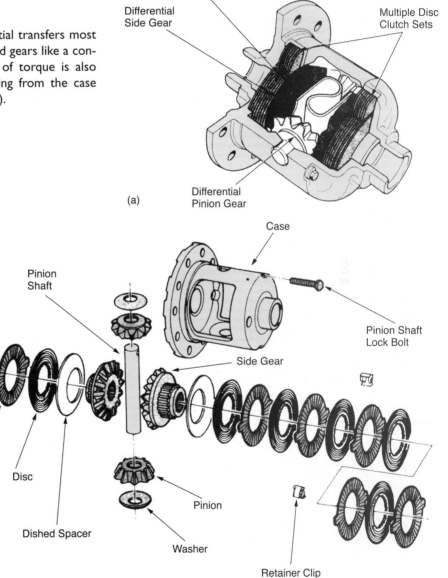

Preload Spring

Differential
Side Gear

Multiple Disc
Clutch Sets

Differential
Pinion Gear

(a)

Case

Pinion Shaft
Lock Bolt

Pinion
Shaft

Side Gear

Disc

Plate

Pinion

Dished Spacer

Washer

Retainer Clip

(b)

FIGURE 11-20 Cutaway (a) and exploded (b) views of a limited slip differential using clutch plates. (Courtesy of Ford Motor Company)

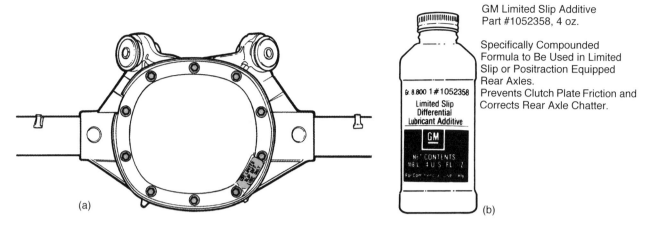

(a)

GM Limited Slip Additive
Part #1052358, 4 oz.

Specifically Compounded
Formula to Be Used in Limited
Slip or Positraction Equipped
Rear Axles.
Prevents Clutch Plate Friction and
Corrects Rear Axle Chatter.

(b)

FIGURE 11-21 (a) An axle equipped with limited slip will normally have a tag at the filler plug indicating the need for a special lubricant. (b) The lubricant is usually a modified gear oil; it can also be an additive. (Portions of materials contained herein have been reprinted with permission of General Motors Corporation, Service and Parts Operations, License Agreement #0310807)

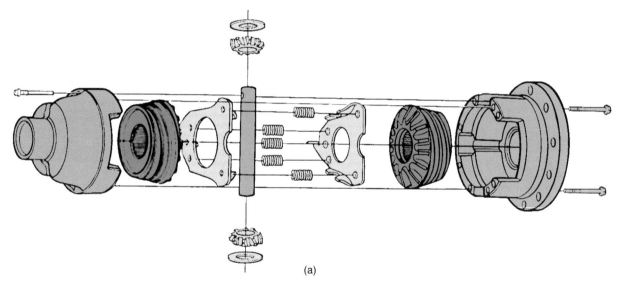

(a)

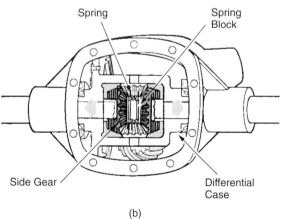

Spring

Spring Block

Side Gear

Differential Case

(b)

FIGURE 11-22 Exploded (a) and cutaway (b) views of a limited slip differential that uses cone-type clutches. (Portions of materials contained herein have been reprinted with permission of General Motors Corporation, Service and Parts Operations, License Agreement #0310807)

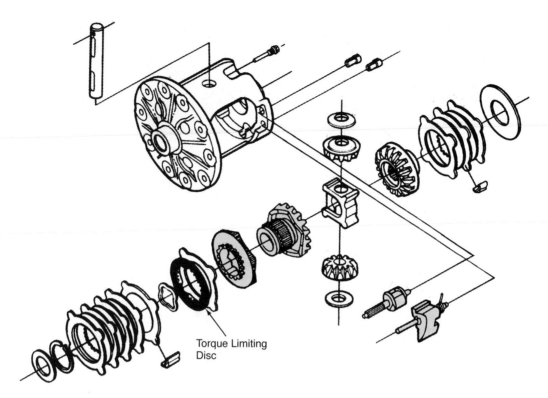

Torque Limiting
Disc

FIGURE 11-23 This clutch-locking differential operates as a limited slip differential until there is a wheel-to-wheel speed difference of 100 rpm or more. At that point, the governor weights will move outward and cause the mechanism to lock up the clutch pack. (Portions of materials contained herein have been reprinted with permission of General Motors Corporation, Service and Parts Operations, License Agreement #0310807)

11.3.2.2 Eaton Locker Differential The Eaton "locker" differential used in some pickups and light trucks includes a governor, latching mechanism, and differential cam gear (Figure 11-23). Normally, this unit will operate as a limited slip differential, but if a wheel-to-wheel speed difference of 100 rpm or more occurs, the unit will lock up. Lockup occurs because the spinning cam in the case turns the governor weights fast enough to fly outward; this, in turn, causes the latching operation, which, in turn, causes the cam gear to rotate relative to the cam side gear, which, in turn, locks up the clutch pack.

11.3.2.3 Self-applying Clutch Differential Some limited slip differentials use self-applying clutches. They do not maintain a constant preload on the clutch packs, so differential action during normal driving is free of clutch drag. These differentials used a four-pinion differential with two separate differential pinion shafts. The two shafts called mate shafts, are fitted into the case in an opposing manner, with ramplike attachments to the case (Figure 11-24). While going down the road, the two shafts, stay centered by pushing toward each other with equal force, because of the equal driving loads and differential gear separation forces. If one wheel loses traction, the driving

load on one of the pinion shafts drops off. The load on the other pinion shaft causes it to lag behind the differential case and move sideways because of the case ramps. This pressure from the differential pinion gears through the axle gear applies the clutch on the side with good traction. The result is that this differential applies the clutch needed to drive the other wheel from the one with poor traction.

11.3.2.4 Viscous Coupling Differential Viscous coupling differentials use a stack of intermeshed clutch plates that run in a bath of silicone fluid and are not spring loaded (Figure 11-25). The thickness of the fluid causes a drag that tries to keep the two sets of plates at the same speed. A unique feature of silicone fluid is that the amount of drag increases as the slip speed of the plates increases. Single-wheel spinning tends to lock up the differential. The plates and silicone fluid must be isolated within a chamber inside the differential case and must be kept separate from the gear oil in the axle.

11.3.2.5 Hydraulic Applied Clutch Differential Normally, a limited slip differential cannot be used on the front axle. If both front wheels turn at the same speed, the vehicle cannot turn; it will travel straight ahead. A recent development is the **Hydra-Lok**

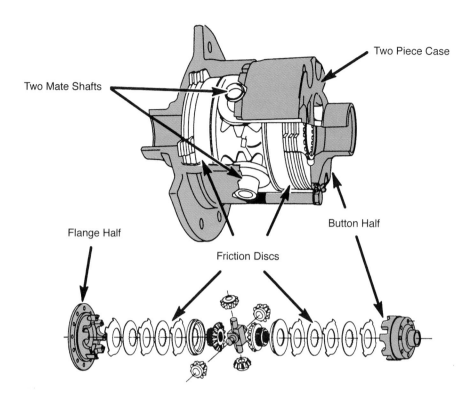

FIGURE 11-24 This limited slip differential uses the action of the pinion mate shafts and ramps in the differential case to apply pressure on the clutch pack and send torque to the wheel with traction. (Courtesy of DaimlerChrysler Corporation)

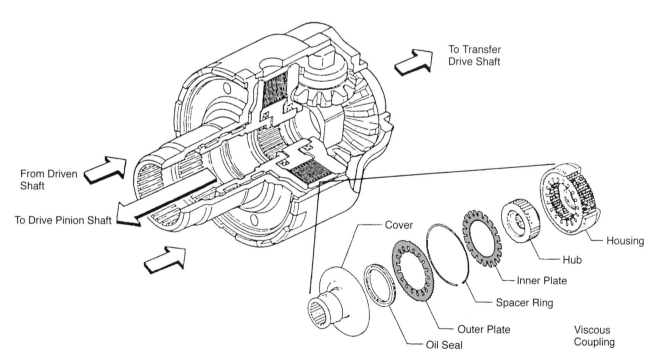

FIGURE 11-25 Viscous coupling. Silicone fluid will let the inner and outer plates slip enough for normal differential action on turns, but it will resist total slippage so as to continuously deliver a certain amount of torque to each wheel or shaft. This particular unit is the interaxle differential for an AWD vehicle. (Courtesy of Subaru of America, Inc.)

FIGURE 11-26 A Vari-Lock (Hydra-Lok) differential includes a gerotor oil pump that is driven when the axles operate at different speeds. If there is too much speed differential, the fluid pressure can apply the internal clutch to reduce wheel spin. (Courtesy of DaimlerChrysler Corporation)

differential from Dana–Spicer (Figure 11-26). Jeep uses the name **Vari-Lock** for this differential. This differential uses a set of clutch plates between one axle gear and the differential case, and these clutch plates have a clearance for free running. There is also a gerotor oil pump built into the differential case. The fluid pressure developed is dependent on the speed difference between the axle gear and the case. The fluid pressure applies the clutch plates so torque will be transferred to both drive axles. The Hydra-Lok differential can be tuned to operate in both a front and rear drive axle.

11.3.2.6 Torsen® Differential The **Torsen®** differential is a pure mechanical worm gear differential (Figure 11-27). The name is derived from "torque sensing." Two helical gears, called "side gears," are connected to the axle shafts. Three pairs of worm gears are mounted in the differential case, and these are called "element gears." Each element gear has the worm gear in the center and a spur gear at each end. The spur gears mesh with the spur gears of the mating element gear. If one of the element gears rotates in the case, its mate must rotate in the opposite direction. Note that all three pairs of element gears must rotate at the same time. Gleason, the company that developed Torsen® differentials, calls the element and side gears *Invex gearing*.

11.4 AXLE SHAFTS

The axle shafts transfer the torque from the differential side gears to the drive wheels, and support the weight of the vehicle on most passenger vehicles and pickups. Axles are forged steel to give them the necessary strength to transfer the torque. The inner ends are splined to match the splines of the differential side gears. Axle shafts can be classified into two categories: the way the axle is loaded and how the axle is retained in the housing.

All modern RWD passenger vehicles use **semi-floating axles.** The inner end floats because it is supported by a gear, not a bearing (Figure 11-28a). The outer end uses a bearing in the end of the housing. This bearing transfers the load of the vehicle onto the axle, which, in turn, transfers it to the wheel. If the axle were to break outboard of the bearing, the wheel would fall off and the vehicle would drop.

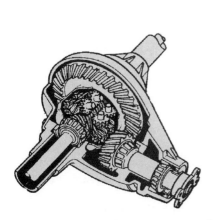

FIGURE 11-27 A cutaway view of an axle with a Torsen® differential (left), the Torsen® Invex gear train (center), and an exploded view of a Torsen® differential. (Courtesy of Zexel Torsen, Inc.)

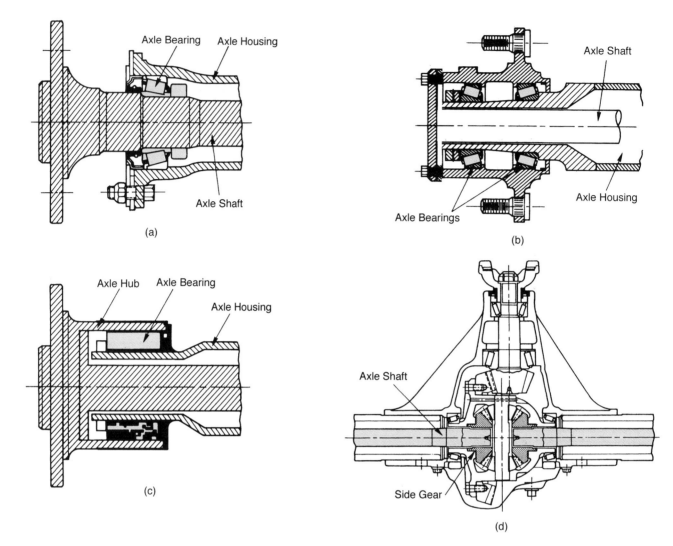

FIGURE 11-28 Modern passenger vehicles use semifloating axles (a). Most trucks use full-floating axles (b). Some older vehicles use three-quarter-floating axles (c). In all cases, the inner end of the axle floats in the differential side gear (d).

All heavy trucks use a **full-floating axle** design (Figure 11-28b). The wheel hub uses a pair of large tapered roller bearings that transfer all of the vehicle loads except torque from the axle housing to the wheel (Figure 11-29). The axle shaft slides into mesh with the axle gear and is bolted to the hub. The axle shaft can be removed, and the vehicle will still roll down the road.

A few older vehicles used **three-quarter-floating axles** (Figure 11-28c). This design uses a single roller or ball bearing between the hub and axle housing. Vertical loads pass from the hub through this bearing to the housing, but cornering loads, which try to pull the axle out of the housing, act on the axle. If the axle breaks, it can slide out of the housing.

11.4.1 Axle Retention

Semifloating axle shafts in passenger vehicles are either **bearing retained** at the outer end of the housing or **C-clip retained** at the inner end. In a bearing-retained axle, the inner race of the axle bearing and a retaining ring are pressed onto the axle. The retaining ring ensures that the axle cannot slide out of the bearing (Figure 11-30). The bearing is held in place in the housing by a retainer plate that is bolted to the end of the axle housing. The brake backing plate is usually secured with the same bolts.

With a C-clip-retained axle, the axle shaft has a hardened surface to serve as the inner race for the bearing; the outer race with a group of rollers is pressed into the end of the housing (Figure 11-31). The inner end of

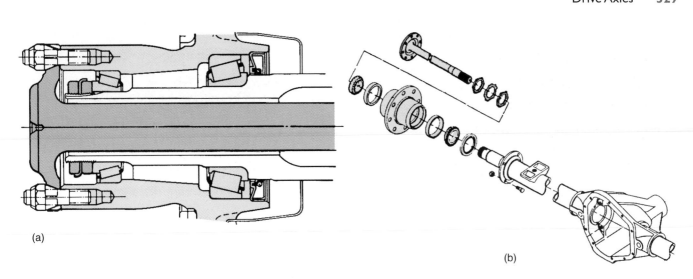

(a)

(b)

FIGURE 11-29 Cutaway (a) and exploded (b) views of a full-floating axle and hub. Note the wheel bearing supporting the hub and how the axle is attached to it.(Portions of materials contained herein have been reprinted with permission of General Motors Corporation, Service and Parts Operations, License Agreement #0310807)

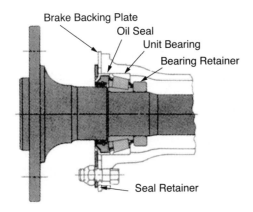

FIGURE 11-30 This bearing-retained axle is held in the axle housing by the seal retainer. (Portions of materials contained herein have been reprinted with permission of General Motors Corporation, Service and Parts Operations, License Agreement #0310807)

the axle has a groove for the C-clip and a hardened end where it contacts the differential pinion shaft. The axle gear has a recess that the C-clip fits into. The differential pinion shaft must be removed to allow the axle to be slid inward so that the C-clip can be removed or replaced in its groove. Sliding the axle outward positions the C-clip into the recess of the axle gear, and sliding the differential pinion shaft into place locks things together. The C-clip limits the outward movement of the axle, and the differential pinion shaft limits the inward movement. This axle style will have a slight amount of end play; a bearing-retained axle should have no end play. If a C-clip axle breaks anywhere from the C-clip groove outward, the axle can slide out of the rear axle housing.

11.5   LUBRICATION

A drive axle is normally filled with gear oil to a point just below the filler opening (Figure 11-32). A few axles, however, are filled at a level lower than this. The action of the ring gear running in the bath of oil distributes the oil through the housing. Many carriers provide a trough to ensure adequate oiling of the front pinion shaft bearing. A vent is installed in the housing to relieve pressures generated as the gears and oil warm up.

The gear oil is kept in the housing by one or more grease seals in each end of the axle housing and at the drive pinion shaft (Figure 11-33). The pinion shaft seal normally seals against the surface of the driveshaft flange, and the axle seals against the machined surfaces of the axle. In some cases, the axle seal is part of the axle bearing.

11.5.1   Drive Axle Lubricants

The gear oils used in drive axles are very similar to those described in Section 6.12; the major differences are the **extreme pressure (EP)** additives and friction modifiers. The gear oil used with hypoid gear sets must be GL-4 or GL-5; GL-5 has about twice as much EP additive as GL-4. This additive forms a wear-resistant coating on the metal surface of the teeth to prevent metal-to-metal contact as the pinion gear slides across the ring gear tooth.

The gear oil used in drive axles with limited slip differentials must have a friction modifier. The **friction modifier** increases the slipperiness of the lubricant to prevent the stick/slip problem. A friction modifier reduces the

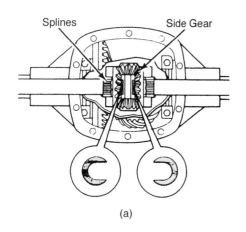

(a)

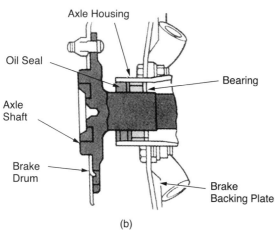

(b)

FIGURE 11-31 A C-lock (a) holds the inner end of the axle in the side gear while the outer end of the axle is supported by a straight roller bearing (b). (Portions of materials contained herein have been reprinted with permission of General Motors Corporation, Service and Parts Operations, License Agreement #0310807)

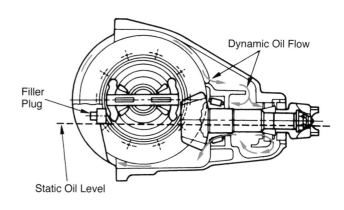

FIGURE 11-32 In most axles the gear oil level is at the bottom of the filter opening. When the axle operates, the ring gear will produce a dynamic oil flow to lubricate all the parts. (Portions of materials contained herein have been reprinted with permission of General Motors Corporation, Service and Parts Operations, License Agreement #0310807)

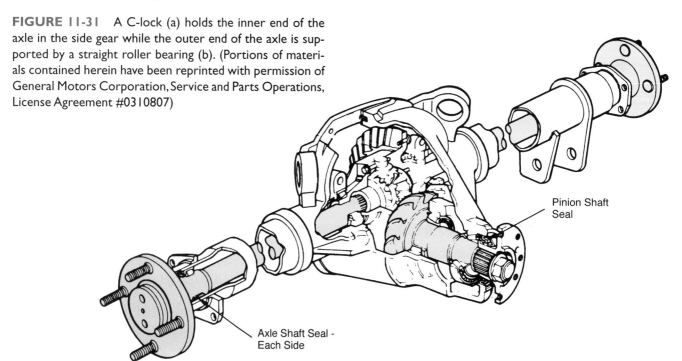

FIGURE 11-33 The gear oil is kept in the housing by seals at each axle shaft, the drive pinion shaft, and gaskets or sealant at each cover. (Courtesy of Ford Motor Company)

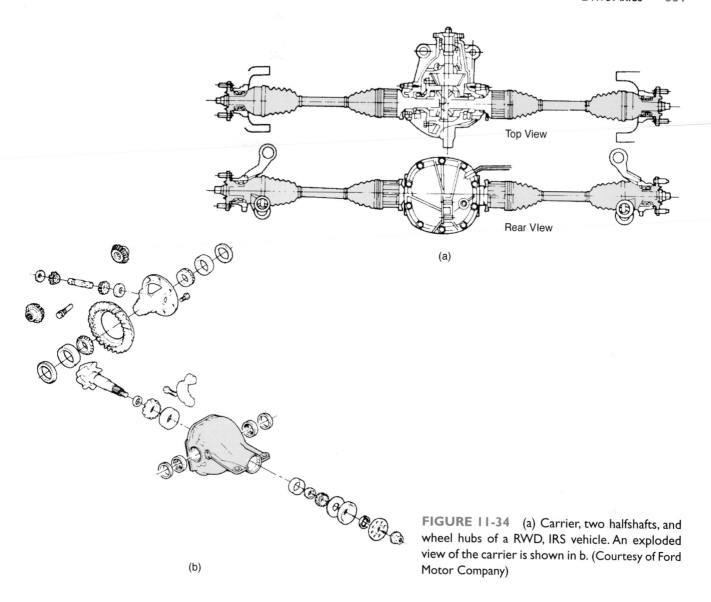

Top View

Rear View

(a)

(b)

FIGURE 11-34 (a) Carrier, two halfshafts, and wheel hubs of a RWD, IRS vehicle. An exploded view of the carrier is shown in b. (Courtesy of Ford Motor Company)

load-carrying ability of the lubricant; normally, no more of this additive is used than is necessary.

11.6 INDEPENDENT REAR SUSPENSION

On vehicles with **independent rear suspension (IRS),** the wheels are supported by the suspension system; driveshafts, also called halfshafts, connect them to the axle assembly (Figure 11-34). The axle housing is very short, slightly bigger than the carrier, and short output shafts are used to connect the axle gears to the U-joint halfshaft flanges.

11.7 AXLE IDENTIFICATION

Occasionally, a technician needs to identify the particular axle that is used in a vehicle. Many manufacturers build axle assemblies of differing torque capacity and install the one most suited for the engine size and vehicle weight. The diameter of the ring gear is often used to classify the various axle assemblies. The Ford 9-in. axle is larger and can carry more torque than the smaller 8-in. axle used in smaller vehicles with smaller engines. Ford's integral carrier axle assemblies are built in 6.75-in., 7.5-in., and 8.5-in. sizes. The 6.75-in. axle assembly is used in compact and subcompact installations, the 8.5-in. axle is used in full-size vehicles,

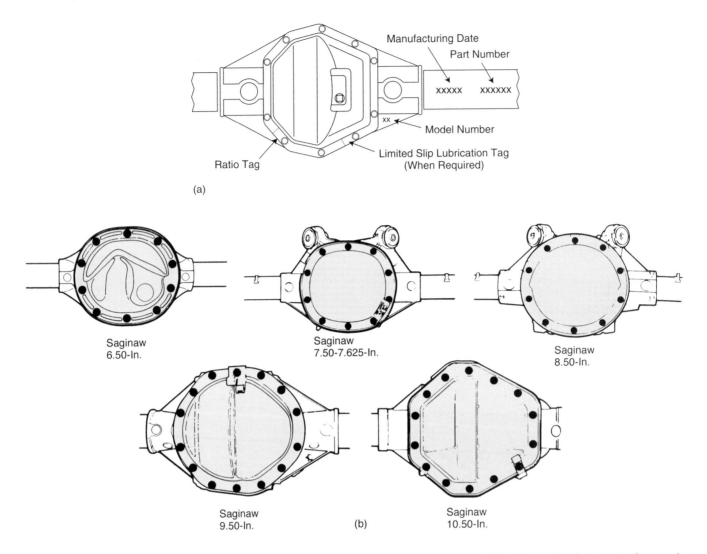

Manufacturing Date
Part Number

xxxxx   xxxxxx

xx ← Model Number

Limited Slip Lubrication Tag
(When Required)

Ratio Tag

(a)

Saginaw
6.50-In.

Saginaw
7.50-7.625-In.

Saginaw
8.50-In.

Saginaw
9.50-In.

(b)

Saginaw
10.50-In.

FIGURE 11-35 (a) A drive axle can be identified by a tag or markings on the housing. (b) A quick identification is often made by the shape of the cover and number of mounting bolts. (a is courtesy of Dana Corporation; b: Portions of materials contained herein have been reprinted with permission of General Motors Corporation, Service and Parts Operations, License Agreement #0310807)

and the 7.5-in. axle is used for vehicle sizes between these two. The size number refers to the rough-cut diameter of the gear blank.

In some cases, the particular axle assembly can be identified by looking at the shape of the cover or by counting the number of mounting bolts. The GM 10-bolt and 12-bolt axle assemblies illustrate this—if the rear cover has 10 mounting bolts, the ring gear also has 10 bolts. In most cases, a more precise identification can be made from the numbers or letters on a tag retained by one of the rear cover mounting bolts or stamped into the axle housing (Figure 11-35).

The axle ratio can be determined from this tag or by counting the number of turns the driveshaft makes to get one turn of the tires. On limited slip

differential axles, this is easier because both tires will rotate together; but on an open differential the tires will rotate unevenly and make accurate counting difficult.

◄ SERVICE TIP ►

The most accurate method of determining gear ratios, if the ring and pinion gears are exposed, is to read the tooth number markings on the ring gear or count the number of teeth on the two gears. Now divide the tooth count of the ring gear by that of the pinion gear, and the result is the ratio.

◀ SERVICE TIP ▶

The axle ratio can often be identified from the tag attached to the axle housing or by the coding on some axles.

◀ SERVICE TIP ▶

The axle ratio can be determined by counting the number of revolutions of the driveshaft that are required to turn the wheels one revolution. The most accurate method of doing this is to lock one of the tires using the parking brake or a block (Figure 11-36). Now, turn the driveshaft until the free tire turns 20 revolutions, and divide the drive-shaft revolutions by 10. For example, if you count 23 1/3 turns of the driveshaft to 20 turns of the free tire, the gear ratio is 2.33:1. Remember that with one wheel locked, the differential will cause the other wheel to turn twice as fast.

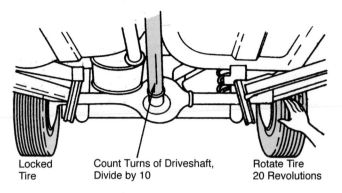

Locked Tire — Count Turns of Driveshaft, Divide by 10 — Rotate Tire 20 Revolutions

FIGURE 11-36 The quickest and most accurate method of determining a rear axle ratio is shown here. If the driveshaft rotates 37 1/3 turns while the free tire rotates 20 turns, the ratio is 3.73:1.

REVIEW QUESTIONS

The following questions are provided to help you study as you read the chapter.

1. Another name for a drive axle is a _____.

2. The ring and pinion gears are machined as a _____ set. If one of the gears needs replacement, the other must also be replaced.

3. The outer ends of the ring gear teeth are called the _____ and the inner ends are known as the _____.

4. The _____ of the ring gear tooth is above the pitch line and the _____ is below it.

5. The _____ side of the ring gear tooth is the drive side and the _____ side is the coast side.

6. The clearance between the ring gear and the drive pinion gear teeth is called _____.

7. _____ and _____ gear sets normally have index marks that are used to time the gears during installation.

8. The two common ways that a drive pinion is mounted in the carrier are _____ _____ and _____ mounted.

9. The four adjustments that are typically done during a drive axle overhaul are
   a. drive pinion _____
   b. drive pinion bearing _____
   c. _____
   d. carrier bearing _____

10. The drive pinion bearing preload is typically adjusted by tightening the _____ _____ nut, which crushes a collapsible spacer.

11. Most removable carriers use _____ adjusters and integral carriers use _____ for backlash and carrier bearing preload adjustments.

12. The differential allows the two drive wheels to rotate at different _____ when turning a corner.

13. The axle shaft used in passenger vehicle drive axles are _____ _____ and the axles used in heavy-duty trucks are of the _____ _____ design.

14. _____ _____ axles are held in the drive axle by _____ or a bearing _____.

15. The gear oil used in most limited slip differentials must have a _____ _____ to prevent the stick/slip problem common with these differentials.

CHAPTER QUIZ

The following questions will help you check the facts you have learned. Select the answer that completes each statement correctly.

1. In a rear axle, the drive pinion gear works with
   a. a ring gear to change the direction of the power flow.
   b. side gears to provide differential action.
   c. a ring gear to provide a gear reduction.
   d. all of these.

2. Two students are discussing the hypoid gears. Student A says that the concave side of the ring gear tooth is called the drive side. Student B says that the heel is the smaller, inner end of the ring gear tooth. Who is correct?
   a. Student A   c. Both A and B
   b. Student B   d. Neither A nor B

3. An overhung pinion uses A. three pinion bearings, B. a wide spacing between the two tapered roller bearings. Which is correct?
   a. A only   c. Both A and B
   b. B only   d. Neither A nor B

4. Which of the following is not true about a hypoid gear set?
   a. The pinion gear is mounted below the ring gear centerline.
   b. A special type of gear oil is required.
   c. This is an efficient gear set with very little friction.
   d. Special procedures are required to adjust it.

5. Two students are discussing axle shafts. Student A says that a broken axle will cause a no-drive condition. Student B says a broken semifloating axle can let a wheel fall off. Who is correct?
   a. Student A   c. Both A and B
   b. Student B   d. Neither A nor B

6. A ring and pinion with a 3.76:1 ratio is classified as
   a. hunting.   c. partial nonhunting.
   b. nonhunting.   d. none of these.

7. A straddle-mounted pinion uses A. three pinion bearings, B. a wide spacing between the two tapered roller bearings. Which is correct?
   a. A only   c. Both A and B
   b. B only   d. Neither A nor B

8. The differential case
   a. provides a mounting point for the ring gear.
   b. encloses the differential gears.
   c. is supported by the carrier bearings.
   d. all of these.

9. An integral carrier axle assembly
   a. is stronger than a comparable removable carrier assembly.
   b. is easier to service than a removable carrier assembly.
   c. uses full-floating axles in most cases.
   d. all of these.

10. Most limited slip differentials transfer torque through A. the differential gears, B. one or two clutch stacks. Which is correct?
    a. A only   c. Both A and B
    b. B only   d. Neither A nor B

11. Limited slip differentials require a special lubricant to prevent the plates from A. sticking, B. wearing. Which is correct?
    a. A only   c. Both A and B
    b. B only   d. Neither A nor B

12. As a rear axle assembly is put together, the carrier bearings are adjusted to get the correct amount of A. backlash between the ring and pinion gears, B. clearance at the bearings. Which is correct?
    a. A only   c. Both A and B
    b. B only   d. Neither A nor B

13. Two students are discussing the assembly of a rear axle center section. Student A says that with an overhung pinion gear, a thicker shim between the gear and its rear bearing will increase the load on the bearing. Student B says that this will move the pinion gear deeper into the ring gear. Who is correct?
    a. Student A   c. Both A and B
    b. Student B   d. Neither A nor B

14. When a car with a limited slip differential turns a corner, the A. clutch plate surfaces must slide across each other, B. pressure on the plates is reduced because of the differential gear action. Which is correct?
    a. A only   c. Both A and B
    b. B only   d. Neither A nor B

15. Full-floating axles are A. not designed to carry heavy loads, B. normally bolted to the drive wheel hub. Which is correct?
    a. A only   c. Both A and B
    b. B only   d. Neither A nor B

16. The ring and pinion gear set has 11 teeth on the pinion and 41 teeth on the ring gear. What is the ratio?

17. What would the ratio be if the pinion gear had 11 teeth and the ring gear had 42?

18. While checking the axle ratio, you find that it takes 34 1/2 turns of the driveshaft to produce 20 turns of one rear tire; the other one is locked. What is the gear ratio?

Chapter 12

DRIVE AXLE SERVICE

LEARNING OBJECTIVES

After completing this chapter, you should be able to:

1. Perform the maintenance operations needed to keep a drive axle operating properly.
2. Diagnose the cause of the common drive axle problems.
3. Recommend the proper repair procedure.
4. Remove and replace an axle shaft, axle bearings, and axle seals.
5. Remove and replace a removable carrier.
6. Overhaul a drive axle, making all necessary adjustments and checks.
7. Be able to complete the ASE tasks for content area E, Rear-Wheel-Drive Axle Diagnosis and Repair.

TERMS TO LEARN

backlash	gear marking compound
backlash variation	pinion bearing preload
bearing spacer	pinion depth
carrier bearing preload	ring gear runout
collapsible spacer	service spacer
contact pattern	shim
crush sleeve	

12.1 INTRODUCTION

Drive axle service includes the following maintenance operations:

- Checking the gear oil level
- Diagnosing problems
- Removing and replacing axle shafts
- Removing and replacing the carrier or entire axle for repairs
- Overhauling and adjusting the carrier

12.2 GEAR OIL CHECKS

The gear oil used in most drive axles is 90-weight or 120-weight gear oil and should be hypoid quality GL-4 or GL-5. If the axle has a limited slip differential, the gear oil must meet the requirements for that differential type. A label is normally located near the filler opening on those axles to indicate the fluid required.

To check drive axle gear oil level:

1. Raise and securely support the vehicle on a hoist or jack stands so that you have access to the axle. The vehicle should be raised so that the drive axle is in its normal position relative to level.
2. Locate the gear oil-level plug, clean the area around it, and remove the plug (Figure 12-1). Be prepared for fluid to run out of the opening.

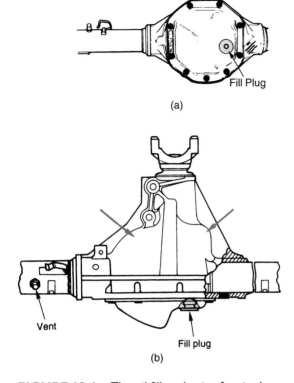

Fill Plug

(a)

Vent

Fill plug

(b)

FIGURE 12-1 The oil filler plug is often in the rear cover (a); it can also be at the front of the carrier housing (b). (Portions of materials contained herein have been reprinted with permission of General Motors Corporation, Service and Parts Operations, License Agreement #0310807)

3. In most axles the gear oil level should be even with the bottom of the opening.

◀ **SERVICE TIP** ▶

If you cannot see the gear oil level, carefully insert your finger into the opening and bend it downward, using it as a level indicator (Figure 12-2).

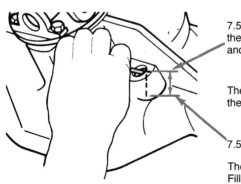

7.5 Inch Axles Built After 2/1/79 Identified with the Suffix One (1) on the I.D. Tag, and All 6.75 and 8.5 Axles

The Lube Level Should Be Up to the Bottom of the Fill Hole

7.5 Inch Axles Built Before 2/1/79

The Correct Lube Level Is 1-1/4 Inches Below the Fill Hole on 7.5 Inch Axles. Measure It with an L-Shaped Gauge

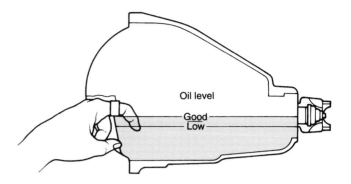

Oil level
Good
Low

FIGURE 12-2 The oil level is usually even with the bottom of the fill opening; if necessary, your finger can be used as a kind of dipstick to determine the level.

◀ **SERVICE TIP** ▶

The fluid level on some Ford axles should be a specified distance below the opening and requires a special dipstick, which can be shop-made (Figure 12-3).

REAL-WORLD FIX A 1994 Dodge Caravan 4×4 (100,000 mi) had a leak in the rear drive axle, pinion shaft area. The seal was replaced using OEM parts, but the vehicle came back with a seal leak.

FIX

On the advice of other technicians, the fluid level was dropped 1″ below the fill hole, and this stopped the leak.

AUTHOR'S NOTE

In a case like this, the technician should consult service information. Adjusting a fluid level to below the proper fill level should only be done with the owner's approval.

FIGURE 12-3 On this axle, the oil level should be 1 1/4 in. below the fill opening; a shop-made tool can be made to check it. (Courtesy of Ford Motor Company)

◀ SERVICE TIP ▶

It should be noted that a high fluid level can flood the axle seals and can cause gear oil to leak into the brake drums. If the fluid level is too low, gear and bearing wear and overheating will occur.

◀ SERVICE TIP ▶

While checking gear oil level, be sure to note its condition. Gear oil normally has a mildly unpleasant smell. Its color should be the same as that of new oil. Metal particles in the oil indicate internal problems.

REAL-WORLD FIX A 1997 Ford F150 (46,000 mi) had a binding condition in the rear end when starting off and making either a right or left turn. It had a stick/slip feeling.

FIX

The rear axle fluid was drained and replaced. This fixed the problem.

AUTHOR'S NOTE

It is assumed that the proper limited slip lubricant was used.

REAL-WORLD FIX A 1997 5.9 L Dodge extended cab 4×4 had a vibration that felt like a clutch chatter that happened mostly on turns. The vehicle had an antispin rear axle.

FIX

A friction modifier additive was added to the rear axle, and the chatter was eliminated.

12.3 PROBLEM DIAGNOSIS

Most drive axle problems are related to noise, vibration, leaks, and failure to transmit power. One of the problems that a technician faces when diagnosing complaints of noise and vibration is isolating them to the drive axle or other driveline component. This can be done by conducting a road test and several in-shop tests. Leaks and no-drive problems can be diagnosed in the shop (Figure 12-4).

Problem diagnosis normally begins with the customer's complaint, which should include an exacting description of the type of noise or vibration and when it occurs. This is followed up by a road test over various types of road surfaces through the speeds where the complaint occurs. The road test should include the following driving conditions:

- **Drive:** light-to-moderate throttle acceleration
- **Cruise:** enough throttle to maintain a constant speed
- **Float:** just enough throttle to keep engine load off the drivetrain as the car slows
- **Coast:** closed throttle deceleration
- **Coast while in neutral:** isolates transmission noises

If vibrations are the problem, the technician should note where the movement is most noticeable—in the car seat, steering wheel, instrument panel, floor pan, or hood and front fenders. Rear axle problems show up mostly in the seat or floor pan.

It should be remembered that some sounds will telegraph and appear to come from locations other than the real source of the problem. Sounds in the driveshaft, exhaust system, and body floor pan can do this, making locating the problem source more difficult. Remember the following when diagnosing sound and vibration problems:

- Tire noise changes with road surfaces and is speed sensitive. It is not affected by torque.
- Drivetrain noise and vibrations are usually torque sensitive and will often change relative to speed or driving conditions.
- Wheel bearing noise and vibration are load sensitive and will often change due to weight transfer as a vehicle turns a corner.
- Driveshaft vibrations occur relative to engine speed in high gear (1:1 ratio), whereas axle vibrations are slower because of the gear ratio in the drive axle.

◀ SERVICE TIP ▶

Some particular axles are noisy because of less than perfect machining. The noise type is often a whine that occurs during light throttle, medium speed, and deceleration. Although it is annoying, if the noise does not occur under heavy loads or does not increase with additional mileage, it is not an indication of failure.

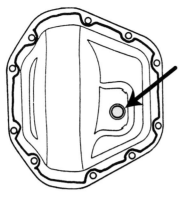

(a) Check Fluid Level

(b) Road Test

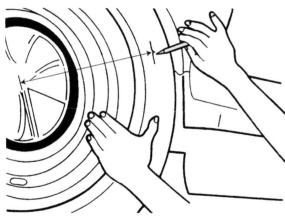

(c) Check Total Lash

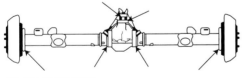

(d) Check Bearings

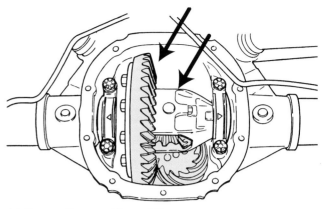

(e) Remove Cover and Inspect Gears

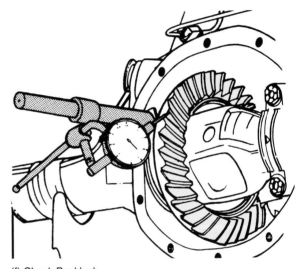

(f) Check Backlash

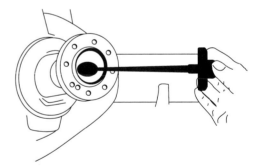

(g) Check Bearing Preload

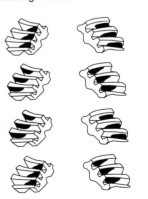

(h) Check Contact Pattern

FIGURE 12-4 Drive axle problem diagnosis usually begins with a check of the gear oil level and a road test. Depending on the nature of the problem, it can include a check of the total lash in the axle, checks of the bearings and gears, and adjustments.

REAL-WORLD FIX A 1993 Jeep Wrangler (100,000 mi) felt like the brakes were applied when operated in either 4-High or 4-Low. 2WD operation was normal, but it would not go faster than 10 mph in 4-High. Removal of the rear driveshaft allowed normal operation from the front drive axle. All four tires were the same diameter, and a check showed a 4.10:1 ratio in the front axle and a 4.11 ratio in the rear.

F I X

A more careful inspection revealed a 3.73 ratio in the rear axle even though it had a tag showing 4.11. The technician had found "41" and "11" on the rear ring gear that he thought meant 4.11. This marking indicates a 41-tooth ring and 11-tooth pinion; "41" divided by "11" equals 3.73. Changing the rear gear set fixed this problem.

REAL-WORLD FIX A 1988 Nissan Pathfinder came in for major service, and the transmission and drive axle were drained and refilled with new fluids. The tires were rotated, and the rear brake pads and rotors were replaced at the same time. The vehicle worked fine during the road test, but two days later, it returned with a shudder from the rear wheels. In an attempt to cure this problem, the tires were replaced to their original position and the rotors were replaced with new OEM rotors, but this did not help.

F I X

It was determined that the rear axle had a limited slip differential. A limited slip additive was put into the differential, and this cured the problem.

12.3.1 Noise

Drive axle noise problems normally fall into one of these categories:

- **Gear noise:** howling or whining; often is torque sensitive but can be continuous.
- **Bearing noise:** can be a high-pitched, whistlelike sound but is usually a rough growl or rumble. Bearings will often make a "wow-wow" type of sound at the speed frequency of the spinning shaft.
- **Clunk:** heavy metallic slapping noise during reversal of power flow or engagement of power from neutral. It is caused by excessive slack or lash in the drivetrain and can be felt in the drive axle.
- **Chuckle:** a rattling noise, similar to something against spinning bicycle spokes, during decelera-

tion below 40 mph (64 kph). It is often caused by excessive clearance in the differential.

- **Chatter on corners:** a vibration or noise as the vehicle turns a corner, especially after prolonged straight driving. Often called a *chuckle*, commonly caused by a stick/slip condition at the clutch plates of a limited slip differential.

◀ SERVICE TIP ▶

While diagnosing noise problems, remember that they can come from the exhaust system (both normal air-transmitted noises and noises from metal-to-metal contact between the exhaust system and the vehicle body or frame), tires, and wind. Drivetrain noises can usually be heard while the vehicle is operated and being supported on a hoist or jack stands. Vehicle loads can be simulated by applying the brake for short periods of time.

◀ SERVICE TIP ▶

When changing the lubricant in a limited slip differential to cure a chatter problem, drive the vehicle through 10 to 12 figure-8 turns. This should work the new lubricant between the clutch plates.

◀ SERVICE TIP ▶

A diagnostic tool, Chassis Ear, consists of a headset and six sensors that can be attached to locations under the vehicle. The vehicle can be driven on a road test while the technician listens to six different locations underneath. This should help locate the noise source (Figure 12-5).

While diagnosing noise problems, a technician may use a chart like the one in Figure 12-6 as a guide to help locate the source of the problem. A complete road test and shop tests must also be performed to confirm that the problem is in the drive axle.

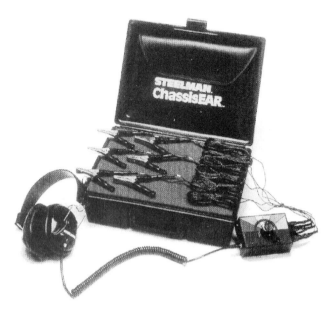

FIGURE 12-5 A Chassis Ear has a microphone attached to each of the six clamps that are connected to various locations under the vehicle. The technician makes a road test while wearing the headset, and turns the selector switch to locate the source of an under-car noise. (Courtesy of Steelman)

REAL-WORLD FIX A 1992 Ford F350 4×4 (385,000 km) had a bucking condition under acceleration. The condition increased under load but was not speed related. It occurred to a lesser degree during deceleration. The driveline and springs were inspected, but no faults were found. A broken transmission mount was replaced, but this did not help. The shock absorbers were replaced. U-joints were checked for binding and angles; these were okay. The rear driveshaft was removed, and the problem went away when the vehicle was driven using only the front drive axle.

FIX

The rear axle cover was removed, and inspection revealed a cracked differential case. There was evidence that the case spread and contacted the drive pinion under load. Differential replacement fixed this problem.

12.3.2   Drive Axle and Differential Total Backlash

A drivetrain clunk during a power change can be caused by too much internal **backlash**.

To check total drive axle backlash (Figure 12-7):

1. Raise and securely support the vehicle on a hoist or jack stands. You need access to the drive axle and the wheels must be free to turn.

Rear Axle Diagnosis

Condition	Cause
Noise in all driving modes	• Road and tires • Front wheel bearings • Incorrect driveline angles
Noise changes with type of road surface	• Road and tires
Noise tone lowers with vehicle speed	• Tires
Noise louder on turns	• Differential pinion and side gears • Axle bearings
Noise in one or more driving modes	• Ring and pinion gears
Noise while vehicle is standing still and while driving	• Engine • Transmission
Clunk on change of speed or direction of power flow	• Worn differential shaft or thrust washers • Worn U-joints
Continuous low-pitched whir	• Worn drive pinion bearings
Chatter on corners	• Wrong gear oil
Irregular knock on rough roads	• Worn limited slip clutch plates • Excess axle shaft end
Vibration	• Tire runout or imbalance • Driveshaft problems • Bent axle shaft • Excess companion flange runout

FIGURE 12-6 A technician will use a chart like this to help locate the cause of a drive axle problem.

2. Lock the driveshaft and drive pinion companion flange by clamping a bar to the companion flange and the body or rear suspension.

3. Block the left wheel so that it cannot turn.

4. Turn the right wheel slowly in one direction until it stops, loading all of the lash to one side. Using chalk, place a mark on the side of the tire 12 in. (305 mm) from the center of the wheel.

5. Hold the chalk steady and rotate the tire in the opposite direction until it stops.

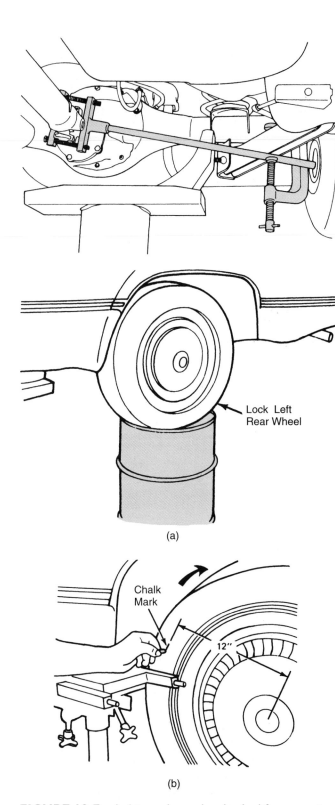

(a)

(b)

FIGURE 12-7   A drive axle can be checked for excessive play in the differential by blocking one drive wheel and the driveshaft (a) and then measuring the distance that the free tire rotates (12 in. out from the tire center) using a piece of chalk (b). The chalk mark should be 1 in. or shorter. (Courtesy of Ford Motor Company)

6. Measure the length of the chalk mark and the amount of lash in the drive axle. More than 1 in. (25.4 mm) of lash is excessive and indicates that something in the axle is worn. This is usually a differential problem. If the lash is less than 1 in., the clunk is being caused by another part in the drivetrain.

12.3.3   Bearing Noise Check

The road test may indicate faulty drive pinion or axle bearings. During part of this check, you will be working around a spinning tire and driveshaft. Make sure that you have no loose clothing, hair, or other body parts that could become entangled.

To check drive pinion and axle bearings:

1. Raise and support the vehicle securely on a hoist or jack stands so that the wheels are free to turn. Release the parking brake.
2. Grip each wheel and attempt to move it up and down and in and out.

◄   **SERVICE TIP**   ►

A bearing-retained axle should have no movement in either direction. Any free play indicates a faulty bearing.

◄   **SERVICE TIP**   ►

A C-clip-retained axle should allow only a barely perceptible vertical motion and between 0.005 and 0.030 in. (0.13 and 0.7 mm) of in-and-out motion, or axle shaft end play. Excessive motion indicates faulty axle bearings or too thin a C-clip for the axle groove.

3. If axle shaft end play seems excessive, place index marks on the tire and wheel and the brake drum and remove them. Mount a dial indicator on the axle flange, position the stylus on the brake assembly, and move the axle shaft in and out while you read the amount of end play on the dial indicator (Figure 12-8).
4. With the tire and wheel in place, rotate the tire; it should rotate smoothly and quietly.

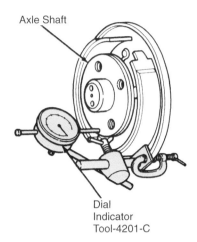

Axle Shaft

Dial
Indicator
Tool-4201-C

FIGURE 12-8 Axle shaft end play can be checked by mounting a dial indicator onto the brake assembly or axle housing with the indicator stylus on the axle. The indicator will measure the end play as the axle is moved in and out. (Courtesy of Ford Motor Company)

5. Start the engine and drive the wheels at idle speed in high gear. Carefully place your fingers lightly against the axle housing close to the brake assembly and under the drive pinion shaft close to the companion flange (Figure 12-9).

◀ **SERVICE TIP** ▶

You should feel smooth, irregular motions from the inside of the drive axle. A bad bearing will usually cause a harsh, rough feel and normally will make a rough growling noise.

6. If roughness is noticed at the drive pinion, stop the engine and disconnect the driveshaft from the companion flange. Now check for end play and side play of the drive pinion shaft; there should be none. If there is no play, use a low-reading in.-lb torque wrench and measure the torque required to turn the pinion shaft (Figure 12-10).

◀ **SERVICE TIP** ▶

Normal axle preload should be about 8 to 30 in.-lb (0.9 to 3.4 N-m) of torque. Brake drag can cause much higher readings. A low reading or any free play of the shaft indicates faulty drive pinion bearings.

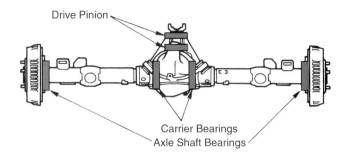

Drive Pinion

Carrier Bearings
Axle Shaft Bearings

Warning: Rotating Shafts and Wheels Can Be Dangerous. You Can Snag Clothes, Skin, Hair, Hands, etc. This Can Cause Serious Injury or Death.

FIGURE 12-9 A faulty rear axle bearing can usually be located by listening and feeling next to the bearing as the vehicle is operated on a hoist or stands. Be careful when doing this because of the rotating shafts and wheels. (Portions of materials contained herein have been reprinted with permission of General Motors Corporation, Service and Parts Operations, License Agreement #0310807)

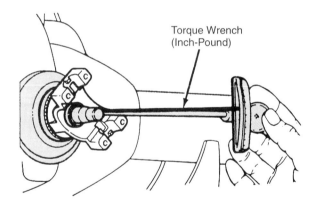

Torque Wrench
(Inch-Pound)

FIGURE 12-10 Drive pinion and axle preload is measured by disconnecting the driveshaft and using a torque wrench to measure the torque required to rotate the pinion shaft. (Courtesy of Ford Motor Company)

REAL-WORLD FIX A 1995 Mustang (46,000 mi) had a rhythmic tire-like noise coming from the left rear that was only heard on smooth roads. All four tires were replaced with no change. A leaking left rear axle seal was replaced along with the bearing, but this did not help either.

FIX

Checking inside the axle housing showed galling of the axle gear and differential case. Replacement of these differential parts repaired this problem.

REAL-WORLD FIX The rear wheel bearings on a 1992 Subaru SVX (113,000 mi) were replaced a year ago because they were very noisy. The vehicle returned after 19,000 miles with the same noise; the wheel bearings have failed. The technician was concerned about the early failure.

FIX

The technician discovered that the new OEM bearings were filled with a Vaseline-like grease for shipping. This grease must be cleaned out and the bearing packed with the proper grease. Proper bearing service procedures must be followed to ensure complete bearing life.

12.3.4 Vibration Check

The vibration checks for a drive pinion shaft and companion flange are a continuation of the driveshaft checks described in Section 10.3.3.2. The companion flange runout is checked by placing the dial indicator stylus on the companion flange (Figure 12-11).

◀ SERVICE TIP ▶

More than 0.005 in. (0.1 mm) of runout indicates a faulty companion flange or bent drive pinion shaft.

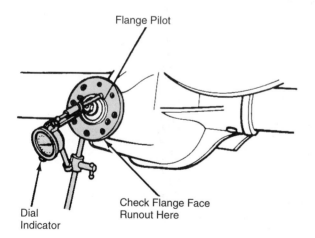

Flange Pilot

Check Flange Face Runout Here

Dial Indicator

FIGURE 12-11 Runout of the pinion drive flange is measured with a dial indicator, as shown here. (Courtesy of Ford Motor Company)

◀ SERVICE TIP ▶

If there is more than 0.060 in. (1.5 mm) of runout in either direction, proceed to step 3.

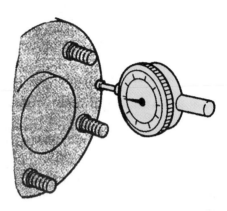

FIGURE 12-12 This dial indicator is set up to measure axle flange lateral runout, which can cause the wheel to wobble. (Courtesy of Ford Motor Company)

A bent axle shaft will cause runout at the wheel flange, which, in turn, produces wheel and tire runout.

To check wheel mounting flange runout:

1. Raise and securely support the vehicle on a hoist or jack stands.
2. Rotate the wheel while you observe the tire tread to determine if there is any lateral (side-to-side) or radial (vertical) runout.
3. Place an index mark on the wheel stud closest to the valve stem, and remove the tire and wheel. Place an index mark on the brake drum next to the marked stud and remove the brake drum.
4. Check flange lateral runout by mounting a dial indicator onto the axle housing or brake assembly and positioning the indicator stylus against the axle flange just outward of the wheel studs (Figure 12-12). The stylus should be positioned parallel to the axle.
5. Rotate the axle and note the amount of dial indicator movement. This is the amount of axle lateral flange runout.

◀ SERVICE TIP ▶

A runout of 0.005 in. (0.1 mm) or less is acceptable; if the runout is more than this, the axle should be replaced.

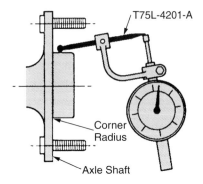

FIGURE 12-13 This dial indicator is set up to measure radial runout of the drum and wheel pilot, which can cause the wheel to run off center. Note the wiggle bar (T75L-4201-A). (Courtesy of Ford Motor Company)

6. Check flange radial runout by moving the dial indicator 90° so that the stylus is parallel to the flange (Figure 12-13). The wheel studs usually interfere with this mounting, so an alternative is to check the runout of the wheel studs. To do this, position the stylus on the side of a wheel stud and rotate the axle so that the stylus is at the highest point. This is where the indicator needle reverses direction. Rotate the dial so that the zero aligns with the needle. Carefully pull the stylus back, rotate the axle to position a second stud un-der the stylus, and read the amount of runout between these two studs. Repeat this procedure on each of the studs and determine the difference between the readings at the lowest and the highest studs.

◄ **SERVICE TIP** ►

A runout of 0.030 in. (0.76 mm) or less is acceptable; if the runout is more than this, the axle should be replaced.

A vibration can also be caused by damage inside the axle assembly. This can be confirmed by operating the axle with the tires, wheels, and brake drums removed, as described in Section 10.3.3.4. Vibrating motion of the axle housing would confirm the source of the vibration.

12.3.5   Leaks

Most gear oil leaks will be found at the axle shaft seals, drive pinion seals, rear cover, or carrier-to-housing gasket. The repairs for these are described in the service sections that follow. Occasionally, a leak is encountered in a porous casting or a faulty weld in the housing (Figure 12-14).

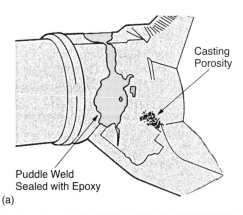

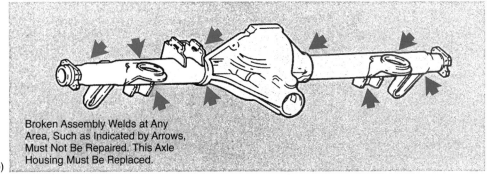

FIGURE 12-14 Some axle oil leaks can be caused by a porous casting or cracked welds. A casting problem can be repaired using epoxy sealant (a); a cracked weld requires housing replacement (b). (Courtesy of Ford Motor Company)

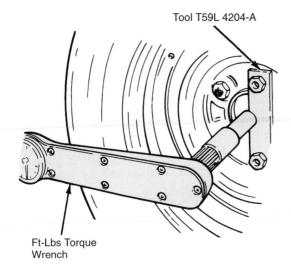

Tool T59L 4204-A

Ft-Lbs Torque Wrench

FIGURE 12-15 A special tool has been attached to two wheel studs, allowing a torque wrench to be used to measure the torque required to turn this wheel while the opposite wheel is on the ground with the transmission in neutral. A low reading indicates a worn limited slip differential. (Courtesy of Ford Motor Company)

◀ SERVICE TIP ▶

A porous casting can be repaired using epoxy. A leaky weld is a sign of a potentially dangerous stress crack or fracture, and the housing should be replaced.

12.3.6 Limited Slip Differential Check

This check is used to confirm the differential's ability to drive both wheels (if a limited slip differential seems not to deliver power to both wheels while one has poor traction).

To check a limited slip differential:

1. Attach an adapter to one of the rear hubs (Figure 12-15). Some adapters require removal of the wheel and tire.

2. Either raise the wheel with the adapter off the floor, leave the other wheel on the floor and place the transmission in neutral, or raise both wheels off the floor and place the transmission in park or in gear.

3. Connect a torque wrench to the adapter and measure the torque required to turn the wheel. Disregard the breakaway torque needed to get the wheel turning.

4. Compare your reading with the manufacturer's specifications.

◀ SERVICE TIP ▶

If no specifications are available, some technicians will use a rule of thumb of 35 to 40 ft-lb (48 to 54 N-m) minimum. Readings lower than this indicate a badly worn clutch pack in the differential.

◀ PROBLEM SOLVING ▶

Imagine that you are working in a general automotive repair shop and these problems are brought to you.

Case 1

The concern with a 10-year-old RWD vehicle was a clunk noise when shifted from neutral to drive or reverse. This was confirmed on your road test. When you get the vehicle raised on the rack, you find that both U-joints are good, but with the driveshaft and the left rear wheel locked, there is 1 1/2 in. of lash at the right tire. What do you think is the problem with this vehicle? How would you confirm your diagnosis?

Case 2

The vibration begins at about 35 mph with the pickup's transmission in either high or second and continues up to 55 mph. It seems to be coming from the back end. What should you do next to locate its cause? What possible rear axle problems could cause it?

12.4 ON-VEHICLE SERVICE OPERATIONS

On-vehicle operations include axle shaft, axle bearing, axle seal, and drive pinion seal replacement. Removal and replacement of a removable carrier and overhaul of an integral carrier can also be done on-vehicle.

Passenger car axles are semifloating and are retained in the housing by either a C-clip at the inner end of the axle or by the axle bearing retainer at the outer end. Axle service includes removing the axle for bearing or seal replacement and bent or broken axle replacement (Figures 12-16 and 12-17). Replacing damaged wheel studs can be done without removing the axle.

C–Lock Retained Axle

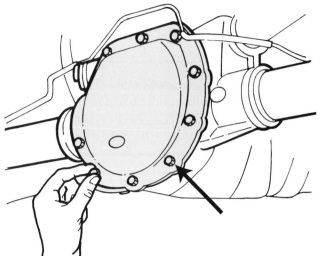

(a) Drain Fluid and Remove Cover

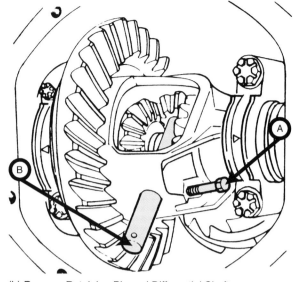

(b) Remove Retaining Pin and Differential Shaft

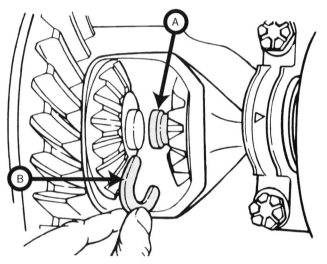

(c) Remove C–Lock

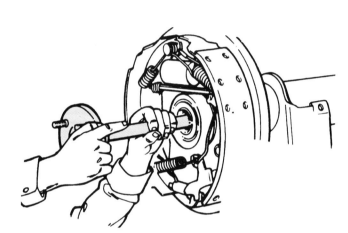

(d) Remove Axle

FIGURE 12-16 Procedure to remove a C-lock axle.

Bearing Retained Axle

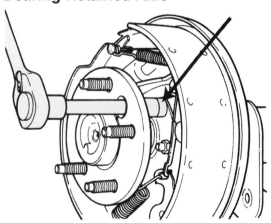

(a) Remove Retainer Nuts/Bolts

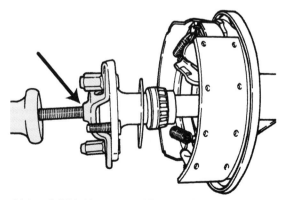

(b) Attach Slide Hammer and Remove Axle

FIGURE 12-17 Procedure to remove a bearing retained axle.

12.4.1   C-Clip Axle Shaft Removal and Replacement

Most modern integral carrier axle assemblies use a C-clip-type of axle shaft.

◀ SERVICE TIP ▶

The housing must have a removable cover to allow access to the C-clips.

To remove a C-clip axle:

1. Raise and securely support the vehicle so that you have access to the axle housing.
2. Remove the tire and wheel and brake drum.
3. Place a drain pan under the axle housing to catch the gear oil. Remove the rear cover attaching bolts. Be sure to note the location of any special clips or tags for proper replacement.
4. Remove the differential shaft retaining pin (Figure 12-18).

◀ SERVICE TIP ▶

The differential shaft retaining pin is hardened and has a tendency to break.

◀ SERVICE TIP ▶

In some vehicles, the differential shaft retaining pin uses left-hand threads. Check the bolt head before trying to remove it.

◀ SERVICE TIP ▶

If the differential shaft retaining pin should break, a special tool is available that will force the pinion shaft out of the differential, shearing off the broken retaining pin (Figure 12-19). Some technicians remove a broken pin using carbide drill bits and left-hand easy-outs. Others use special reverse-direction drill setups and reverse-spiral carbide drill bits.

FIGURE 12-19   In some differentials, the pinion shaft lock bolt tends to break during removal. This tool is used to force the differential pinion shaft out, shearing off a broken lock bolt without damaging the differential case. (Courtesy of Borroughs)

For Access to the Axle Shaft Retainers, Remove the Differential Pinion Shaft Lock Bolt

Then Slide the Pinion Shaft Out of the Case

NOTE:
The Differential Gears Can Now Be Removed. If They Do Not Require Removal, Install the Shaft and Lock Bolt Back into the Case After Removing the "C" Washers.

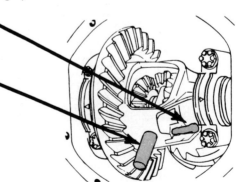

FIGURE 12-18   Removing the lock bolt allows removal of the differential pinion shaft. (Courtesy of Ford Motor Company)

5. Remove the differential pinion shaft by rotating the differential one-half turn, tapping the pinion shaft inward an inch or so, rotating the differential back, inserting a punch into the retaining pin hole, and pulling the pinion shaft out of the differential (Figure 12-20).

◀ SERVICE TIP ▶

Note that the differential pinions and thrush washers can rotate out of position while the pinion shaft is removed.

6. Push the axle inward and remove the C-clip from its groove (Figure 12-21).

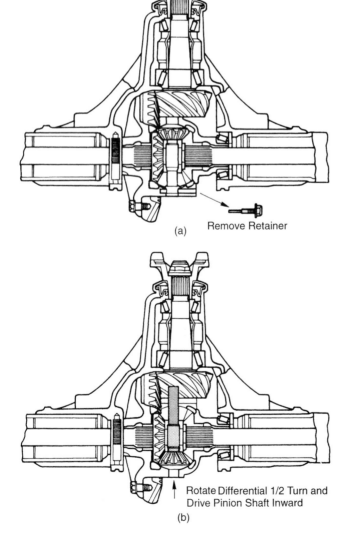

(a)   Remove Retainer

Rotate Differential 1/2 Turn and Drive Pinion Shaft Inward

(b)

7. Pull the axle out of the housing, supporting it so that it does not drag across the seal.

To replace a C-clip axle:

1. Oil the axle bearing in the housing and the seal area on the axle.

2. Insert the axle into the housing, supporting it so that it does not drag across the seal.

◀ SERVICE TIP ▶

When the inner end strikes the carrier bearing, grip the axle flange so that you can lift the inner end to the center of the differential; push inward so that the axle splines will center the differential side gear (Figure 12-22).

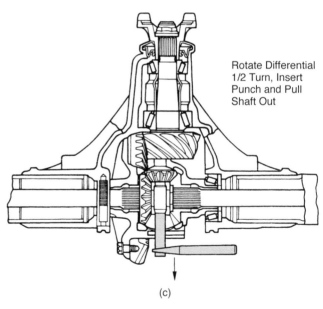

Rotate Differential 1/2 Turn, Insert Punch and Pull Shaft Out

(c)

FIGURE 12-20 If the pinion shaft does not slide out easily (a), rotate the differential one-half turn, drive the pinion shaft inward enough to expose the lock pin hole (b), rotate the differential one-half turn, insert a punch into the lock pin hole, and pull the shaft out (c).

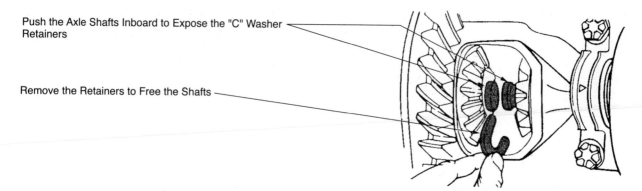

Push the Axle Shafts Inboard to Expose the "C" Washer Retainers

Remove the Retainers to Free the Shafts

FIGURE 12-21 After the pinion shaft has been removed, the axle can be slid inward and the C-clip removed from its groove. (Courtesy of Ford Motor Company)

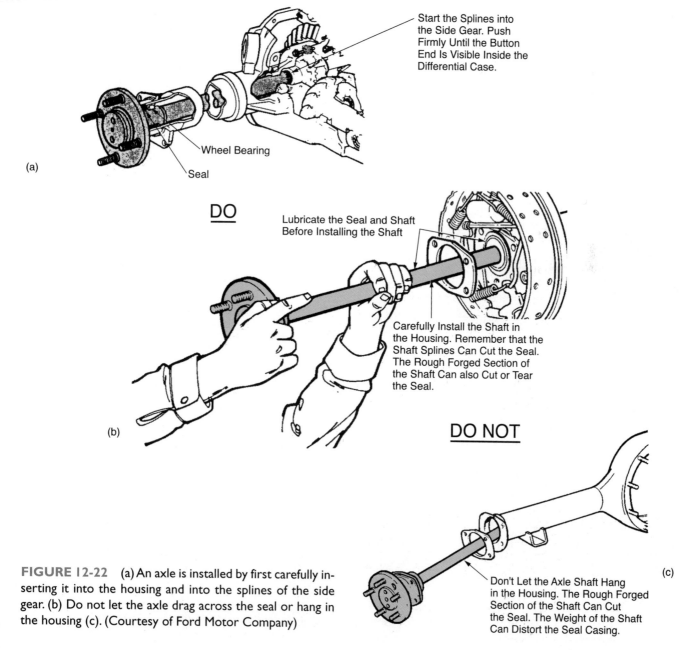

Start the Splines into the Side Gear. Push Firmly Until the Button End Is Visible Inside the Differential Case.

Wheel Bearing

Seal

(a)

DO

Lubricate the Seal and Shaft Before Installing the Shaft

Carefully Install the Shaft in the Housing. Remember that the Shaft Splines Can Cut the Seal. The Rough Forged Section of the Shaft Can also Cut or Tear the Seal.

(b)

DO NOT

Don't Let the Axle Shaft Hang in the Housing. The Rough Forged Section of the Shaft Can Cut the Seal. The Weight of the Shaft Can Distort the Seal Casing.

(c)

FIGURE 12-22 (a) An axle is installed by first carefully inserting it into the housing and into the splines of the side gear. (b) Do not let the axle drag across the seal or hang in the housing (c). (Courtesy of Ford Motor Company)

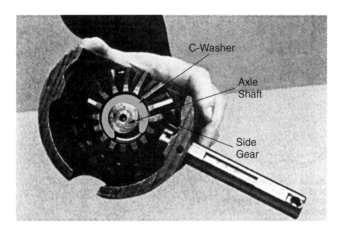

FIGURE 12-23 When the C-clip is in the axle groove and the axle is pulled back outward, the C-clip becomes locked in place in the side gear. (Courtesy of Ford Motor Company)

FIGURE 12-25 A shim has been cut and is being installed behind the C-clip to reduce the amount of axle end play. (Courtesy of Ford Motor Company)

3. Place the C-clip into its groove in the axle and slide the axle outward so that the C-clip becomes captured in its recess in the side gear (Figure 12-23).
4. Slide the differential pinion shaft in place, making sure to align the hole for the retainer pin.
5. Replace the retainer pin and, on threaded pins, tighten it to the correct torque (Figure 12-24).
6. Test your installation by pulling the axle in and out. It should have about 0.005 to 0.030 in. (0.12 to 0.76 mm) of end play.

◄ SERVICE TIP ►

Some manufacturers have C-clips of various thicknesses available to correct axle end play; others recommend adding a shim to correct excess end play (Figure 12-25).

7. On rear covers using gaskets, clean off the old gasket, install the cover using a new gasket, and tighten the bolts to the correct torque. On covers using formed-in-place gaskets, clean off all of the old sealant and oil from the housing and cover surfaces and run a bead of sealant on the housing surface circling each bolt hole (Figure 12-26). Replace the cover and tighten the bolts to the correct torque.
8. Fill the axle to the proper level with the correct lubricant.
9. Replace the brake drum and wheel and tire.

12.4.2 Bearing-Retained Axle Shaft Removal and Replacement

A bearing-retained axle is used in most axle assemblies with a removable carrier; it is also used in some integral carrier axles.

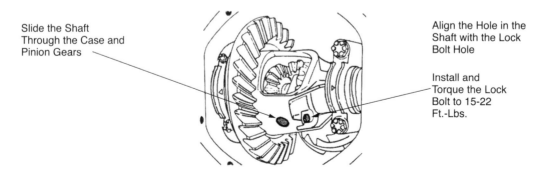

FIGURE 12-24 Installation of the differential pinion shaft locks the axle and C-clip in place. Be sure to tighten the lock pin to the correct torque. (Courtesy of Ford Motor Company)

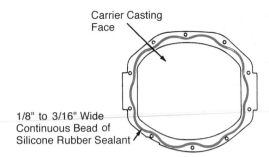

Carrier Casting Face

1/8" to 3/16" Wide Continuous Bead of Silicone Rubber Sealant

Typical Bead Installation. Parts Must Be Assembled within 15 Minutes After the Application of Sealant. Gasket Surface of Houing and Carier Must Be Free of Oil.

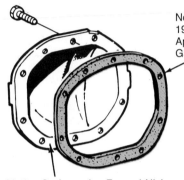

Non-Hardening Sealer (C3AZ-19562-A or Equivalent) May Be Applied to Both Sides of the Gasket if Necessary.

Be Sure the Mating Surfaces Are Free of Nicks, Bumps or Creases. Use a Torque Wrench to Be Sure of Even Pressure.

FIGURE 12-26   To seal the rear cover, axle housings use either a gasket or a formed-in-place gasket of sealant. (Courtesy of Ford Motor Company)

To remove a bearing-retained axle:

1. Raise and support the vehicle securely on a hoist or jack stands.
2. Remove the tire and wheel. Remove the brake drum.
3. Remove the nuts that secure the axle bearing retainer to the axle housing (Figure 12-27).
4. Attach an adapter and slide hammer to the axle flange. Using the slide hammer, pull the axle and bearing loose from the housing (Figure 12-28).

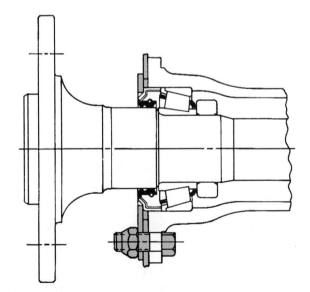

FIGURE 12-27   The bearing retainer bolts are being removed to allow removal of a bearing-retained axle. The hole in the axle flange allows the use of a socket and extension. (Courtesy of Dana Corporation)

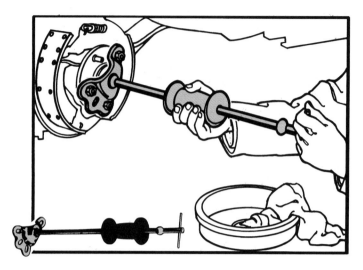

FIGURE 12-28 A slide hammer with an adapter for the wheel flange is used to pull a bearing-retained axle from the housing. (Courtesy of OTC Tools)

◀ SERVICE TIP ▶

Most axle flanges include a hole so that a socket and extension bar can be used to remove and replace the retainer bolts.

5. Pull the axle out of the housing, supporting it so that it does not drag on the seal.

To replace a bearing-retained axle:

1. Oil the seal area of the axle. On some axles the seal is inside the axle bearing and needs no oil.
2. Insert the axle into the housing, supporting it so that it does not drag across the seal. When the inner end strikes the carrier bearing, grip the axle flange so that you can lift the inner end to the center of the differential; push inward so the axle splines engage the differential side gear.
3. Tap the outer end of the axle, if necessary, to move the axle bearing into its recess in the housing. As it enters, align the retainer with its bolts and install and tighten the nuts to pull the bearing and axle into place.
4. Tighten the retainer nuts to the correct torque (Figure 12-29).
5. Replace the brake drum and the wheel and tire.

FIGURE 12-29 After the axle has been replaced, tighten the retainer nuts to the correct torque. (Courtesy of Dana Corporation)

12.4.3 Full-Floating Axle Shaft Removal and Replacement

The full-floating axle is used in light-, medium-, and heavy-duty trucks and in many larger pickups and vans. Axles are removed to replace the shaft, gain access to the wheel bearings, allow removal of the hub and brake drum on some units for access to the brakes, and allow removal of the carrier.

To remove a full-floating axle shaft:

1. Remove the bolts that attach the axle shaft flange to the hub (Figure 12-30).
2. Using a soft hammer, strike the axle flange to break the gasket loose.
3. Slide the axle out of the housing.

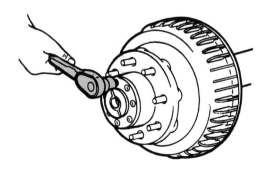

FIGURE 12-30 Removing the axle flange bolts allows the axle to be slid out of the housing. This allows access to the axle, wheel bearings, and brakes. (Portions of materials contained herein have been reprinted with permission of General Motors Corporation, Service and Parts Operations, License Agreement #0310807)

To replace a full-floating axle shaft:

1. Thoroughly clean the hub and axle flange surface, and place a new gasket in position.
2. Slide the axle into the housing. When the inner end meets the carrier, grip the axle flange and lift the inner end as you push inward so the axle splines engage the differential side gear.
3. Replace the axle flange-to-hub retaining bolts and tighten them to the correct torque.

12.4.4 C-Clip Axle Bearing and Seal Removal and Replacement

The C-clip axle uses a roller bearing with a snug-fitting case and outer race in the axle housing. A smooth section of the axle shaft serves as the inner race for the bearing. When replacing a bearing or seal, the bearing race area of the axle should be checked for wear, roughness, and damage. If the bearing surface is damaged, the axle should be replaced.

<h2 style="text-align:center">◄ SERVICE TIP ►</h2>

A bearing that is offset sideways is available from aftermarket sources to run on an unworn portion of the shaft (Figure 12-31).

The axle seal, which is located next to the bearing, seals against a smooth area of the shaft.

<h2 style="text-align:center">◄ SERVICE TIP ►</h2>

The axle seal surface can become worn and should be checked during seal replacement.

Both the bearing and the seal are removed from the housing using a slide hammer and special adapter (Figure 12-32). Pull the seal first and then, if desired, the bearing (Figure 12-33). After they are removed, the recesses where they fit should be checked for scratches or gouges that might let gear oil past the seal.

Another special tool is required to install the bearing. It should be slightly smaller than the diameter of the bearing and have a face that meets almost all of the face of the bearing so as not to damage the bearing during installation (Figure 12-34). The new bearing is driven straight into the housing to the end of its recess. The

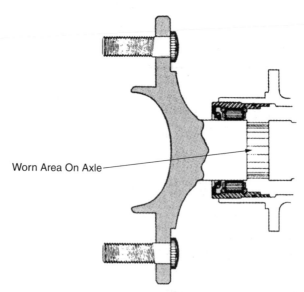

Worn Area On Axle

FIGURE 12-31   Axle bearing failure on a C-clip axle can ruin the axle. This bearing and seal assembly moves the bearing sideways, allowing an unworn portion of the axle to be used as the inner race. (Courtesy of CR Services)

same installation procedure and type of tool is used to install the new seal (Figure 12-35).

<h2 style="text-align:center">◄ SERVICE TIP ►</h2>

If the new axle seal does not have a coating on its outer shell, it is recommended that the outer edge of the shell be coated with RTV or nonhardening gasket sealant.

12.4.5 Bearing-Retained Axle Bearing and Seal Removal and Replacement

The bearing-retained axle bearing is press fit onto the axle shaft and should be removed carefully to prevent injury from possible bearing explosion. Most modern

Remove the Axle Shaft Seal with a Slide-Hammer
Tool as Shown

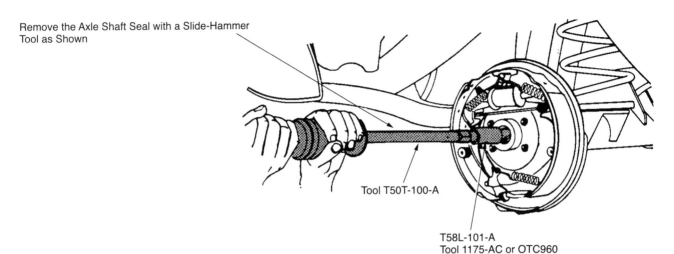

Tool T50T-100-A

T58L-101-A
Tool 1175-AC or OTC960

FIGURE 12-32 The bearing and seal are normally removed from the housing with a slide hammer and adapter. (Courtesy of Ford Motor Company)

Axle Housing

Bearing

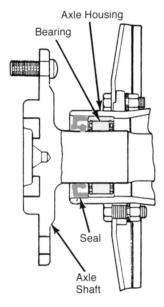

Seal

Axle
Shaft

FIGURE 12-33 The axle seal is just inside the end of the housing and the bearing is inside it. (Portions of materials contained herein have been reprinted with permission of General Motors Corporation, Service and Parts Operations, License Agreement #0310807)

axle bearing removal tools enclose the bearing completely and thus will contain an exploding bearing.

◀ **SERVICE TIP** ▶

When a bearing separator is used, a section of large iron pipe or a used starter or generator housing can be placed over the bearing to enclose it (Figure 12-36).

Bearing

Driver
Handle
J-8092

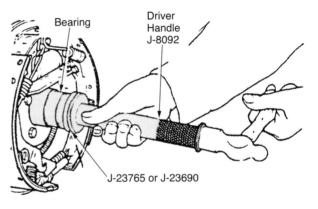

J-23765 or J-23690

FIGURE 12-34 An axle bearing is driven into the housing with a special driver and hammer. (Portions of materials contained herein have been reprinted with permission of General Motors Corporation, Service and Parts Operations, License Agreement #0310807)

Axle Shaft Seal Installer
J-23771, 7 1/2-In., 7 5/8-In. and
J-21128, 8 1/2-In. Axle

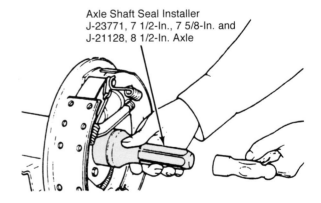

FIGURE 12-35 An axle seal is driven into the housing with a seal installer and hammer. (Portions of materials contained herein have been reprinted with permission of General Motors Corporation, Service and Parts Operations, License Agreement #0310807)

FIGURE 12-36 A bearing could explode as it is being pressed off the axle. An old starter housing can be placed over the bearing as a scatter shield when a bearing separator is used under the bearing. This assembly can be used in a press with relative safety.

On some axles, the seal is mounted alongside the bearing and is removed and replaced using the procedure described in Section 12.4.4. Other axles use a seal that is part of the bearing.

To remove and replace a bearing pressed on an axle shaft:

1. Position the axle so that the lock ring rests on the edge of the anvil portion of a vise or a sturdy benchtop. Using a hammer and cold chisel, make a series of six or eight cuts into the ring (Figure 12-37). Strike each location once or twice using fairly strong blows to expand the ring slightly so that it will relax its grip on the axle.
2. Select an adapter of the correct size to fit the bearing, and install the adapter and fixture on the axle (Figure 12-38).
3. Place the fixture in the bed of a press and press the axle out of the bearing and lock ring (Figure 12-39).

◀ **SERVICE TIP** ▶

Be ready to catch the axle as it moves through the bearing because it will fall freely after moving an inch or so.

FIGURE 12-37 The axle bearing retainer ring should be cut or stretched using a drill and chisel to make six to eight chisel blows before trying to press the bearing off the axle. (Courtesy of Dana Corporation)

Some axles use tapered roller bearings, which require a slightly different removal procedure because the rollers prevent the attachment of an adapter to the inner race. On these bearings, cut the bearing cage so that it and the rollers can be removed, and then attach an adapter or bearing separator to the inner race (Figure 12-40).

To press a bearing onto an axle:

1. Clean the bearing retainer and the end of the axle, and place the bearing retainer onto the axle.
2. Place the bearing onto the axle and press the axle into the bearing to the correct position (Figure 12-41).
3. Place the lock ring onto the axle and press the axle into the ring until the ring contacts the bearing.

FIGURE 12-38   This tool set encloses the bearing in a collet as it attaches the bearing to the press fixture to allow the safe removal of the bearing. (Courtesy of OTC Tools)

12.4.6 Lug Bolt/Wheel Stud Removal and Replacement

Lug bolts are held in the axle flange by an interference fit between a serrated portion of the bolt and the hole in the flange. Replacement lug bolts are sized using several dimensions, as shown in Figure 12-42. A lug bolt can often be removed using a hammer to give the lug bolt a firm tap on its end (Figure 12-43a); however, it is possible to bend the axle flange this way.

◄ SERVICE TIP ►

If the bolt is too tight, fit a U-joint press, some suspension bushing presses, or a C-clamp and short pipe section over the axle flange and damaged bolt, and tighten the press/clamp to push the bolt inward (Figure 12-43b).

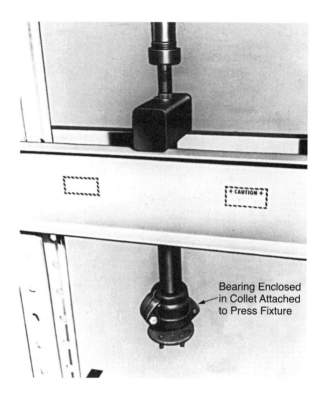

FIGURE 12-39   The fixture shown in Figure 12-38 has been placed in a press, and the axle is being forced from the bearing. (Courtesy of OTC Tools)

The new bolt is installed by placing it in position, setting a stack of flat washers over the threads, and tightening the lug nut to pull the bolt in place using socket wrench (Figure 12-44).

◄ SERVICE TIP ►

Do not use an impact wrench to install a wheel stud. The impact wrench's pounding action can strip the wheel stud serrations.

12.4.7 Pinion Shaft Seal Replacement

A leaking pinion shaft seal can be replaced in-vehicle without removing the pinion shaft from the carrier or drive axle/carrier from the vehicle. The driveshaft flange is removed and then the seal is removed and replaced. An important requirement while performing this operation is to not disturb the drive pinion bearing preload adjustment. Measuring the drive axle preload in step 2 provides the information for tightening the pinion nut in step 8.

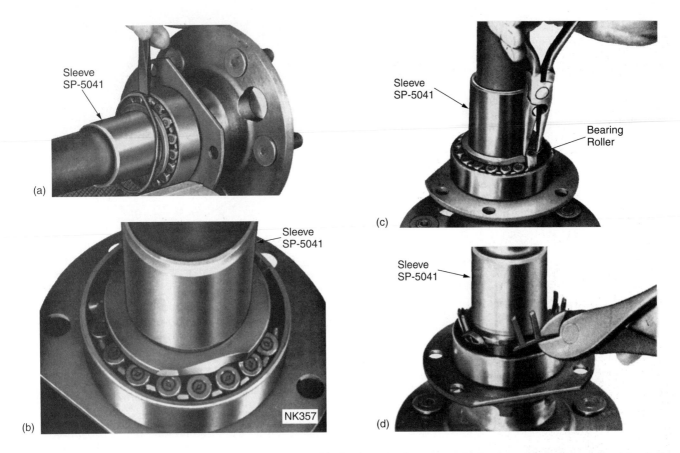

FIGURE 12-40 A safe procedure to remove a tapered roller bearing from the axle is to cut the bearing cage (a), grind a notch in the inner race (b), lift out the rollers (c) and remaining part of the cage (d), and attach an adapter to the inner race. Note the use of a sleeve to protect the seal area on this axle. (Courtesy of DaimlerChrysler Corporation)

To remove and replace a drive pinion seal:

1. Disconnect the driveshaft from the companion flange, and support the driveshaft so it does not hang from the front U-joint.
2. Measure the torque required to rotate the pinion shaft (pinion and carrier bearing preload) using a low-reading torque wrench, and record this measurement (Figure 12-45).
3. Remove the drive pinion nut and companion flange as described in Section 12.4.6.

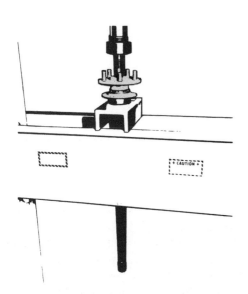

FIGURE 12-41 The axle is being pressed into the bearing and retainer plate. (Courtesy of OTC Tools)

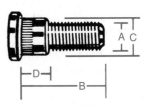

FIGURE 12-42 Critical dimensions for a wheel stud. (Courtesy of Dorman Products)

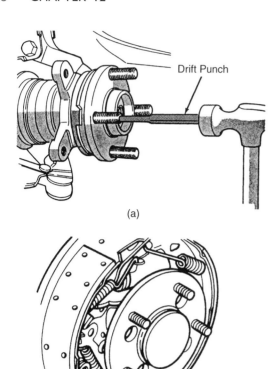

(a)

(b)

J-5504

FIGURE 12-43 (a) Sometimes a damaged wheel stud can be removed with a punch and firm tap from a hammer. (b) A tight stud should be removed using a pressing tool so as not to bend the axle flange. (a is courtesy of DaimlerChrysler Corporation; b: Portions of materials contained herein have been reprinted with permission of General Motors Corporation, Service and Parts Operations, License Agreement #0310807)

4. Check the sealing surface on the companion flange to ensure a good, smooth surface.

5. Remove and replace the seal. If the new seal does not have a coating on the outer surface, apply a thin film of RTV sealant before installing it.

6. Apply a thin film of gear oil to the lip of the seal and the sealing surface of the flange, and replace the companion flange.

7. Install a new pinion nut, and tighten the nut until the bearing preload is slightly greater than that recorded in step 2. The pinion nut should be very tight.

8. Replace the driveshaft.

REAL-WORLD FIX The drive axle pinion shaft seal in a 1989 S10 Blazer (166,000 mi) was replaced, but it still leaked. The seal was replaced again along with a repair sleeve on the companion flange surface, but it still leaked. A careful visual inspection during this last repair did not reveal any problems.

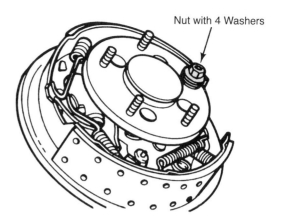

Nut with 4 Washers

FIGURE 12-44 A new wheel stud is installed by tightening the lug nut against a stack of flat washers. (Portions of materials contained herein have been reprinted with permission of General Motors Corporation, Service and Parts Operations, License Agreement #0310807)

FIX

While replacing the seal for the third time, the technician determined that the leak was along the splines between the pinion shaft and the companion flange and around the seal shell. A check of the axle housing vent tube showed that it was open. Replacement of the seal with the addition of a sealant on the outer surface and on the inner surface of the companion flange washer fixed this problem.

◀ **PROBLEM SOLVING** ▶

Imagine that you are working in a general automotive repair shop and these problems are brought to you.

Case 1

The pickup you're working on has a bad axle seal. You removed the differential cover, but as you try to remove the differential shaft retaining bolt, the head snaps off. What will you do now so that you can remove this hardened, broken-off remainder of the bolt that is still holding the differential shaft in place?

Case 2

The problem began with axle gear oil on the brakes, and you pulled the bearing-retained axle. You check in the axle housing to pull the grease seal, but there is no seal in there and there is no sign of a sealing surface on the axle. Where is the seal?

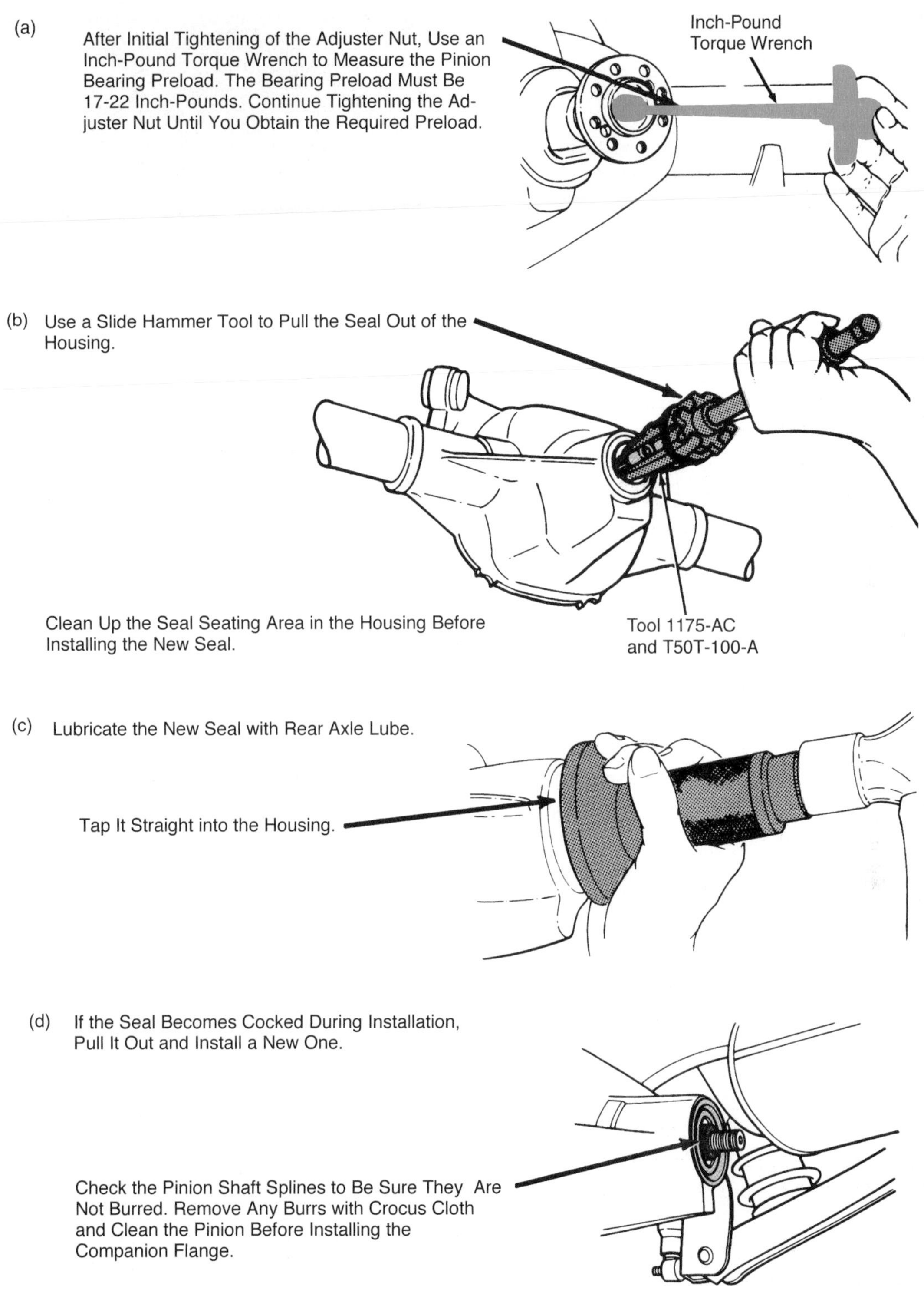

(a) After Initial Tightening of the Adjuster Nut, Use an Inch-Pound Torque Wrench to Measure the Pinion Bearing Preload. The Bearing Preload Must Be 17-22 Inch-Pounds. Continue Tightening the Adjuster Nut Until You Obtain the Required Preload.

Inch-Pound Torque Wrench

(b) Use a Slide Hammer Tool to Pull the Seal Out of the Housing.

Clean Up the Seal Seating Area in the Housing Before Installing the New Seal.

Tool 1175-AC and T50T-100-A

(c) Lubricate the New Seal with Rear Axle Lube.

Tap It Straight into the Housing.

(d) If the Seal Becomes Cocked During Installation, Pull It Out and Install a New One.

Check the Pinion Shaft Splines to Be Sure They Are Not Burred. Remove Any Burrs with Crocus Cloth and Clean the Pinion Before Installing the Companion Flange.

FIGURE 12-45 A leaky drive pinion seal is repaired by first measuring the axle preload (a), removing the pinion flange and the seal (b), replacing the seal (c), checking the shaft splines and flange (d), and replacing the flange and tightening the nut to get a slightly higher preload than measured in step a. (Courtesy of Ford Motor Company)

12.5   CARRIER REMOVAL AND REPLACEMENT

On removable carrier axles, the carrier is removed from the axle housing to service or repair the differential, ring and pinion gears, and any of the bearings.

To remove a carrier:

1. Raise and securely support the vehicle on a hoist or jack stands.
2. Remove the axles as described in Section 12.4.2.
3. Remove the driveshaft as described in Section 10.4.2.
4. Place a drain pan under the axle assembly, and remove the nuts or bolts that are securing the carrier to the housing. Also remove the copper washers used to seal the studs (Figure 12-46).
5. Be ready to support the heavy carrier as you break the gasket seal and remove the carrier from the housing.

To replace a carrier:

1. Clean the gasket surface on the axle housing and carrier and remove any old grease and debris from the bottom of the housing.
2. On housings using studs, place a new gasket in position on the housing. If cap screws are used, place the gasket on the carrier (Figure 12-47).

Use Copper Washer

Install Washer Behind Tag

FIGURE 12-46 After removing the axles, this carrier can be detached by removing the nuts and copper washers and lifting the carrier housing from the axle housing. (Courtesy of Ford Motor Company)

3. Set the carrier in position, install the washers and nuts or cap screws, and tighten them to the correct torque.
4. Replace the axles as described in Section 12.4.2.
5. Replace the driveshaft as described in Section 10.4.2.

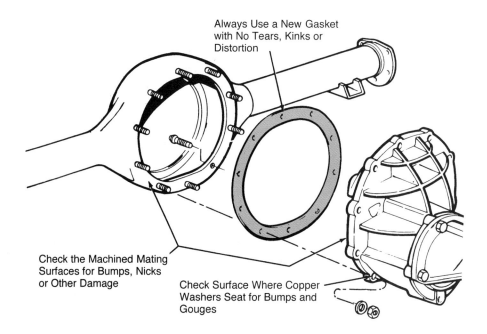

Always Use a New Gasket with No Tears, Kinks or Distortion

Check the Machined Mating Surfaces for Bumps, Nicks or Other Damage

Check Surface Where Copper Washers Seat for Bumps and Gouges

FIGURE 12-47 A new gasket should be used when replacing a carrier. (Courtesy of Ford Motor Company)

12.6 CARRIER OVERHAUL

Carrier overhaul includes:

- An inspection of the gears and bearings before teardown
- A check for ring gear runout
- Removal and replacement of the differential and ring gear
- Removal and replacement of the pinion gear
- Inspection and repair of the differential
- Assembly adjustments for pinion depth, pinion bearing preload, backlash, and carrier bearing preload (Figure 12-48)

Due to the variety of carriers, there are at least two ways of making each of these adjustments. **Pinion depth** can be adjusted by a **shim** right next to the gear of an overhung pinion, or it can be adjusted by a shim at the bearing retainer of a straddle-mounted pinion. In most carriers, **pinion bearing preload** is adjusted using a collapsible bearing spacer. Some carriers, however, use a solid spacer and shims. Backlash and carrier bearing preload can be adjusted using threaded adjusters in some axles; most modern axles use shims for these two adjustments.

For secure support during the overhaul procedure, removable carriers are normally mounted in fixtures attached to a shop bench (Figure 12-49). Most integral carriers are overhauled in the vehicle, or the axle assembly can be removed and overhauled at the bench. The parts needed to rebuild a carrier assembly are normally purchased as needed. Some suppliers market installation kits, which include the parts needed during the installation and adjustment of a ring and pinion gear (Figure 12-50).

12.6.1 Inspection Before Teardown

Inspection begins with a complete cleanup.

◄ SERVICE TIP ►

On C-clip axle units, be aware that the differential gears can fall out; you may want to slide the differential pinion shaft back in place to hold them.

After cleaning, visually inspect the ring gear and differential gears for obvious damage. The surface of the teeth should be smooth and have a polished sheen.

Common ring gear wear appears as a rough, scored tooth surface or chipped or nicked teeth (Figure 12-51).

◄ SERVICE TIP ►

Occasionally, a ring gear will wear in a smooth pattern, with the only noticeable wear being a step near the bottom of the teeth.

Rotate the pinion shaft and the differential. They should roll smoothly without any end play; both sets of bearings should be preloaded.

REAL WORLD FIX A 1997 Jeep Grand Cherokee (44,000 mi) had a whine when operated between 55 and 70 mph. It was most noticeable under light deceleration, but not present under cruise or acceleration. The rear axle was inspected, and the ring and pinion gears and the bearings appeared questionable. They were replaced, but this did not help. The front axle was inspected, and the carrier bearing appeared bad. All the bearings were replaced, but this did not help. The ring and the pinion appeared good, but the contact pattern ran the full length of the gear tooth on one side.

FIX

A test using a Chassis Ear indicated the noise to be coming from the front axle. The ring and pinion gear set was replaced and adjusted to a correct contact pattern. This fixed the problem.

12.6.2 Ring Gear Runout

Ring gear runout is checked if there is evidence of damage to the ring gear. Runout is usually caused by a faulty or bent differential case or an improper mounting of the ring gear onto the case. Because gear runout will cause backlash to change, it is sometimes referred to as **backlash variation.**

To check ring gear runout:

1. Mount a dial indicator so that the indicator stylus is on the back of the ring gear and at a 90° angle to the gear surface (Figure 12-52a). The runout of a differential case can be checked using a similar procedure (Figure 12-52b).

2. Rotate the ring gear and observe the amount of indicator needle movement. This is the amount of runout.

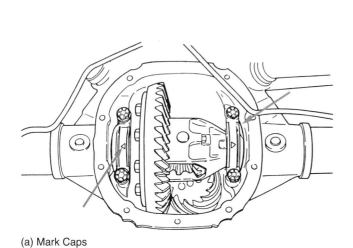

(a) Mark Caps

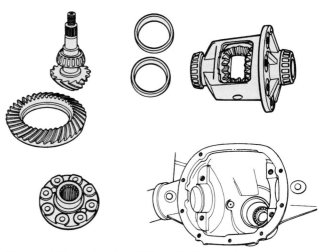

(d) Inspect Gears, Bearings, Differential Case and Gears, Housing, and Companion Flange

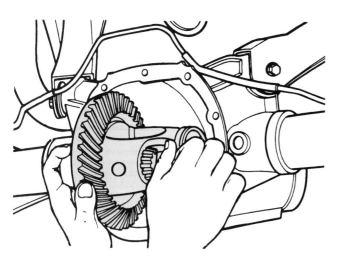

(b) Remove Caps, Differential, and Bearings with Cups

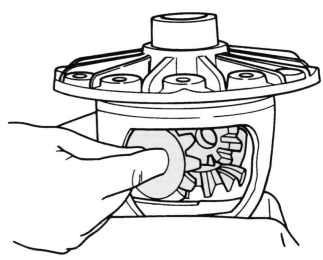

(e) Check Differential Gears

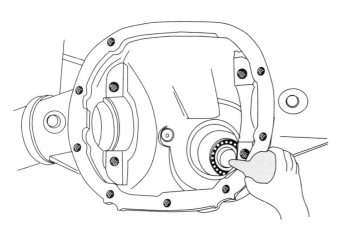

(c) Remove Companion Flange and Remove Drive Pinion Gear

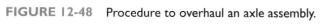

FIGURE 12-48 Procedure to overhaul an axle assembly.

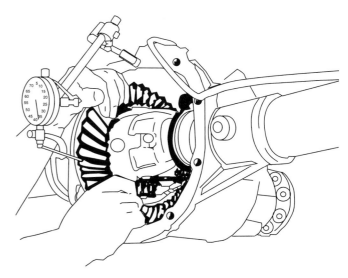

(f) Assemble Axle and Make Adjustments

FIGURE 12-49 This carrier is supported securely using a bench support. (Courtesy of Ford Motor Company)

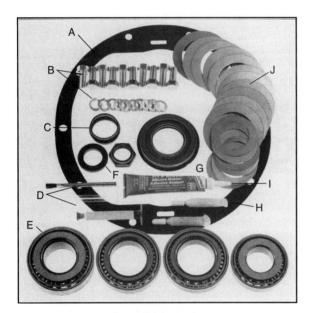

A. Cover Gasket
B. Ring Gear Bolts and Washers
C. Crush Sleeve
D. Marking Compound and Brush
E. Pinion and Carrier Bearings
F. Pinion Nut and Washer
G. Pinion Seal
H. Thread Locking Compound
I. Silicone Sealer
J. Pinion and Carrier Shims

FIGURE 12-50 This ring and pinion installation kit includes all the parts needed for installation and adjustment of a ring and pinion gear. (Courtesy of Richmond Gear)

Scored Teeth

Nicks or Ridges on Tooth Edge

Cracked Teeth

Drive Side Knock

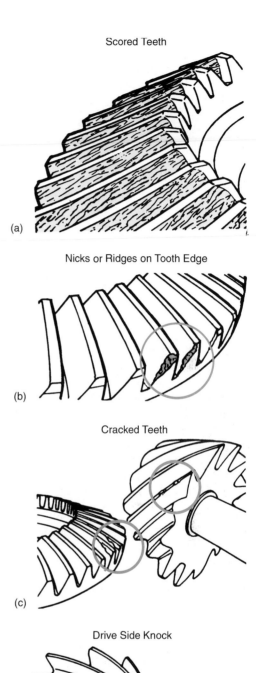
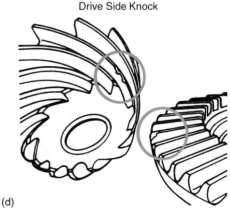

FIGURE 12-51 Noisy gear operation can be caused by scored teeth (a) or cracked or chipped teeth (b, c, and d). (Courtesy of Ford Motor Company)

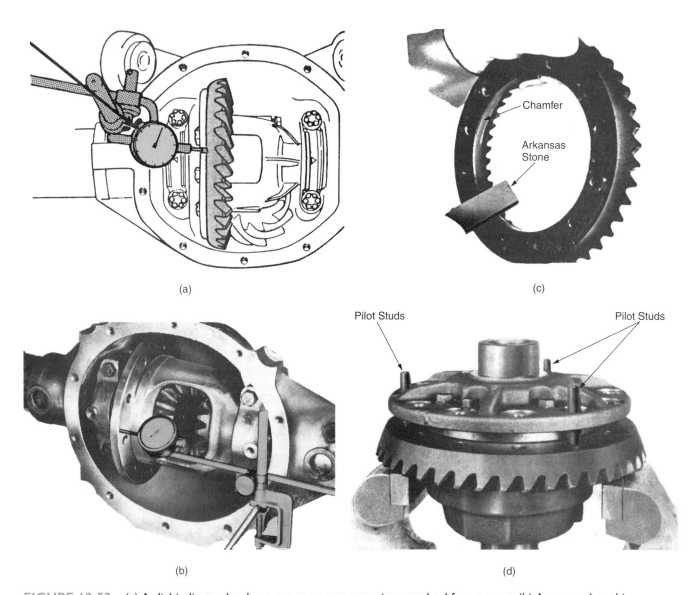

(a)

(c)

(b)

(d)

FIGURE 12-52   (a) A dial indicator has been set up to measure ring gear backface runout. (b) Among other things, excessive runout can be caused by runout of the ring gear mounting flange. When replacing a ring gear on the case, be sure to remove any burrs that might interfere with the seating (c) and to use pilot studs for bolt alignment (d). (a is courtesy of Ford Motor Company; b, c, and d are courtesy of DaimlerChrysler Corporation)

◀ **SERVICE TIP** ▶

Runout can sometimes be corrected by the following process:

1. Remove the ring gear from the differential case.
2. Clean them both thoroughly.
3. Remove any metal burrs or raised metal from the case.
4. Replace the gear, tightening the bolts evenly and to the correct torque.

◀ **SERVICE TIP** ▶

One manufacturer limits the maximum allowable runout to 0.004 in. (0.1 mm). Others have no specification for runout. Instead, they specify that the backlash must not be less than the minimum specification at the tightest point or larger than the maximum specification at the loosest point.

It should be noted that left-hand threads are used on many ring gear bolts. It should also be noted that some manufacturers recommend discarding the old ring gear bolts if they are removed and installing new ones.

12.6.3 Differential Removal

◀ **SERVICE TIP** ▶

An experienced technician will loosen the ring gear mounting bolts before removing the differential if there is a chance he/she might remove the ring gear from the differential case. These bolts are normally very tight, and the differential is hard to hold when it is out of the carrier. While still in the carrier, the differential case can be held stationary by placing a block of wood between the ring and pinion gears or by placing a box wrench on one of the ring gear bolts and against the side of the carrier.

◀ **SERVICE TIP** ▶

Don't forget to check the ring gear bolt heads for markings that indicate left-hand threads, usually an "L."

◀ **SERVICE TIP** ▶

The bores of the carrier bearing caps are normally machined after they are mounted on the carrier. This means that the cap will fit properly only in the original position. Index marks should be put on them before removal to ensure proper replacement.

To remove a differential:

1. Using a punch and hammer or permanent marker, place index marks on each of the bearing caps (Figure 12-53).

FIGURE 12-53 Index marks should be placed on the bearing caps before removal to ensure proper replacement. (Courtesy of DaimlerChrysler Corporation)

◀ **SERVICE TIP** ▶

Some bearing caps are factory marked with an arrow; even so, this only shows you half of what you need. Mark the caps so you can tell the right and left sides.

2. On threaded adjusters, remove the adjustment locks, the carrier bearing cap mounting bolts, and the bearing caps (Figure 12-54). On shim-adjusted carriers, remove the bearing cap mounting bolts and the bearing caps.

◀ **SERVICE TIP** ▶

You can lift the bearing cap bolts about halfway out of their holes and use them as a handle to help remove the caps.

3. On threaded adjusters, remove the adjuster and lift the differential with bearing cups out of the carrier (Figure 12-55). Mark or tag the bearing cups so that they won't be mixed up.

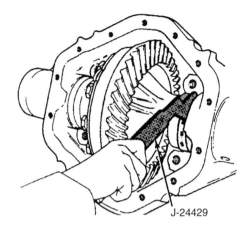

J-24429

FIGURE 12-54 Loosening the threaded adjusters removes the preload and allows for easy removal of the adjusters and bearing caps. Keep each set of bearing cup, cap, and adjuster separate to ensure reinstallation onto the proper side. (Portions of materials contained herein have been reprinted with permission of General Motors Corporation, Service and Parts Operations, License Agreement #0310807)

Some manufacturers recommend the use of a spreader tool to stretch the carrier and take the pressure off the shims and bearings. When using a spreader tool, do not spread the carrier any farther than the manufacturer's limits, or 0.015 in.

◀ **SERVICE TIP** ▶

Some differentials can be removed by placing a box wrench on one of the ring gear bolts and turning the pinion gear so that the wrench pushes against the carrier and lifts up the differential. As the differential is removed from the carrier, tag or mark the shims and bearing cup from each side so they won't be mixed up.

◀ **SERVICE TIP** ▶

On shim-adjusted carriers, the preload at the shims should be too tight to allow easy removal of the differential (Figure 12-56). Most differentials can be pried out of the carrier, but be careful not to damage the gasket surface on the carrier.

◀ **SERVICE TIP** ▶

The drive pinion gear is held in place by the companion flange, and the self-locking nut that secures it is very tight. You can expect to exert 150 to 300 ft-lb (203 to 407 N-m) of torque to break it loose.

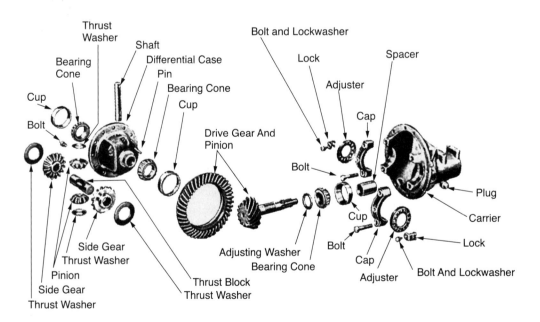

FIGURE 12-55 With the caps removed, the differential case with differential and ring gear can be removed from the housing. (Courtesy of DaimlerChrysler Corporation)

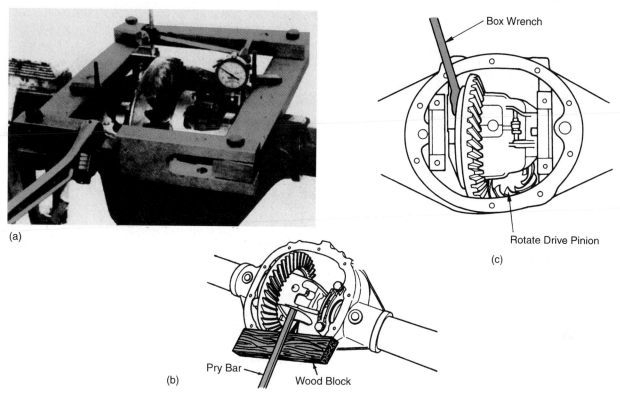

(a)

Box Wrench

Rotate Drive Pinion

(c)

Pry Bar — Wood Block

(b)

FIGURE 12-56   (a) Some manufacturers recommend the use of a case spreader to spread the housing (0.015 in. maximum) so that the differential case can be removed. (b) Often, however, the differential case can be pried out of the housing using a pry bar and block of wood to protect the gasket surface; note that the bearing caps are in place with the bolts loosened. (c) Some differentials can be lifted from the housing by placing a box wrench onto one of the ring gear bolts and rotating the drive pinion shaft. (a courtesy of Dana Corporation; b is courtesy of Ford Motor Company)

12.6.4 Pinion Gear Removal

To remove a drive pinion:

1. Place index marks on the end of the pinion shaft and the companion flange so that you can replace the flange back on the same spline (Figure 12-57).

2. Attach a holding tool to the flange. Use a socket and the longest handle available to loosen the nut (Figure 12-58). A torque multiplier is very helpful. Once loosened, a ratchet handle can be used to remove the nut.

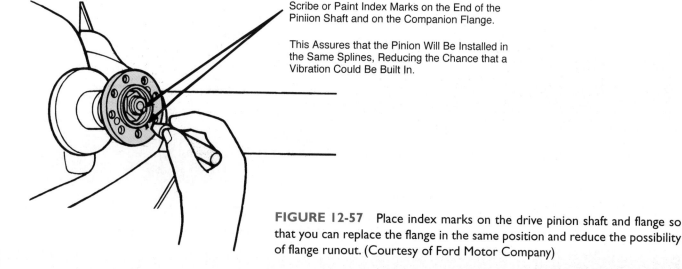

Scribe or Paint Index Marks on the End of the Piniion Shaft and on the Companion Flange.

This Assures that the Pinion Will Be Installed in the Same Splines, Reducing the Chance that a Vibration Could Be Built In.

FIGURE 12-57   Place index marks on the drive pinion shaft and flange so that you can replace the flange in the same position and reduce the possibility of flange runout. (Courtesy of Ford Motor Company)

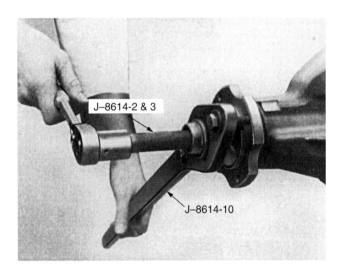

FIGURE 12-58   When attached to the pinion flange, this tool will provide the leverage needed to hold the pinion flange as the drive pinion nut is loosened and tightened. It can also be used as a puller when removing the flange (inset). (Courtesy of Kent-Moore)

Use One Hand to Reach Through the Rear of the Housing and Hold the Pinion So It Will Not Fall and Be Damaged.

With a Soft-Faced Hammer, Gently Tap on the Shaft to Free the Pinion.

Remove the Pinion Assembly Through the Rear of the Housing.

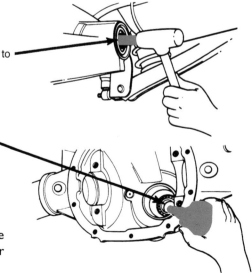

FIGURE 12-59   A soft hammer is usually needed to drive the pinion shaft from the bearings. (Courtesy of Ford Motor Company)

3. Slide the companion flange off the drive pinion shaft. If necessary, use a puller to remove the flange.

◀ SERVICE TIP ▶

Driving off a flange by hammering on the lugs could bend it and cause a future vibration.

4. Use a soft hammer or brass punch to tap the pinion shaft into the carrier (Figure 12-59). Be ready to catch the pinion gear as it slides out.

12.6.5 Pinion Shaft Seal Replacement

A leaking pinion shaft seal can be replaced in-vehicle without removing the pinion shaft from the carrier or drive axle/carrier from the vehicle. The drive shaft flange is removed and then the seal is removed and replaced. An important requirement while performing this operation is to not disturb the drive pinion bearing preload adjustment. Measuring the drive axle preload in Step 2 provides the information for tightening the pinion nut in Step 8.

To remove and replace a drive pinion seal:

1. Disconnect the drive shaft from the companion flange, and support the driveshaft so it does not hang from the front U-joint.
2. Measure the torque required to rotate the pinion shaft (pinion and carrier bearing preload) using a low reading torque wrench and record this measurement (see Figure 12-73)

3. Remove the drive pinion nut and companion flange as described in Section 12.6.4.

4. Check the sealing surface on the companion flange to insure a good, smooth surface.

5. Remove and replace the seal. If the new seal does not have a coating on the outer surface, apply a thin film of RTV sealant before installing it.

6. Apply a thin film of gear oil to the lip of the seal and the sealing surface of the flange, and replace the companion flange.

7. Install a new pinion nut, and tighten the nut until the bearing preload is slightly greater than that recorded in step 2. The pinion nut should be very tight.

8. Replace the drive shaft.

12.6.6 Inspection of Bearings and Gears

After disassembly, the parts should be cleaned in solvent and inspected to ensure their usability. Gears are checked in the same manner as transmission gears; this procedure is described in Section 8.5.4. Bearing inspection is also similar to that described for transmission bearings in Section 8.5.5 (Figure 12-60). Bearings to be reused should be oiled to prevent rusting.

The inside of the carrier or axle housing should be cleaned. Worn drive pinion bearing cups are normally removed from the carrier using a punch and hammer (Figure 12-61).

◄ **SERVICE TIP** ►

New cups are installed by driving them into place using a bearing cup driver and hammer. An old cup is sometimes used as the driving tool.

Never hammer directly on the new cup. The drive pinion seal should be checked to make sure that it is in good condition. The seal lip must not have excess wear, be cut or torn, nor be overly hardened. Many technicians will replace this seal during each overhaul. Also, make sure that the sealing surface on the companion flange is not damaged or worn (Figure 12-62).

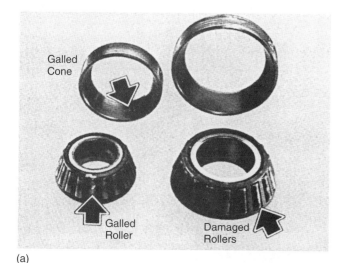

(a)

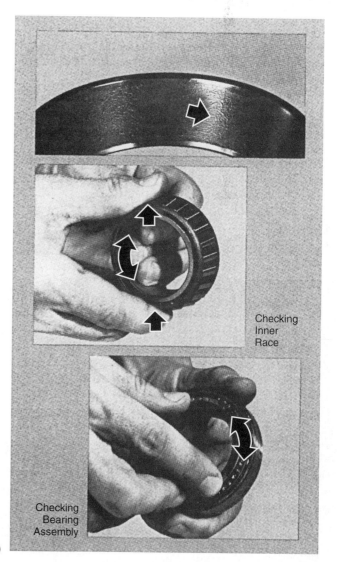

(b)

FIGURE 12-60 (a) Used tapered roller bearings and their cups should be inspected for damage. (b) It is also a good practice to press them together as you rotate them so that you can feel for any damage. (Courtesy of Ford Motor Company)

◀ **SERVICE TIP** ▶

Normally during disassembly, the carrier bearings are left on the differential case unless the case bearings, or a shim behind the bearing, needs to be replaced. Also, the rear drive pinion bearing is left in place unless the drive pinion, bearing, or pinion depth shim needs to be replaced. In some cases, the bearing is ruined during removal. A sturdy puller and step plate are required to remove a carrier bearing (Figure 12-63). The new bearing is normally pressed into place.

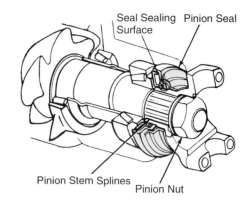

FIGURE 12-62   When the drive pinion is replaced, a new drive pinion seal should be used and the sealing surface of the flange should be inspected carefully. (Courtesy of Ford Motor Company)

FIGURE 12-61   (a) A damaged bearing cup can be driven out of the housing using a long punch (b and c). A special tool can be used to pull the new bearing cup into position, making sure that it is completely seated. (a: Portions of materials contained herein have been reprinted with permission of General Motors Corporation, Service and Parts Operations, License Agreement #0310807; b and c are courtesy of Ford Motor Company)

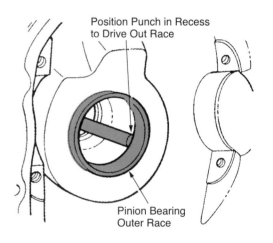

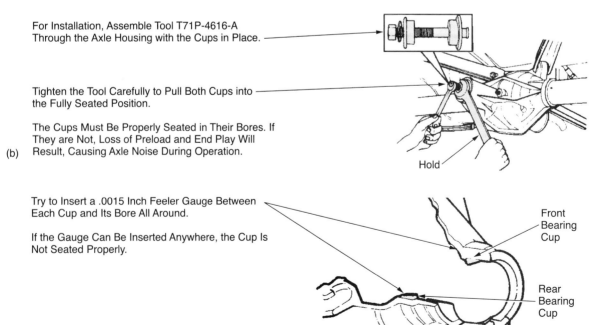

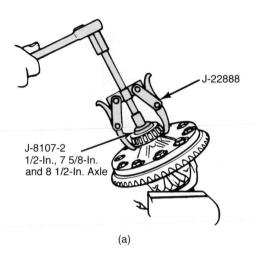

J-22888

J-8107-2
1/2-In., 7 5/8-In.
and 8 1/2-In. Axle

(a)

FIGURE 12-63   (a) A two-jaw bearing puller and adapter at the axle opening are being used to remove the differential side case/carrier bearing. (b) The new bearing is installed using a press. (a: Portions of materials contained herein have been reprinted with permission of General Motors Corporation, Service and Parts Operations, License Agreement #0310807; b is courtesy of Ford Motor Company)

Place the New Bearng on the Hub of the Case.

Use Tool T57L-4221-A to Align the Bearing on 7.5 or 8.5 Axle. (On 6.75 Axle, Use T79P-4220-A.)

Press the Bearing On Until the Tool Bottoms.

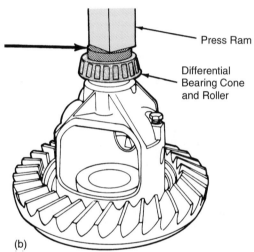

Press Ram

Differential Bearing Cone and Roller

(b)

REAL-WORLD FIX A 1998 Ford F150 (115,000 mi) had bad drive axle bearings, so the pinion and carrier bearings were replaced. The proper synthetic gear oil and friction modifier were put in the axle. A road test revealed a rhythmic thumping noise during deceleration. With the vehicle on a lift, the noise came from the axle housing.

FIX

The ring and pinion gears were replaced even though a close inspection revealed only a scuff mark on the coast side of a ring gear tooth. The gear replacement cured this problem.

12.6.7   Drive Pinion Depth Shim Selection

Pinion depth is the first step in the adjustment sequence on most carriers (Figure 12-64). On overhung pinion gears, the pinion depth shim selection is the first step in reassembly. This shim places the drive pinion gear in the proper position relative to the ring gear and carrier (Figure 12-65). All pinion gears use a depth shim to adjust for minor manufacturing tolerances of the gear and carrier. Pinion depth is affected by the machining of the gear and carrier, as well as by the rear bearing.

◄ SERVICE TIP ►

The pinion depth shim is usually located between the rear bearing and the pinion gear head. On some carriers it is located under the rear bearing cup (Figure 12-66). If a carrier is assembled with the wrong pinion depth shim, it will need to be disassembled so that the shim can be changed.

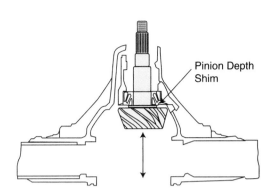

(a) Adjust Pinion Depth

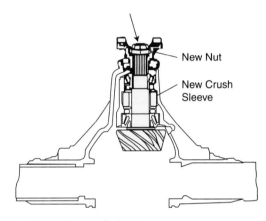

(b) Adjust Pinion Bearing Preload

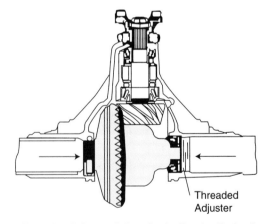

(c) With Threaded Adjuster, Adjust Carrier Bearing Preload

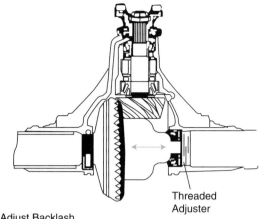

(d) Adjust Backlash

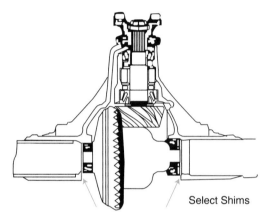

e) With Shim Adjustment, Select Shims for Carrier Bearing Preload and Backlash Adjustments

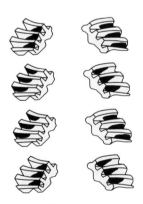

(f) Run Contact Pattern to Check Adjustments

FIGURE 12-64 Procedure to adjust most drive axle assemblies.

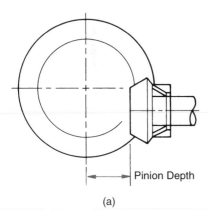

(a)

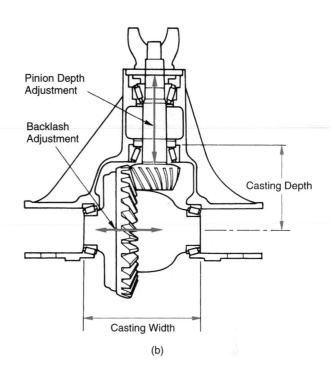

(b)

FIGURE 12-65 (a) The drive pinion must be positioned at the design distance from the ring gear center. (b) Shims are used at the drive pinion gear to compensate for variations in the casting depth, and shims or threaded adjusters are used at the carrier bearings to compensate for variations in the casting width when adjusting the ring and pinion gear.

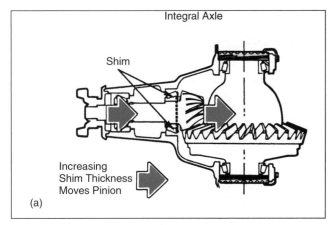

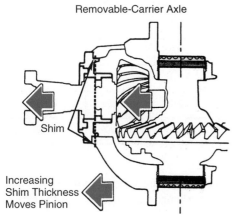

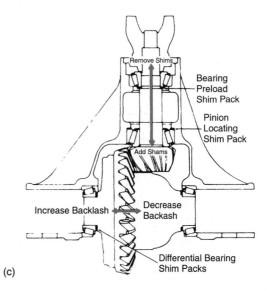

(c)

FIGURE 12-66 (a) Pinion depth shims are usually positioned between the pinion gear head and the rear pinion bearing. Sometimes they are between the bearing support and the housing (b) or between the rear bearing cup and the housing (c). (a and b are courtesy of Ford Motor Company; c is courtesy of Dana Corporation)

◀ SERVICE TIP ▶

Some adjustments require that you insert a shim, press the bearing in place, and then check to see if you inserted a shim of the correct size. If you need to change the shim, you must pull the tight-fitting bearing back off. Some technicians make up slip-fit bearings so the shim can be easily changed. Slip-fit bearings are made by honing the bearing ID to enlarge it slightly. If using a slip-fit bearing, be sure to check the bearing width and compensate for any width difference with the new bearing.

◀ SERVICE TIP ▶

Straddle-mounted pinion gears allow for easy depth shim change and adjustment because the shim is located under the bearing retainer.

There are different methods used to determine the correct size for a pinion depth shim: (1) + or − markings on the pinion gear, (2) gauge block and fixtures, (3) contact patterns, and (4) pinion depth micrometer with gear depth marking. At one time, many passenger vehicle drive pinion gears were marked with a + or − and a number that indicated the position of that gear relative to a perfect gear. The + or − indicated the direction, and the number (up to about 0.005 in.) indicated the distance. This number was etched or painted on the head or stem of the gear (Figure 12-67). When a ring and pinion gear set is replaced, the technician checks the markings on both the old and new pinion gears and changes the shim to compensate for any difference. These markings are no longer used by all manufacturers.

Most vehicle manufacturers use a set of pinion depth gauge blocks to select the correct depth shim. These gauges are installed in the carrier, usually using the rear drive pinion bearing (Figure 12-68). Most gaug-

(a)

Old Pinion Marking	New Pinion Marking								
	−4	−3	−2	−1	0	+1	+2	+3	+4
+4	+0.008	+0.007	+0.006	+0.005	+0.004	+0.003	+0.002	+0.001	0
+3	+0.007	+0.006	+0.005	+0.004	+0.003	+0.002	+0.001	0	−0.001
+2	+0.006	+0.005	+0.004	+0.003	+0.002	+0.001	0	−0.001	−0.002
+1	+0.005	+0.004	+0.003	+0.002	+0.001	0	−0.001	−0.002	−0.003
0	+0.004	+0.003	+0.002	+0.001	0	−0.001	−0.002	−0.003	−0.004
−1	+0.003	+0.002	+0.001	0	−0.001	−0.002	−0.003	−0.004	−0.005
−2	+0.002	+0.001	0	−0.001	−0.002	−0.003	−0.004	−0.005	−0.006
−3	+0.001	0	−0.001	−0.002	−0.003	−0.004	−0.005	−0.006	−0.007
−4	0	−0.001	−0.002	−0.003	−0.004	−0.005	−0.006	−0.007	−0.008

(B)

FIGURE 12-67   (a) This pinion gear has a +4 marking on it, which means its best running position is 0.004 in. more than the nominal mounting point. (b) If it is replaced, a chart can be used to determine the change needed in the depth shim. (Courtesy of Dana Corporation)

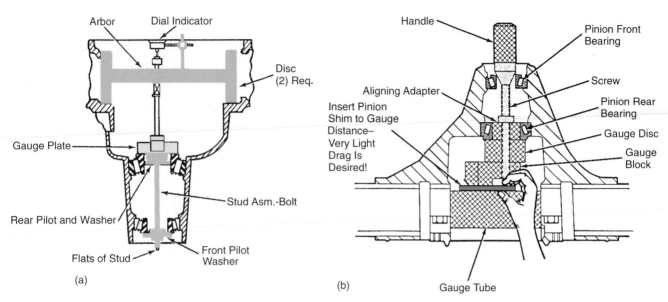

FIGURE 12-68 (a) Some pinion depth gauging tools use a dial indicator to indicate the size of the depth shim needed. (b) With others, the actual shim size is used. (a: Portions of materials contained herein have been reprinted with permission of General Motors Corporation, Service and Parts Operations, License Agreement #0310807; b is courtesy of Ford Motor Company)

ing sets can be used only on the carriers they are designed for. There is no universal gauge set or procedure for all drive axles.

◀ **SERVICE TIP** ▶

The only universal method of checking pinion depth is a gear **contact pattern.** After the carrier is assembled and adjusted, a **gear marking compound** is put on the ring gear, and the gears are rolled against each other. Improper depth will cause a high or low contact, as well as contact that is toward the toe on one side of the tooth and toward the heel on the other (Figure 12-69). The major drawback with this method is that you have to remove the differential and disassemble the drive pinion gear in order to change the shim with an overhung pinion. The process of making and interpreting a contact pattern is described in Section 12.6.10.

Because these procedures (except for the contact pattern) vary among different models, it will be necessary to follow the procedure given by the vehicle or equipment manufacturer. If using a contact pattern, assemble the new parts using the original depth shim or the nominal size recommended by the manufacturer. This shim should put the pattern in the ballpark so that cor-

◀ **SERVICE TIP** ▶

Some aftermarket drive pinion gears are marked with the actual setting distance on the head of the gear (Figure 12-70). A special depth micrometer is mounted in the carrier bearing bores to measure this distance. It is usually the distance from the center of the ring gear to the head of the pinion gear. If the distance measured is different from the pinion gear marking, the shim size is changed to make the adjustment.

rection can be made with the fewest number of shim changes.

The pinion gear and bearings on straddle-mounted pinion gears are installed in the bearing retainer, and pinion bearing preload adjusted as described in Section 12.6.8. This assembly is installed into the carrier using the original depth shim or the nominal shim recommended by the manufacturer. Backlash and carrier bearing preload are adjusted as the ring gear and differential are installed (Section 12.6.9), and a contact pattern is rolled (Section 12.6.10). The contact pattern is read to determine if pinion depth is correct. If it is not, the bearing retainer is removed, the depth shim is increased or decreased, the bearing retainer and pinion gear are reinstalled, backlash is readjusted to compensate for the pinion gear movement, and a new contact

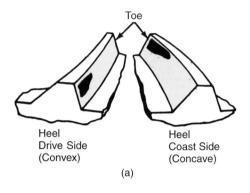

Toe

Heel
Drive Side
(Convex)

Heel
Coast Side
(Concave)

(a)

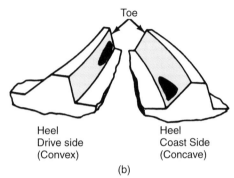

Toe

Heel
Drive side
(Convex)

Heel
Coast Side
(Concave)

(b)

FIGURE 12-69 (a) If the pinion gear is too far away from the ring, it will contact the ring at the heel of the drive side and the toe of the coast side. (b) If it is too close, the contact will be at the toe of the drive side and the heel of the coast side. (Portions of materials contained herein have been reprinted with permission of General Motors Corporation, Service and Parts Operations, License Agreement #0310807)

pattern is rolled. This procedure is repeated until the correct contact pattern is obtained.

◀ SERVICE TIP ▶

If the pinion gear is going to be moved deeper into the ring gear, be aware that the pinion gear will contact the ring gear. Move the ring gear away from the pinion gear before making this adjustment. Increase the backlash, and then move the pinion gear.

12.6.8 Drive Pinion Bearing Preload Adjustment

After installation of the pinion depth shim and rear bearing, the bearing spacer is placed on the pinion shaft and the pinion gear is installed in the carrier. The

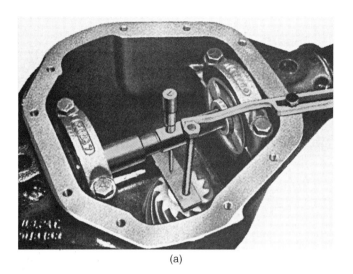

(a)

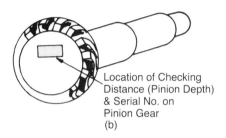

Location of Checking
Distance (Pinion Depth)
& Serial No. on
Pinion Gear
(b)

FIGURE 12-70 (a) A pinion depth micrometer is measuring the distance from the ring gear centerline to the end of the pinion gear. (b) The measured distance should be the same as that etched on the pinion gear. (a is courtesy of DaimlerChrysler Corporation; b is courtesy of Richmond Gear)

bearing spacer will be either a collapsible **crush sleeve** or a fixed-length solid spacer. This spacer keeps the two tapered roller bearings apart as the companion flange nut is tightened. The spacer allows the bearings to be squeezed against their races just tight enough to obtain the proper preload. The length of a fixed spacer is adjusted by adding or removing thin selective-size shims. A crush sleeve starts out too long and is collapsed to the proper length as the drive pinion nut is tightened. Collapsing a crush sleeve takes a substantial amount of force.

◀ SERVICE TIP ▶

A **collapsible spacer** is normally replaced with a new one each time the pinion gear is removed or the nut is removed from the pinion shaft.

◄ **SERVICE TIP** ►

In emergencies, the spacer can be reused by adding a shim right next to it.

◄ **SERVICE TIP** ►

An experienced technician is concerned with two things while adjusting pinion bearing preload. One of these is the actual adjustment. If the bearings are too loose, the pinion gear can change mesh contact with the ring gear; this will cause noise and probable gear failure. If the bearings are too tight, a power loss will result because of the excess drag, and bearing failure will probably occur. The pinion shaft nut is the other concern. It must be tight enough to retain the preload. This is a self-locking, prevailing torque nut that should never be reused. If it is too loose on the pinion threads, it can back off and allow pinion bearing preload to disappear. The amount of torque is specified by manufacturers; a rule of thumb is a minimum of 125 ft-lb (167N-m).

◄ **SERVICE TIP** ►

It is recommended that the pinion shaft be in a vertical position during the preload adjustment. In this way, gravity moves the shaft downward and centers it in the bearing cone (Figure 12-71).

To adjust drive pinion bearing preload using a collapsible spacer:

1. Lubricate the bearings and slide the pinion gear with the rear bearing, depth shim, and new collapsible spacer into the carrier through the front bearing and seal (Figure 12-72).
2. Lubricate the splines and seal area, and install the companion flange, being sure to align the index marks.
3. Oil the inner face of the new nut and install it on the pinion shaft.
4. Attach a holding tool to the flange and begin tightening the nut.

◄ **SERVICE TIP** ►

As the nut tightens onto the flange, rotate the pinion shaft to help seat the bearings. From this point on, rotate the pinion a turn or so for every half-turn of the nut. It is also a good practice to tap on the casting with a steel hammer to help seat the bearings.

5. Continue tightening the nut as you check two things: the minimum torque to obtain the preload using a high-reading, foot-pound torque wrench and the amount of preload using a very low-reading inch-pound torque wrench (Figure 12-73). Stop tightening when the preload is within specifications.

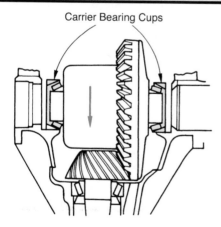

FIGURE 12-71 When checking for the size of the backlash and carrier bearing preload shims, remember that the carrier bearing cups will try to spread from the weight of the differential and thus try to give a false reading.

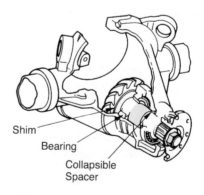

FIGURE 12-72 When the drive pinion is replaced, a new collapsible spacer and nut should be used. The bearings, seal, spline, and nut should be lubricated. (Courtesy of Ford Motor Company)

◀ SERVICE TIP ▶

If the drive pinion preload occurs at too low a tightening torque, install a new nut and collapsible spacer and repeat this operation.

◀ SERVICE TIP ▶

Note that the bearing preload specification will vary depending on whether new or used bearings or a new seal is used. New bearings or a new seal usually require a higher amount of preload.

To adjust drive pinion bearing preload using a solid spacer:

1. Install the solid spacer onto the pinion shaft with a starting shim that should be thicker than needed (Figure 12-74).
2. Follow steps 1 through 4 of the procedure used with a collapsible spacer. Tighten the nut to about 50 ft-lb (68 N-m) of torque.
3. If there is no free play, measure the bearing preload as described in step 5 of the collapsible spacer procedure. If the preload is within specifications, you have the correct shim; go to step 8. If the preload is too high, the starting shim will have to be replaced

with a thicker one. If the preload is too low, a thinner shim is needed. If there is no preload, as expected, continue to step 4.

4. Mount a dial indicator on the carrier and position the indicator stylus on the end of and parallel to the pinion shaft (Figure 12-75).
5. Move the pinion shaft through its free play and read the amount of dial indicator needle movement to determine the amount of free play.
6. Determine the amount of shim change by subtracting a factor specified by the manufacturer and the amount of free play from the size of the starting shim.

◀ SERVICE TIP ▶

To select the correct preload shim, if there is a starting shim size of 0.030, 0.010 in. of free play, and a factor of 0.003, the procedure would be 0.030—0.010—0.003—0.017, for a shim size of 0.017in.

7. Remove the pinion gear and replace the starting shim with the size just determined. Repeat steps 1 through 3.
8. Tighten the pinion nut to the correct torque and check pinion bearing preload as described in step 3.

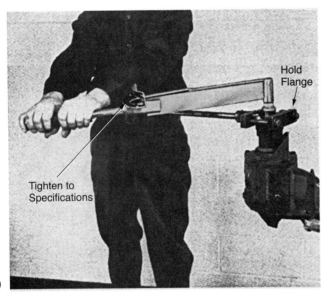

Hold Flange

Tighten to Specifications

(a)

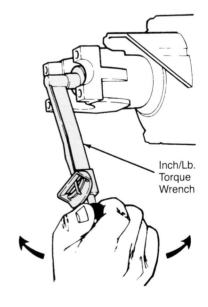

Inch/Lb. Torque Wrench

(b)

FIGURE 12-73   (a) The drive pinion nut should require a minimum amount of torque to crush the collapsible spacer. (b) From this point, the nut is tightened until the correct preload is reached. (Courtesy of Ford Motor Company)

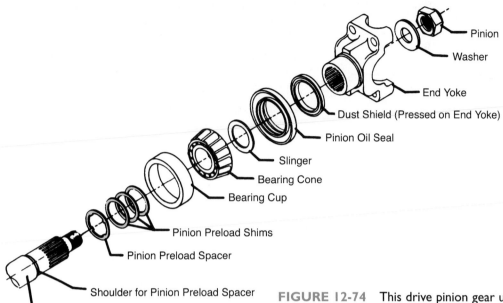

FIGURE 12-74 This drive pinion gear uses a solid spacer and a set of shims to adjust pinion bearing preload. (Courtesy of Dana Corporation)

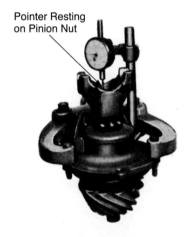

FIGURE 12-75 Drive pinion end play is measured using a dial indicator. (Courtesy of Ford Motor Company)

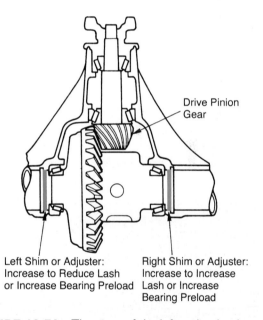

Left Shim or Adjuster: Increase to Reduce Lash or Increase Bearing Preload   Right Shim or Adjuster: Increase to Increase Lash or Increase Bearing Preload

FIGURE 12-76 The sizes of the left and right shims are used to adjust ring gear backlash and bearing preload. (Portions of materials contained herein have been reprinted with permission of General Motors Corporation, Service and Parts Operations, License Agreement #0310807)

12.6.9 Backlash and Carrier Side Bearing Preload Adjustments

These two adjustments are made at the same time as part of the installation of the ring gear and differential into the carrier. Backlash is the operating clearance between the ring and pinion gears. It is adjusted by moving the ring gear toward the pinion gear (toward the right side) to reduce the amount of backlash, or away from the pinion (toward the left side) to increase backlash (Figure 12-76). Incorrect backlash will cause the contact pattern on both sides of the gear tooth to be too close to the heel or too close to the toe.

Carrier bearing preload places enough pressure on the carrier bearings to hold the ring gear in proper mesh with the pinion gear without putting unnecessary load and drag on the bearings. The amount of preload is increased by moving the two carrier bearing cups toward each other, and it is reduced by moving them away from each other. These adjustments are made using the threaded adjusters or by changing the shims.

◀ SERVICE TIP ▶

After carrier bearing preload has been adjusted, the overall preload of the carrier should increase a noticeable amount from the pinion bearing preload.

During manufacture of a carrier, the bearings and gears are adjusted using a single, cast-iron production shim at each carrier bearing. The sizes of these two shims are carefully selected to provide the proper backlash and carrier bearing preload. The production shims are normally replaced with a fixed-size **service spacer** and a selective-size shim when the carrier is adjusted. This replacement provides the shim size range that is required to readjust the slightly worn bearings and gears.

To adjust backlash and carrier bearing preload using threaded adjusters:

1. Set the differential with bearing cups in place into the carrier.
2. Place the threaded adjusters in position and thread them next to the bearing cups (Figure 12-78).
3. Turn the adjusters to move the ring gear completely into mesh with the pinion gear so that there is no backlash and no clearance at the bearings.

◀ SERVICE TIP ▶

Be sure to align the index marks on the gear teeth of nonhunting and partial nonhunting gear sets (Figure 12-77).

◀ SERVICE TIP ▶

Rotate the differential to seat the bearings as the adjustments are made.

4. Install the bearing caps, making sure to align your index marks. Align the bearing caps by threading the bolts into their holes as you hold the caps upward; then drop the caps into position. (Figure 12-79).

◀ SERVICE TIP ▶

When the caps drop, they should sit right next to the carrier; if they don't, the adjuster is probably cross-threaded.

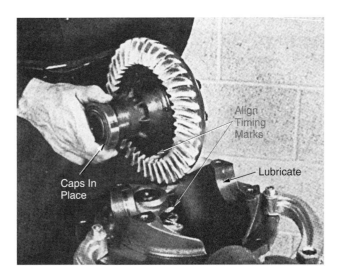

FIGURE 12-77 With threaded adjusters, the differential with bearing cups in place is set into the case. Make sure to align the timing marks on nonhunting gear sets. (Courtesy of Ford Motor Company)

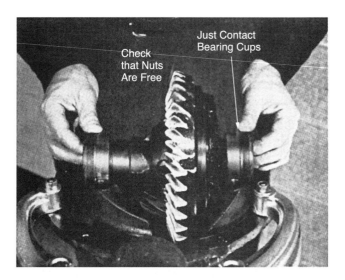

FIGURE 12-78 The threaded adjusters are set into place and rotated in their threads to just contact the cups; move the cups into contact with the bearings, and bring the ring gear into contact with the pinion gear. (Courtesy of Ford Motor Company)

FIGURE 12-79 Start the bearing cap bolts into their threads; the bearing caps should drop into alignment with the threaded adjusters. Be sure to align the bearing cap index marks. (Courtesy of Ford Motor Company)

5. Tighten the bearing cap bolts so they are snug, about 10 to 20 ft-lb (13 to 27 N-m) of torque. Rotate the differential to seat the bearings.

6. Turn the adjusters to push the differential case to the left so that there is a slight backlash and then back to the right until the backlash just disappears; this should be zero backlash with no load between the gears.

◄ SERVICE TIP ►

Note that an adjuster can only push inward on a bearing cup and that the other adjuster must be backed off to allow its bearing cup to move away. Thread the right adjuster inward so there is no clearance at the bearings with no preload.

7. Mount a dial indicator on the carrier. Position it so that the indicator stylus is on the tip of a ring gear tooth and parallel to the ring gear in one plane while being as close as possible to tangent with the ring gear in the other plane (Figure 12-80).

8. Hold the pinion gear stationary while you try to rotate the ring gear back and forth. There should be no backlash or indicator needle motion.

9. Keep the left-side adjuster stationary as you thread the right-side adjuster inward. Recheck backlash as you do this, and stop adjusting when the backlash is within specifications.

◄ SERVICE TIP ►

Because the right-side adjuster was stationary as the left-side adjuster was turned inward, carrier bearing preload is also being increased.

10. Confirm the preload adjustment by
    a. marking the right-side adjuster position and backing the adjuster off about one-half turn,
    b. slowly turning the right-side adjuster back inward as you watch the rollers of that bearing (Figure 12-81b); at some point, when the adjuster contacts the bearing cone, the rollers should begin to rotate,
    c. turning the adjuster inward at least one full adjuster lock hole but not more than two; stop at the point where the adjuster lock will line up.

    OR:
    a. back off the left adjuster one notch,
    b. set up a dial indicator with stylus touching the side of the left bearing race (Figure 12-81c),
    c. turn the right bearing adjuster inward until the dial indicator shows movement of the race,
    d. remove the dial indicator and turn the left adjuster back inward one notch,
    e. turn the right adjuster inward one to two notches further.

    OR: Set up a dial indicator between the carrier bearing caps to measure case spread (Figure 12-82). As the adjuster is turned inward to preload the bearings, the case will spread apart and the amount of spread can be read on the dial indicator. Some manufacturers provide a case spread specification.

    OR: Measure the increase in torque required to rotate the drive pinion shaft as described in Section 16.6.3.

11. Tighten the bearing cap bolts to the correct torque and rotate the differential to seat the bearings.

◄ SERVICE TIP ►

Test your carrier bearing preload adjustment by trying to rock the ring gear through its backlash using just the tip of your finger. You should not be able to move it unless you hook your fingertip on a gear tooth.

12. Recheck backlash at four or more points around the ring gear, making sure that the backlash is

(a)

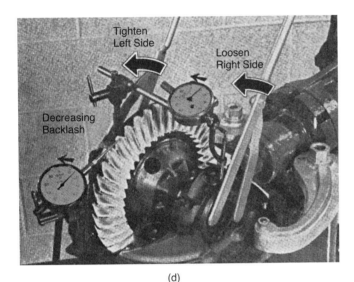

Tighten
Left Side

Loosen
Right Side

Decreasing
Backlash

(d)

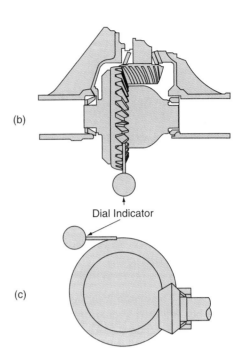

(b)

Dial Indicator

(c)

FIGURE 12-80 (a) A dial indicator is set up with the indicator stylus on a tooth of the ring gear; the ring gear is rocked back and forth against a stationary pinion gear to measure backlash. The indicator stylus should be parallel to the ring gear (b) and pointed straight toward the outer edge (c). (d) Backlash is adjusted by loosening one adjuster while tightening the other one. The second dial indicator in (d) is measuring case spread to adjust for the correct carrier bearing preload. (a and d are courtesy of Ford Motor Company)

within specifications and that there is not too much variation. Readjust the adjusters if backlash is incorrect; at this time, you should turn one adjuster out one notch and then the other one in one notch to maintain the bearing preload. If there is an excessive amount of backlash variation, check the ring gear runout as described in Section 12.6.2.

13. Install the adjuster locks, and tighten their bolts to the correct torque.

To adjust backlash and carrier bearing preload using shims:

1. Set the differential with the bearing cups and ring gear into the carrier.

2. Use a group of shims, spacers, and feeler gauge pairs on each side, between the bearing cups and the carrier, so that there will be zero backlash and preload at the ring and pinion gears as well as re-

moving any clearance at the bearings (Figure 12.83).

◄ **SERVICE TIP** ►

Note that gravity tries to move the bearing cups outward from the bearings, and this can cause false readings.

◄ **SERVICE TIP** ►

Insert two feeler gauges, one at each side of the shim, below the bearing cup boss so that the shims will not cock and cause a false reading.

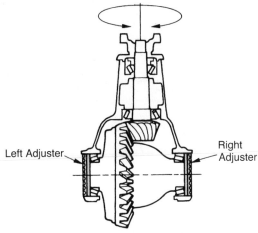

Left Adjuster

Right Adjuster

1. Measure Drive Pinion Bearing Preload.
2. Turn Carrier Bearing Adjusters Inward to Increase
   1. to New Value.
3. Recheck Backlash.

(a)

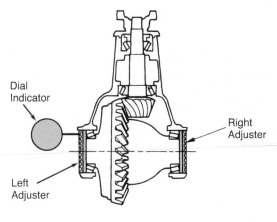

Dial Indicator

Right Adjuster

Left Adjuster

1. Set Up Dial Indicator on Left Bearing Race.
2. Turn Right Adjuster Inward Until Dial Indicator Shows Movement.
3. Turn Indicator 1 or 2 Notches Farther.
4. Recheck Backlash.

(c)

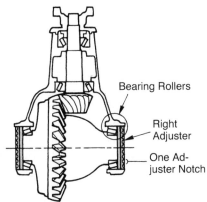

Bearing Rollers

Right Adjuster

One Adjuster Notch

1. Turn Right Adjuster Inward Until Bearing Roller Moves.
2. Turn Adjuster 1 to 2 Notches Further.
3. Recheck Backlash.

(b)

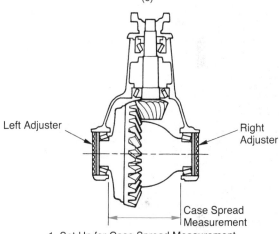

Left Adjuster

Right Adjuster

Case Spread Measurement

1. Set Up for Case Spread Measurement.
2. Turn Adjuster Inward to Increase Case Spread by Proper Value.
3. Recheck Backlash.

(d)

FIGURE 12-81 Four methods of adjusting carrier bearing preload. Note that once the bearings are preloaded properly, the adjusters must be turned in equal but opposite motions if backlash must be readjusted.

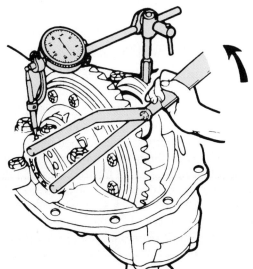

FIGURE 12-82 Turning the adjuster as shown will reduce the amount of case spread and preload on the carrier bearings and increase backlash slightly. The amount of case spread can be read on the dial indicator. (Courtesy of Ford Motor Company)

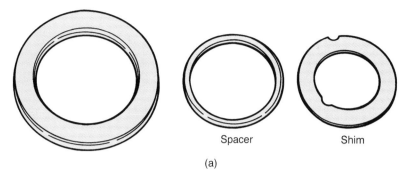

Spacer   Shim

(a)

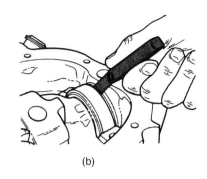

(b)

Equal Thickness

NK369A

(c)

FIGURE 12-83 (a) Cast-iron production shim (OEM use), service spacer, and shim used to adjust backlash and carrier bearing preload. (b) After measuring for the required shim, a shim and spacer will be inserted between the bearing cup and housing. (c) Two feeler gauges, inserted below the middle of the race will give more accurate measurements. (a and b: Portions of materials contained herein have been reprinted with permission of General Motors Corporation, Service and Parts Operations, License Agreement #0310807); c is courtesy of DaimlerChrysler Corporation)

◀ **SERVICE TIP** ▶

The feeler gauges should have a slight but definite drag. Be sure to rotate the differential during the final readings to ensure that the bearings are seated.

3. Add the total amount of spacer, shims, and feeler gauges used on each side, and record these shim pack numbers (Figure 12-84).

4. Adjust the shim pack numbers to obtain the correct amount of backlash by subtracting the specified amount from the left side and adding this amount to the right side.

◀ **SERVICE TIP** ▶

Moving 0.002 in. (0.05 mm) of shim size will change the amount of backlash about 0.001 in. (0.03 mm).

5. Adjust the shim packs to obtain the correct preload by adding the specified amount to each shim pack. This will be about 0.004 to 0.006 in. (0.1 to 0.15 mm) to each side.

6. Install the selected a shim. It will be necessary to use a soft hammer or a special tool to tap the second shim into place (Figure 12-85).

7. Install the bearing caps, and tighten the bolts to the correct torque.

8. Rotate the differential several turns to make sure that there is no binding and to seat the bearings. Measure the backlash as described in step 7 of the procedure for threaded adjusters. Measure the backlash at four or more locations around the ring gear to ensure that any variation is within the limits and that the backlash is within specifications. If there is too much or too little backlash, move some of the shim pack from one side to the other to correct it.

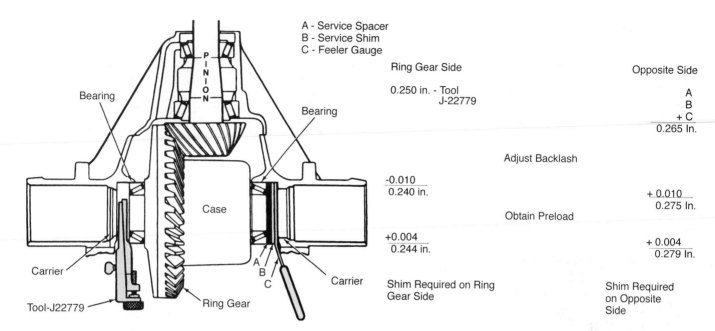

A - Service Spacer
B - Service Shim
C - Feeler Gauge

Ring Gear Side	Opposite Side
0.250 in. - Tool J-22779	A B + C 0.265 In.
Adjust Backlash	
-0.010 0.240 in.	+ 0.010 0.275 In.
Obtain Preload	
+0.004 0.244 in.	+ 0.004 0.279 In.
Shim Required on Ring Gear Side	Shim Required on Opposite Side

Bearing

PINION

Bearing

Case

Carrier

Carrier

Tool-J22779

Ring Gear

FIGURE 12-84 Procedure used to measure and determine the correct shims. Note that in this example, a special tool (J-22779) is used to measure the gap on the left side, while a service spacer, shim, and feeler gauge are used on the right side. (Portions of materials contained herein have been reprinted with permission of General Motors Corporation, Service and Parts Operations, License Agreement #0310807)

◀ **SERVICE TIP** ▶

An alternative method of adjusting backlash and carrier bearing preload is to start with too small a shim at the left side and add enough shims to obtain zero bearing clearance and preload. Now, measure the backlash and adjust the shim packs to correct the amount of backlash. Next, increase the size of both shim packs to adjust the bearing preload (Figure 12-86).

12.6.10   Tooth Contact Pattern Check

Most technicians use a contact pattern as a quality control check to ensure that the gear set is adjusted correctly. It may take a few minutes but can save much more time and frustration by preventing a comeback. A contact pattern is also used during a preteardown as a diagnostic check.

Rolling a contact pattern is done by coating the ring gear with a marking compound and then turning the pinion gear so that its contact rubs the marking compound off the ring gear. At one time, white lead was

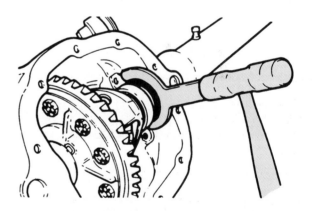

FIGURE 12-85 The last shim should be rather tight to install. It should be driven into place using either a soft hammer or special tool. (Portions of materials contained herein have been reprinted with permission of General Motors Corporation, Service and Parts Operations, License Agreement #0310807)

used as the marking compound, but it is no longer available. Marking compound is available from some gear or vehicle manufacturers (GM gear marking compound, part number 1052351).

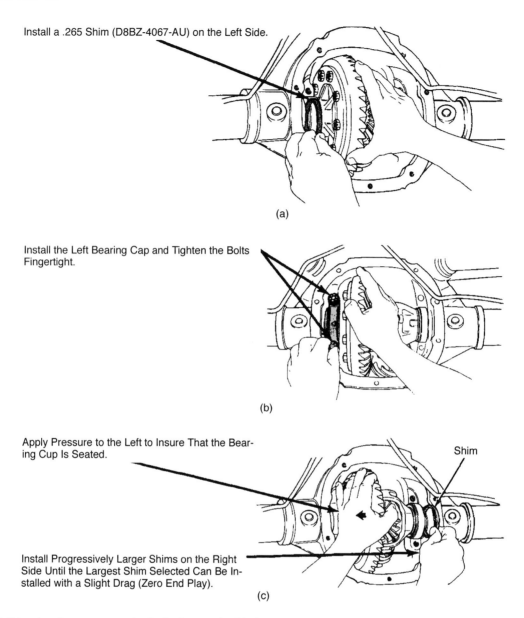

Install a .265 Shim (D8BZ-4067-AU) on the Left Side.

(a)

Install the Left Bearing Cap and Tighten the Bolts Fingertight.

(b)

Apply Pressure to the Left to Insure That the Bearing Cup Is Seated.

Shim

Install Progressively Larger Shims on the Right Side Until the Largest Shim Selected Can Be Installed with a Slight Drag (Zero End Play).

(c)

FIGURE 12-86   An alternative method of adjusting backlash and carrier bearing preload is to install a shim on the left side (a), install the left side cap and snugly tighten the bolts (b). Install a shim that is large enough to provide a slight drag on the right side (c). Install the right cap and tighten the bolts (d). Rotate the ring gear to seat the bearings (e) and measure backlash (f), adjust the shims as necessary to correct backlash (g), and adjust shim sizes to get the proper bearing preload (h). (Courtesy of Ford Motor Company)

◀ **SERVICE TIP** ▶

A very good substitute is artist's oil paint in either white or yellow. Foot powder in an aerosol form can also be used; it is fast but tends to cake if you have to make an adjustment and roll a second pattern.

◀ **SERVICE TIP** ▶

It is best to roll a pattern in one revolution around the ring gear in each direction, leaving a pattern on both the drive and coast sides of the tooth. Going over a tooth twice tends to smear the pattern and average out the two contacts, possibly hiding a problem. Some sources use a drive-side-only pattern, but

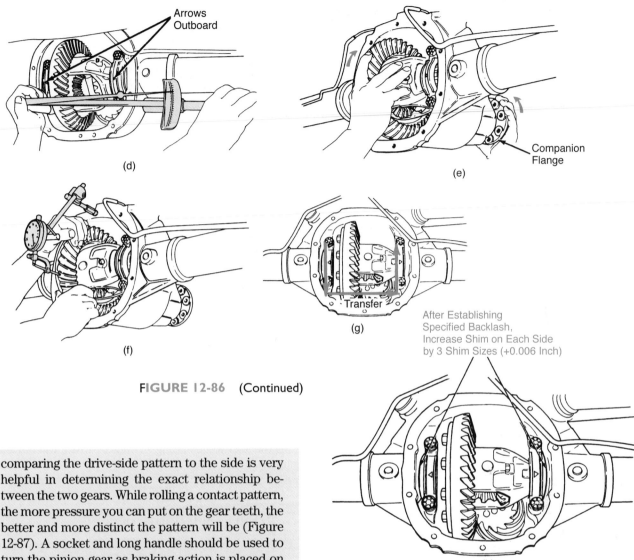

FIGURE 12-86 (Continued)

comparing the drive-side pattern to the side is very helpful in determining the exact relationship between the two gears. While rolling a contact pattern, the more pressure you can put on the gear teeth, the better and more distinct the pattern will be (Figure 12-87). A socket and long handle should be used to turn the pinion gear as braking action is placed on the ring gear by a bar, block of wood, wrench on a ring gear bolt, or parking brake (Figure 12-88).

The pattern should appear as an elongated oval, about half the length of the gear tooth. The center of the oval should be slightly toward the toe of the tooth and midway up the tooth (Figure 12-89). Under load, the tooth deflects more at the toe, and this will move the contact pressure more toward the heel. The pattern should not have a sharp or straight edge at either the top or bottom. Also, it should be located in the same position on both sides of the tooth.

Gear adjustments will affect the pattern in the following manner:

- Decreasing the backlash moves the ring gear closer to the pinion and will move both the drive-side and coast-side patterns lower and toward the toe.

- Increasing the backlash moves the ring gear away from the pinion and will move both the drive-side and coast-side patterns higher and toward the heel.

- Changing the depth shim to move the pinion deeper, or closer to the ring gear, will move the drive-side pattern toward the toe and the coast-side pattern toward the heel (with the same backlash).

- Moving the pinion shallower, or away from the ring gear, will move the drive-side pattern toward the heel and the coast-side pattern toward the toe (with the same backlash).

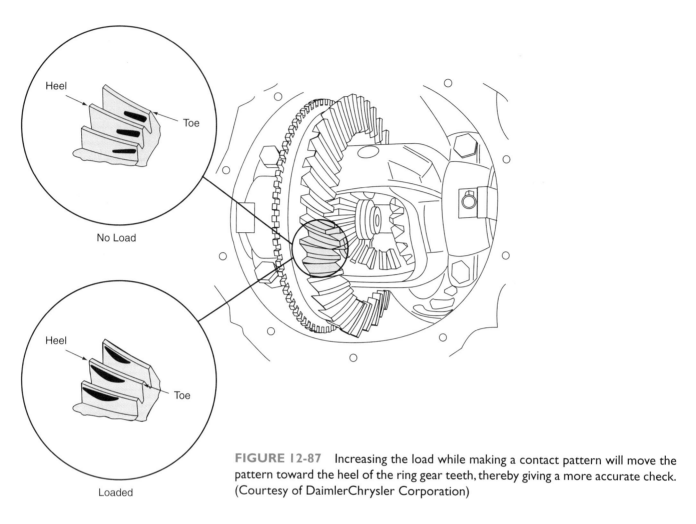

FIGURE 12-87 Increasing the load while making a contact pattern will move the pattern toward the heel of the ring gear teeth, thereby giving a more accurate check. (Courtesy of DaimlerChrysler Corporation)

FIGURE 12-88 A gear contact pattern is the final check for a gear adjustment. The more pressure you apply between the ring and pinion gears, the sharper the contact pattern will be. Here a box wrench is on one of the ring gear bolts to load it while the pinion gear is being turned with a socket and ratchet handle.

To roll a contact pattern:

1. Apply a very thin film of marking compound on both sides of the ring gear teeth (Figure 12-90). If there is a possible problem, coat all of the teeth; if you are not concerned with ring or pinion gear runout, coat a 6- to 10-tooth section.

2. Either use a wrench to turn the pinion gear as you brake the ring gear, or vice versa. Rotate the pinion gear through the marking compound once in each direction.

3. Check the pattern on both sides of the ring gear teeth and compare the pattern to those shown in Figure 12-91.

◀ **SERVICE TIP** ▶

If you coated the entire ring gear, check for a pattern variation. One steady change in pattern indicates ring gear runout; two or more changes in pattern indicate pinion gear runout (Figure 12-92).

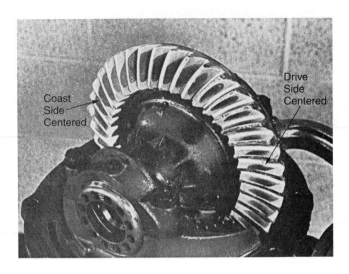

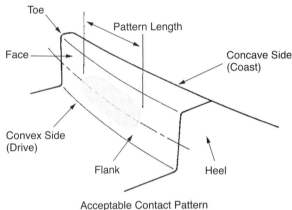

Acceptable Contact Pattern

FIGURE 12-89 The ideal contact pattern will be about one-half the length of the gear tooth and slightly off-center toward the toe on both the drive and coast sides of the tooth. (Courtesy of Ford Motor Company)

FIGURE 12-90 The marking compound (artist's oil paint) should be applied in a very thin coating over the entire gear tooth.

4. If the pattern shows good contact, complete reassembly of the axle. If the pattern is incorrect, adjust the ring or pinion as necessary and roll another pattern to check your adjustment.

12.6.11 Limited Slip Differential Service

In most cases, this operation involves disassembly and reassembly of the differential with a replacement of worn parts. It can also include adjusting the clearance or preload of the clutch packs and a bench check for rotating torque. Cone clutch limited slip differentials use a split case, which makes disassembly easy; plate clutch units are serviced through the case window (Figure 12-93). This means that you have to rotate the differential gears to the

FIGURE 12-91 An incorrect pattern indicates what adjustment is needed. (Courtesy of Dana Corporation)

Pattern Interpretation
(Ring Gear)

Drive Side   Coast Side
Heel   Toe   Toe   Heel

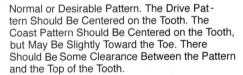
Normal or Desirable Pattern. The Drive Pattern Should Be Centered on the Tooth. The Coast Pattern Should Be Centered on the Tooth, but May Be Slightly Toward the Toe. There Should Be Some Clearance Between the Pattern and the Top of the Tooth.

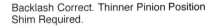
Backlash Correct. Thinner Pinion Position Shim Required.

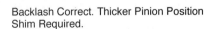
Backlash Correct. Thicker Pinion Position Shim Required.

Pinion Position Shim Correct. Decrease Backlash.

Pinion Position Shim Correct. Increase Backlash.

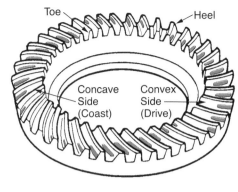

FIGURE 12-92 A pattern that changes as it goes around the ring gear is caused by ring gear runout (one pattern change) or pinion gear runout (several pattern changes).

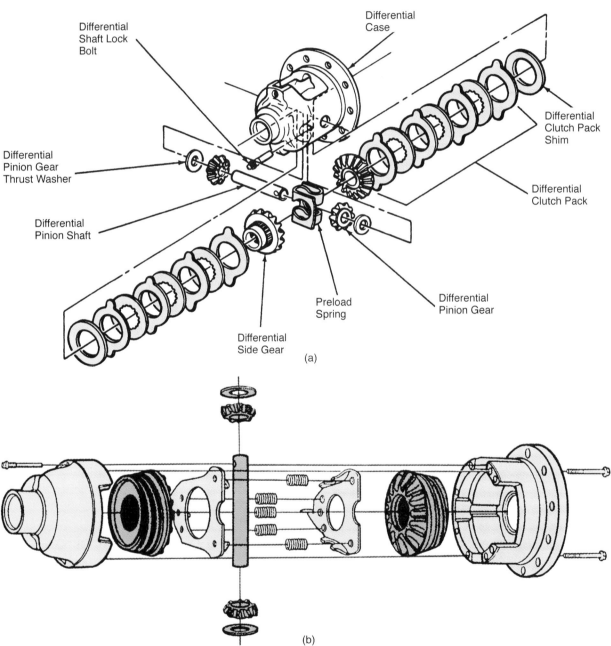

FIGURE 12-93 Exploded views of plate clutch (a) and cone clutch (b) and limited slip differentials. (a is courtesy of Ford Motor Company; b: Portions of materials contained herein have been reprinted wih permission of General Motors Corporation, Service and Parts Operations, License Agreement #0310807)

window or from the window to their proper position against the resistance of the clutch packs' preload.

◄ SERVICE TIP ►

If the clutch plates are to be reused, they should be replaced in their original positions. Restacking the plates in different positions will result in increased wear and diminished performance.

To disassemble a plate clutch limited slip differential:

1. Carefully remove the S-shaped preload spring by tapping it through the window using a punch and hammer, or pulling it out with pliers (Figure 12-94).
2. Roll the differential pinions around to the case windows, and remove them.

◄ SERVICE TIP ►

In some units, there is enough preload on the clutch plates to require the use of a gear rotator (Figure 12-95).

3. Remove the side gear and clutch packs as a group, and tag or mark them so that they can be reassembled on the same side of the differential.
4. Clean the parts by wiping the friction surfaces with a cloth; do not use solvent on them. The differential case and pinion gears can be washed in solvent.
5. Inspect the differential parts as described in Section 8.5.9. The clutch plates or cones should be checked for scores, grooves, or galling.

Reassembly of most limited slip differentials is a reverse of the disassembly procedure. Be sure to lubricate all of the friction surfaces with the recommended gear oil for that differential. Some differentials use a shim to set the clutch pack for the correct preload or clearance; this adds a step in the reassembly procedure for determining the pack height and shim size (Figure 12-96).

◄ SERVICE TIP ►

The clutch pack surfaces must be thoroughly lubricated with the proper lubricant during assembly (Figure 12-97). One manufacturer recommends soaking them in the lubricant for 20 minutes.

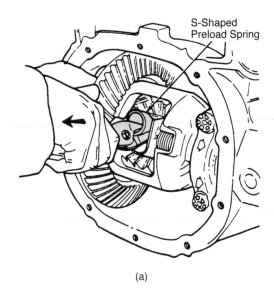

(a)

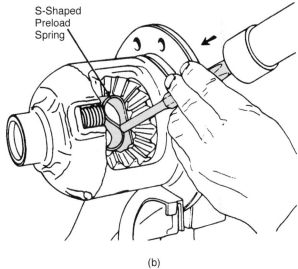

(b)

FIGURE 12-94 The preload spring on this differential can be removed using a pair of pliers (a) or a soft drift punch (b). (Courtesy of Ford Motor Company)

Tools are available to bench check a limited slip differential to make sure that there is enough holding power at the clutches (Figure 12-98).

◄ SERVICE TIP ►

A pair of old axle shafts may also be used to make a bench check of limited slip clutch holding power.

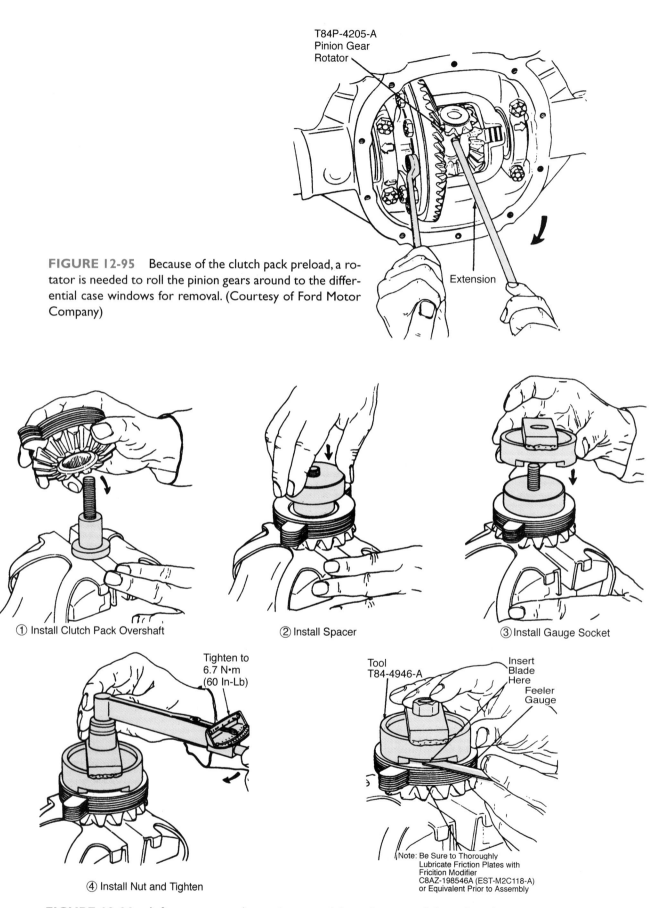

T84P-4205-A
Pinion Gear
Rotator

Extension

FIGURE 12-95 Because of the clutch pack preload, a rotator is needed to roll the pinion gears around to the differential case windows for removal. (Courtesy of Ford Motor Company)

① Install Clutch Pack Overshaft

② Install Spacer

③ Install Gauge Socket

Tighten to
6.7 N•m
(60 In-Lb)

④ Install Nut and Tighten

Tool
T84-4946-A

Insert
Blade
Here

Feeler
Gauge

Note: Be Sure to Thoroughly
Lubricate Friction Plates with
Fricition Modifier
C8AZ-198546A (EST-M2C118-A)
or Equivalent Prior to Assembly

FIGURE 12-96 A five-step procedure using a special gauging set is followed to determine the pack height and the shim size needed to obtain the correct pack preload. (Courtesy of Ford Motor Company)

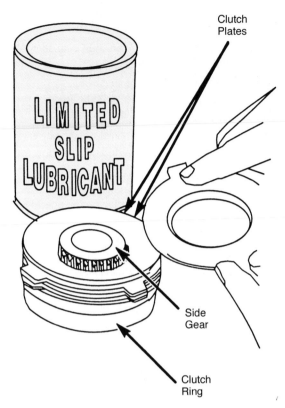

Clutch
Plates

Side
Gear

Clutch
Ring

FIGURE 12-97   The clutch plates should be lubricated, using the proper lubricant for that differential, as they are assembled. (Courtesy of DaimlerChrysler Corporation)

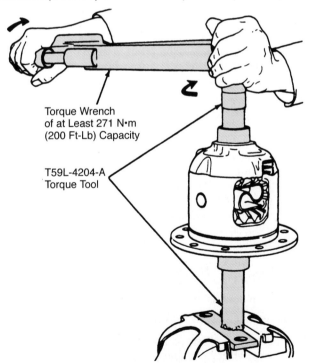

Torque Wrench
of at Least 271 N•m
(200 Ft-Lb) Capacity

T59L-4204-A
Torque Tool

FIGURE 12-98   Torque tools allow the breakaway torque of this limited slip differential to be measured before the differential is installed into the carrier. (Courtesy of Ford Motor Company)

◄ SERVICE TIP ►

In some differentials, the inner hub of the clutch pack is separate from the axle gear. An axle should be slid through them to keep the two sets of splines aligned as the assembly is tightened.

◄ PROBLEM SOLVING ►

Imagine that you are working in a general automotive repair shop and these problems are brought to you.

Case 1

You've just finished assembling the carrier and are adjusting backlash. The specification is 0.004 to 0.008 in. You adjusted the backlash to 0.006 in., but when you recheck it, you measure 0.004 in. at one tooth and 0.010 in. at another. Is this acceptable? If not, what is probably wrong? What should you do next?

Case 2

You've assembled the Ford 9-in. axle and completed the adjustments. When you run a tooth contact pattern, the contact shows high on the heel of the drive side and on the toe of the coast side with almost a straight line at the outer edges. What does this mean? What should you do to correct it?

Case 3

You've just assembled a Dana 60 rear axle (Salisbury style) and you encounter the same problem as in Case 2. Do you need to make the same correction? If so, what do you need to do to make it?

REVIEW QUESTIONS

The following questions are provided to help you study as you read the chapter.

1. The oil level in a drive axle is usually even with the _____ of the fill opening.

2. Drive axle diagnosis starts with a _____ test and a _____ level check.

3. The four driving conditions used to diagnose a drive axle problem are
   a._____
   b._____
   c._____
   d._____

4. _____ is the driving condition when the throttle is closed and the vehicle is decelerating.

5. To remove a _____ retained axle, the differential pinion shaft must be removed.

6. A hole in the axle _____ allows for access to the bolts that secue the axle retainer.

7. _____ axles are removed by unbolting the axle flange bolts and sliding the axle out of the housing.

8. After the axle is removed, the axle seal is easily removed with a _____ _____ and an adapter.

9. Before pressing a bearing off an axle, the _____ _____ must be removed.

10. Before removing the carrier bearing caps, they should be _____ to identify the side and direction for reinstallation.

11. Drive pinion _____ is most often adjusted by a _____ behind the rear drive pinion bearing.

12. Integral carriers use shims to adjust carrier bearing preload and backlash. Adding a shim to the ring gear side of the carrier and removing an identical-size shim from the other side will _____ backlash.

13. Carrier bearing preload is adjusted in an integral carrier by adding a _____ shim to each side of the carrier.

14. The ideal ring and pinion contact pattern will be about _____ _____ the length of the gear tooth and slightly off center toward the toe.

15. The clutch plates of a limited slip differential should be throughly _____ as the differential is assembled.

CHAPTER QUIZ

The following questions will help you check the facts you have learned. Select the answer that completes each statement correctly.

1. While discussing drive axle gear oil checks, Student A says that the oil level should be even with the bottom of the filler hole in all drive axles. Student B says that a tag is mounted at the filler hole of axles that require special lubricant. Who is correct?
   a. Student A
   b. Student B
   c. Both Student A and Student B
   d. Neither Student A nor Student B

2. A drive axle makes a howling sound during drive conditions. Student A says this is probably caused by a faulty ring and pinion gear adjustment. Student B says it could be caused by a bad axle bearing. Who is correct?
   a. Student A
   b. Student B
   c. Both Student A and Student B
   d. Neither Student A nor Student B

3. The vehicle owner's complaint is a clunking noise when the transmission is shifted from reverse to drive. This is probably caused by A. excessive ring gear backlash B. wear in the differential. Which is correct?
   a. A only
   b. B only
   c. Both A and B
   d. Neither A nor B

4. A vehicle makes a chattering noise while turning corners, which is most noticeable after driving straight for a few miles. Student A says that this is a fairly common problem with limited slip differentials and that it might be cured by changing the gear oil. Student B says that this type of noise is caused by a chipped differential pinion gear or worn differential pinion shaft. Who is correct?
   a. Student A
   b. Student B
   c. Both Student A and Student B
   d. Neither Student A nor Student B

5. Student A says that an axle shaft is held in the housing by a C-clip, which keeps the shaft from coming out of the differential side gear. Student B says that the bolts holding

the brake backing plate to the axle housing also hold some axles in place. Who is correct?

a. Student A

b. Student B

c. Both Student A and Student B

d. Neither Student A nor Student B

6. Student A says that excessive radial play of the axle at the outer end can be caused by a worn axle. Student B says that a gear oil leak onto the brakes can be caused by a bad seal or a gear oil level that is too high. Who is correct?

a. Student A

b. Student B

c. Both Student A and Student B

d. Neither Student A nor Student B

7. Student A says that some axle bearings can explode as they are being pressed from the shaft. Student B says that the axle bearing used on most C-clip axles comes without an inner race. Who is correct?

a. Student A

b. Student B

c. Both Student A and Student B

d. Neither Student A nor Student B

8. Student A says that a carrier with faulty drive pinion bearings should be removed from the vehicle and overhauled at the repair bench. Student B says that with integral carrier axles, this can be done with the carrier in the vehicle. Who is correct?

a. Student A

b. Student B

c. Both Student A and Student B

d. Neither Student A nor Student B

9. Student A says that ring gear runout can be caused by sloppy installation of the ring gear onto the differential case. Student B says that ring gear runout can cause the backlash to be okay at one portion of the ring gear and not okay at another. Who is correct?

a. Student A

b. Student B

c. Both Student A and Student B

d. Neither Student A nor Student B

10. As a carrier is disassembled, it should be checked for

a. worn or damaged ring and pinion gears.

b. rough bearings.

c. excessive lash in the differential.

d. all of these.

11. A thicker drive pinion shim will move the pinion gear A. inward and deeper into the ring gear, B. outward and less deep into the ring gear. Which is correct?

a. A only

b. B only

c. Both A and B

d. Neither A nor B

12. Student A says that if you install a thicker shim at the ring gear side carrier bearing, the backlash will decrease. Student B says that this will increase carrier bearing preload. Who is correct?

a. Student A

b. Student B

c. Both Student A and Student B

d. Neither Student A nor Student B

13. Student A says that part of the tightening force you put on the pinion nut is making the collapsible spacer shorter. Student B says that a new nut and collapsible spacer should be used when you install a pinion gear. Who is correct?

a. Student A

b. Student B

c. Both Student A and Student B

d. Neither Student A nor Student B

14. Student A says that a contact pattern close to the heel on both the drive and coast sides of the gear tooth is caused by improper pinion depth. Student B says that contact toward the heel on the drive side and toward the toe on the coast side is caused by excessive backlash. Who is correct?

a. Student A

b. Student B

c. Both Student A and Student B

d. Neither Student A nor Student B

15. Student A says that carrier bearing preload is adjusted using a dial indicator and that backlash is adjusted by carefully watching the gear movement. Student B says that backlash that is only 0.001 in. tight at one location is okay if it is within specifications everywhere else. Who is correct?

a. Student A

b. Student B

c. Both Student A and Student B

d. Neither Student A nor Student B

Chapter 13

FOUR-WHEEL DRIVE THEORY

LEARNING OBJECTIVES

After completing this chapter, you should be able to:

1. Understand the requirements and limits for 4WD and AWD.
2. Identify the parts of a transfer case and know the purpose for each.
3. Trace the power flow through the major types of transfer cases for each gear range.
4. Identify the parts of a front drive axle assembly and know the purpose for each.
5. Identify the different types of hubs used on front drive axles.

TERMS TO LEARN

all-wheel-drive (AWD)	interaxle differential
automatic hub	locking hub
bevel gear	mechanical hub
center differential	open design
closed knuckle	part-time 4WD
front drive axle	planetary gear
full-time 4WD	transfer case
integrated wheel end dis-	twin-traction axle
connect	viscous coupling

13.1   INTRODUCTION

Four-wheel drive (4WD) for cars, pickups, and light trucks has steadily evolved from the somewhat crude but rugged Jeep of World War II to some very sophisticated sport coupes and sport utility vehicles of today. 4WD can be based on a vehicle with front engine–RWD, front engine–FWD, or rear engine–RWD.

A 4WD vehicle needs a drive axle at both the front and rear ends; of course, the front drive axle must be steerable. One or both of these axles can be a solid axle design, as described in Chapter 11, or one or both axles can be of an independent suspension design. Solid axles are more rugged and less expensive, but the independent suspension designs have better ride and handling qualities (Figure 13-1).

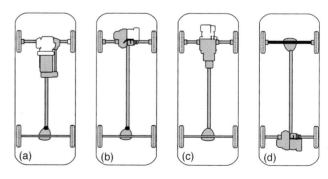

FIGURE 13-1   4WD can be based on a front engine, RWD vehicle (a), a front engine FWD vehicle with either a transverse (b) or lengthwise (c) engine, or a rear engine vehicle (d).

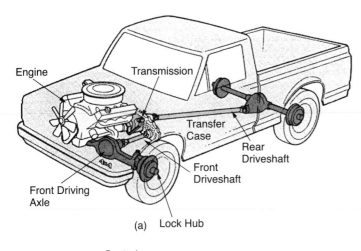

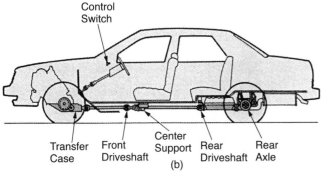

FIGURE 13-2 (a) The 4WD pickup uses a transfer case to split and engage the power flow to the front drive axle when the driver wants 4WD. (b) The AWD car uses a transfer case to split the power flow between the front differential in the transaxle and the rear drive axle. (Courtesy of Ford Motor Company)

In this chapter we concentrate on the 4WD utility vehicle, which is the most common 4WD vehicle. Most of these vehicles are based on a front engine–RWD platform, with the major additions to the drivetrain being a **transfer case** and a **front drive axle** (Figure 13-2).

13.2 TRANSFER CASES

The transfer case is the gear assembly used to control the power flow to the front axle and somewhat to the rear axle. In some FWD-based vehicles, the transfer gears are built into the transaxle. In short-wheelbase vehicles, the transfer case is attached directly to the transmission; and in many instances, the transmission

extension and mainshaft are modified so that the transfer case and transmission form a more compact package (Figure 13-3). In some vehicles where there is ample space, the transfer case is a separate unit, and a U-joint or short driveshaft is used to couple it with the transmission.

Both integral and separate transfer cases have one input shaft and two output shafts, one to each drive axle. Power is sent to the rear driveshaft almost all of the time. Some transfer cases include a neutral. An internal dog clutch or synchronizer assembly is used to control the power flow to the front driveshaft. Many 4WDs use a floor-mounted shift lever to engage or disengage this dog clutch. Normally, this is done with the vehicle stopped. However, some modern transfer cases use electronic controls for this shift, which can be made with the vehicle in motion—that is "on the fly." These cases have a magnetic clutch that synchronizes the speeds of the clutch parts and an electric shift control motor that moves the clutch into engagement (Figure 13-4).

Many transfer cases include a gear mechanism to provide a lower range, a reduction of around 2:1. Control of low range is by either the same lever that controls the 2WD–4WD shift, a separate lever, an electronic control using the electric shift control motor, or vacuum controls and motors. Low range is limited to 4WD operation because it doubles the torque to the drive axles, and this is often more than one axle is designed to handle. There are essentially two styles of transfer cases: those that use gears to drive the front output shaft and those that use a chain and sprockets.

There are two major types of 4WD vehicles and transfer cases, and these are part-time and full-time styles. **Full-time 4WD** is also called all-wheel-drive (AWD) or any-time 4WD. Traditional, pickup, and Jeep-based vehicles use part-time 4WD that is designed to be used off-road. **Part-time 4WD** has a positive, mechanical connection between the front and rear driveshafts when shifted into 4WD. 4WD is used only where there is poor traction because the front or rear tires must be able to slip on the road surface while cornering. Gear train bind up will occur if turns are made on pavement. Modern AWD vehicles include a center differential that allows the front and rear driveshafts to be driven at different speeds to prevent drivetrain binding. AWD transfer cases that deliver power to both driveshafts all of the time are called *mechanically active*. A few modern AWD vehicles are passenger car-based, and AWD is used to enhance driving on wet or icy roads.

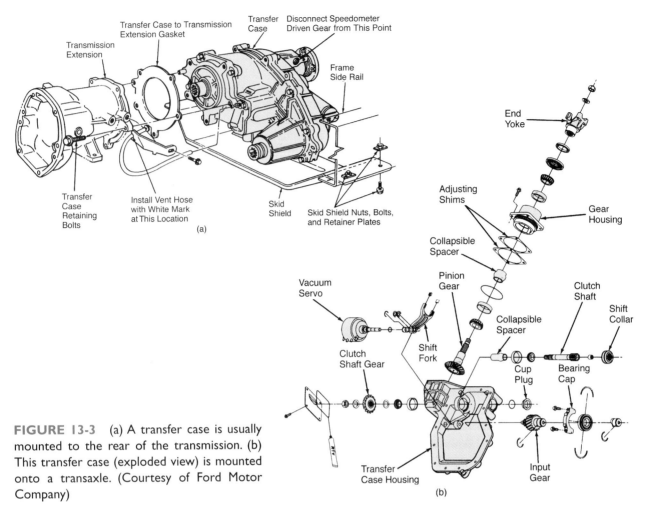

FIGURE 13-3 (a) A transfer case is usually mounted to the rear of the transmission. (b) This transfer case (exploded view) is mounted onto a transaxle. (Courtesy of Ford Motor Company)

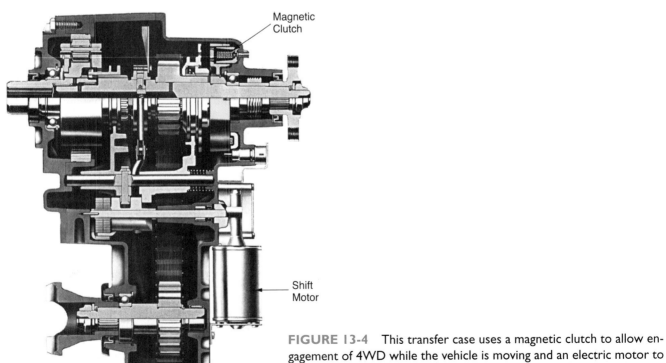

FIGURE 13-4 This transfer case uses a magnetic clutch to allow engagement of 4WD while the vehicle is moving and an electric motor to complete the 2WD–4WD shift and to make the shift into low range. (Courtesy of BWD Automotive Group)

13.2.1 AWD Transfer Cases

Full-time 4WD or **all-wheel drive (AWD)** transfer cases maintain constant power to both the front and rear axles and include a **center differential,** or **interaxle differential,** between the front and rear output shafts (Figure 13-5). Remember that as a vehicle turns a corner, the outside wheels go faster than the inside ones, and the front wheels go faster than the rear wheels because of the different turning radius of each wheel (Figure 13-6). The differential used with AWD is often a **bevel gear** type like that used in transaxles and rear drive axles. It can also be a **planetary gear** type or a **viscous coupling** type (Figure 13-7). Some planetary differentials are designed to split torque unevenly; one, for example, splits torque so that 35% goes to the front axle and the remaining 65% goes to the rear axle.

Most center differentials, however, split torque equally. It is possible, though, to lift one wheel and not get enough torque to the other three wheels to move the vehicle (Figure 13-8). Thus, a center differential includes a lockout. With the lockout, at least both driveshafts and one wheel at each end will be driven.

Some modern AWD vehicles use *smart transfer cases* that automatically lock up or drive both or either output shaft as needed for the driving conditions. Some act through electronic sensors, noting tire slippage and applying an internal clutch using an electric motor. Others use a hydraulically applied internal clutch much like the Quadra-Trac II (Hydra-Lok) limited slip differential (Figure 13-9).

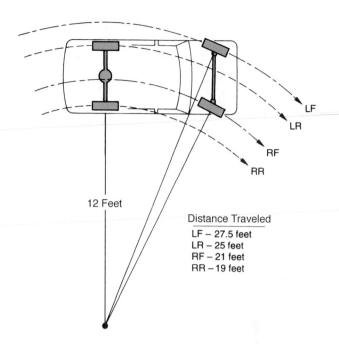

FIGURE 13-6 If a vehicle makes a right-angle turn with an inside rear wheel radius of 12 ft, the four tires will travel the distances indicated in the same amount of time; the outside front tire will have to go about 70% faster than the inside rear tire.

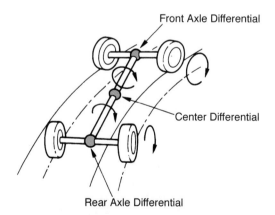

FIGURE 13-5 An AWD car has a center differential to split the torque between the front and rear axles, allowing the axles to travel at different speeds. The differentials in the front and rear axles split torque between each pair of wheels and allow the wheels to travel at different speeds.

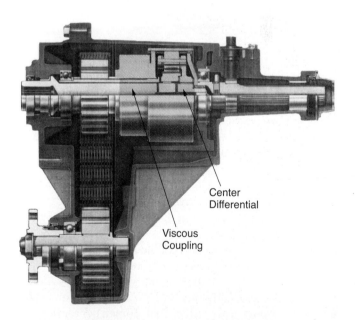

FIGURE 13-7 Single-speed AWD transfer case that includes a center, planetary gear type of differential with a viscous coupling to control the differential. This differential will split the torque so that 65% goes to the rear axle and 35% to the front. (Courtesy of BWD Automotive Corporation)

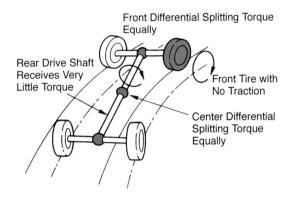

FIGURE 13-8 If the center and front differential split torque equally, an AWD vehicle can become stuck when one wheel loses traction, as shown here.

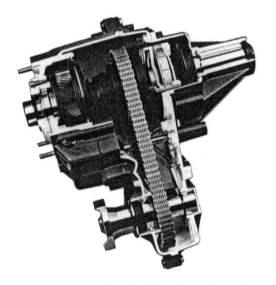

FIGURE 13-9 The Quadra-Trac II on-demand transfer case includes a gerotor oil pump that is driven when the front and rear driveshafts operate at different speeds. If there is too much speed differential, the fluid pressure can apply the internal clutch to transfer torque to each one.

AWD vehicles must have four equal-diameter tires. Unequal diameters produce different axle speeds, and this will cause excessive wear at the drive axle or center differential. A viscous coupling at the center differential will not last if it has to operate constantly.

At this time, some AWD vehicles produced by Audi, Land Rover, Lexus, Toyota, and VW use a Torsen® differential for the center differential. Torsen center differentials are designed with a torque bias ratio of 2.5:1 to 3.5:1. This differential type allows the two driveshafts to operate at different speeds without spin-out problems at the front or rear and smooth turning action (Figure 13-10). The Torsen differential is mechanically active.

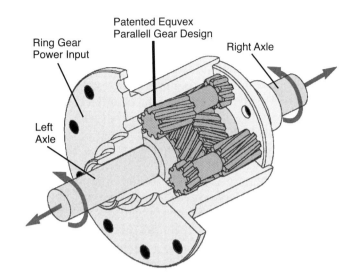

FIGURE 13-10 A cutaway view of a Torsen T-2 differential from a drive axle. A transfer case version will have a different housing. Note that the Iquvex gear train floats in the outer housing. (Courtesy of Zexel Torsen, Inc.)

There are essentially two styles of transfer cases: those that use gears to drive the front output shaft and those that use a chain.

◀ **SERVICE TIP** ▶

It is normally recommended to use the manufacturer's recommendation for the fluid type and amount. If a unit is noisy or experiences hard shifting, a fluid replacement might cure the problem. A lubrication guide showing the recommendation of a leading rebuilder of manual transmissions and transfer cases is given in Appendix B.

13.2.2 Gear-Drive Transfer Case

The gear-drive transfer case uses a set of six gears on three shafts with two sliding shift assemblies (Figure 13-11). Three of the gears transfer power to the front output for 4WD, and all but one of the gears are used in 4L (4WD–low range). Most early transfer cases were of this design.

There are three ways for power to flow through this transfer case plus neutral (Figure 13-12). In 2H (2WD–high range), the sliding dog clutch (range clutch) on the upper shaft couples the input shaft to the rear output shaft so that power can pass straight

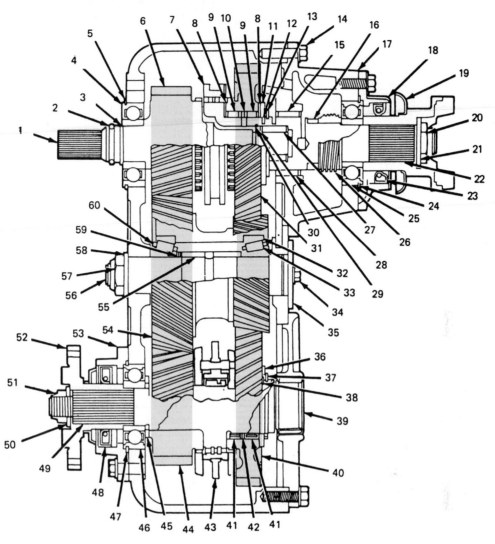

1.	Input Shaft	18.	Rear Bearing	32.	Idler Gear Shaft Bearing
2.	"O" Ring		Retainer		Cup
3.	Snap Ring	19.	Rear Yoke Assembly	33.	Idler Shaft Bearing
4.	Bearing	20.	Locknut		Cone
5.	Snap Ring	21.	Washer	34.	Idler Shaft Cover
6.	Input Shaft Gear	22.	Rear Output Shaft		Bolts and
7.	Sliding Clutch	23.	Bearing Retainer		Lockwasher
8.	Tanged Bronze Thrust		Seal	35.	Idler Shaft Gear
	Washer	24.	Snap Ring		Cover and Gasket
9.	Roller Bearings	25.	Bearing	36.	Thrust Washer
10.	Spacer	26.	Speedometer Gear	37.	Snap Ring
11.	Thrust Washer	27.	Pilot Bearings	38.	Thrust Washer Pin
12.	Thrust Washer Pin	28.	Rear Output Shaft	39.	Rear Bearing
13.	Snap Ring		Front Bearing		Retainer and Output
14.	Bolt and Lockwasher	29.	Washer		Shaft Cover
15.	Needle Bearings	30.	Bearing Retainer	40.	Front Wheel Drive
16.	Spacer	31.	Rear Wheel Drive		Low Gear
17.	Rear Output Shaft		Low Gear	41.	Roller Bearings
	Housing				

42.	Spacer
43.	Synchronizer
44.	Front Wheel Hi-Gear
45.	Spacer
46.	Bearing
47.	Snap Ring
48.	Seal
49.	Front Output Shaft
50.	Washer
51.	Locknut
52.	Output Yoke
53.	Bearing Retainer
54.	Idler Gear
55.	Idler Gear Spacer
56.	Idler Shaft
57.	Locknut
58.	Washer
59.	Bearing Cone
60.	Bearing Cup

FIGURE 13-11 A gear-drive transfer case uses a gear arrangement as shown here. (Portions of materials contained herein have been reprinted with permission of General Motors Corporation, Service and Parts Operations, License Agreement #0310807)

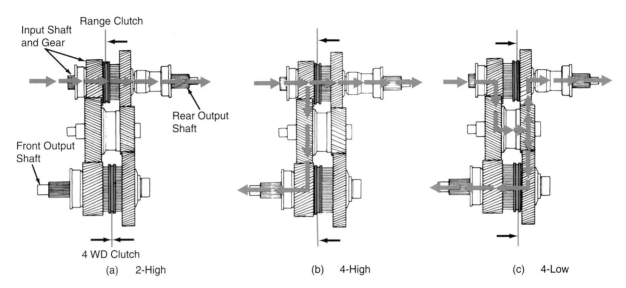

FIGURE 13-12   Power flow through a gear-drive transfer case in 2H (a), 4H (b), and 4L (c). Note the positions of the upper and lower shift collars (range and 4WD clutches). (Courtesy of Ford Motor Company)

through at a 1:1 ratio to the rear wheels. In 4H, the upper clutch is still engaged as it was in 2H, and the lower sliding dog clutch is moved to couple the high gear on the lower shaft with the lower, or front, output shaft. Now power passes through the front gears of the gear train to drive the front wheels at a 1:1 ratio. In 4L, both sliding clutches are moved to the rear. Power to the rear output shaft now passes through the idler gear set, and power to the front output shaft passes through the front-drive low gear. Both output shafts will be driven at a reduced speed because of the gear ratios. Neutral occurs when the range clutch is between high and low ranges.

◀ **SERVICE TIP** ▶

A full-time AWD vehicle with an active transfer case should never be operated with either the front or rear wheels stationary. Severe transfer case damage will occur if one pair of wheels is spinning and the other pair is stopped. This applies to emission testing using a dynamometer.

13.2.2.1 Haldex All-Wheel-Drive System. The Haldex system is currently being used on several European vehicles. The major part is a coupling that can be installed onto the rear drive axle to connect it to the

FWD system, or it can connect a front drive axle to a RWD vehicle drivetrain (Figure 13-13). The coupling uses a multidisc clutch that is applied hydraulically when there is an excessive speed difference between the input and output shafts (Figure 13-14). Hydraulic pressure to apply the clutch is generated in the clutch when the input and output shafts turn at different speeds. When there is no speed difference, there will be no pressure. The clutch application rate is controlled electronically using software designed for the particular vehicle.

13.2.3 Chain-Drive Transfer Case

This is a very popular style of transfer case. There is some variety in these units, but each uses a large silent chain to transfer power from the upper shaft to the lower, front output shaft (Figure 13-15). There are three ways for power to flow through this transfer case plus neutral (Figure 13-16). Low range is provided by a set of planetary gears. Power enters the gear set through the carrier of the gear set, which is connected to the input shaft; a dog clutch is used to control the power flow for 4WD to the drive-chain sprocket.

In high range, the planetary gears are locked up by shifting the sun gear into mesh with both the planet pinion gears and the planet carrier. In low range, the sun gear is shifted so that it is in mesh with only the planet pinions, and the ring gear is held

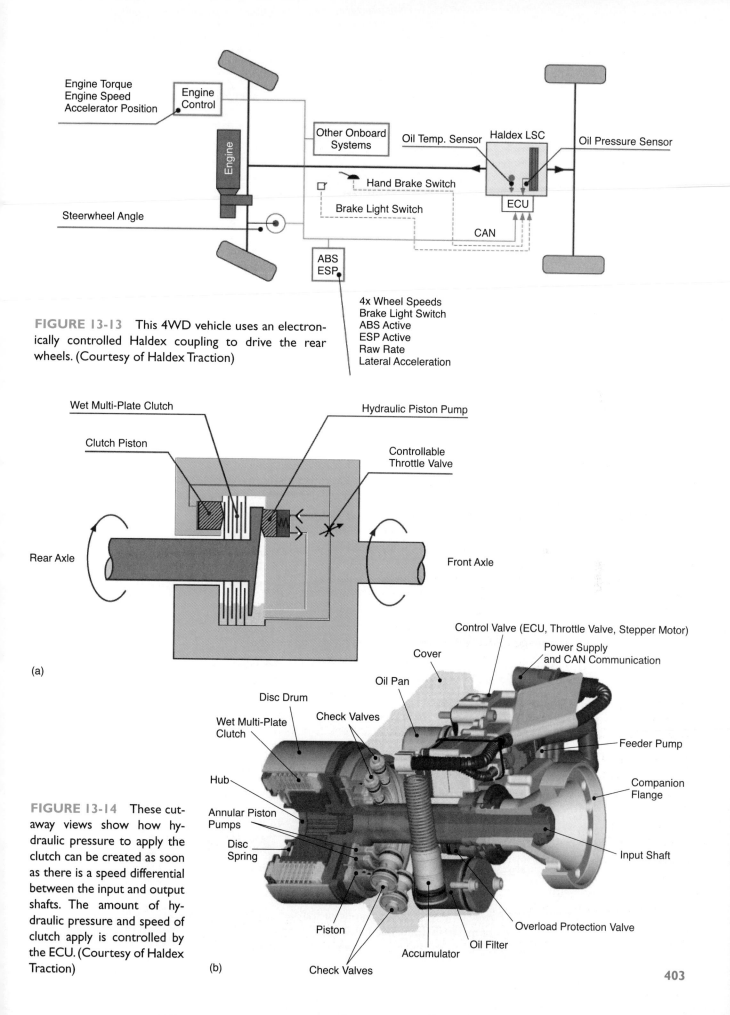

FIGURE 13-13 This 4WD vehicle uses an electronically controlled Haldex coupling to drive the rear wheels. (Courtesy of Haldex Traction)

Engine Torque
Engine Speed
Accelerator Position

Engine Control

Engine

Steerwheel Angle

Other Onboard Systems

Oil Temp. Sensor

Haldex LSC

Oil Pressure Sensor

Hand Brake Switch

Brake Light Switch

ECU

CAN

ABS
ESP

4x Wheel Speeds
Brake Light Switch
ABS Active
ESP Active
Raw Rate
Lateral Acceleration

Wet Multi-Plate Clutch

Hydraulic Piston Pump

Clutch Piston

Controllable
Throttle Valve

Rear Axle

Front Axle

(a)

FIGURE 13-14 These cutaway views show how hydraulic pressure to apply the clutch can be created as soon as there is a speed differential between the input and output shafts. The amount of hydraulic pressure and speed of clutch apply is controlled by the ECU. (Courtesy of Haldex Traction)

Control Valve (ECU, Throttle Valve, Stepper Motor)

Power Supply
and CAN Communication

Cover

Oil Pan

Disc Drum

Check Valves

Wet Multi-Plate
Clutch

Feeder Pump

Companion
Flange

Hub

Annular Piston
Pumps

Disc
Spring

Input Shaft

Piston

Overload Protection Valve

Accumulator

Oil Filter

Check Valves

(b)

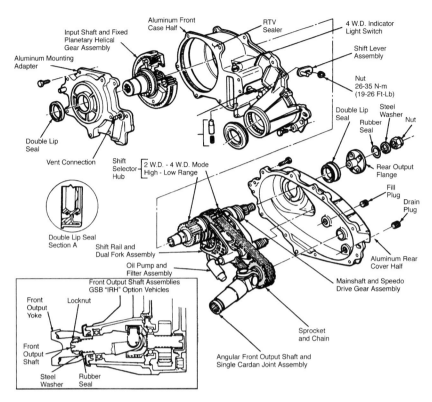

FIGURE 13-15 A chain-drive transfer case uses a Morse chain to transfer power to the front output shaft. (Courtesy of Ford Motor Company)

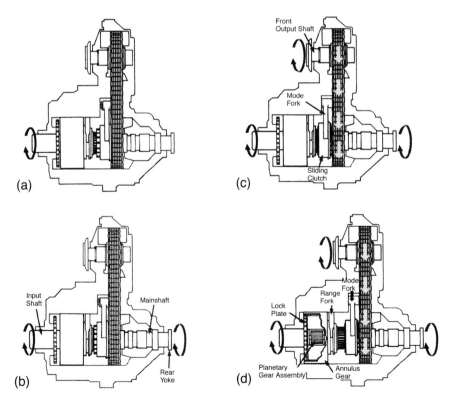

FIGURE 13-16 Power flow through a chain-drive transfer case in neutral (a), 2H (b), 4H (c), and 4L (d). (Portions of materials contained herein have been reprinted with permission of General Motors Corporation, Service and Parts Operations, License Agreement #0310807)

stationary. Now when the sun gear is driven, the planet gears will be forced to "walk" around the inside of the ring gear, and the carrier will be driven at a reduced speed. In AWD transfer cases, the output from the planetary gear set enters the differential, which has one output to the rear output shaft and another to the sprocket of the drive chain for the front output shaft (Figure 13-17).

13.3 FRONT DRIVE AXLES

Except for the outer ends of the axle housing, which allow steering, most early 4WD utility vehicles use a solid front drive axle that is essentially the same as the one used in the rear (Figure 13-18). The carrier is normally offset to the side so that the front driveshaft can pass alongside the engine, and the carrier itself is the same as the rear carrier.

Some front drive axle assemblies include a feature that allows disconnecting one of the axle shafts (Figure 13-19). A collar is shifted to connect or disconnect the two parts of the shaft. Either a vacuum or electric shift motor is used for this with the controls being activated by shifting the transfer case into or out of 4WD.

Many Ford pickups and utility vehicles use a swing-axle style of independent suspension (Figure 13-20). This unit, called a **twin-traction axle,** has two axle assemblies that have their inner ends connected to the vehicle frame through a pivot bushing. The left-side axle assembly supports the carrier and the left steering knuckle. The right-side axle assembly supports the right steering knuckle. The right-side shaft is much longer than the left, and it is a three-piece assembly with two Cardan U-joints.

Most modern 4WD light trucks and utility vehicles use a version of a short–long arm (SLA) suspension similar to that used by many RWD passenger cars. This suspension produces much better ride quality and handling features (Figure 13-21)

A steering knuckle support, which has provision for the steering pivots, is formed into the outer ends of the front drive axle housings. Some early units and larger units in use today use a **closed knuckle,** which has a large rounded housing that encloses a CV joint; these units use a pair of tapered roller bearings for the steering pivots (Figure 13-22). Most modern front drive axles use an **open design** with ball joints for the steering pivots and a Cardan U-joint (Figure 13-23).

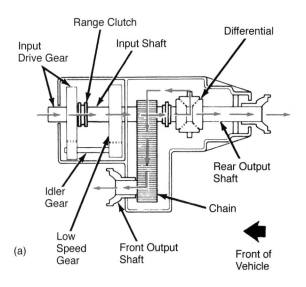

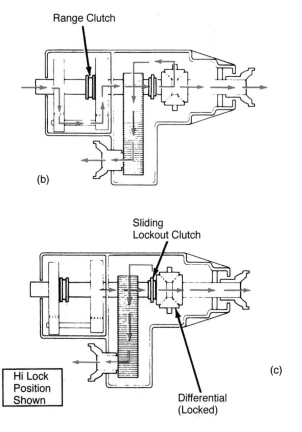

FIGURE 13-17 Power flows through an AWD transfer case in HI (a), LO (b), and HI Lock with the differential locked up (c). (Courtesy of Ford Motor Company)

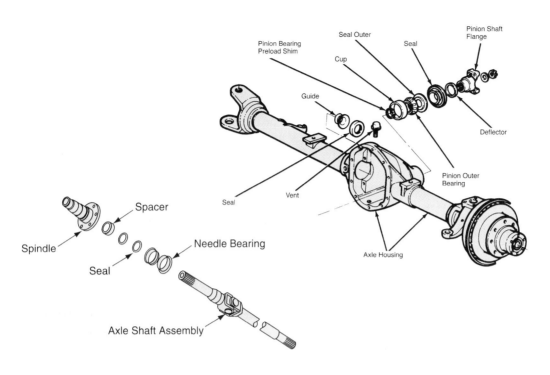

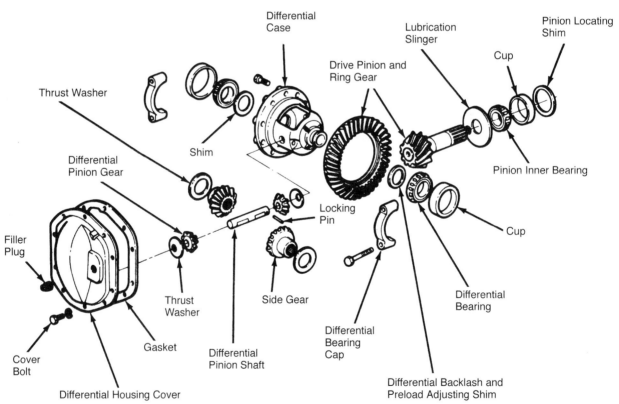

FIGURE 13-18 Exploded view of a front drive axle. (Courtesy of Ford Motor Company)

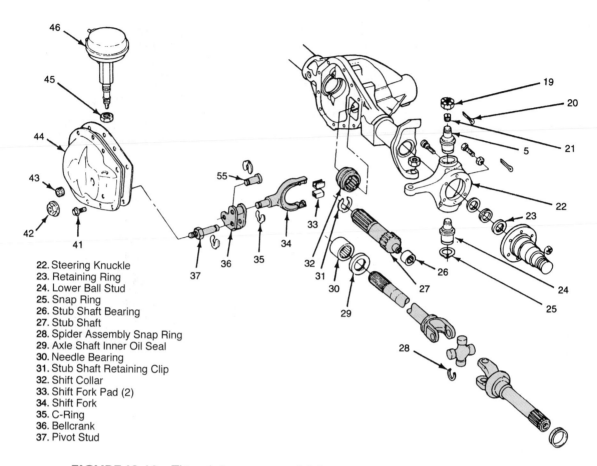

22. Steering Knuckle
23. Retaining Ring
24. Lower Ball Stud
25. Snap Ring
26. Stub Shaft Bearing
27. Stub Shaft
28. Spider Assembly Snap Ring
29. Axle Shaft Inner Oil Seal
30. Needle Bearing
31. Stub Shaft Retaining Clip
32. Shift Collar
33. Shift Fork Pad (2)
34. Shift Fork
35. C-Ring
36. Bellcrank
37. Pivot Stud

FIGURE 13-19 This axle has a vacuum shift feature that allows disconnecting the left axle. (Courtesy of DaimlerChrysler Corporation)

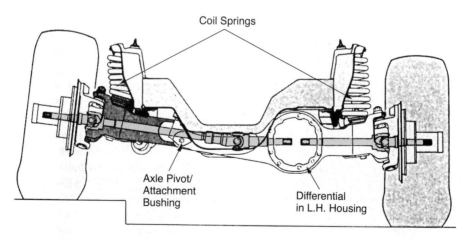

FIGURE 13-20 A twin-traction drive axle allows independent front suspension. (Courtesy of Ford Motor Company)

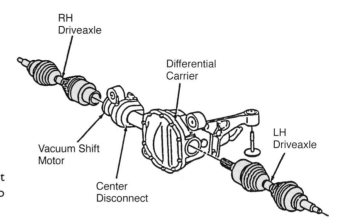

FIGURE 13-21   Front axle assembly for independent front suspension (IFS); note the axle assemblies, which are similar to those of a FWD car. (Courtesy of Ford Motor Company)

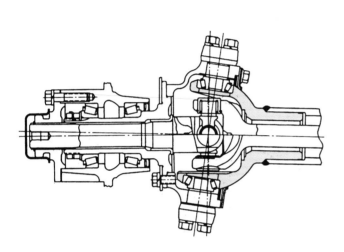

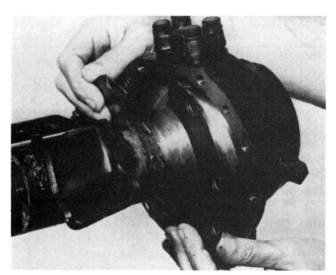

FIGURE 13-22   A closed-end axle encloses the CV joint in a round chamber, keeping it clean and lubricated. (Courtesy of Dana Corporation)

Most axle shafts consist of two pieces: An inner axle that connects to the axle gear in the differential, the U-joint, or CV joint; and an outer axle that connects to the wheel hub. In most cases, a special hub unit is used to make the connection at the wheel hub. Some

◄   **SERVICE TIP**   ►

The front axle of many part-time 4WD vehicles does not get used very often; it is common to go many months without 4L or 4H being used. During this time, the oil will drain off the bearings and gears, and rusting, corrosion, or other deterioration can occur. It is recommended that the vehicle be driven in 4H a short distance, 10 to 20 yards or meters, every month or so to recoat the parts of the drive axle with gear oil.

4WDs mount the differential carrier to the vehicle frame or body and use a fully independent suspension that is similar to that of some FWD cars.

13.3.1   Integrated Wheel End Disconnect

The transfer case can only disconnect the power from the driveshaft to the other drive axle. This is the front axle of RWD-based vehicles or the rear axle of vehicles based on FWD designs. But, the wheels of that axle will still drive the axle shaft and gears as well as the driveshaft, causing unnecessary wear and a loss of about 0.5 mpg.

Many 4WD vehicles are equipped with special hubs that can be manually manipulated to lock or unlock the power flow; other hubs operate automatically. An **integrated wheel end disconnect** system has been recently developed that is used to connect or disconnect the outboard CV joint with the wheel hub. This is con-

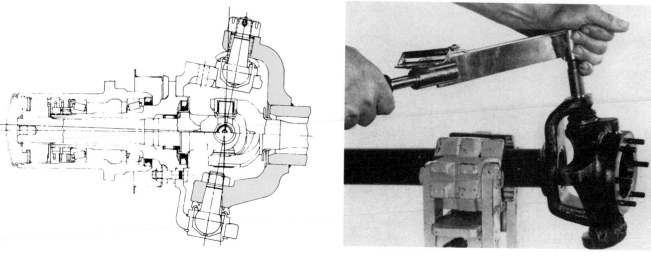

FIGURE 13-23   An open-end axle uses a standard Cardan U-joint exposed to the elements. (Courtesy of Dana Corporation)

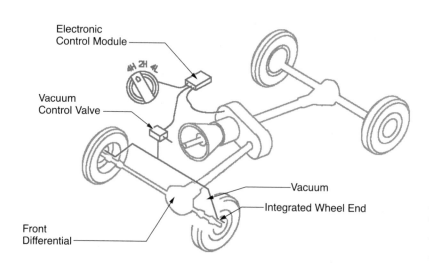

FIGURE 13-24   This wheel end disconnect system can connect or disconnect torque transfer from the CV joints to the wheel hubs. The vacuum control system is controlled by the vacuum control valve and the electronic 4WD controls. (Courtesy of Wam Industries)

trolled by a 4WD electronic control so that the wheel ends connect when 4WD is engaged and disconnect when shifted back to 2WD (Figure 13-24).

A coupler, which resembles a synchronizer sleeve, is used to connect the CV joint with the wheel hub (Figure 13-25). The coupler is released by vacuum and moved to engagement by a wave spring. Vacuum remains at the release piston during 2WD operation. A vacuum loss will cause the wheel ends to engage; if the system should fail, 4WD operation is available. The vacuum signal comes from the engine intake manifold and is controlled by a vacuum control valve. The control valve is controlled by the 2WD–4WD mode switch.

13.3.2   Wheel Hub

Several styles of hubs are used to connect the front drive axle to the wheel hub. In some cases, it is simply a unit with internal splines that is bolted directly to the wheel hub. A simple hub is not used on some modern vehicles because it will drive the front axle and driveshaft while the transfer case is in 2WD. This drag causes wear, a loss of power, and reduced fuel mileage.

Many 4WD utility vehicles use a type of **locking hub** so that the 4WD gearing can be disconnected during normal driving (Figure 13-26). There are two major types of locking hubs: mechanical and automatic.

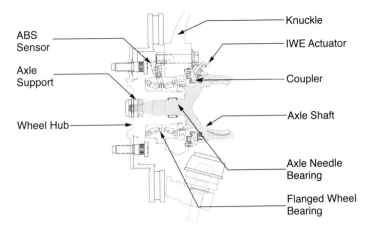

FIGURE 13-25 On an integrated wheel end, the coupler is moved to the left by a wave spring to lock the wheel hub to the axle shaft/CV joint housing. The coupler is moved to the right by vacuum to disconnect the wheel hub from the axle shaft. (Courtesy of Wam Industries)

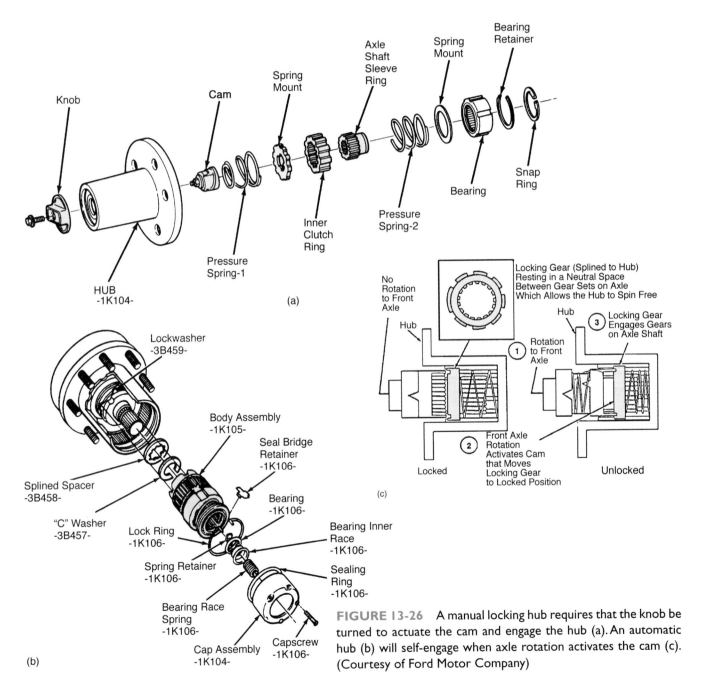

FIGURE 13-26 A manual locking hub requires that the knob be turned to actuate the cam and engage the hub (a). An automatic hub (b) will self-engage when axle rotation activates the cam (c). (Courtesy of Ford Motor Company)

Mechanical hubs contain a dog clutch that is shifted by rotating the hub unit manually to engage or disengage the dog clutch (lock the hub) or disengage it. The hub engages when an internal cam moves a spline on the clutch hub into mesh with a spline in the wheel hub. Some hubs have an automatic feature in which rotation of the axle causes the cam in the hub to operate. Some early **automatic hubs** used a two-direction, one-way clutch that allowed the axle to drive the hub in addition to the dog clutch. Automatic hubs allow the driver to engage 4WD without having to get out and go to the hubs to lock them. They also include a method of manually engaging the dog clutch so that they will stay locked in engagement.

4WD hubs use tapered roller wheel bearings much like a 2WD vehicle, only larger (Figure 13-27). Besides the diameter, the major difference is that two nuts are used. An inner nut is used to adjust bearing clearance, and an outer nut is used to lock or jam the inner one. A washer, which also serves to lock the adjustment, separates the two nuts.

Locking and automatic hubs are disliked by some motorists, usually those that don't understand their operation. Some manufacturers use axle disconnect mechanisms; these use a vacuum or electric motor to move a shift collar that couples the two-piece axle shaft for 4WD and uncouples it in 2WD. The axles and differential gears will rotate in 2WD, but the ring and pinion gears are not driven.

◀ SERVICE TIP ▶

After 4WD operation, one manufacturer recommends driving in reverse for 10 feet to ensure release of the automatic hubs. If one or both hubs remain engaged, drive axle noise or wear can occur.

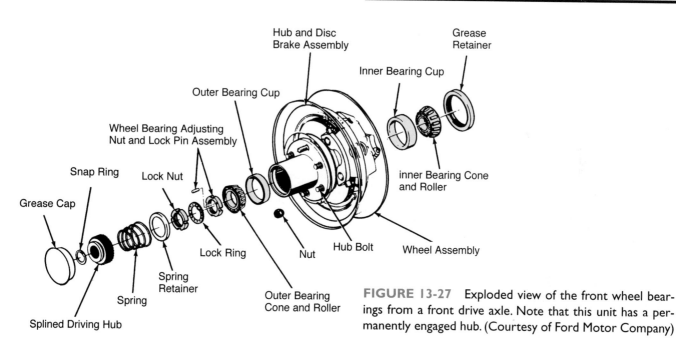

FIGURE 13-27 Exploded view of the front wheel bearings from a front drive axle. Note that this unit has a permanently engaged hub. (Courtesy of Ford Motor Company)

REVIEW QUESTIONS

The following questions are provided to help you study as you read the chapter.

1. A typical transfer case will have _____ input and _____ output shafts.

2. Full-time four-wheel-drive or all-wheel-drive vehicles use a center _____.

3. Excessive wear in the center differential or drive axle could be caused by unequal _____ diameters.

4. The two most popular types of transfer cases are _____ and _____ drives.

5. The front drive axle uses a _____ _____ so that 4WD can be disconnected during normal road driving.

6. Four-wheel-drive front axle hubs are either _____ or self-locking.

CHAPTER QUIZ

The following questions will help you check the facts you have learned. Select the answer that completes each statement correctly.

1. A transfer case is used to A. control the power flow to the second driveshaft, B. provide a gear reduction for additional torque. Which is correct?
   a. A only
   b. B only
   c. Both A and B
   d. Neither A nor B

2. To transfer power to the front output shaft, a transfer case uses A. a helical gear train, B. a large silent chain. Which is correct?
   a. A only
   b. B only
   c. Both A and B
   d. Neither A nor B

3. An AWD transfer case must include a
   a. shifter for the front output shaft.
   b. differential.
   c. low-range gear set.
   d. all of these.

4. Low range in many transfer cases A. is available only while in 2WD mode, B. sends the power flow through a planetary gear set. Which is correct?
   a. A only
   b. B only
   c. Both A and B
   d. Neither A nor B

5. At its outer ends, a 4WD front drive axle uses A. CV joints, B. Cardan U-joints. Which is correct?
   a. A only
   b. B only
   c. Both A and B
   d. Neither A nor B

6. A 4WD vehicle has automatic front hubs; the control on the hubs is to A. prevent one front wheel from spinning while the other one is not, B. disengage the hub from the driving axle for driving on the road. Which is correct?
   a. A only
   b. B only
   c. Both A and B
   d. Neither A nor B

Chapter 14

4WD SERVICE

LEARNING OBJECTIVES

After completing this chapter, you should be able to:

1. Perform the maintenance operations needed to keep a 4WD vehicle operating properly.
2. Diagnose the cause of the problems unique to 4WD vehicles.
3. Remove and replace a transfer case.
4. Overhaul a transfer case.
5. Remove, replace, and service front drive axle components.
6. Be able to complete the ASE tasks for content area F, Four-Wheel Drive Component Diagnosis and Repair.

TERMS TO LEARN

double-lip seal   torque bias check

14.1   INTRODUCTION

Service of a 4WD drivetrain is an extension of the areas covered in Chapters 8, 10, and 12. A transfer case is serviced in almost the same manner as a transmission. The driveshaft for the second drive axle is essentially the same as that used at the rear of a RWD vehicle. The additional drive axle is often a copy of a RWD drive axle with provision for steering. The *wheel end* of the drive axle has a U-joint or CV joint in the axle and a steering knuckle in the axle housing. It is important that the technician be able to identify the important features of the particular 4WD vehicle being worked on (Figure 14-1).

Service operations include checking gear oil levels; lubricating U-joints and slip joints; and diagnosing noise, vibration, and failure to operate correctly. Major service operations include rebuilding transfer cases, driveshafts, drive axles, and wheel hubs. Because the driveshaft and drive axle service operations are described in earlier chapters, in this chapter we concentrate on transfer case and wheel hub service, items unique to 4WD.

14.2   GEAR OIL CHECKS

Most transfer cases have a gear oil-level plug in the side of the case for checking the oil level (Figure 14-2). As in a transmission, the gear oil level should be at the bottom of this opening. Some transfer cases use ATF and others use gear oil; you should always use the type of lubricant specified by the manufacturer. A lubricant guide is included as Appendix B. The front drive axle normally uses the same gear oil-checking methods and lubricant as the rear drive axle.

Contaminated gear oil should be replaced by draining the old oil and filling the transfer case with new oil of

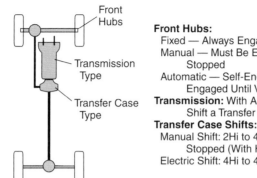

Front Hubs:
  Fixed — Always Engaged
  Manual — Must Be Engaged or Disengaged Manually with the Vehicle
    Stopped
  Automatic — Self-Engage when Power Is Sent to Them, Some Will Remain
    Engaged Until Vehicle Direction is Reversed
Transmission: With Automatic Transmissions, It Is Extremely Difficult to
    Shift a Transfer Case from Neutral to Hi or Lo Range
Transfer Case Shifts:
  Manual Shift: 2Hi to 4Hi, 4Hi to 4Lo, and 4Lo to 4Hi — Vehicle Must Be
    Stopped (With Hubs Locked, 2Hi to 4Hi Shift Can Be Made in Motion)
  Electric Shift: 4Hi to 4Lo and 4Lo to 4Hi Vehicle Must Be Stopped

FIGURE 14-1   The operating characteristics of vehicles with part-time 4WD vary depending on the type of front hubs, transmission, or transfer case.

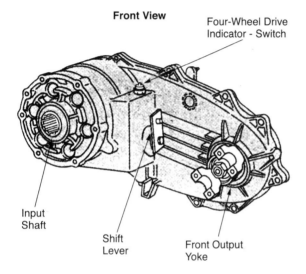

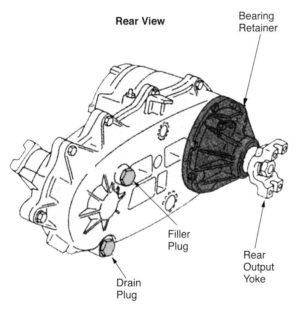

FIGURE 14-2   In most transfer cases, the oil level should be even with the bottom of the filler plug opening. (Courtesy of Ford Motor Company)

the correct type to the proper level. Many transfer cases include a drain plug so oil change is relatively easy.

◀ SERVICE TIP ▶

Some vehicles use a transfer case made from magnesium with an aluminum oil-level plug. The plug has a small head, and it tends to seize. A wrench will easily slip and round off the small plug head. It is recommended that if the plug does not unscrew using a reasonable amount of force, to heat the case area surrounding the plug. Use a hot-air device for this; *DO NOT* use a torch because the magnesium case can ignite and cause a serious fire.

REAL-WORLD FIX An AWD 2000 Chevrolet Astro (38,000 mi) had an odd skip-miss feeling during acceleration while hot. All the engine management features had been checked, and it appeared that the engine was running properly. Tire diameters were checked, and they all measured within 1/8″ of each other. The transfer case was drained and refilled with the proper fluid, but this did not help.

FIX

A second transfer case fluid change was recommended, and this fixed the problem. This transfer case can have a stick/slip problem, similar to a limited slip differential.

14.3 PROBLEM DIAGNOSIS

4WD components have the same type of problems as other drivetrain parts: noise, vibration, and failure to transmit power. The diagnostic procedure is similar to

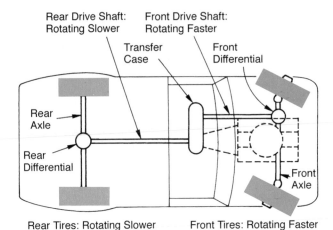

Rear Drive Shaft: Rotating Slower   Front Drive Shaft: Rotating Faster

Transfer Case   Front Differential

Rear Axle

Rear Differential

Front Axle

Rear Tires: Rotating Slower   Front Tires: Rotating Faster

FIGURE 14-3   As a vehicle turns a corner, the rear tires, drive axle, and driveshaft turn more slowly than the ones at the front. If both front and rear axles are driven at the same speed, the gears in a transfer case will bind up.

that described in Chapters 8, 10, and 12. However, the technician should pay particular attention to isolating the problem at the source—either the transmission or the transfer case, for example. When trying to isolate a problem, it is possible in some units to operate the transfer case in its different modes and the transmission in its different gears.

◄ SERVICE TIP ►

A condition unique to 4WD that may be considered a problem by some vehicle owners is driveline wind-up. This operation, which should be avoided, occurs when a part-time 4WD vehicle is operated on dry pavement with the transfer case in 4WD and the front hubs engaged (Figure 14-3). The different rotating speeds of the front and rear wheels will cause a bind-up condition in the drivetrain. The result will be a hop, skip, or bounce of the front or rear tires and a transfer case locked in gear. Driveline wind-up can be removed by lifting a wheel off the ground or, more simply, by driving the vehicle in a circle in a direction opposite to what made the wind-up. With some electric-shifted transfer cases, wind-up can cause a delay in shifting out of 4WD.

Some automatic hubs will not disengage under certain conditions. These hubs are designed to engage automatically when the driving action of the front axles

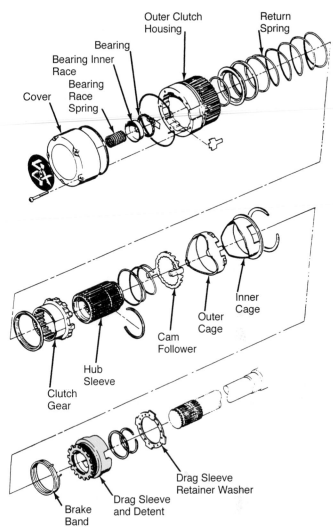

Outer Clutch Housing   Return Spring

Bearing

Bearing Inner Race

Bearing Race Spring

Cover

Inner Cage

Outer Cage

Cam Follower

Hub Sleeve

Clutch Gear

Drag Sleeve Retainer Washer

Drag Sleeve and Detent

Brake Band

FIGURE 14-4   In an automatic locking hub, the drag sleeve will cause hub engagement when driven by the front axle and hub sleeve. (Portions of materials contained herein have been reprinted with permission of General Motors Corporation, Service and Parts Operations, License Agreement #0310807)

causes the internal cam to lock up the hub (Figure 14-4). With some vehicles, these hubs need to be released by shifting the transfer case to 2WD and driving in the opposite direction for at least 10 ft (3 m). If this is not done, the front hubs can remain engaged, which will cause front wheel rotation to drive the axle, differential, and opposite axle or both axles, ring and pinion gears, and driveshaft. This can produce a noise problem and unnecessary wear.

Some transfer cases include a viscous coupling that acts as a limited slip coupling between the front and rear driveshafts (Figure 14-5). A special procedure, called a *torque bias check*, is used to check this coupling. The **torque bias check** measures the torque required to rotate one front wheel that is raised off the ground while the other three wheels are on the ground,

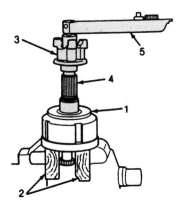

FIGURE 14-5 The torque bias of this viscous coupling (1) from a transfer case is being checked; a turning resistance that is too small indicates a faulty viscous coupling. (Courtesy of DaimlerChrysler Corporation)

the transfer case is in 4WD, and the transmission is in neutral. A worn viscous coupling is indicated if the readings are low. Check service information for specifications and the exact checking procedure.

◀ SERVICE TIP ▶

In cases of early or premature viscous coupling failure, check for mismatched tire diameter (excessive driving with a compact spare tire can cause this) or a failure to drive one of the wheels. A broken axle or CV joint might go unnoticed until the coupling fails.

REAL-WORLD FIX A 1998 GMC pickup (42,000 mi) had a noise in 4WD and would not shift out of 4WD until coasting in second gear. A Chassis Ear indicated the whining noise to be coming from the transfer case. Disassembly and inspection of the transfer case showed nothing wrong. The chain and sprockets were replaced, but this did not help.

FIX

A careful check of tire size showed 5/32″ deeper tread on the rear tires, and a check of tire circumference showed 98″ at front and 99″ at the rear. Replacement of the worn front tires fixed this problem.

AUTHOR'S NOTE

Proper tire rotation would have kept the tire wear even and prevented this problem.

◀ SERVICE TIP ▶

A complaint of "locked in 4WD," early failure of a viscous coupler, a transfer case trouble code, or wheel hop on corners can be easily caused by the tires. Low tire pressure, as little as 5 psi, or unequal tire diameters, 1/4″ ($6\frac{1}{2}$ mm) or more difference in circumference, can affect operation. All four tires must be the same brand, type, and size. Tire circumference can be checked quickly and easily by wrapping a tape measure around the tread (Figure 14-6).

◀ SERVICE TIP ▶

Some chain-drive transfer cases can experience drive-chain failure. The unit will be low on fluid and will have a stretched, worn chain with a brownish color from overheating. This problem is caused by a tendency of the ATF lubricant to aerate, mist, and leave the transfer case through the vent. After repair, changing to 30-weight motor oil, which does not mist, should cure this problem.

REAL-WORLD FIX A 1995 Chevrolet K 1500 pickup (88,000 mi) came in with a complaint of an intermittent hard pull to the right. A road test showed that this occurred while driving in 4WD; it was also difficult to shift out of 4WD after making a turn. A check showed proper voltage from the transfer case switch to the front axle actuator. The front axle actuator was replaced, but this did not help.

FIX

Following advice, the tires were checked. They were all the same age and brand, but three of them were 265/75R16 and one was 245/75R16. Replacement of this tire with a 265/75R16 fixed this problem.

◀ PROBLEM SOLVING ▶

Imagine that you are working in a general automotive repair shop and these problems are brought to you.

Case 1

An 8-year-old 4WD pickup uses a manually shifted transfer case, and the driver's complaint is that after he uses 4WD, he has a very difficult time shifting from 4WD to 2WD. What are the possible faults with this vehicle? Where should you begin your diagnosis?

Case 2

The driver's complaint is that his truck does not work in 4WD. He got stuck in some sand and had to be pulled out because only the rear tires were being driven. What are the possible faults with this vehicle? Where should you begin your diagnosis?

14.4 IN-VEHICLE SERVICE

In-vehicle service varies depending on the particular transfer case. With some transfer cases, in-vehicle service is limited to front and rear output shaft seal replacement. The output shaft and bearings can be removed from the main case for service or parts replacement in some gear drive units. Some transfer cases are shifted by vacuum controls, which can be checked, repaired, and adjusted in-vehicle (Figure 14-7). Modern electronic-shifted units have switches, sensors, electrical wiring, and shift motors that can be checked and replaced (Figure 14-8). Due to this large variety, it is recommended to refer to the "In-Vehicle Service" section of the manufacturer's service manual. Electronic and vacuum controls are described more completely in Chapter 15.

REAL-WORLD FIX A 1987 Jeep Wrangler (13,500 mi) front axle did not engage. An inspection showed broken and brittle vacuum hoses, some falling off their connectors. The vacuum harness, with most of the lines, was replaced.

FIX

After securing a vacuum diagram, it was determined that a vent was plugged. Cleaning this vent (after repairing the vacuum lines) fixed this problem.

◀ SERVICE TIP ▶

Many 4X4 vehicles are driven in 2WD mode for long periods of time. During this period, the shift motor tends to get sluggish and often will not operate when 4WD operation is desired. It is recommended to shift into 4WD for a short operation every month. A light tap with a hammer has helped some sluggish motors get back into operation.

FIGURE 14-6 The measuring tape wrapped around the tire shows that the circumference is 90 3/4″. The other three tires should measure close to the same.

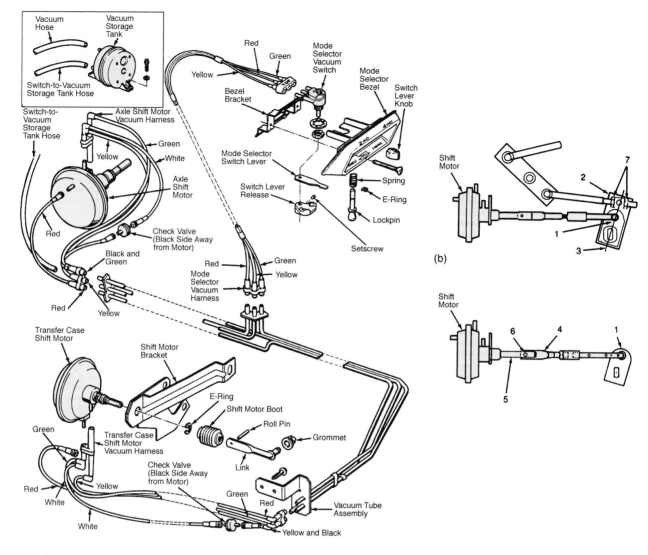

Vacuum Hose

Vacuum Storage Tank

Switch-to-Vacuum Storage Tank Hose

Switch-to-Vacuum Storage Tank Hose

Axle Shift Motor Vacuum Harness

Green

Yellow

White

Axle Shift Motor

Red

Black and Green

Red

Yellow

Check Valve (Black Side Away from Motor)

Transfer Case Shift Motor

Shift Motor Bracket

E-Ring

Shift Motor Boot

Roll Pin

Grommet

Green

Transfer Case Shift Motor Vacuum Harness

Link

Check Valve (Black Side Away from Motor)

Red

Yellow

White

White

Green

Red

Yellow and Black

Vacuum Tube Assembly

Red

Green

Yellow

Bezel Bracket

Mode Selector Vacuum Switch

Mode Selector Bezel

Switch Lever Knob

4WD

2WD

Mode Selector Switch Lever

Switch Lever Release

Spring

E-Ring

Lockpin

Setscrew

Red

Green

Yellow

Mode Selector Vacuum Harness

Shift Motor

2

7

1

3

(b)

Shift Motor

6

4

1

5

(a)

FIGURE 14-7 (a)This vehicle uses vacuum controls to shift the transfer case and drive axle into 2WD or 4WD. (b) Each of the vacuum shift motors includes an adjustment in the linkage to help ensure proper operation. (Courtesy of Daimler-Chrysler Corporation)

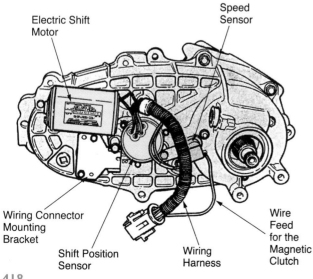

Electric Shift Motor

Speed Sensor

Wiring Connector Mounting Bracket

Shift Position Sensor

Wiring Harness

Wire Feed for the Magnetic Clutch

FIGURE 14-8 This transfer case uses an electric shift motor to make the shifts. Note the motor and the speed and shift position sensors. (Courtesy of Ford Motor Company)

REAL-WORLD FIX A 1994 Ford Aerostar AWD van (163,000 km) would not stay in park. It would hold for a short while, but then roll a short distance, hold and then roll again. Another shop replaced the transfer case and controller, but this did not help. There were no trouble codes.

FIX

An inspection revealed that the inner splines on the right front axle were stripped. Replacement of this axle fixed this problem.

REAL-WORLD FIX A 1990 Jeep Cherokee part-time 4X4 (172,000 km) had a complaint of driveline noise in 4WD mode and slippage in 4-High when under load. The noise was sometimes a single clunk, sometimes a grinding noise.

FIX

Close inspection of the vacuum hoses for the shift mechanism showed leaks at the front axle servo; apparently, when under load and with low vacuum, it would shift out of 4WD. Replacement of these hoses fixed the problem.

14.4.1   Transfer Case Shift Linkage Adjustment

Manually shifted transfer cases include a provision for adjusting the shift linkage to ensure that the dog clutches are properly engaged or disengaged in the various lever positions. The actual adjustment will vary among the different makes and models; always consult the proper service manual.

REAL-WORLD FIX A 1975 Chevrolet 4X4 pickup (120,000 mi) transfer case jumped out of 4WD shortly after engagement. The front hubs were replaced, but this did not help.

FIX

This problem was caused by the shift linkage being out of adjustment. A simple adjustment fixed this vehicle.

To adjust transfer case shift linkage:

1. Remove the shift boot so that you have access to the gearshift mechanism (Figure 14-9).

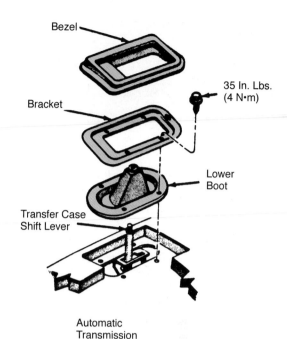

FIGURE 14-9   Removing the shift lever boot provides access to the linkage adjustment. (Courtesy of Daimler-Chrysler Corporation)

2. Place the lever in the correct position; sometimes a spacer of a certain size is specified to position the lever properly (Figure 14-10).

3. Disconnect the linkage rod swivel/trunnion from the shift lever; it should slide freely in and out of the lever. If not, adjust the trunnion position so that it is a free fit in the lever hole (Figure 14-11).

Most front hubs can be removed, disassembled, cleaned, inspected, and replaced, using whatever new parts may be necessary.

REAL-WORLD FIX A 1991 Ranger 4X4 (76,000 mi) came in with a clicking, ratchet-like sound at the front axle. One front hub was replaced, and now the vehicle is back, making the same sound.

FIX

A binding U-joint was found in the front axle; replacement of this joint fixed this noise problem.

14.4.2   Front Hub Removal and Replacement

Some front hubs are removed simply by removing the bolts at the wheel hubs and sliding them off the axle

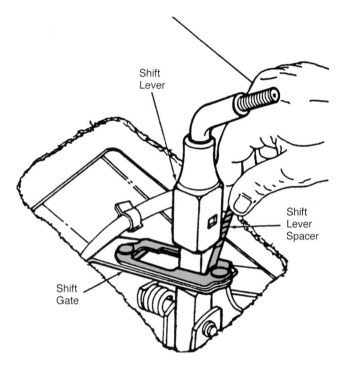

FIGURE 14-10 A spacer is installed between the shift lever and the shift gate to place the lever in the proper position. (Courtesy of DaimlerChrysler Corporation)

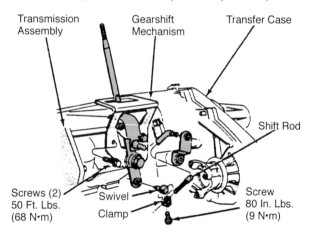

FIGURE 14-11 With the shift lever properly positioned, the shift rod is adjusted so that it is the proper length. (Courtesy of DaimlerChrysler Corporation)

and hub (Figure 14-12). Other hubs have an internal snap ring that secures the splined inner sleeve to the axle; these hubs require partial disassembly in order to remove this snap ring. Some front hubs are built entirely in the wheel hub so that the wheel hub encloses the wheel bearings along with the locking mechanism. To remove the hub and rotor in these units, the locking mechanism must be removed to gain access to the wheel-bearing locking and adjusting nuts.

It is highly recommended that you follow the procedure given in the manufacturer's service manual. Hub replacement is the reverse of the disassembly procedure.

REAL-WORLD FIX The front hubs on a Ford F-150 (88,000 mi) failed. This was the third set; the prior set was an updated version.

F I X

The automatic hubs were replaced with a set of stronger, manually locking hubs. This cured this problem.

14.4.3   Wheel Hub and Rotor Removal, Replacement, and Bearing Adjustment

A 4WD hub and rotor unit is held onto the hollow spindle by a pair of tapered roller wheel bearings. These bearings are similar to those used on a passenger vehicle but larger so that the drive axle shaft can pass through the hub (Figure 14-13). Two nuts hold the bearing adjustment. The inner nut serves to adjust the wheel bearing clearance; a locking washer or ring is positioned next to it to prevent its rotation, and the outer locknut secures all of these together. Various styles of locking rings are used, depending on the manufacturer. Special wrenches are usually required for removal and replacement of these nuts (Figure 14-14).

To remove a 4WD hub and rotor:

1. Raise and support the vehicle securely on a hoist or jack stands.
2. Remove the wheel and tire.
3. Remove the brake caliper from its mounts and suspend it securely so that it does not fall and damage the hose (Figure 14-15).
4. Remove the portions of the outer hub to gain access to the wheel bearing nuts.
5. Remove the outer locknut, locking washer, and inner nut. Rock the hub and rotor to work the outer bearing to a position where you can grip it and remove it.
6. Slide the hub and rotor off the spindle (Figure 14-16).

To reinstall the hub and rotor, reverse this procedure. Be sure to clean, lubricate, and adjust the wheel bearings properly; to install the brake mounts correctly; and to tighten the bolts and wheel lug nuts to the correct torque.

To adjust a wheel bearing:

1. With the hub on the spindle and the wheel bearings installed, torque the inner adjusting nut to

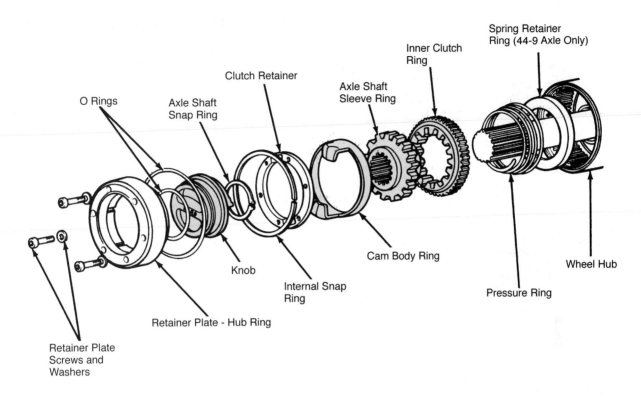

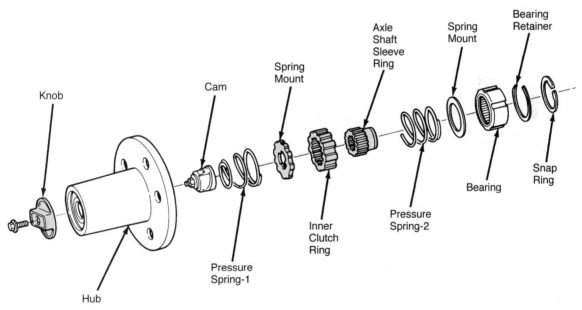

FIGURE 14-12 These two free-running hubs use a knob that is rotated to engage or disengage the hub from the drive axle and sleeve ring. (Courtesy of Ford Motor Company)

about 15 to 20 ft-lb (20 to 27 N-m). Rotate the hub during this operation to completely seat the bearings.

2. Loosen the adjusting nut one-quarter to one-half turn, keeping the wheel hub stationary.

3. Retighten the adjusting nut to the specified torque, which should be about 5in.-lb (0.5 N-m).

4. Position the locking washer so that the inner adjusting nut will not be able to rotate from the position where you just set it.

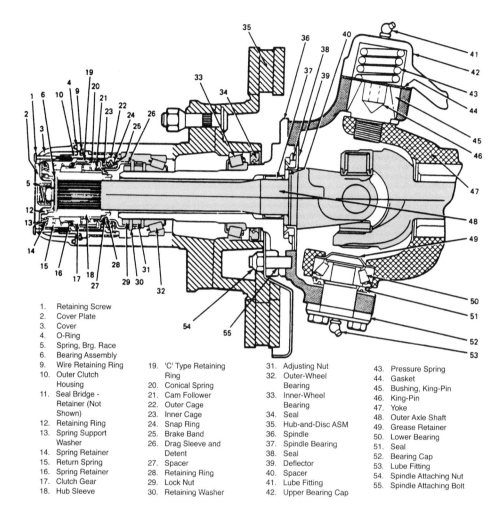

1. Retaining Screw
2. Cover Plate
3. Cover
4. O-Ring
5. Spring, Brg. Race
6. Bearing Assembly
9. Wire Retaining Ring
10. Outer Clutch Housing
11. Seal Bridge - Retainer (Not Shown)
12. Retaining Ring
13. Spring Support Washer
14. Spring Retainer
15. Return Spring
16. Spring Retainer
17. Clutch Gear
18. Hub Sleeve

19. 'C' Type Retaining Ring
20. Conical Spring
21. Cam Follower
22. Outer Cage
23. Inner Cage
24. Snap Ring
25. Brake Band
26. Drag Sleeve and Detent
27. Spacer
28. Retaining Ring
29. Lock Nut
30. Retaining Washer

31. Adjusting Nut
32. Outer-Wheel Bearing
33. Inner-Wheel Bearing
34. Seal
35. Hub-and-Disc ASM
36. Spindle
37. Spindle Bearing
38. Seal
39. Deflector
40. Spacer
41. Lube Fitting
42. Upper Bearing Cap

43. Pressure Spring
44. Gasket
45. Bushing, King-Pin
46. King-Pin
47. Yoke
48. Outer Axle Shaft
49. Grease Retainer
50. Lower Bearing
51. Seal
52. Bearing Cap
53. Lube Fitting
54. Spindle Attaching Nut
55. Spindle Attaching Bolt

FIGURE 14-13 Cutaway view of a 4WD front hub, spindle, and steering knuckle. (Portions of materials contained herein have been reprinted with permission of General Motors Corporation, Service and Parts Operations, License Agreement #0310807)

5. Install the outer locknut and tighten it to the specified torque.

14.4.4 Axle Shaft Removal and Replacement

The inner end of the axle shaft of a front drive axle floats in the differential side gear in the same manner as in a rear axle assembly. The outer end, however, is substantially different in that it contains a U-joint or CV joint and is retained by the wheel hub and spindle (Figure 14-17).

REAL-WORLD FIX A 1993 F-150 4X4 had a squeaking noise coming from the front axle whenever the front hubs were engaged or in 4WD mode.

FIX

Careful inspection located the cause of the noise to be the axle housing seal. Coating the new seal lip with silicone grease cured this noise problem.

(a)

(b)

FIGURE 14-14 Four special wrenches used for 4WD wheel bearing locknuts and retaining nuts. (Courtesy of OTC Tools)

FIGURE 14-15 The brake caliper has been removed from its mounts and is suspended from the spring using a wire hook to prevent it from falling and possibly damaging the brake hose.

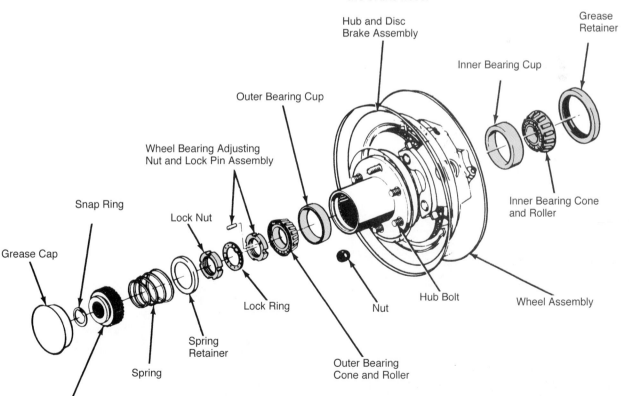

FIGURE 14-16 Exploded view of a 4WD wheel bearing. Note that the hub is permanently engaged with the axle through the splined driving hub and that a lock ring and lock pin are used to keep the wheel bearing adjusting nut from rotating. (Courtesy of Ford Motor Company)

423

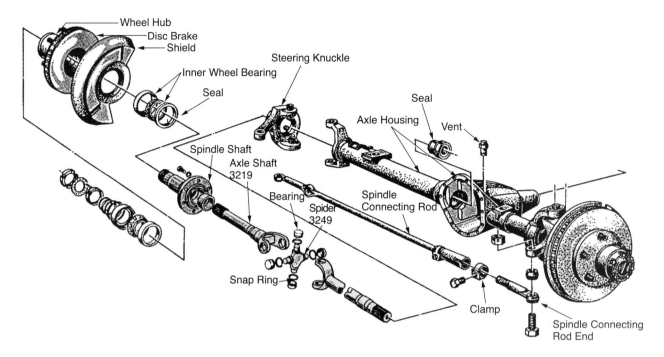

FIGURE 14-17 Solid front drive axle housing with the left-side axle shaft and hub assembly. (Courtesy of Ford Motor Company)

To remove a front axle shaft:

1. Raise and securely support the vehicle on a hoist or jack stands.
2. Remove the wheel hub and rotor as described in Section 14.4.2.
3. Remove the spindle from the steering knuckle (Figure 14-18).
4. Pull the axle shaft assembly out through the steering knuckle, being careful in some housings not to drag it across the seal (Figure 14-19).

FIGURE 14-18 After the brake assembly and hub are removed, the spindle can be removed; sometimes a tap from a soft hammer is needed to break it loose. (Courtesy of Dana Corporation)

FIGURE 14-19 With the spindle removed, the axle shaft assembly can be slid through the opening in the steering knuckle. (Courtesy of Dana Corporation)

Axle installation is essentially the reverse of the removal procedure. Be careful not to damage the seals in the axle housing and spindle. During the installation, the inner end of the axle must be inserted into the differential side gear.

Front drive axles have an inner axle seal to prevent gear oil from traveling out of the housing. The seal's location, usually deep in the housing, can make this seal difficult to remove and replace.

REAL-WORLD FIX The leaking front axle seals on the 1992 GMC pickup (70,000 miles) were replaced using OEM seals. The seals on this and similar pickups still had leakage, and the technician was concerned because he was sure the installing methods were correct.

FIX

A Technical Service Bulletin (TSB) was located addressing this problem. The axle shafts should be replaced due to poor surface finish that causes seal wear. The metal part of the seal should be coated with the proper sealant and the housing vent should be cleaned. Following these practices fixed this seal leak.

AUTHOR'S NOTE

TSBs should always be checked when a repair does not go right; also make sure that the particular TSB applies to the vehicle being worked on. There is an updated vent hose for some vehicles.

14.5 TRANSFER CASE REMOVAL AND REPLACEMENT

The transfer case on some longer-wheelbase vehicles is a separate gearbox that is coupled to the transmission by a U-joint or short driveshaft. The removal of these units is a matter of disconnecting the input and two output U-joints, the shift linkage, and the frame mounts. However, most transfer cases used on utility vehicles and pickups are bolted to the rear of the transmission and can be removed by following the procedure described here. A service manual for the vehicle you are working on should also be followed when doing this job.

To remove a transfer case:

1. Raise and support the vehicle securely on a hoist or jack stands.
2. Remove any skid plates and brace rods that block access to the transfer case or that are attached to it.
3. Disconnect the front and rear driveshafts, being sure to make index marks so that the shafts can be reinstalled in the same position.
4. Disconnect the speedometer cable and shift connections. Some mechanical shift levers must be disconnected from inside the vehicle.
5. Support the transfer case using a transmission jack, and remove the bolts that secure the transfer case to the transmission (Figure 14-20).

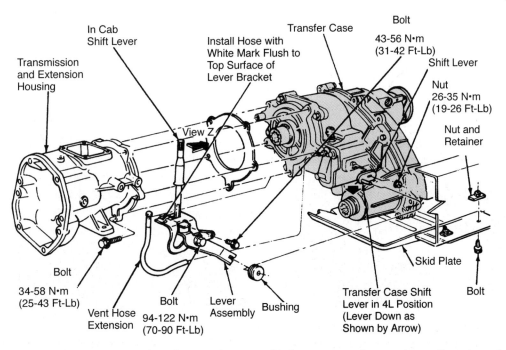

FIGURE 14-20 Because of its shape and center of balance, a transfer case is usually awkward to support as it is removed from the transmission and the vehicle. (Courtesy of Ford Motor Company)

6. Slide the transfer case off the rear of the transmission, and remove it from the vehicle.

Installation of most transfer cases is the reverse of the removal procedure. Make sure that the gasket and seals between the transfer case and the transmission are in good condition and that the bolts are tightened to the correct torque. Some units use a **double-lip seal** to block lubricant flow between the transmission and transfer case.

14.6   TRANSFER CASE OVERHAUL

A chain-drive transfer case has three shafts: one input and two outputs (Figure 14-21). The input shaft and output shaft for the rear axle are often piloted into each other and are supported by a pair of bearings. This assembly also contains a dog clutch to couple the two shafts together for 2H and 4H, a sprocket to drive the chain, a dog clutch to engage this sprocket for 4H and 4L, often a planetary gear set for low range, a method of shifting this gearset, and sometimes a differential for full-time 4WD. The third shaft, which is also mounted on a pair of bearings, is the output shaft for the front axle. This shaft is much simpler, with only a sprocket that is driven by the chain in 4WD modes. Most chain-drive transfer cases have a two-part split aluminum case that opens up to allow easy access to all of the internal parts and shift mechanism.

A gear-drive transfer case has four shafts (Figure 14-22). As in the chain-drive units, the input and rear output shafts are piloted into each other and are supported by a pair of bearings. The idler and front output shafts are also supported by a pair of bearings. A dog clutch, which is shifted one way for 2H and 4H power flows and the opposite way for 4L power flow, is mounted on the input and rear output shafts. The idler shaft supports one double gear, which transfers power to the front output shaft for 4H and 4L and to the rear output shaft for 4L. The front output shaft supports two gears and a dog clutch, which is used to engage 4H and 4L power flows. Most gear-drive transfer cases are cast-iron, with a cover plate that can be removed for inspection of the internal parts and removal of the larger parts. A retainer or cover plate is used at most of the bearings to allow removal of the bearings or bearing shims, which are used for bearing adjustments.

Because overhaul procedures and adjustments vary somewhat in these units, a service manual is required when repairing transfer cases. Most of the operations are the same as those used in transmissions, transaxles, and drive axles. These operations include disassembly, gear and bearing inspection, shift fork clearance and operation, chain wear check, shaft inspection, seal replacement, and reassembly with adjustments for gear end float and bearing clearance or preload (Figure 14-23).

1. Oil Seal	19. Facings	37. O-Ring	55. Clutch Hub
2. Front Adapter	20. Shift Rail	38. Shift Lever	56. Snap Ring
3. Snap Ring	21. Range Shift Fork	39. Crescent Ring	57. Drive Hub
4. Snap Ring	22. Pump Plunger	40. Roller	58. Snap Ring
5. Bearing	23. Output Shaft	41. Pin	59. Bearing
6. Thrust Washer	24. Plunger Spring	42. Front Driveshaft	60. Shift Fork Return Spring
7. Snap Ring	25. Range Shift Sleeve	43. Snap Ring	61. Rear Cover
8. Thrust Plate	26. 4WD Sender	44. Bearing	62. Needle Bearing
9. Sun Gear	27. Detent Spring	45. Bearing Retainer	63. Filler and Drain Plugs
10. Planet Carrier	28. Detent Plunger	46. Retaining Clip	64. Speedometer Drive Sleeve
11. Input Shaft	29. Main Housing	47. Snap Ring	
12. Pump Retainer	30. C-Ring	48. Drive Sprocket	65. Retaining Clip
13. Pump Rear Cover	31. Set Screw	49. Snap Ring	66. Speedometer Gear
14. Pump Body	32. Shift Cam	50. Spacer	67. Oil Seal
15. Pump Front Cover	33. Cup Plug	51. Drive Sprocket	68. Rear Drive Shaft Yoke
16. Pump Pickup	34. Bearing	52. Drive Chain	69. Seal
17. Chip Magnet	35. Snap Ring	53. Lockup Shift Collar	70. Washer
18. Lockup Shift Fork	36. Oil Seal	54. Clutch Spring	71. Yoke Nut

FIGURE 14-21   Identification Key

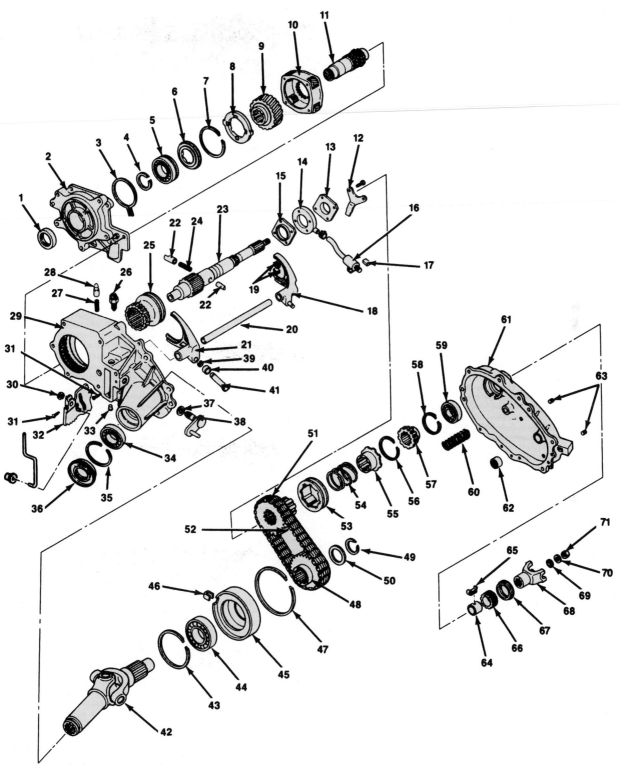

FIGURE 14-21 An exploded view of a chain-drive transfer case. A service manual should be used for the disassembly, rebuilding, and reassembly of this unit. (Courtesy of Ford Motor Company)

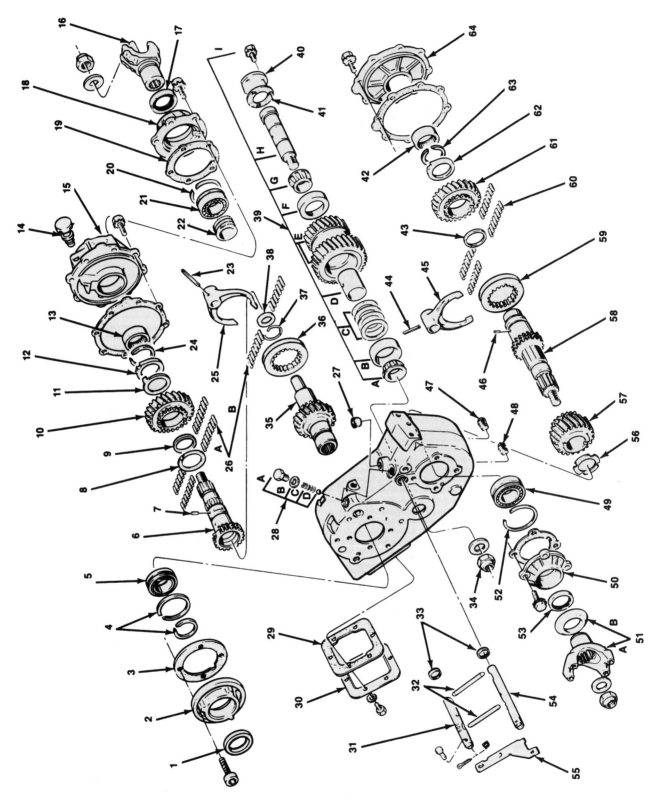

FIGURE 14-22 Exploded view of a gear drive transfer case. A service manual should be used for complete repair procedures. (Courtesy of DaimlerChrysler Corporation)

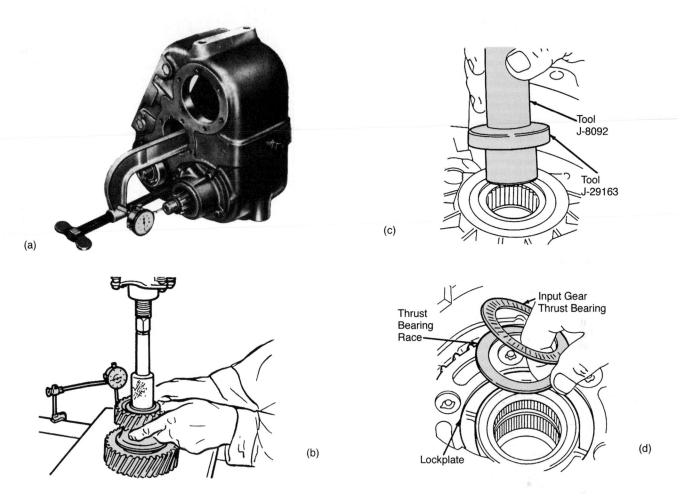

FIGURE 14-23 Some transfer case repair operations include adjustment of shaft end play/preload (a), check of gear end play (b), proper installation of needle bearing thrust washers and races (c), and removal and replacement of bearings (d). (a is courtesy of DaimlerChrysler Corporation; b, c, d: Portions of materials contained herein have been reprinted with permission of General Motors Corporation, Service and Parts Operations, License Agreement #0310807)

REAL-WORLD FIX A 1998 Explorer (86,000 mi) made a grinding noise during the 4-Low to 4-High shift but did not go into gear. The shift motor worked well. The technician was not sure how this unit operated.

FIX

The transfer case was removed and disassembled. Inspection revealed a broken shift fork and damaged shift sleeve. A new sleeve and fork fixed this problem.

REAL-WORLD FIX A 1997 4X4 Chevrolet pickup (101,000 mi) had an intermittent grinding noise from the front drive axle that could occur at any speed. The noise stopped if the transfer case was shifted into 4-High. The

front axle seals and vacuum axle actuator were replaced, but this did not help.

FIX

Advice from other technicians recommended a check of the transfer case output shaft retaining ring. A cracked snap ring was found, and replacement of this ring fixed this problem.

REAL-WORLD FIX A 1997 Explorer (81,000 mi) had a loud whining, whirring noise that occurred during deceleration from speeds above 45 mph. The noise went away when the vehicle was accelerated. The transfer case was removed, inspected, and reassembled. A new drive sprocket was installed during reassembly. The vehicle was given back to the customer but was returned with a complaint of no reverse. A test at the shop, though, showed that everything worked fine.

FIX

This problem was caused by a worn transfer case shift cam. The cam wears in a manner that it appears good until compared with a new part. Replacement of the shift cam fixed this problem.

REAL-WORLD FIX The transfer case of a 1998 Chevrolet Suburban jumped to neutral when the vehicle hit a large dip or bump in the road. The vehicle could be shifted back into gear and driven.

FIX

After disassembly of the transfer case, it was found that the plastic shift fork inserts had broken off. Replacement of the shift forks fixed this problem.

REAL-WORLD FIX A 1994 Toyota Land Cruiser (155,000 mi) had the front CV joints rebuilt at a discount repair center, and one of the joints exploded, locking the wheel to the hub. Both axles were replaced along with the wheel bearings and seals. The drive front axle was inspected for damage. The vehicle came back (two days later) because of a bad pinion whine. Inspection showed roughness on the coast side of the ring gear. No cause of the problem was found so the differential was replaced. The vehicle returned (four days later) because it was binding and making loud scraping noises on turns. The ring gear showed more severe wear on the coast side. Since no definite cause was found, a new drive axle housing, differential, and ring and pinion gear set were installed. A road test revealed gear set whine and a tendency for geartrain bind up.

FIX

A check of the transfer case in this AWD vehicle showed a damaged center differential. Replacement of this faulty differential allowed the front axle to operate without binding.

◀ PROBLEM SOLVING ▶

Imagine that you are working in a general automotive repair shop and these problems are brought to you.

Case 1

The transfer case in the utility vehicle will not shift into low range; the shift seems blocked. The shift in and out of 4WD is OK. This transfer case uses one shift lever for both operations. What is probably wrong in this unit? What will you probably need to do to fix it?

Case 2

The driver's complaint is that the vehicle jumps out of 4WD when a load is put on it. The shifts in and out of 4WD seem normal. Could this be a front axle or hub problem? Where should you begin your diagnosis?

REVIEW QUESTIONS

The following questions are provided to help you study as you read the chapter.

1. The fluid level in a transfer case is checked in a manner similar to that for a _____ transmission.

2. Driveline bind-up can be caused by operating a 4WD vehicle on a hard _____ surface while in 4WD.

3. The symptoms of driveline bind-up are hop, skip, or bounce of the _____ tires and a transfer case that becomes _____ in 4WD.

4. In-vehicle service of a transfer case may be limited to _____ level check and _____ replacement.

5. Some transfer cases use a _____ _____ seal to prevent sharing of fluid between the transmission and the transfer case.

6. Most transfer case _____ procedures are similar to those done when working on a manual transmission, transaxle, or driveaxle.

CHAPTER QUIZ

The following questions will help you check the facts you have learned. Select the answer that completes each statement correctly.

1. While discussing transfer case lubricant, student A says that the lubricant level should be at the bottom of the filler hole, as in many standard transmissions. Student B says that all transfer cases use ATF for lubricant. Who is correct?

   a. Student A

   b. Student B

   c. Both Student A and Student B

   d. Neither Student A nor Student B

2. The transfer case shift lever of a 4WD vehicle is locked in 4H. Student A says that this can be caused by poor driving habits. Student B says that backing up in a circle can often free the shift lever. Who is correct?

   a. Student A

   b. Student B

   c. Both Student A and Student B

   d. Neither Student A nor Student B

3. Student A says that driving with one wheel hub locked and the other free can cause differential wear. Student B says that some vehicles with automatic hubs need to be driven in the opposite direction to release the hubs after 4H or 4L operation. Who is correct?

   a. Student A

   b. Student B

   c. Both Student A and Student B

   d. Neither Student A nor Student B

4. Student A says that to remove a front axle shaft from most 4WD vehicles, you may need a puller to free the hubs from the axle shaft. Student B says that the axle can be pulled out through the steering knuckle after the spindle has been removed. Who is correct?

   a. Student A

   b. Student B

   c. Both Student A and Student B

   d. Neither Student A nor Student B

5. Student A says that most transfer cases resemble automatic transmissions once they are disassembled. Student B says that the same repair procedures are used on all transfer cases. Who is correct?

   a. Student A

   b. Student B

   c. Both student A and student B

   d. Neither student A nor student B

6. Transfer case overhaul includes

   a. gear inspection.

   b. bearing inspection.

   c. bearing clearance adjustment.

   d. all of these.

◀ Chapter 15 ▶

ELECTRICAL/ELECTRONIC DRIVETRAIN THEORY AND SERVICE

LEARNING OBJECTIVES

After completing this chapter, you should be able to:
1. Identify the switches, sensors, and controls used in a manual transmission/transaxle drivetrain.
2. Understand the purpose of these electrical units.
3. Be able to complete the ASE tasks for testing, adjustment, and replacement of switches, sensors, and electrical/electronic components.

TERMS TO LEARN

alternating current (AC)
ammeter
amperes (A, amp)
B−
B+
break (open)
circuit breaker
complete circuit
continuity
control module
diagnostic trouble code (DTC)
digital multimeter (DMM)
diode
direct current (DC)
electronic control module (ECM)

electrostatic discharge (ESD)
fuse
fusible link
gauge (wire)
ground
grounded circuit
high resistance (weak)
integrated microchips
make (close)
malfunction indicator light (MIL)
ohmmeter
ohms (O, Ω)
open
parallel circuit
power source

power train control module (PCM)
protection devices
relay
resistance
schematic
self-induction
sensor
series circuit
shorted circuit

solenoid
switch
symbols (circuit components)
transistors
vacuum motor
volts (V)
watts (W)
wiring diagram

15.1   INTRODUCTION

Except for a few vehicles in the mid-1930s to 1950s that used electric solenoid-operated shifts, manual drivetrain electric control was simply a backup light switch operated by the shift linkage. Electrical/electronic controls for modern vehicles include

- Clutch switches for starter operation
- Backup light switches
- Transfer case shift controls
- Overdrive unit control
- Electronic vehicle speed sensors

These switches or sensors are used to help control the operation of another part of the vehicle, such as the clutch switch that helps control starter operation, or they can be circuits that shift the transfer case.

15.2 ELECTRICAL/ ELECTRONIC BASICS

Occasionally, a drivetrain technician must repair a fault in a switch, wire, or other electrical portion component of the drivetrain. In the past, these parts were simple enough that most mechanics with basic knowledge could fix them. Modern vehicles include many electronic devices that integrate vehicle operating systems, so different systems affect each other. For example, a starting system will not operate without some preliminary action, such as the release of the clutch in the drivetrain.

Electronics usually refers to solid-state systems that are the basis for computer control. These components include transistors, diodes, speed sensors, and integrated microchip devices. Electronic control and sensing devices are rather fragile when compared to other electrical devices but can be extremely long-lived because nothing moves in them but electrons. To understand and become really proficient with electricity and electronic devices, you should take a course in automotive electronics. This explanation is just an introduction to help you understand the electrical features of an automotive drivetrain.

A technician is basically concerned with three measurable features of electricity: **volts, amperes**, and **ohms** (Figure 15-1). Volts (abbreviated as V) are a unit of electrical pressure; some call it electromotive force. Voltage is the force that pushes electric current through a circuit. In a vehicle, voltage is supplied by the battery or alternator when the engine is running. The amount of current flow is measured in amperes (abbreviated as A or amp). Ohms (abbreviated as O or Ω) are units of electrical **resistance**. Resistance limits or controls the amount of current that flows in a circuit. Electric power is measured in **watts**. Wattage is determined by multiplying the voltage by the current flow or amperes (W = V×A).

Electricity requires a **complete circuit** from the energy source, through the component doing the work, and back to the energy source (Figure 15-2). This component is also called the *load*. This circuit is composed of the battery or alternator, wires, switches, and electrical component—all electrical conductors. A modern vehicle has many different electrical circuits, with about a mile (1.6 km) of wire. Each circuit begins at the positive battery (**B+**) connection and ends at the battery negative or **ground (B−)**. Many are simple, one-component circuits; some use a **series circuit** with several components connected in a string; and some use a **parallel**

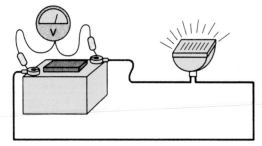

(a) Electrical Pressure Is Measured in Volts

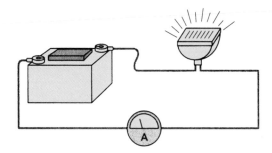

(b) Electrical Flow Is Measured in Amps

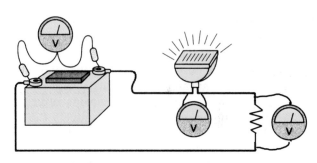

(c) Electrical Resistance Will Cause a Voltage Drop

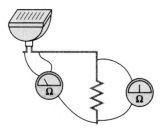

(d) Electrical Resistance is Measured in Ohms

FIGURE 15-1 Volts are a unit of electrical pressure; amperes are a unit of current flow; and ohms are a unit of electrical resistance. Resistance in a circuit will cause a voltage drop.

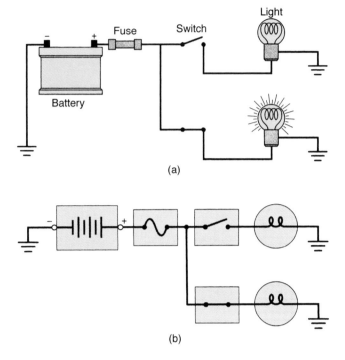

FIGURE 15-2 An electric circuit must be complete for current to flow. This can be shown in the form of a diagram (a) or schematic (b).

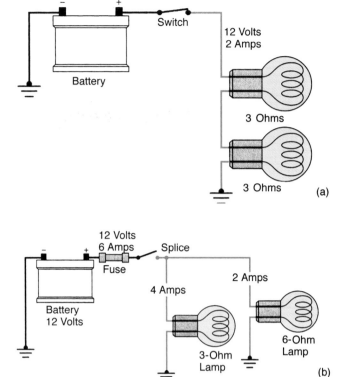

FIGURE 15-3 Series circuit (a) and parallel circuit (b). (Reprinted with the permission of Ford Motor Company)

circuit with branches that allow current flow through separate paths (Figure 15-3). Vehicle manufacturers provide **wiring diagrams** that are maps of these circuits, and these diagrams or **schematics** often use **symbols** for the components to help simplify the diagrams (Figure 15-4).

Most automotive circuits use **direct current (DC)**. DC always travels in one direction, and the flow direction is thought to be from negative to positive (− to +). Most commercial and household electricity is **alternating current (AC);** AC current switches direction many times a second. Most vehicles use 12-volt circuits, and most household and commercial circuits are either 110 or 220 V.

15.2.1 System Components

Most electrical systems have five major components:

1. Power source
2. Protection devices
3. Control devices
4. Connecting wires
5. Output devices

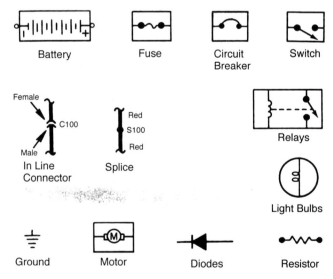

FIGURE 15-4 These symbols are used to show the components of an electrical system. (Courtesy of Everco Industries)

As mentioned, the **power source** for automotive systems is either an alternator or a battery. The battery is used primarily when the engine is not running or when electrical demands exceed the rating or ability of the alternator. When fully charged, the battery voltage is a little over 12.5 V. If electricity is used without the engine running, the voltage will drop as the battery discharges. Before computerized vehicles, most circuits would not work properly if

battery voltage dropped below 9 V; vehicles using computers require at least 10.5 V. When the engine is running, the alternator raises the voltage applied to the circuit to a regulated voltage between 13.6 and 15.6 V (Figure 15-5).

If too much current flows through a circuit, it can cause serious overheating. Current flow is normally determined by the resistance in the output device. The wire size in a circuit is designed to handle the required

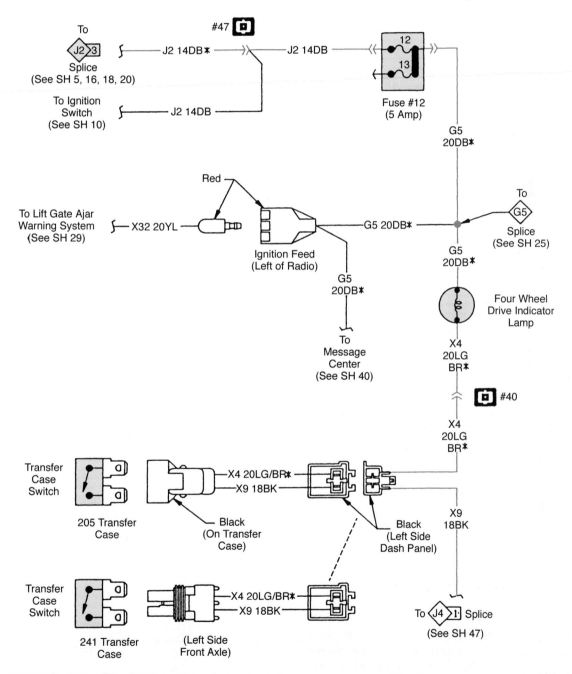

FIGURE 15-5   This 4WD indicator lamp circuit has a power source (J2 splice connector at top left), a fuse to protect it (fuse 12), a switch to control the circuit (lower left), an output (Four Wheel Drive Indicator Lamp), and wires to connect the components. The J4 splice (lower right) completes the connection to ground. (Courtesy of DaimlerChrysler Corporation)

amount of current. **Protection devices** allow enough current flow through a circuit for normal operation. Excessive current flow will cause the protection device to open the circuit and stop current flow. **Fuses, fusible links,** or **circuit breakers** are the protection devices. A fuse is a one-time device that melts at a certain current flow. Fuses are designed to be easily replaced. A fusible link is a one-time protection device that is a short piece of wire about four wire gauge sizes smaller than the wire for that circuit. A current overload causes

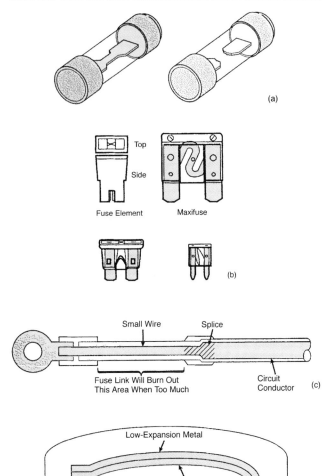

the fusible link to burn out, and the circuit must be repaired by replacing the fusible link. A *circuit breaker* senses current flow, and if amperage becomes excessive, a set of contacts will cycle open to break the circuit. Some circuit breakers reclose after cooling down to return the circuit to operation; others must be closed mechanically by pushing a button or lever (Figure 15-6).

A **switch** is the common *control device* used to **break (open)** a circuit to stop current flow or to **make (close)** a circuit to allow current flow. Most switches offer no resistance (0 Ω) when they are closed and *infinite resistance* (∞ Ω) when they are open. Some switches are combined with rheostats or variable resistors so that they can change the amount of resistance at their various positions. These are normally used to control the brightness of a light or the speed of a motor. A switch can be used to control a unit directly, like a backup light switch and backup light, or indirectly through a relay, such as a clutch switch and a starter.

A **relay** is essentially an electromagnet and a set of switch contacts. The electromagnet is controlled by a switch and requires only a small amount of current to operate. When the magnetic coil is energized by its control circuit, the magnetic pull closes the switch contacts, which, in turn, controls a current flow that can be much larger than what flows through the switch. These are *normally open* (NO) relays. Some relays are *normally closed* (NC); they are opened by the control circuit to stop current flow (Figure 15-7).

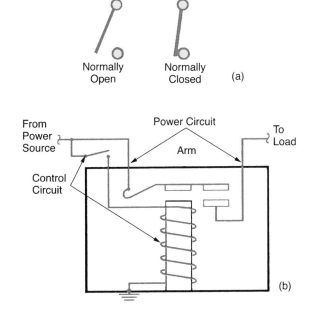

FIGURE 15-6 Circuit protection devices can be fuses with tubular (a) or flat-blade connections (b), a fusible link (c), or a circuit breaker (d). (a, c, and d courtesy of Ford Motor Company; b: Portions of materials contained herein have been reprinted with permission of General Motors Corporation, Service and Parts Operations, License Agreement #0310807)

FIGURE 15-7 A simple switch can be normally open or normally closed (a). Relays use a magnetic coil to close or open (not shown) switch contacts (b). (Courtesy of Ford Motor Company)

The wires used to complete a circuit are normally composed of a copper conductor surrounded by a plastic insulator. Copper is a very good electrical conductor and offers a fairly small amount of resistance. The amount of metal in the wire determines the **gauge** of the wire and the amount of current that it can safely carry (Figure 15-8). Plastic is an extremely poor conductor, so it is a very good insulator; this insulation keeps the current flow contained in the wire. Insulation allows two or more wires to be placed next to each other or alongside a ground.

In most vehicles, the metal body, frame, engine, and transmission provide part of the electrical circuit called the **ground circuit**. The negative (−) sides of the battery and alternator are connected to ground. Each electrical component is also connected to ground, normally by the metal case or frame of the component (Figure 15-9). Some components use a separate ground wire that is fastened to a ground connection to complete a circuit. Engine assemblies use a ground strap to ensure a good ground connection required by high-current starter systems. Most computer circuits include multiple grounds to ensure proper voltage signals.

Output devices for automotive systems include motors, lights, relays, solenoids, heaters, and magnetic clutches. Electromagnetic output devices operate from the magnetic field that is created when electric current travels through a wire. The strength of this magnet is determined by the number of turns of wire in the coil and

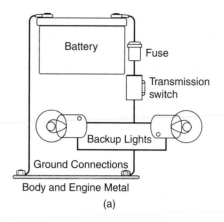

(a)

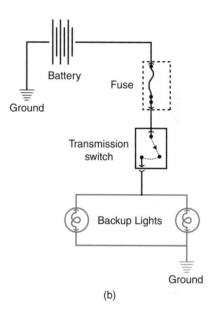

(b)

FIGURE 15-9   Insulated wires are used to conduct electricity to the clutch coil. The metal of the engine forms the ground circuit to complete the circuit back to the battery. This is shown in a diagram (a) and a schematic (b).

the amount of current, which together are called *ampere-turns*. Increasing either the number of turns or amperage increases the magnetic pull. The current flow is determined by the resistance in the wire making up the coil (Figure 15-10).

Wire Size Conversion Table			
Metric Size mm²	AWG Size	Metric Size mm²	AWG Size
.22	24	5.0	10
.5	20	8.0	8
.8	18	13.0	6
1.0	16	19.0	4
2.0	14	32.0	2
3.0	12	52.0	0

(a)

Wiring Color Code

Red
Solid Wire

Red/Wht
Stripe Wire

R/W D
Dotted Wire

R/W H
Hashed Wire

(b)

FIGURE 15-8   Electrical wire is sized by gauge sizes, using an American wire gauge system (a). Wire colors, with stripes, dots, or hash marks, are used to identify particular wires (b). (Courtesy of Everco Industries)

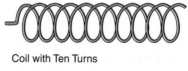

Coil with Ten Turns

Ampere Turns = 10 X Current Flow

FIGURE 15-10   The strength of a magnetic coil is determined by multiplying the number of wire turns by the current flow.

When current flows through the wire coil of a magnetic device such as a relay or clutch coil, it creates a magnetic field. When the current stops flowing, the magnetic field collapses, and this can create problems in computer circuits. When a magnetic field collapses over a coil of wires, high voltage is induced in the coil. This is called **self-induction** and is the operating principle of an ignition coil or transformer. Whenever the current flow to a magnetic coil or relay is shut off, the magnetic field collapses, inducing voltage in the circuit. In most cases the voltage is bled off and does no harm, but it can spike to a voltage high enough to damage solid-state electronic controls. To prevent this, a **diode** is included in some circuits. Connected to each end of a coil, a diode will allow current to pass in one direction but not the other. During normal operation, the diode does nothing but block unwanted current flow past the coil. When the system is shut off, the diode allows the induced current to bleed off around the coil, eliminating the high-voltage spike (Figure 15-11).

15.3 BASIC ELECTRONICS

Solid-state electronics is the basis of modern computers and automotive **control modules**. Solid-state electrical devices are units in which nothing moves except electrons. They include diodes, **transistors,** and **integrated microchips**. These units are quite reliable because there is nothing in them that wears out. They can, however, be easily damaged by rough handling and vibration, high temperatures, high current flow, and high-voltage spikes or **electrostatic discharge (ESD)**. Electronic devices are usually used for sensing and control circuits; they include sensors, control modules, and actuators.

Sensors monitor a variety of measurable functions, such as motion, speed, pressure, and temperature. Many new vehicles use speedometers that have the pointer positioned by the powertrain control module rather than the mechanical speedometer cable of the past. The powertrain control module receives an electrical vehicle speed signal from the vehicle speed sensor (VSS) mounted at the transmission/transaxle.

ABS systems use one or more wheel speed sensors so that the brake control module can determine if the wheel is braking properly or locking up. The wheel speed sensor can be mounted in the rear axle of a pickup using a RWAL (rear-wheel-antilock) system, on the CV joints of a FWD vehicle, on the axle shafts of a RWD vehicle, or on the hub of a nondrive wheel. Some speed sensors are basically a magnet(s) mounted on a rotating shaft and a switch. The magnet will pass the switch and cause it to cycle on each revolution. The ABS

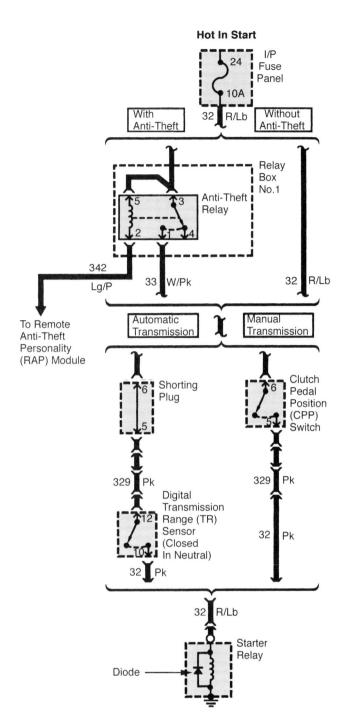

FIGURE 15-11   The starter relay in this circuit contains a diode that will prevent the induced voltage in the coil from becoming great enough to damage the control module. (Courtesy of Ford Motor Company)

wheel speed sensors are a coil of wires wrapped around a magnetic core that is mounted next to a *toothed ring,* also called a *reluctor, sensor ring, toothed rotor, exciter ring, tone wheel, gear pulser, or rotor* (Figure 15-12).

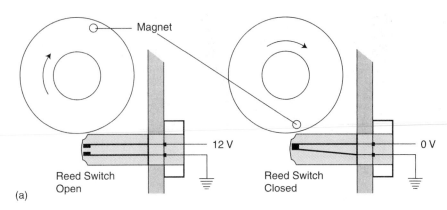

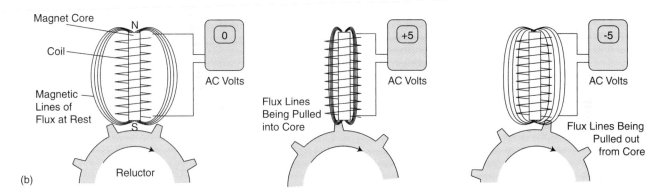

These speed sensors generate an AC electrical signal with a frequency that matches the speed of the wheel.

In an electronic shift transfer case using automatic locking hubs, a shift while moving, on the fly, from 2WD to 4WD can make a fairly severe shift because the front driveshaft and axle must suddenly come up to speed. This is avoided by applying a magnetic clutch to start the gear train moving and bring it up to speed. When the speed sensor indicates the proper speed, the shift motor is operated to complete the shift (Figure 15-13).

The T56 transmission includes a reverse lockout **solenoid** (Figure 15-14). At speeds above a few miles per hour, a spring moves the solenoid to block shifts into reverse. When the vehicle is at rest or moving forward at a very low speed, the vehicle **powertrain control module (PCM)** energizes the solenoid to allow shifts into reverse.

An **electronic control module (ECM)** is programmed to open or close circuits to relays or actuators based on the signal from the various sensors. It looks at input signals that tell it what is occurring, and in turn, it operates the outputs at the proper time (Figure 15-15). Although it is unable to handle the electric current required for a magnetic clutch or motor, a control module can operate a relay that can carry higher current. Units that use small current flows, such as light-emitting diodes (LEDs), can operate directly from the control module (Figure 15-16).

The outputs—that is, any components controlled by the ECM—include the transmission solenoid, transfer case motor and clutch, and any **malfunction indicator lights (MIL)** that inform the driver of operational problems.

15.4 ELECTRICAL CIRCUIT PROBLEMS

Most electrical problems fall into one of four categories: **open, high resistance** or **weak, shorted,** or **grounded.** These problems can occur in either a constant or an intermittent manner; intermittent problems are usually much harder to locate and are often the result of the vehicle's movement, vibration, and changes in temperature. With the proper equipment and knowledge, most electrical components can easily be checked to see if any of these problems are present.

15.4.1 Open Circuits

An unwanted open circuit is an incomplete or broken circuit in which no current can flow and is usually caused by a broken or disconnected wire, a blown fuse or fusible link (probably caused by a short or ground),

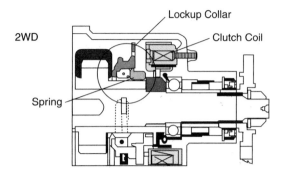

2WD

Lockup Collar

Clutch Coil

Spring

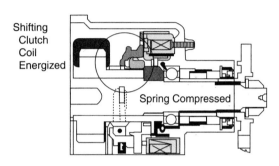

Shifting
Clutch
Coil
Energized

Spring Compressed

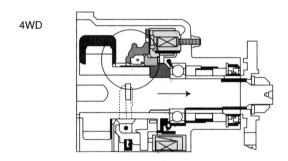

4WD

FIGURE 15-13 When a shift begins, the clutch coil is energized to pull the lockup collar against the rotating hub to start it rotating. When it is rotating at the correct speed, the shift motor is operated to complete the shift. (Courtesy of Ford Motor Company)

or a broken filament in a light bulb. Source voltage is present up to the open point, which makes locating the open rather easy. An open circuit causes a complete current loss. An open or weak circuit can occur at any point between the B+ and the ground connection (Figure 15-17).

15.4.2 High-Resistance Circuits

A high-resistance circuit is similar to an open circuit except that current is reduced (not enough to do the job). This problem is often caused by a loose or corroded connection. A high-resistance circuit causes reduced voltage

at the load, and this is called a *wasted or unwanted voltage drop*. All components that use electrical power cause a voltage drop; the voltage after the working component will always be less than the voltage before the component.

15.4.3 Shorted Circuits

Although some people use the term *short circuit* to describe any electrical problem, a short circuit is most often found only in a wire coil. If the wires lose their insulation and metal of the coil wires touches, current will take the shortest path and bypass some of the circuit or coils. The effect of the short is lower coil resistance because of the shorter path, and this allows an increase in current flow. The strength of the magnet is also reduced due to fewer ampere-turns. Sometimes a short is called a *copper-to-copper* connection. A short can also occur between the wires of two separate circuits if their insulation is damaged (Figure 15-18). This short would allow an unwanted current to flow into the wrong circuit.

REAL-WORLD FIX A 1985 Corvette (116,000 mi) automatic overdrive transmission made an immediate shift into 2nd overdrive when the shifter was moved to 2nd gear. Overdrive disengaged when shifted into 3rd gear, but reengaged immediately when shifted into 4th gear. This was a four-speed transmission with overdrive available in 2nd, 3rd, and 4th. The shifts into overdrive were controlled by a separate switch. A check for power and ground at the ECM and switch showed no problem.

FIX

A careful inspection showed that be transmission wiring was routed through the shift linkage, and the harness was shorting during the 2nd and 4th shifts. Repair of the wires and rerouting the harness fixed this problem.

15.4.4 Grounded Circuits

A grounded circuit is similar to a short except that the bare wire touches ground. This is sometimes called a *short-to-ground* or *copper-to-iron* connection. The grounded circuit completes an unwanted path directly back to battery ground (B−), so that part of the circuit is bypassed. Most of the current will follow the path of least resistance. Depending on where the connection occurs, a grounded circuit can have zero resistance, and the current flow will instantly increase to the limit of the fuse, wire, or battery. This causes a very rapid burnout, and the resulting smoke or burned-out wire is often easy to locate (Figure 15-19).

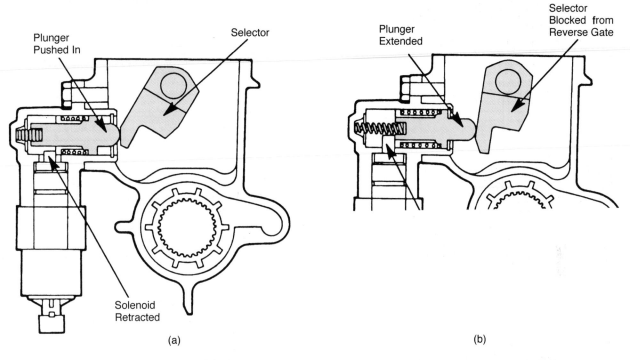

**Energized
Shift Into Reverse Allowed**

Plunger
Pushed In

Selector

Solenoid
Retracted

(a)

**De-Energized
Reverse Locked-Out**

Plunger
Extended

Selector
Blocked from
Reverse Gate

(b)

FIGURE 15-14 The lockout solenoid retracts and allows a shift into reverse when it is energized. This occurs when the PCM determines that the vehicle's speed is less than 3 mph. (Courtesy of DaimlerChrysler Corporation)

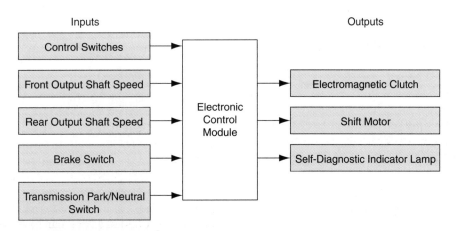

Inputs

Outputs

Control Switches

Front Output Shaft Speed

Rear Output Shaft Speed

Brake Switch

Transmission Park/Neutral
Switch

Electronic
Control
Module

Electromagnetic Clutch

Shift Motor

Self-Diagnostic Indicator Lamp

FIGURE 15-15 The electronic control module for an electronic shift transfer case receives input from three switches and two sensors. When conditions
are right for a shift, it can activate the electronic clutch, shift motor, and indicator light.

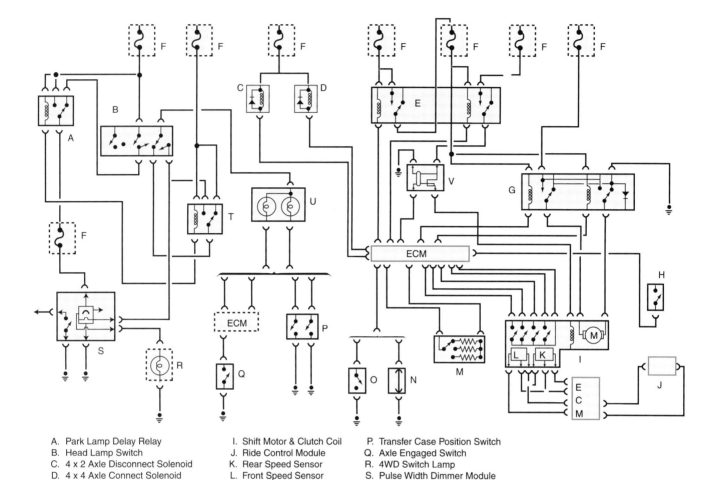

A. Park Lamp Delay Relay
B. Head Lamp Switch
C. 4 x 2 Axle Disconnect Solenoid
D. 4 x 4 Axle Connect Solenoid
E. Battery Saver & Accy Delay Relays
F. Fuses
G. Transfer Case Relay Module
H. Brake On/Off Switch

I. Shift Motor & Clutch Coil
J. Ride Control Module
K. Rear Speed Sensor
L. Front Speed Sensor
M. 4WD Mode Switch
N. Shorting Plug
O. A/T Range Sensor

P. Transfer Case Position Switch
Q. Axle Engaged Switch
R. 4WD Switch Lamp
S. Pulse Width Dimmer Module
T. Dimmer Control Relay
U. 4WD Indicator Lamps
V. Clutch Relay

FIGURE 15-16 The wiring schematic for an electric shift transfer case and electronic control circuit.

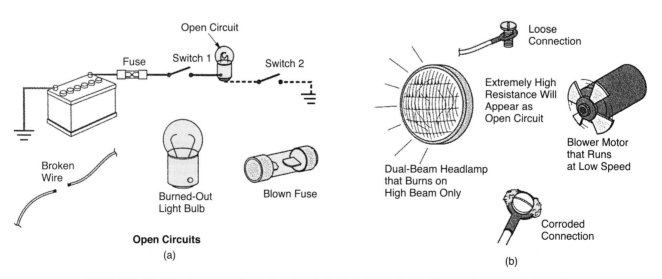

FIGURE 15-17 An open circuit is a break in the circuit that will stop the current flow (a). Corroded or loose connections will cause high resistance, which will reduce the current flow (b). (Reprinted with the permission of Ford Motor Company)

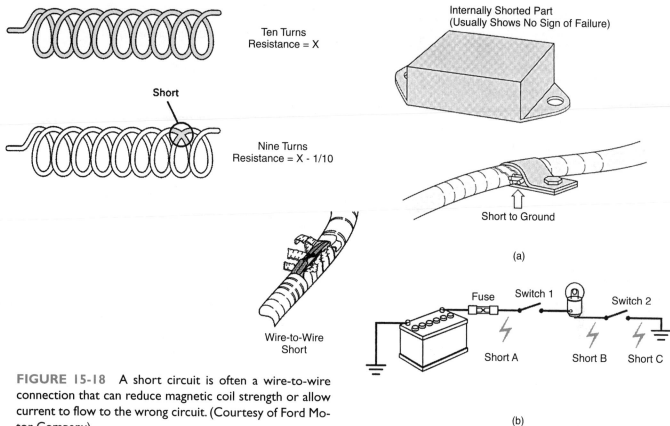

FIGURE 15-18 A short circuit is often a wire-to-wire connection that can reduce magnetic coil strength or allow current to flow to the wrong circuit. (Courtesy of Ford Motor Company)

FIGURE 15-19 A ground circuit allows current to take a shorter path to ground (a); the increased current flow will normally burn out the fuse (b). (Courtesy of Ford Motor Company)

15.5 MEASURING ELECTRICAL VALUES

Technicians commonly use a test light, jumper wire, and analog volt-ohmmeter or multimeter (a combination ammeter, ohmmeter, and voltmeter) for troubleshooting automotive electrical problems. Today, the weathertight connectors on modern vehicles make jumper wire use very difficult (Figures 15-20 and 15-21). The common test light and analog meter should not be used on solid-state circuits because they may cause faulty sensor readings or damage to the electronic components. LED test lights and **digital** voltmeters or **multimeters (DMMs)** can be used safely on any automotive circuit.

Most test lights are system powered and have a ground clip that is connected to vehicle ground and a probe used to contact electrical connections (Figure 15-22). A light in the unit lights up when voltage is contacted. Older units used a simple bulb that could draw several amperes of current. Newer units use an LED in place of the bulb. An LED draws almost no current. Self-powered test lights contain a battery and are like a flashlight with wire probes; when the probes complete a circuit, the light comes on, showing **continuity**.

Multimeters have a selector switch that must be set to the desired function, depending on what you plan to measure (Figure 15-23). Some meters have a range switch that is set to the area where the readings are expected to fall. If in doubt, the range switch is set to the highest reading possible and then reset downward until readings occur. Older meters were of the analog type and used a needle that moved across a scale to indicate readings. Newer meters are digital and display the actual value in a set of digits, and they draw only a very small amount of current from the circuit as you measure the values.

Computer circuits also require care because of possible damage through electrostatic discharge (ESD). ESD is the shock you feel or the spark you see when you touch metal after walking across certain carpets or sliding across some seat coverings. The electrostatic shock you felt was several hundred volts; an ESD discharge like this can easily damage solid-state electronic devices. The symbol shown in

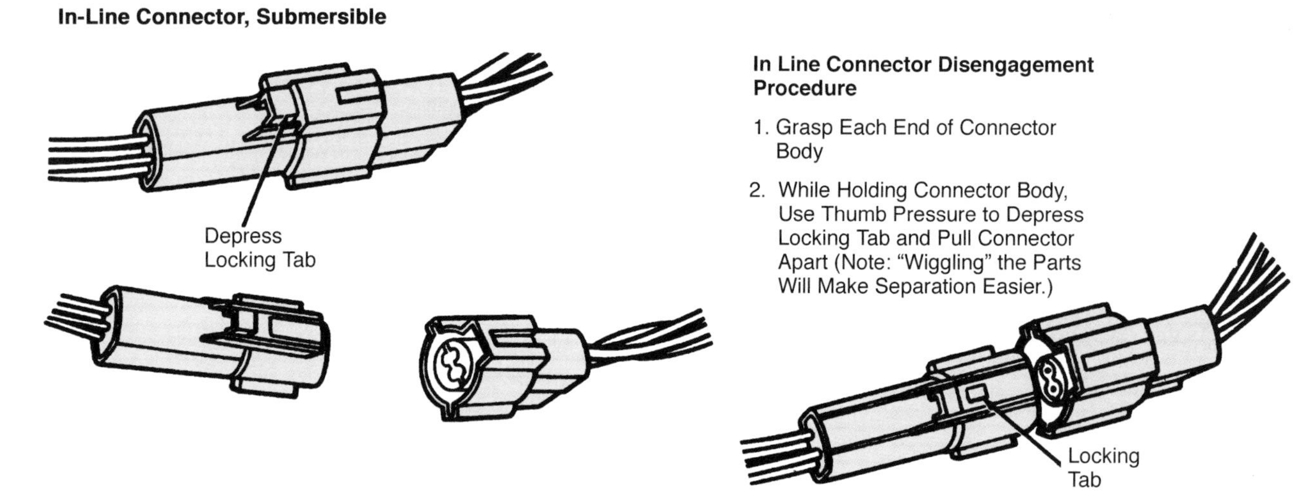

In-Line Connector, Submersible

Depress
Locking Tab

In Line Connector Disengagement Procedure

1. Grasp Each End of Connector Body

2. While Holding Connector Body, Use Thumb Pressure to Depress Locking Tab and Pull Connector Apart (Note: "Wiggling" the Parts Will Make Separation Easier.)

Locking Tab

FIGURE 15-20 Modern electrical components use weathertight connectors with locks to keep the contacts clean and tight. (Courtesy of Ford Motor Company)

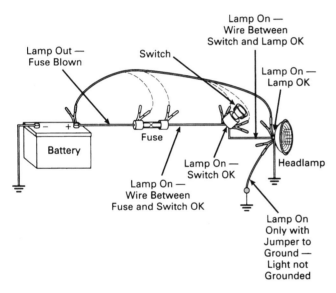

Lamp On — Wire Between Switch and Lamp OK

Lamp Out — Fuse Blown

Switch

Lamp On — Lamp OK

Lamp On — Switch OK

Fuse

Battery

Headlamp

Lamp On — Wire Between Fuse and Switch OK

Lamp On Only with Jumper to Ground — Light not Grounded

FIGURE 15-21 Jumper wires can often be used to by-pass portions of a circuit to determine where the location of the problem is. In this case, there are several possible causes for the lamp not to come on. (Courtesy of Ford Motor Company)

Figure 15-24 is placed on some components and wiring diagrams to indicate components that are easily damaged by ESD. Unless you are connected electrically to the vehicle's ground, do not touch any circuits of that component or its electrical connections. Do not make any electrical measurements or checks on these components unless instructed to do so, and always follow the directions exactly. If directed to make voltage checks, always connect the negative probe to ground first.

Weathertight connectors present a difficult problem when probing for electrical values. You can disconnect the connector and probe the ends, but sometimes this is an inaccurate reading without normal circuit load. Thin probes are available that allow back-probing a connection by sliding the probe into the back of the connector, through the weathertight packing.

◄ SERVICE TIP ►

There are probes are designed to pierce the wire's insulation using a sharp point or tip. If you break the insulation, you should reseal it using an approved sealant to prevent water from leaking in and causing future corrosion.

15.5.1 Measuring Voltage

A voltmeter is used to measure voltage and voltage drop by connecting the negative (−) lead to ground and probing various points along the circuit with the positive (+) lead. The meter will display the actual voltage for that point in the circuit; depending on the circuit and its components, this reading should be B+ (around 12 V) or some lesser value. A zero (0) reading before the last load indicates an open circuit between the probe and B+. A reading less than B+ indicates a voltage drop; this can be good or bad.

Voltage drop can also be measured by connecting the negative (−) lead to the ground side of a component and the positive (+) lead to the B+ side of the compo-

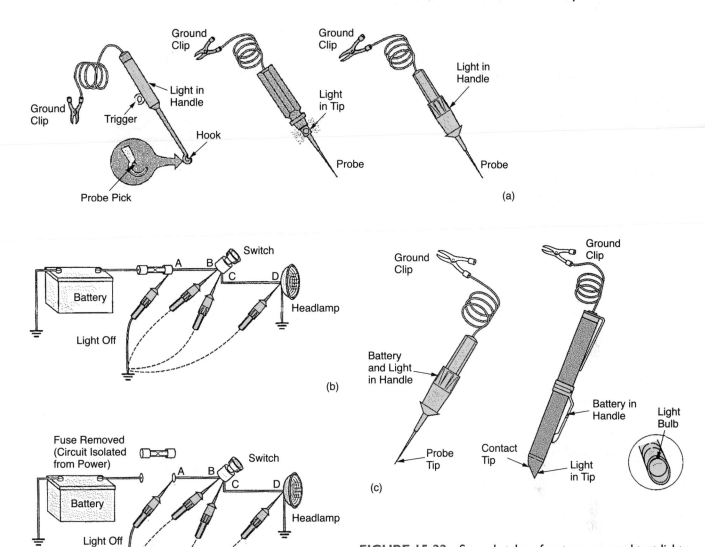

FIGURE 15-22 Several styles of system-powered test lights are available (a). They are used to probe a circuit to locate voltage (b). Self-powered test lights of varied design (c) can be used on isolated circuits (d). (Courtesy of Ford Motor Company)

nent. The reading will be the amount of voltage dropped (used) across that component. It should be noted that voltage drop occurs only while the circuit is on and under load. The total voltage drop in any circuit is always equal to the sum of each voltage drop for all of the components, and this is equal to the source voltage. Usually, all of the voltage drop occurs across the loads (actuator or output device).

◀ SERVICE TIP ▶

Don't forget that a 12-V drop across an component might be okay, *or* it may indicate that the element is open if the circuit is not working (Figure 15-25).

In a simple circuit such as a backup light, there should be B+ voltage right up to the insulated connection to the light, and there should be a 12-V drop across the lightbulb. A small drop across a connection or switch is allowed, but this is usually limited to about 0.1 to 0.2 V per connection. Any drop greater than this indicates a high-resistance problem that will cause a circuit to function below normal, and this should be corrected (Figure 15-26).

15.5.2 Measuring Resistance

An **ohmmeter** is used to measure the resistance in electrical components. The two ohmmeter leads are connected to the two ends of a wire or connections of a component, and the meter displays the resistance

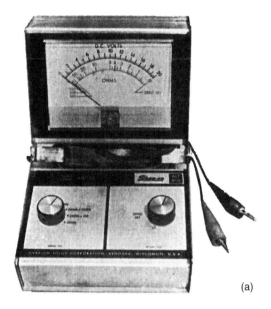

(a)

(b)

FIGURE 15-23   Analog (a) and digital (b) multimeter. Do not use analog meters when testing electronic circuits.

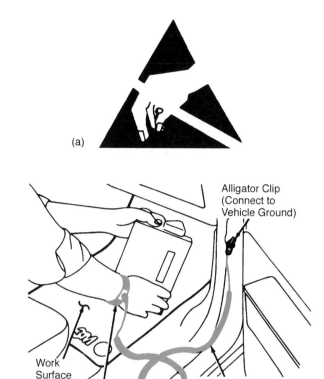

(a)

(b)   Work Surface Mat   Wrist Band   Alligator Clip (Connect to Vehicle Ground)   Ground Cord Assembly

FIGURE 15-24   Extreme care should be used when testing components displaying this ESD symbol (a). A work surface mat and grounding cord (b) can be used to prevent static electricity buildup, which can damage electronic components. (b is courtesy of Ford Motor Company)

◄   **SERVICE TIP**   ►

Many digital meters are self-ranging and give a reading of any resistance value within their ability. They also indicate the range in Ω, kΩ, or MΩ. Analog meters require setting the meter to the range (1k, 10k, 1M, etc.) and recalibrating the meter for each range. An analog meter is calibrated by connecting the leads together and rotating the calibration knob until the meter reads zero. DMMs are designed not to affect solid-state components when making resistance measurements.

value of that component (Figure 15-27). Ohmmeters are self-powered by an internal battery. They must never be connected to a circuit that has power, since the usually higher voltage from the circuit will damage the ohmmeter. Some meters have an internal protective fuse that will burn out to save the meter. Always turn off the power to the circuit or disconnect the power lead when checking components with an ohmmeter. Disconnecting the component will also keep the meter from reading unwanted parts of the circuit.

An ohmmeter is perfect for checking an item such as a clutch magnetic coil when it is off the car (Figure 15-28). If the resistance value matches the specifications, the unit does not have a short circuit and shows *continuity*. Moving one of the leads to

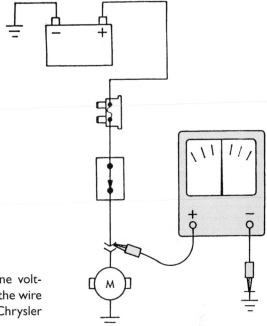

FIGURE 15-25 Voltage is measured by connecting one volt-meter lead (normally the negative) to ground and probing the wire connections with the other lead. (Courtesy of DaimlerChrysler Corporation)

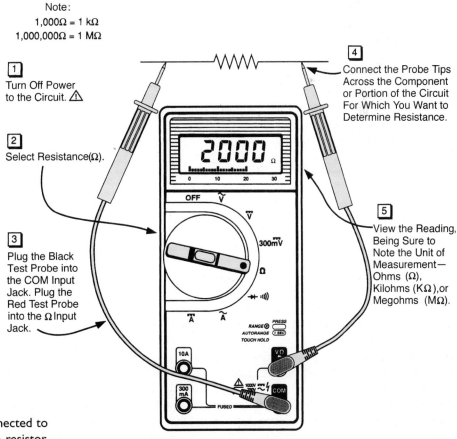

Note:
1,000Ω = 1 kΩ
1,000,000Ω = 1 MΩ

1 Turn Off Power to the Circuit. ⚠

2 Select Resistance(Ω).

3 Plug the Black Test Probe into the COM Input Jack. Plug the Red Test Probe into the Ω Input Jack.

4 Connect the Probe Tips Across the Component or Portion of the Circuit For Which You Want to Determine Resistance.

5 View the Reading, Being Sure to Note the Unit of Measurement— Ohms (Ω), Kilohms (KΩ), or Megohms (MΩ).

FIGURE 15-26 This meter is connected to measure the voltage drop across the resistor. (Courtesy of Fluke Corporation; reproduced with permission)

⚠ Make Sure Power Is Off Before Making Resistance Measurements.

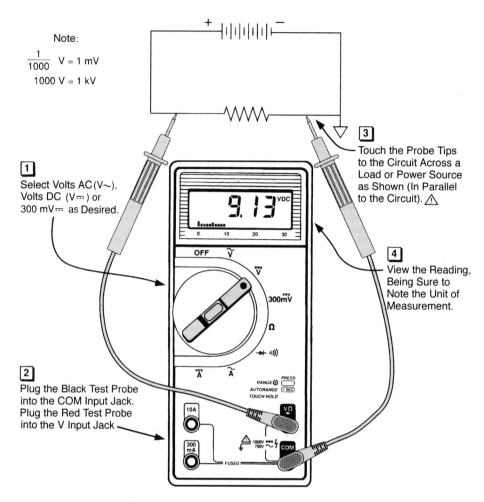

Note:

$\dfrac{1}{1000}$ V = 1 mV

1000 V = 1 kV

1 Select Volts AC (V~),
Volts DC (V⎓) or
300 mV⎓ as Desired.

3 Touch the Probe Tips
to the Circuit Across a
Load or Power Source
as Shown (In Parallel
to the Circuit). ⚠

4 View the Reading,
Being Sure to
Note the Unit of
Measurement.

2 Plug the Black Test Probe
into the COM Input Jack.
Plug the Red Test Probe
into the V Input Jack

FIGURE 15-27 A digital multimeter being used to measure resistance. Be sure to turn off or disconnect the electrical power to the circuit when using ohmmeter functions. (Courtesy of Fluke Corporation; reproduced with permission)

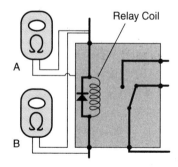

FIGURE 15-28 Ohmmeter A is connected to check for a ground circuit; it should read infinite resistance. Ohmmeter B is measuring the resistance of the coil; if the leads are reversed, it will show a different resistance because of the diode.

the unit's mounting point checks for a grounded coil; the reading should be infinite. A DMM displays *OL* for open leads to indicate infinite (out-of-limits) resistance.

◄ SERVICE TIP ►

When checking components with parallel circuits, don't forget that the meter does not know which path you want to measure; it will include all the possible paths. To be safe, disconnect one end of the component you are measuring.

REAL-WORLD FIX A 1991 Ford Explorer 4X4 (76,000 mi) would not go into 4WD, and none of the indicator lights went on. The wires to the switch and shift control modules all checked okay, but the clutch coil and shift motor did not work. The switches operated properly.

FIX

Tapping on the shift motor got it to shift into 4-High, but not 4-Low. A faulty pin connection was found at the shift motor position switch connector. Disassembly and cleaning the shift motor commutator and brushes, the shift motor position switch, and the connector fixed this problem.

15.5.3 Measuring Amperage

An **ammeter** is used to measure amperage by breaking the circuit and connecting the ammeter in series with the circuit. Some ammeters use an inductive pickup that is simply placed over the wire (Figure 15-29). If the current readings measured in the circuit are less than specifications, a weak circuit with excessive resistance is indicated. If the current readings are higher than specifications, a short or grounded circuit is indicated.

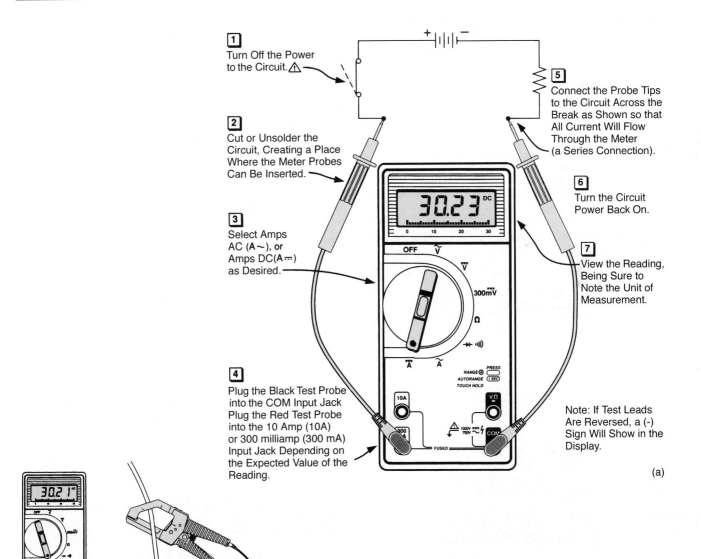

1 Turn Off the Power to the Circuit. ⚠

2 Cut or Unsolder the Circuit, Creating a Place Where the Meter Probes Can Be Inserted.

3 Select Amps AC (A∼), or Amps DC(A⎓) as Desired.

4 Plug the Black Test Probe into the COM Input Jack Plug the Red Test Probe into the 10 Amp (10A) or 300 milliamp (300 mA) Input Jack Depending on the Expected Value of the Reading.

5 Connect the Probe Tips to the Circuit Across the Break as Shown so that All Current Will Flow Through the Meter (a Series Connection).

6 Turn the Circuit Power Back On.

7 View the Reading, Being Sure to Note the Unit of Measurement.

Note: If Test Leads Are Reversed, a (-) Sign Will Show in the Display.

(a)

(b)

FIGURE 15-29 Digital multimeter being used to measure current flow (a). A transformer probe can be used to check current flow without breaking the circuit (b). (Courtesy of Fluke Corporation; reproduced with permission)

15.5.4 Interpreting Measurements

The technician must be familiar with the circuit and its components so that he or she knows what to expect while measuring electrical values. Wiring diagrams are used to follow the current flow through a circuit, much like a road map. At one time, electric circuits were quite simple and easy to follow. Now the technician often has to study the diagram and all the information available for that particular circuit to identify what he or she is working with to understand its operation.

◄ SERVICE TIP ►

Loose connectors can cause intermittent electrical problems. The small, round micropin connectors connect to a pin that is 0.040″. Round micropin connectors can be checked using a #60 drill bit (0.040″). Insert the shank of the drill bit into the connector, and you should feel a snug fit.

◄ SERVICE TIP ►

Exact specifications are often not available for the particular vehicle and circuit being worked on. Sometimes the resistance value or current draw for a clutch, magnetic coils, or relay windings is given, but not always. When testing with a meter, the technician often has to guess what a usable range should be. A known good component can be measured to obtain a reliable value. In most circuits, B+ voltage should be found up to the major output device except for an allowance for a slight voltage drop at the connectors.

REAL-WORLD FIX A 1996 Chevrolet pickup (53,000 mi) would not shift into 4WD. Using a technical service bulletin (TSB) as a guide, the front axle actuator and harness were replaced, but this did not help. Pushing the 2WD switch provided 2WD but no indicator light. Pushing the 4WD switch gave 4WD but both high and low lights remained on. A check for DTCs gets code 2, encoder fault.

FIX

Taking the encoder apart showed corrosion on the printed circuit and connectors. Replacement of this encoder fixed this problem.

AUTHOR'S NOTE

The encoder provides an electric signal for the shift lever position to the control module.

15.6 ELECTRICAL SYSTEM REPAIR

Normally, a faulty electrical component such as a switch, relay, or motor is repaired by removing and replacing it. The R&R operation is usually a rather simple process of disconnecting the wires or connectors, removing the component, installing the new component, and reconnecting the wires and other connections.

◄ SERVICE TIP ►

The new component should be compared with the old one to make sure that it is a proper replacement.

REAL-WORLD FIX A 1996 Toyota 4 Runner (93,000 mi) would not shift into 4WD; the transfer case engaged, but not the front axle. The 4WD indicator light on the instrument panel did not light. The fuses were good.

FIX

Checking a wiring diagram showed a switch on the transfer case that grounds the automatic disconnecting differential (ADD) relay. The ADD relay controls a vacuum that shifts the front differential and turns on the 4WD light. This switch was faulty, and replacing it fixed this problem.

REAL-WORLD FIX A 1996 Chevrolet pickup (110,000 mi) had a faulty U-joint replaced on the front driveshaft and it was determined that the vehicle would not shift out of 4WD. The vehicle had been converted by the dealership from a vacuum shift to an electrical shift.

FIX

Further checking of the shift motor showed a faulty motor and a contaminated electrical wire splice. Replacement of the motor and repair of the splice fixed this problem.

Occasionally, a technician must replace a faulty connector or wire by splicing the wire. A few connectors have the wires molded into them, so replacement requires splicing the new connector to each wire. In most cases, however, individual wires can be removed from the connector. These wires use an end terminal with a locking tang that expands to hold the terminal into the connector. A variety of special terminal disconnecting tools are available. The tool is pushed against the locking tang, and it depresses the tang, allowing the terminal to be pulled out (Figure 15-30).

A wire can be spliced by following a rather quick and easy procedure.

To splice a wire:

1. When replacing a wire, make sure that the new wire is of the same size or larger than the original.
2. If using a connector, slide the two wire ends into the connector (Figure 15-32).

◀ **SERVICE TIP** ▶

A wire stripper can be used as a gauge; the smallest opening that cleanly strips the wire without nicking or cutting the wire strands tells us the wire gauge. Strip off an amount of insulation slightly longer than the splice clip, about 3/8 to 1/2 in. (10 to 13 mm) long (Figure 15-31).

3. Use a crimping tool to squeeze the splice clip firmly onto the bare wire. If not using a connector, push the two wire ends together so that the bare wires overlap, and twist the connection so that the wires are tight (Figure 15-33).
4. Use a soldering gun or iron to heat the wires enough to melt solder, and apply 60/40 rosin-core solder to the hot wires until the solder flows through the joint (Figure 15-34). Do not use acid-core solder!

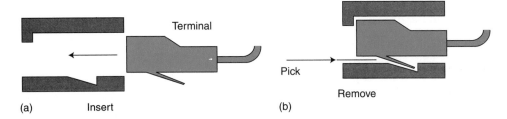

(a)   Insert   (b)

Terminal

Pick

Remove

FIGURE 15-30 A terminal is normally pushed into a weathertight connector until it locks in place (a). A pick is used to unlock the tang to allow the terminal to be removed (b).

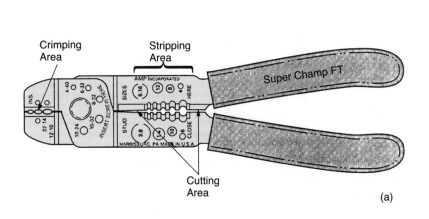

Crimping Area

Stripping Area

Cutting Area

(a)

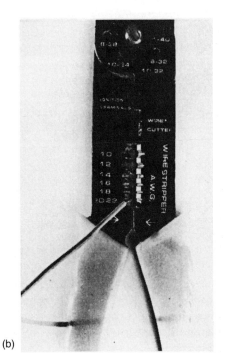

(b)

FIGURE 15-31 Wire stripping/crimping tool (a). The cutting area is used to cut the insulation and pull it off the wire (b). (a is courtesy of Ford Motor Company)

Installation Instructions

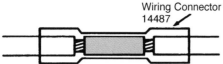

Wiring Connector
14487

1. Strip Wires 23.8mm (.94 Inch), Insert into Crimp Barrel.

2. Crimp Using Crimp Tool for Preinsulated Crimps.

3. Heat Splice with Heat Gun Until Tubing Shrinks and Adhesive Flows from Each End.

FIGURE 15-32 A splice can be made quickly by crimping a wiring connector to the two wires. (Courtesy of Ford Motor Company)

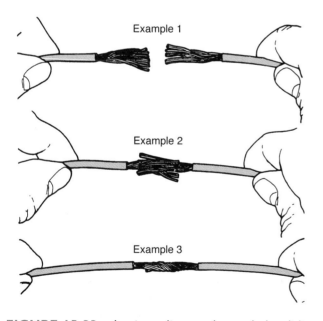

Example 1

Example 2

Example 3

FIGURE 15-33 A wire splice can be made by sliding the bared ends of the wires to overlap and then twisting them to hold them together. This connection should be soldered for security. (Courtesy of DaimlerChrysler Corporation)

FIGURE 15-34 Rosin-core solder should always be used for soldering the wire connection.

FIGURE 15-35 A repaired wire connection should be insulated by wrapping it tightly with tape or using shrink tubing. The tubing will shrink tightly in place when heated with a match.

5. Insulate the splice by wrapping it with either plastic electrical tape or a shrink tube.

◄ SERVICE TIP ►

A shrink tube is a plastic tube that is slid over the splice and heated with a match or hot-air gun so that it shrinks tightly in place to insulate the splice. If using a shrink tube, slide a piece of tube, about 1/2 in. longer than the splice, over the wire before connecting it in step 2. Keep the tube away from the connection while soldering it. After soldering the connection, slide the tube to the proper location and heat it to shrink it and lock it in place (Figure 15-35). If using tape, make sure that the tape wrapping is tight and smooth and looks neat.

15.6.1 Electronic System Self-Diagnosis

Many electronic systems use a control module that performs self-diagnosis on its sensors and its output circuits. If it locates an electrical problem, it will set and display a **diagnostic trouble code (DTC),** which is also called an *error code.* The code can be either *soft* (temporary) or *hard* (semipermanent). A soft code is erased from the control module's memory when the key

Code	Description	Action to Take
—	Inoperative or erratic system errors	Complete tests A through D
1	Microprocessor RAM access error	Replace control module
2	Clutch connector or clutch coil has discontinuity	Go to step F1
3	Front output speed sensor connector or internal circuitry of sensor has discontinuity	Go to step E1
4	Rear output speed sensor connector or internal circuitry of sensor has discontinuity	Go to step E1
5	Both front and rear speed sensor connectors and/or internal circuitry of sensor has discontinuity	Go to step E1
6	Clutch and front sensor connectors and/or clutch coil and/or internal circuitry of sensor have discontinuity	First see step F1, then step E2
7	Clutch and rear sensor connectors and/or clutch coil and/or internal circuitry of sensor have discontinuity	First see step F1, then step E2
8	Clutch and both sensor connections and/or clutch coil and/or internal circuitry have discontinuity	First see step F1, then step E2
9	Mechanical problems that allow clutch plates to slip during clutch engagement (or faulty sensor output signal)	First see step F1, then step E2
10	Both code 9 and code 2	See action for code 9
11	Both code 9 and code 3	See action for code 9

FIGURE 15-36   A diagnostic trouble code (for an electronic shift transfer case) indicates the nature of the problem. The tests and steps listed under the action to take are printed in the service manual.

is turned off; a hard code is erased by performing a special operation, pressing certain control head buttons, or removing a fuse from the control module. This is called *clearing codes*. Some systems can record and display the history of past failures.

◀ SERVICE TIP ▶

Self-diagnosis is very specific to vehicle model and circuit. Follow the exact directions given by the vehicle manufacturer or, if using a portable scanner, the directions given by the manufacturer of that scanner (Figure 15-36).

REAL-WORLD FIX A 1997 Ford F-150 (82,000 mi) had an intermittent 4WD shift problem. When the problem occurred, there was no light at the 4WD switch. Wiggling the wires and tap testing did not help. The Generic Electrical Module (GEM) was replaced, but this did not help. A check for DTCs sometimes showed a B1355, ignition run circuit open, but the problem did not last long enough to check thoroughly. It was noticed that the seat belt warning light did not function while the problem occurred.

FIX

A check of the power supply showed a loose fuse for this circuit. Replacement of the fuse block fixed this problem.

REAL-WORLD FIX A 1997 Ford Aerostar (17,000 mi) flashed Code 9, sensor output signal or mechanical problem. It displayed the code at 15 mph on a straight, level road.

FIX

Checking the signal from the front axle sensor during a road test showed a faulty signal, and disassembly showed dirt packed under the sensor. Replacement of this sensor fixed this problem.

Self-diagnosis is entered or begun by pushing a particular combination of buttons on the control head or using a jumper wire in the data link connector. The codes resulting from self-diagnosis will be displayed on (1) the control head display, (2) a handheld scanner unit, or (3) a voltmeter or test light or the display light. A scanner is a tool used to enter self-diagnosis, display trouble codes, and perform diagnostic checks (Figure 15-37). In most systems the trouble code is read as a one- or two-digit number; some systems display the code by a pattern of pulses from a voltmeter or flashes of a light.

The trouble code number indicates the nature of the problem. This number is usually keyed to a series of tests that must be performed to locate the exact fault. These tests usually involve measuring voltage or resistance at particular locations in the circuit and are found in any good service manual (Figure 15-38).

REAL-WORLD FIX The 4X4 Cancel lamp on a 1997 Ford F-150 (85,000 mi) began flashing during highway driving after a long run. If the vehicle was stopped and shifted into park, the problem was temporarily fixed. A generic scanner indicated three DTCs, but it could not read them. A check of TSBs showed a related problem; it recommended replacement of the output shaft speed sensor gear if it became loose on the shaft.

FIX

Replacement of this gear fixed this problem.

AUTHOR'S NOTE

Later, the technician learned that he could read the code number on his scanner.

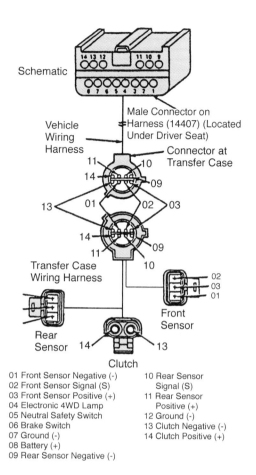

01 Front Sensor Negative (-)
02 Front Sensor Signal (S)
03 Front Sensor Positive (+)
04 Electronic 4WD Lamp
05 Neutral Safety Switch
06 Brake Switch
07 Ground (-)
08 Battery (+)
09 Rear Sensor Negative (-)
10 Rear Sensor Signal (S)
11 Rear Sensor Positive (+)
12 Ground (-)
13 Clutch Negative (-)
14 Clutch Positive (+)

FIGURE 15-38 It is often necessary to probe connector terminals to determine if the proper electrical signal is at each terminal. (Courtesy of Ford Motor Company)

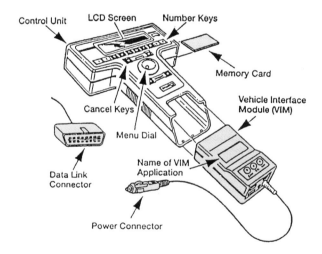

FIGURE 15-37 This scan tool is connected to the vehicle's 12-V power and the data link connector to run specific diagnostic tests or retrieve diagnostic trouble codes. (Courtesy of Ford Motor Company)

After the fault is located and repaired, the codes must be cleared. With soft codes, this is easily done by turning off the key. Hard codes are cleared by performing specific operations at the control head or on the scan tool. Removing control module fuses or the battery cable will also clear codes.

◄ SERVICE TIP ►

Disconnecting the battery will erase all the electronic memories of most cars, including clock settings and station presets for the radio, often resulting in an irate vehicle owner.

◄ SERVICE TIP ►

Removing a control module fuse erases the memory of that control module only but can also cause other problems. Some vehicles will use a portion of the engine or powertrain control module for transfer case shift control, and this also controls other engine or transmission operations.

◄ SERVICE TIP ►

Some vehicles use adaptive learning, and this programs the control module to the driver's driving style over about 100 miles of driving. If this memory is lost, the vehicle will operate differently until it relearns. This may cause some customer concern.

After any faults have been repaired and the codes erased, most technicians will road test the vehicle and rerun self-diagnosis to make sure that all the faults have been corrected.

REAL-WORLD FIX A 1992 Explorer (142,000 km) shifted between 2WD and 4WD but not into 4WD, low range. Connecting power and ground to the shift motor at the controller connector caused the motor to run and shift the transfer case. There was no voltage output from the controller for this shift.

F I X

Additional tests to check the output confirmed a controller problem. Replacement of the controller fixed this problem.

REAL-WORLD FIX A 1994 Chevrolet Blazer (128,000 mi) would not shift into 4-High. The green and amber indicator lights blinked when the switch was pressed, but the shift did not occur. The front axle vacuum motor received vacuum in low range but not in high range. Low range worked properly.

F I X

The ECM was reprogrammed back to its default settings by disconnecting the battery for $2\frac{1}{2}$ minutes and then turning the ignition on and off five times. This operation fixed this problem.

REAL-WORLD FIX The 4X4 light on an AWD 1995 Ford Aerostar (102,000 mi) flashed two times, paused two, and then repeated. The technician's service information indicated there was no self-diagnosis. A check of power and grounds at the transfer case and control module showed no problems, and the front and rear speed sensors seemed to be working properly.

F I X

Another technician provided information from a different source revealing that the blinking light indicated code 2, open clutch coil. An ohmmeter check of the clutch coil confirmed an open circuit. Replacement of the transfer case clutch coil fixed this problem.

REAL-WORLD FIX A 1992 AWD Ford Aerostar (125,000 mi) had a problem at 45 to 50 mph. It made a loud growling noise from the front, pulled hard to the right, and then pulled to the left. An inspection of the front wheel bearings, axles, CV joints, differential, and transfer case showed no problem. The front brake pads, rotors, and calipers were replaced, but this did not help.

F I X

This vehicle uses an automatic transfer case, and the front speed sensor failed. It sent a signal to the ECM to lock up the transfer case at the wrong time. Replacement of the front speed sensor fixed this problem.

15.7 VACUUM CONTROLS

Some 4WDs use **vacuum motors** to shift the transfer case between high and low ranges or the front drive axle into or out of operation. The vacuum control circuit begins at the engine, passes through small hoses, is controlled by one or more valves, and ends at one or more vacuum motors. In some ways, vacuum controls are similar to electrical controls. They include (1) a power source—the intake manifold, (2) control devices—the vacuum switch, (3) connecting hoses in place of the wires, and (4) an output device—the vacuum motor or diaphragm.

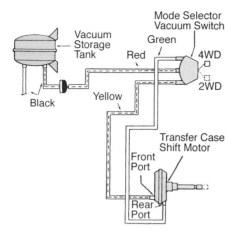

FIGURE 15-39 This vacuum circuit is used to shift a transfer case between 2WD and 4WD. The vacuum storage tank is connected to the intake manifold for the vacuum source. (Courtesy of DaimlerChrysler Corporation)

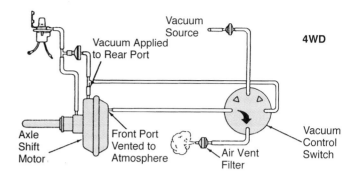

FIGURE 15-40 The vacuum control switch, mounted at the instrument panel, is used to control the vacuum to the shift motor ports. (Courtesy of DaimlerChrysler Corporation)

The vacuum source is in the intake manifold. A vacuum is really an air pressure lower than atmospheric; a vacuum is generated when the throttle plate is partially closed. Most systems use a one-way check valve and vacuum reservoir to maintain a continual supply of vacuum under all conditions (Figure 15-39). The control switch is a vacuum valve that shuttles the vacuum between different hose ports. It usually sends the vacuum signal to one hose of the vacuum motor while opening the other hose to atmospheric pressure. The control switch can be instrument-panel-mounted for manual control or remote-mounted and controlled by some other method. The axle shift motor shown in Figure 15-40 is controlled by a control switch mounted on the transfer case; when the transfer case is shifted into 4WD, the control switch causes the shift motor to engage the drive axle.

Vacuum hoses are small-diameter plastic or rubber tubes that are slid over a connector and held in place by the elastic nature of the tubing. A molded connector is sometimes used to hold a group of tubes to a control valve. Most vacuum motors use a flexible diaphragm to separate two sides of a sealed housing. When vacuum is supplied to one side and atmospheric pressure supplied to the other, the pressure differential forces the diaphragm toward the vacuum side (Figure 15-41).

◀ SERVICE TIP ▶

At a common manifold vacuum of 20 in. of mercury, the pressure differential will be 10 psi. A 4-in. diaphragm has an area of 12.5 square inches, and if a 10-psi pressure difference is acting on it, a force of 125 lb will be generated.

Vacuum controls are fairly easy to check by using a vacuum gauge to test for vacuum. The gauge reading will indicate if the signal is where it should be or has become lost because of a leaky hose or diaphragm (Figure 15-42). Vacuum controls have become less common on modern vehicles because they tend to disrupt the engine fuel mixture. This can cause lean misfire that will increase exhaust emissions.

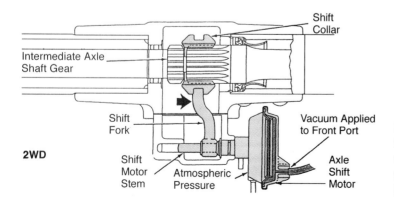

FIGURE 15-41 In 2WD mode, vacuum is applied to the right side of the shift motor's diaphragm, and this moves the diaphragm, shift fork, and shift collar to the right to disconnect the axle shaft. (Courtesy of DaimlerChrysler Corporation)

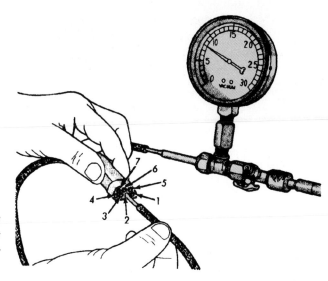

FIGURE 15-42 Vacuum circuits and devices are checked by applying a vacuum signal to the various ports and seeing if they hold vacuum or operate properly. (Courtesy of DaimlerChrysler Corporation)

REVIEW QUESTIONS

The following questions are provided to help you study as you read the chapter.

1. The three measurable features of electricity are

   a. _____

   b. _____

   c. _____

2. _____ is a measurement of electrical pressure.

3. An _____ is the measure of electrical flow.

4. An _____ is the unit of measurement of electrical resistance.

5. Electricity must have a complete _____ from the power source through the fuses, switch, and component loads back to the power source.

6. Fuses, fusible links, and circuit breakers are examples of circuit _____ devices.

7. A _____ is an electromechanical switch that controls a large current flow with a small current flow.

8. _____ are used to monitor measurable functions, such as motion, speed, pressure, and temperature.

9. An _____ _____ _____ (ECM) uses _____ inputs to open or close relays, lights, or other actuator circuits.

10. A _____ circuit will not allow any _____ to flow.

11. A high _____ in a circuit will reduce the amount of voltage and current to the load.

12. When checking circuit voltage at a load, a voltage of less than source voltage indicates a _____ _____.

13. _____ are self-powered by an internal battery.

14. _____ need to be connected in series when measuring the current flow of the circuit.

15. A _____ _____ _____ (DTC) can be accessed through the _____ _____ _____ (MIL) and will indicate the nature of a problem and the circuit affected.

CHAPTER QUIZ

The following questions will help you check the facts you have learned. Select the answer that completes each statement correctly.

1. Which of the following is the unit for electrical pressure?

   a. amperes   c. volts

   b. ohms   d. resistance

2. Most automotive electrical systems use AC current.

   a. True

   b. False

3. A fusible link is usually four wire sizes _____ than the wire used in that particular circuit.

   a. larger   c. Both a and b

   b. smaller   d. Neither a nor b

4. Which of the following would be considered the output device in an electronic transfer case shift control?

   a. shift motor

   b. transfer case select switch

   c. powertrain control module

   d. transfer case relay

5. Which of the following would be considered the input device in an electronic transfer case shift control?

   a. shift motor

   b. transfer case select switch

   c. powertrain control module

   d. transfer case relay

6. In a vehicle with a manual transmission, the clutch switch is connected to the

   a. starter motor.   c. ignition switch.

   b. starter relay.   d. both a and b.

7. Which of the following test instruments can be used on any automotive electrical circuit?

   a. test light   c. analog multimeter

   b. ohmmeter   d. DMM

8. Modern electrical devices can be damaged by

   a. electrostatic discharge.

   b. excess heat.

   c. rough handling.

   d. all of these

9. Which of the following is true concerning ohmmeters?

   a. Ohmmeters are self-powered.

   b. Ohmmeters are used to check live circuits.

   c. Ohmmeters measure resistance.

   d. Both a and c.

10. An example of a short circuit is

    a. a magnetic coil with a resistance specification of 5 to 7 ohms that measures 0.5 ohm.

    b. a burned-out lightbulb.

    c. a burned wire that lost its insulation and touches ground.

    d. any of these.

11. A broken wire is an example of a/an _____ circuit.

    a. short   c. grounded

    b. open   d. weak

12. The backup lights are very dim; this is caused by

    a. a short.   c. an open circuit.

    b. high resistance.   d. a short to ground.

13. A SUV will not shift into 4WD. Student A says that the shift motor could be stuck. Student B says that sometimes the shift motor will work if you tap it with a small hammer. Who is correct?

    a. Student A   c. Both A and B

    b. Student B   d. Neither A nor B

◀ Chapter 16 ▶

EXTRADUTY AND HIGH-PERFORMANCE DRIVETRAINS

16.1 INTRODUCTION

In this chapter we describe the variety of heavy-duty and aftermarket drivetrain components used for extraduty, specialized, and off-road applications. These components range from almost-stock units to units manufactured specifically for racing application and, in some cases, for very specific operations. For example, the clutches designed for drag racing, NASCAR, and "Indy" cars are quite different from each other as well as from a stock unit.

For the most part, the components described in this chapter are not found in the average parts house; many are available through speed shops that deal in high-performance parts. Most of these parts are not serviced in the average repair shop, and in some cases, their installation will void manufacturers' warranties or could be in violation of clean-air standards in some states.

There are as many reasons for modifying the drivetrain as there are a variety of vehicles. For example, the owner of a pickup with a heavy-duty clutch or transmission gear set installed to handle the added load of pulling a heavy trailer, a camper, or R/V may try to improve fuel mileage with an auxiliary transmission, an off-roader may install a locking-style differential in a 4WD, or a hot-rodder may change rear axles to handle the torque from increased engine performance. Racing places special demands on a drivetrain. In almost all forms of racing, the most important criteria are the ability to transfer torque, overall light weight, light inertial or rotational weight, small physical size, sufficient endurance, and the ability to shift gears quickly and pre-

cisely. Unlike stock components, cost and ease of repair are secondary in importance.

16.2 RACE CAR DRIVETRAIN DESIGN FACTORS

The physical weight of a drivetrain component is simply how much it weighs. This weight places a burden on the vehicle in that the tires and springs must carry the weight, and the mass must be accelerated and decelerated when the vehicle changes speed. This mass is also affected by inertia. The greater the mass, the more difficult it is to change speed. In addition, this mass causes weight to transfer from side to side during turns, from front to rear during acceleration, and from rear to front during braking. Normally, the overall weight will be kept as low as possible and as low in the vehicle as possible to keep the center of gravity close to the ground.

The amount of rotating weight or mass in the drivetrain (Figure 16-1) is usually referred to as the moment of inertia (MOI). This mass resists changes in engine speed and also vehicle speed when the engine is connected to the drive wheels. A heavy flywheel, for example, is often used to maintain a fairly constant, rotating low speed. A 4WD operating at crawl speeds over a boulder or very rough road can benefit from the effects of a heavy flywheel and clutch. However, this setup would greatly inhibit a sprint car's ability to accelerate rapidly. Moment of inertia is the amount of mass and

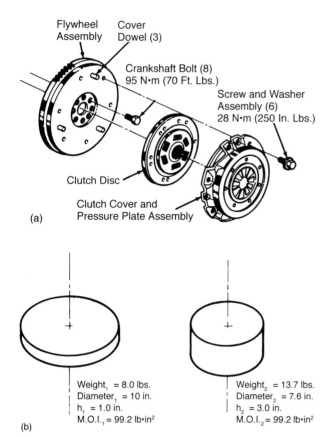

(a)

(b)

Weight$_1$ = 8.0 lbs.
Diameter$_1$ = 10 in.
h$_1$ = 1.0 in.
M.O.I.$_1$ = 99.2 lb·in^2

Weight$_2$ = 13.7 lbs.
Diameter$_2$ = 7.6 in.
h$_2$ = 3.0 in.
M.O.I.$_2$ = 99.2 lb·in^2

FIGURE 16-1 (a)The rotating mass of the flywheel and pressure plate assembly generates a rotating inertia to dampen engine torsional vibrations and prevent engine stalling as the clutch is let out. The amount or moment of inertia is determined by the amount and diameter of the mass. (b) In this example, an 8-lb flywheel can have the same moment of inertia as a 13.7-lb flywheel. (a is courtesy of DaimlerChrysler Corporation; b is courtesy of Tilton Engineering)

where it is located relative to the center of the shaft. The formula used to compute moment of inertia is

$$MOI = M \times r^2$$

where:

MOI = moment of inertia
M = mass
r^2 = radius $\times$ radius

A study of this formula reveals that doubling the mass or overall weight will double the moment of inertia, but if the radius is doubled, the moment of inertia will increase greatly, about four times. An increase in the moment of inertia of the drivetrain will make the engine work harder to accelerate, and the brakes will have

to work harder to slow the vehicle. The energy transfer during braking will be lost as heat.

The accelerating ability of most race cars is limited by tire traction. This is the amount of grip between the tires and the road surface. You are probably familiar with tire spin, which occurs when too much power is sent to the tires for the traction available. Some engineers and many race car teams look at traction as the amount of grip in pounds or newtons; this is a product of several factors, as shown in Figure 16-2. Notice that maximum traction occurs at a 10 to 25 percent slip rate and that the amount of traction drops off rapidly when the slip rate or amount of tire spin increases (Figure 16-3). A spinning tire has very little traction. An experienced driver tries to sense wheel spin during acceleration and will reduce the amount of throttle when spin occurs (Figure 16-4).

Wheel spin occurs when the driving torque on the tires exceeds the traction force. It does no good to have

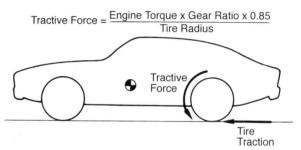

FIGURE 16-2 Wheel spin will occur if tractive force exceeds traction. Traction is a product of the weight on the tire and the coefficient of friction between the tire tread and the road surface.

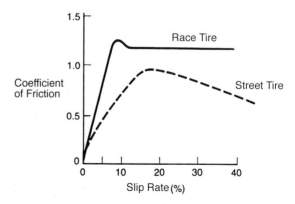

FIGURE 16-3 The coefficient of friction is the greatest at a 10 to 25 percent slip rate of the tire to the road. Note how a race tire generates a higher coefficient of friction than a street tire.

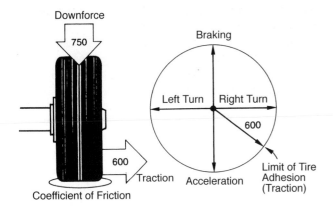

FIGURE 16-4 With this particular coefficient of friction and downforce, this tire can generate 600 lb of traction; this traction force, called the circle of traction, is the same in all directions—forward, sideways, or rearward.

Vehicle with: 300 ft.-lb. of torque; 26-inch diameter tires on drive wheels; transmission 1st gear ratio of 2.2 : 1

Axle ratio	Overall ratio	Tractive force	Top speed (5,000 rpm)
3.08	6.77	133	125.62
3.42	7.55	148	113.13
3.73	8.26	162	103.73
4.10	9.02	170	94.37
4.56	10.03	197	84.84
4.88	10.74	211	79.28
5.13	11.29	221	75.42
5.38	11.4	232	71.91

FIGURE 16-5 The tractive force has been calculated for a first-gear ratio of 2.2:1 and eight different axle ratios. The top speed with a transmission ratio of 1:1 has been included for the same axle ratios. Calculations such as this are often done when selecting transmission and axle ratios for a particular track.

more torque at a drive wheel than traction conditions permit unless the driver is completely capable of sensing wheel spin as it begins and can react to it instantly or the vehicle has electronic traction control. Slider or slipper-style clutches used in drag racing are designed to transfer only part of the engine torque to the drivetrain and gradually increase that amount until full lockup occurs a few seconds later.

Electronic traction control systems are available on many new vehicles and are being used on some modern racing vehicles. These units sense wheel spin using the same electronic sensors as the antilock braking system. When the system detects wheel spin (the rear wheels will be turning faster than the front wheels), the system will either reduce engine power and/or apply the brakes to keep the maximum amount of wheel spin within prescribed limits. This makes driving a fairly high horsepower car easier and safer on wet or icy roads. Wheel torque is a product of engine torque times gear ratio, as described in Section 3.6.

When a road race team selects the gearing to use at a particular track, the two major considerations are the slowest corner and the fastest straightaway (Figure 16-5). The car must be able to accelerate out of the slowest corner with gearing that multiplies torque to a point of or just below wheel spin. The highest-speed gearing should let the engine almost reach redline, or maximum rpm, at the end of the fastest straightaway. The speed difference between these two points and the torque curve of the engine determine the number of gears needed in the transmission. A wide variation in speed or a "peaky" engine with a narrow torque band may require a four-, five-, or six-speed transmission. A small speed difference with an engine that has a wide torque band can use a one-, two-, or three-speed transmission. In this

case, many race teams will remove the unused gears from the transmission; this saves inertial drag and power loss from the frictional drag. By removing some of the gear sets, some four- and five-speed transmissions can become two- or three-speed transmissions.

The gearing to adjust engine speed to the fastest point on the track is at the final drive or rear axle ring and pinion gears and the tire diameter. As in a passenger car, this is determined by the formula for speed (mph) in Section 3.6. The gearing for the slowest-speed section is the transmission gear ratio times the final drive ratio.

16.3 CLUTCHES

A heavy-duty, extraduty, racing-style clutch must follow all the operating principles given in Chapter 4. To transmit more torque, a clutch must have greater surface area (larger diameter or multiple plates), a higher spring or clamping pressure, or a higher coefficient of friction. Each of these brings a disadvantage, so a compromise is usually the needed.

Normally, a clutch and flywheel are considered a unit. A larger-diameter clutch for some engines requires a flywheel with a larger friction surface area and bolt-hole drilling for the pressure plate. A heavy clutch assembly and heavy flywheel are grouped together when a large amount of inertial mass is desired for low-rpm operation. The flywheel used with a lightweight clutch on an engine that revs to very high rpm should also be lightweight and of a material that will not explode from centrifugal force (Figure 16-6). When a small-diameter clutch assembly is chosen for a very low mounted engine in a car with almost no ground clearance, the flywheel must also be of a small diameter and a special starter is required.

Many early high-performance clutches increased their torque-transmitting power simply by changing the springs, adding the maximum number of springs possible, or using stronger, higher-rate springs. Of course, this increased the amount of pedal effort required to release the clutch and the load on the throw-out bearing and crankshaft thrust bearing. If your left leg wasn't strong enough, you couldn't drive the vehicle. Current designs have made more use of centrifugal assist (Figure 16-7).

The spring clamping power only needs to be strong enough to provide the initial clamping force, and the added clamping force from centrifugal force takes care of the torque increase as the engine speed increases.

Small-diameter clutches use multiple discs to transmit the required amount of torque (Figure 16-8). This requires a floater plate between each disc, support stands for the pressure plate to compensate for the added height, and a pressure plate with increased travel so that each disc will have a sufficient air gap when released. When these clutches are used with aluminum flywheels and pressure plates, a harder plate must be positioned next to the aluminum to protect it. This plate is called a *heat shield, wear plate, floater,* or *facing.*

Racing-clutch discs commonly use organic facing, metallic-sintered iron facing, or ceramic–copper facing (Figure 16-9). Organic facing is preferred for a smoother,

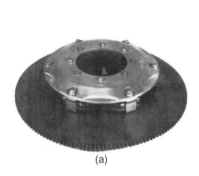

(a)

FIGURE 16-6 (a) This small-diameter multi-plate clutch is designed for racing operations whe moment of inertia and overall weight are important. (b) Flywheels of smaller diameters are also available to reduce inertia and lower the engine in the chassis. (Courtesy of Tilton Engineering)

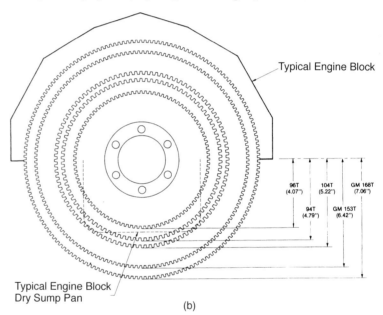

(b)

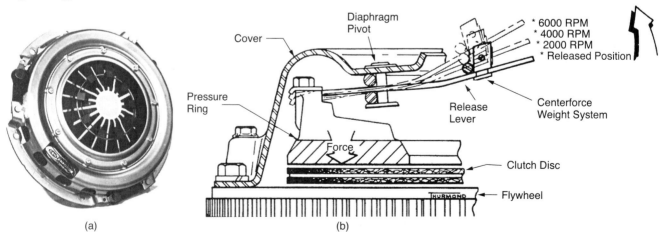

(a)   (b)

FIGURE 16-7 Weights have been added to the release levers of this diaphragm clutch to increase clamp load and torque capacity. (Courtesy of Centerforce Clutches)

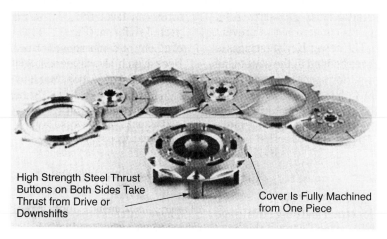

High Strength Steel Thrust Buttons on Both Sides Take Thrust from Drive or Downshifts

Cover Is Fully Machined from One Piece

FIGURE 16-8 Three-plate racing clutch; the open design offers clean and cool operation. (Courtesy of Tilton Engineering)

less aggressive application; the other two materials are preferred for higher-temperature use. The newer metallic clutches have smoother engagement characteristics, which are similar to those of the organic materials. Street-type discs are normally dampened and include a Marcel. Rigid, undampened discs are used for most competition installations. When solid discs without a Marcel are used, the amount of pressure-plate travel required to release the clutch is very short.

The different facing materials can be identified rather easily by appearance. Most organic facing looks like normal asbestos or nonasbestos facing; sintered iron facing is a full-circle facing that should have heat expansion slots cut across it; and ceramic–copper facing is in rather small pads, with 3 to 10 pads used on each side of the disc. The ceramic–copper pads can be attached to a disc having three or six arms or a full-circle disc. When attached to a full-circle disc, the disc must have expansion slots cut across it to prevent warpage from heat expansion. The newer Kevlar facing is in the form of pads or pucks that are bonded to the plate. One clutch design intended for high-performance street and drag race use incorporates two different fac-

Organic Facing

Metallic Facing

FIGURE 16-10 This dual friction disc has an organic facing on one side and a metallic facing on the other to generate more torque capacity with smooth operation. (Courtesy of Centerforce Clutches)

ing materials. This disc uses a nonasbestos, synthetic composite material facing on one side and a powdered metallic facing on the other (Figure 16-10).

16.3.1 High-Performance Clutch

These clutches are designed for street and drag strip use in production vehicles. In most cases they are very

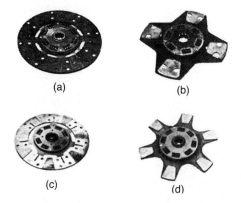

(a)

(b)

(c)

(d)

FIGURE 16-9 The variety of clutch discs includes organic facing (a), copper–metallic facing (b), combination facing (c), and sintered iron facing (d) in both dampened and rigid designs. (Courtesy of McLeod Industries, Inc.)

similar to the Borg and Beck, diaphragm, and Long-style stock units. Depending on the supplier, they can include a pressure plate assembly with a heavier and stronger cover, nodular iron pressure rings, improved springs, and improved pivots and contacts between the cover and the pressure ring. Some firms can tailor the centrifugal assist weights to the expected shift rpm (Figure 16-11). Adding weight to the fingers of a Long or diaphragm clutch or adding rollers to a Borg and Beck clutch allows a reduction in the spring strength for easier pedal operation. But if too much weight is added, the clutch cannot be released above certain rpms.

To remove the danger of explosions at high rpm, high performance pressure-plate assemblies are used with high-rpm flywheels and discs.

16.3.2   Slider Clutch

Slider clutches are designed for drag strip use. They are also used in tractor- and truck-pulling vehicles and mud racing. Slider clutches solve a problem encountered with very high horsepower vehicles, such as top-fuel, supercharged dragsters and funny cars. The engines in these cars produce much more torque than the tires can transfer to the ground. If the clutch locks up completely with the vehicle standing still, the tires will spin, or if there is enough traction so that they don't spin, the vehicle may do an extremely high wheel stand. If the tires spin, they will create a lot of tire smoke but not much acceleration. The clutch used on such a car is designed to slip and not lock up until the car is some distance

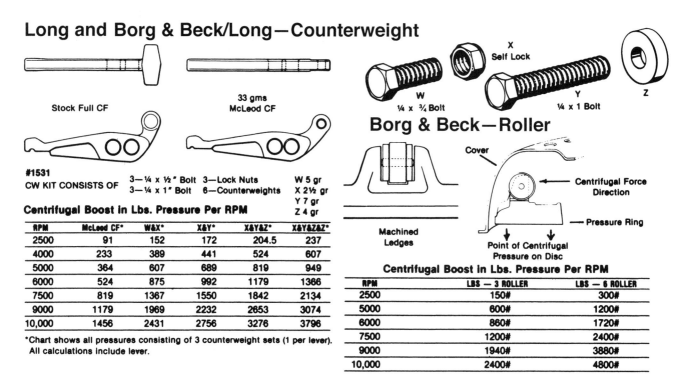

Long and Borg & Beck/Long—Counterweight

Stock Full CF

33 gms
McLeod CF

#1531
CW KIT CONSISTS OF

3—¼ x ½" Bolt   3—Lock Nuts
3—¼ x 1" Bolt   6—Counterweights

W 5 gr
X 2½ gr
Y 7 gr
Z 4 gr

Centrifugal Boost in Lbs. Pressure Per RPM

RPM	McLeod CF*	W&X*	X&Y*	X&Y&Z*	X&Y&Z&Z*
2500	91	152	172	204.5	237
4000	233	389	441	524	607
5000	364	607	689	819	949
6000	524	875	992	1179	1366
7500	819	1367	1550	1842	2134
9000	1179	1969	2232	2653	3074
10,000	1456	2431	2756	3276	3796

*Chart shows all pressures consisting of 3 counterweight sets (1 per lever).
All calculations include lever.

X
Self Lock

W
¼ x ¾ Bolt

Y
¼ x 1 Bolt

Z

Borg & Beck—Roller

Machined
Ledges

Cover

Centrifugal Force
Direction

Pressure Ring

Point of Centrifugal
Pressure on Disc

Centrifugal Boost in Lbs. Pressure Per RPM

RPM	LBS — 3 ROLLER	LBS — 6 ROLLER
2500	150#	300#
5000	600#	1200#
6000	860#	1720#
7500	1200#	2400#
9000	1940#	3880#
10,000	2400#	4800#

(a)

Adjustable Pressure Plate

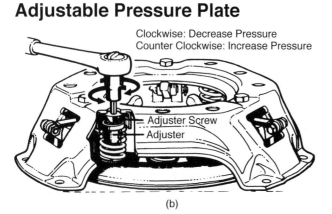

Clockwise: Decrease Pressure
Counter Clockwise: Increase Pressure

Adjuster Screw
Adjuster

(b)

FIGURE 16-11 (a) These Long and Borg & Beck pressure-plate assemblies have various-sized weights that can be added to obtain increased rpm clamp loads. (b) Some of these clutches also offer adjustments for the static spring load. (Courtesy of McLeod Industries, Inc.)

down the track. This style of clutch is adjustable, to allow control over the initial torque transfer and the lockup point (Figure 16-12). The slipping of the clutch generates a lot of heat, requiring exotic materials in construction and a large amount of maintenance. The clutch in some top-fuel cars has a life of four runs or

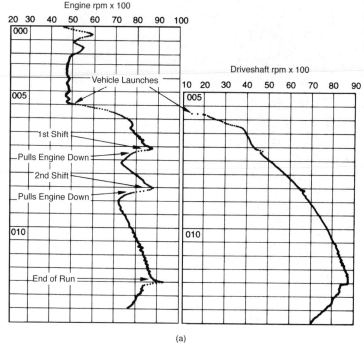

(a)

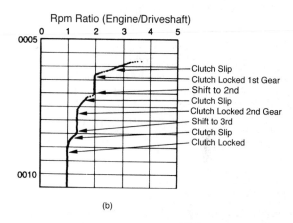

(b)

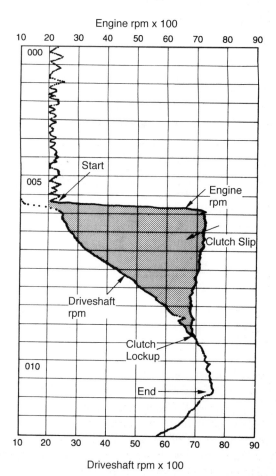

(c)

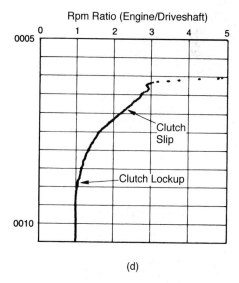

(d)

FIGURE 16-12 Onboard computer tape recording of the engine rpm and the driveshaft rpm (a) and the engine-to-driveshaft gear ratio (b) from a top-alcohol dragster during a 6.16-second, 225-mph run; note the clutch slippage at launch and after each shift. A similar tape for a top-fuel car shows the engine rpm and the driveshaft rpm (c) and the engine-to-driveshaft ratio (d) during a 4.9-second, 187-mph run; note the clutch slippage during the first 3 seconds. (a and b are Courtesy of Racepak)

less, about 1 mile (1.6 km). Most top-fuel teams replace the clutch discs and floater plates every run. The proper adjustment and maintenance of this clutch is as important as any other factor in producing a good run.

There are two major styles of slider clutches: lever clutches and pedal clutches. Lever clutches are strictly centrifugal clutches with all the clutch clamp load coming from centrifugal force acting on one or more sets of levers—as many as 18 levers. Springs are used in lever clutches to provide plate clearance and to release the clutch at low engine speeds. The strength of these springs adjusts the stall rpm, which is the point at which the clutch begins to apply. The shape, weight, and initial angle of the primary levers and the centrifugal force acting on them push the pressure plate against the clutch plates to engage the clutch (Figures 16-13 and 16-14). A lever clutch can have up to four sets of levers that operate at different times in a sequence determined by throw-out bearing

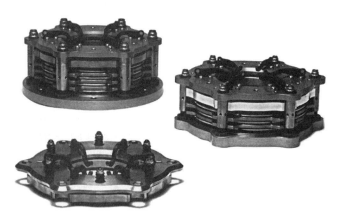

FIGURE 16-13   One-, three-, and four-disc slider clutch. These clutches are applied by centrifugal force acting on the release lever arms. The springs in the centrifugal clutch release the clutch and provide resistance for stall speed. (Courtesy of L & T Slider Clutches and Joel Gelfand)

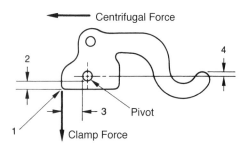

FIGURE 16-14   Lever arm. Some of the factors that affect slider clutch timing and force are the radius of the pressure point (1), the distances from the pivot point (2 and 3), the weight, and height of release bearing contact point (4). (Courtesy of L & T Slider Clutches)

FIGURE 16-15   This slider clutch has several sets of lever arms; release bearing movement allows the second and third sets of arms to increase clamp pressure. (Courtesy of L & T Slider Clutches)

movement (Figure 16-15). The second-, third-, and fourth-stage levers have different length projections where they contact the throw-out bearing. As the bearing moves away from the clutch, another set of levers can become effective and add its force to the clamp load, making the clutch stronger. Adjustments for a lever clutch include initial plate clearance; release spring resistance; weight, shape, and mounting angle for each set of levers; and the rate of throw-out bearing movement.

A pedal clutch engages when the clutch pedal is released and a spring causes pressure-plate movement, much like that of a conventional clutch. This clutch is used on cars that require a high rpm before clutch engagement. After engagement, a set of levers increases clamp load with increased rpm, much like a lever clutch.

Both of these clutch styles are multiplate clutches with the number of plates determined by horsepower. A top-fuel dragster usually uses four plates; a pulling tractor uses five.

16.3.3   Button Clutch

The clutches used in short track, circle track, NASCAR, and road racing (which includes Indy and formula cars) are often called *button clutches* because of their relatively small diameter. The diameter is kept as small as possible to reduce the moment of inertia. Most short and circle track cars use a clutch with a static load. The clutches are engaged as the vehicle leaves the pits and not used again until the race is over. Some of these cars use a simple mechanical dog clutch, which is the lightest arrangement possible but which can only be engaged with the engine shut off. A newer type of dog clutch, called a *coupler*, includes a cone clutch (Figure

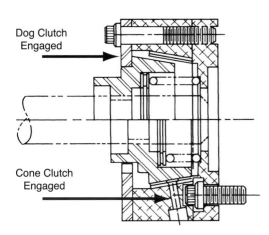

FIGURE 16-16   Dog Clutch Engaged / Cone Clutch Engaged

FIGURE 16-16   This coupler combines a dog clutch with a small cone clutch. Depressing the clutch pedal causes cone clutch application, which can start the vehicle moving, and releasing the pedal allows the spring to engage the steel splines. (Courtesy of RAM Automotive)

FIGURE 16-17   Closed-design multiplate racing clutch; note how the floater plates are splined to the outer ring, which also serves to support the pressure-plate assembly. (Courtesy of Quarter Master Industries)

16-16). Pushing the clutch pedal downward engages the cone clutch, which provides the initial engagement to move the car. Releasing the pedal engages the splines of the dog clutch and gives positive lockup.

When the vehicle has to shift gears during a race, dynamic friction and the heat and wear that it generates become important factors. Early multiplate clutches were enclosed in a ring that tended to trap debris and heat, both of which were detrimental to clutch operation (Figure 16-17). Modern clutches are of an open design that operates cleaner and cooler and also has a much lower moment of inertia.

Clutch heat is an important factor with Formula 1 cars. Every part of these vehicles is as lightweight as possible in order to improve vehicle performance. A very-high-speed engine with poor, low-rpm torque at a standing start for a race has a potential for engine stalling or clutch burnout. Some of these clutches have

the ability to withstand only one or two all-out engagements. A modern, space-age innovation is to use carbon–carbon friction surfaces on the flywheel and a pressure plate with carbon–carbon discs (Figure 16-18). This material is very light in weight and can withstand temperatures as high as 3000°F (1650°C). It is also very expensive. Its coefficient of friction does not fade with heat; in fact, the amount of friction increases. Carbon–carbon will operate at temperatures that can melt the clutch and remove the temper and strength from the pressure spring. The moment of inertia of this material is about one-third less than a metallic clutch of equal power. Carbon–carbon clutches have an extremely low wear rate, often lasting four times longer than clutches using metallic facing.

16.3.4   Performance Clutch Linkage

The linkage used to operate the clutch is usually a simplified version of the linkage used in passenger vehicles. Many builders use the tried-and-true rule "the simpler, the better." Linkage is either mechanical or hydraulic.

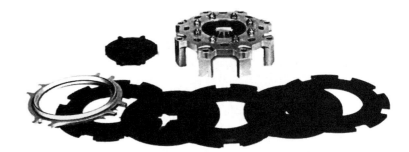

FIGURE 16-18   The black color of the discs and floater plates and drive hub identify this carbon clutch. It will handle 600 ft-lb of torque and has a total weight of only 3.3 lb and a moment of inertia of 14.7 lb-in². (Courtesy of Tilton Engineering)

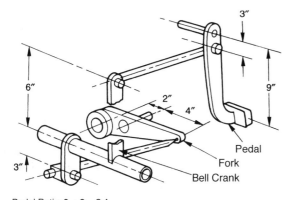

3″
9″
6″
2″
4″
Pedal
Fork
3″
Bell Crank

Pedal Ratio: 9 ÷ 3 = 3:1
Bell Crank Ratio: 6 ÷ 3 = 2:1
Fork Ratio: 4 ÷ 2 = 2:1
Overall Ratio: 3 × 3 × 2 = 18:1

(a)

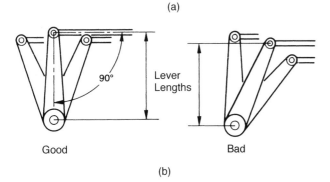

90°
Lever
Lengths

Good   Bad

(b)

FIGURE 16-19   (a) A typical mechanical linkage should be as simple as possible with lever lengths designed to provide the release force needed with short, fast operation. (b) The lever should be positioned so the lever and the operating rod form a 90° angle at the midpoint of the motion.

Mechanical linkage consists of the pedal, the lever on the throw-out bearing cross shaft or release lever, and a rod or tubing that connects them (Figure 16-19). If possible, the clutch rod should be designed so that it transmits tension or a pulling force rather than a compression or pushing force, which tends to bend the rod.

The lever and the clutch rod should always make a right (90°) angle to each other when they are at the midpoint of their travel. Clutch pedal–to–throw-out bearing travel ratio is controlled by the lever lengths at the clutch pedal and cross shaft lever. Pedal free travel is adjusted by an adjustable-length clutch rod.

Hydraulic clutch systems are usually more efficient and easier to set up, although they cost more and offer more possibility for problems. As in a stock vehicle, the clutch pedal operates a master cylinder, which, in turn, operates the hydraulic release bearing (Figure 16-20). Clutch pedal–to–throw-out bearing travel ratio is adjusted by changing the diameter of the master cylinder. The release bearing can be operated by a slave cylinder through a release lever or directly by a hydraulic release bearing. Some aftermarket hydraulic release bearings are designed to replace the transmission front bearing retainer/ throw-out bearing quill. Some are threaded to provide an adjustment for throw-out bearing positioning. Like production vehicle hydraulic clutch systems, a hydraulic system requires fluid, bleeding, and possible fluid replacement.

16.3.5   Cautions and Considerations

Probably the greatest possibility for injury comes from an exploding flywheel or pressure plate. The centrifugal force from high engine rpm and the extreme loads can cause the clutch and flywheel to fly apart. Many stock flywheels and pressure rings are made from gray cast iron, which is rather brittle. It is difficult to say at what particular rpm rate a flywheel will explode, but the force that is released can be very destructive. In regard to safe operating rpm values, material with gray cast iron is the worst, nodular or ductile cast iron is better, and steel billet or aluminum is the best. Safe operating rpm is also affected by clutch and flywheel condition; heat checks in the flywheel or pressure ring surface are stress raisers, which can lead to failure. Normally, a

(a)

(b)

FIGURE 16-20 Custom hydraulic systems are available from master cylinder and pedal assemblies (a) combined with a slave cylinder (b). This adjustable slave cylinder with release bearing is designed to replace the transmission input shaft bearing. (Courtesy of Tilton Engineering)

good ductile iron flywheel and pressure ring can be operated safely at speeds up to 7500 rpm.

The rules of most race car sanctioning bodies specify what clutches and flywheels can or must be used and if scatter shields or explosion-containing containers shields must be used (Figure 16-21). These are called *clutch cans* in drag racing. Some racing classes require periodic inspection and certification of the bell housing/clutch can. On vehicles driven on the street, it is wise to use good, undamaged components. If the engine is to be operated at speeds much faster than stock, the clutch and flywheel should be replaced with ones rated for the higher rpm or explosion-containing devices should be used around the clutch housing.

FIGURE 16-21 This bell housing is formed from steel and is designed to keep an exploding pressure plate or flywheel contained. (Courtesy of McLeod Industries, Inc.)

If a performance clutch replacement is planned, it is recommended that advice be obtained from the various aftermarket clutch manufacturers. After you identify your vehicle and the type of driving you expect to do, they can recommend the best replacement parts and sometimes tailor them to your particular needs.

16.3.6   Installation and Service

With the exception of slider clutches, heavy-duty or competition clutches are serviced, adjusted, installed, and repaired using the same practices, procedures, and cautions described in Chapter 5. Wear and damage occur in the same manner as in passenger vehicle clutches, only faster in most cases.

As mentioned previously, slider clutch pressure plates include adjustments, which vary slightly among manufacturers. The two major adjustments for any clutch are clutch pedal free play and pedal travel. As in a production vehicle, free play ensures clearance between the throw-out bearing and release levers or fingers. The pedal travel adjustment prevents the clutch from disengaging any more than necessary. The diaphragm spring used in many clutches can be damaged if it is pushed too far past center. There are several ways of checking pedal travel to determine the point where the clutch becomes completely released. In most high-performance vehicles, a stop is put under the clutch pedal so that it cannot travel any farther than needed (Figure 16-22). Some racers will increase their clutch pedal free travel to the point where the pedal bottoms out at the floor pan at the point of release.

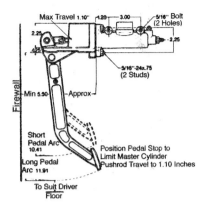

FIGURE 16-22 A pedal stop limits excessive pedal motion, which can cause overstroking and damage to the pressure plate spring or release bearing. (Courtesy of Tilton Engineering)

16.4   TRANSMISSIONS

With most stock, street-driven vehicles, transmission changes are limited to stock units that were made available for a particular chassis or body design. Some RWD vehicles have a variety of models with interchangeable transmissions. For example, some mid-1970s GM cars will accept a Saginaw three-speed, Saginaw four-speed, Muncie three-speed, Muncie four-speed, or Borg-Warner T10 transmission with very few changes. The Muncie and Borg-Warner transmissions are stronger than the Saginaw units with a choice of gear ratios (Figure 16-23). Most vehicles are manufactured with some variety in gear ratios available for the various vehicle models, with the lowest ratios generally being used in station wagons and pickups.

If you try to swap a late-model five- or six-speed transmission into an earlier vehicle, be aware that these units use an electronic speedometer, and GM units are designed so that the top of the case is rotated 17° to the left. Some of these units are available in aftermarket

Four-Speed

Gear	T10						Muncie		Top Loader	
1st	2.43	2.64	2.64	2.88	2.88	3.42	2.20	2.52	2.32	2.78
2nd	1.61	1.75	1.60	1.91	1.74	2.28	1.64	1.88	1.69	1.93
3rd	1.23	1.34	1.23	1.33	1.33	1.46	1.27	1.29	1.29	1.36
4th	1.00	1.00	1.00	1.00	1.00	1.00	1.00	1.00	1.00	1.00

Tremec Transmissions: Five-Speed / Six-Speed

Gear	T5				TR-3450	TR-3550	T-45	T56			
1st	3.35	3.75	3.97	3.76	3.82	3.27	3.37	1st	2.66	2.97	3.36
2nd	1.93	2.19	2.34	2.18	2.31	1.98	1.99	2nd	1.78	2.07	2.07
3rd	1.29	1.41	1.46	1.42	1.42	1.34	1.33	3rd	1.30	1.43	1.35
4th	1.00	1.00	1.00	1.00	1.00	1.00	1.00	4th	1.00	1.00	1.00
5th	0.72	0.72	0.85	0.81	0.74	0.68	0.67	5th	0.74	0.80	0.80
								6th	0.50	0.62	0.62
Rev.	3.15	3.53	3.71	3.76	3.82	3.01	3.22	Rev.	2.90	3.28	3.28
TC	175	225	230		335	350	250–325	TC	450	400	350

TC: Torque capacity in lb-ft

FIGURE 16-23 Available gear ratios for the T10, Muncie, and Top Loader four-speeds; the T5 and Tremec 3450 and 3550 and T-45 five-speeds; and T-56 six-speed transmissions.

versions with more standard features that make installation easier in older vehicles.

For racing, most stock-based classes will use stock transmissions as a cost-saving factor. In many cases, a stock transmission that has the correct gear ratios is selected, and this unit is run in a stock form. If it should fail, another unit is usually available at a wrecking yard. In some classes of racing, a stock transmission shifts too slowly and modifications are required.

16.4.1   Transmission Modifications

Modifications of a transmission begin with a good, careful rebuild. If a transmission is expected to perform under the more severe conditions, all the gears, bearings, shafts, and cases must be in nearly perfect condition. Any burrs on the speed gear clutching teeth or synchronizer sleeves should be removed, as described in Chapter 8. Transmission modifications include:

- Altering the synchronizer assemblies
- Improving lubrication for the speed gears
- Improving the bearing surfaces for the speed gears
- Reducing end play to the minimum allowance

If the transmission is to be shifted in a normal manner so that synchronizing action is maintained, the following checks and service operations should be performed:

- Polish the cone surface of the speed gears.
- Use blocker rings that have a thread width of 0.002 to 0.004 in. (0.05 to 0.1 mm) (Figure 16-24). Make sure that the rings are round by coating the gear cone with a felt marker or Prussian Blue and twisting the ring into place; it should make contact completely around the cone. Using a needle file, cut six equally spaced slots across the threads. Remove all burrs from the chamfered areas of the rings.
- Make sure that the synchronizer sleeve slides freely over the hub, blocker ring, and speed gear clutching teeth.

If the transmission is to be speed shifted, the synchronizer tends to block shifts too effectively and slows them down. Two stages of modifications can be made; both will make the transmission difficult to shift slowly without grinding the gears. The first stage is to leave out the blocker rings, energizer springs, and/or synchronizer keys. The second stage is to remove every other speed gear clutch tooth and every other spline end from the synchronizer sleeve (Figure 16-25). Using a small grinding stone, this is a rather slow, tedious job. It also

(a)

(b)

FIGURE 16-24 To ensure fast, smooth shifting, the blocker ring–to–speed gear fit should be perfect. (a) Coat the cone surface of the gear with a marking pen or machinist dye and slightly rotate the ring against it; the dye should be removed all the way around the cone. (b) Filing wiping grooves across the ring will help the ring begin synchronizing operation quicker. (Portions of materials contained herein have been reprinted with permission of General Motors Corporation, Service and Parts Operations, License Agreement #0310897)

creates more backlash in the transmission, which shows up during a power change.

You can bench check synchronizer shifting ability by assembling the gear train on the mainshaft, leaving out the synchronizer energizer springs and snap rings (Figure 16-26). Then with the main drive gear in position, stand the gear train on end with the front end up; the synchronizer sleeves should drop into their rear-shifted positions. It might be necessary to rotate the gears slightly to align the teeth. Next, reverse the position so that the rear end is up, and again, the sleeves should drop into their front-shifted positions. Any hanging up of the sleeves indicates a problem that needs to be corrected.

FIGURE 16-25   The dog teeth on the main drive and speed gears have been replaced with rings having teeth spaced more widely apart. Also, the sleeve has teeth with a much wider spacing. These gears will shift much faster than stock.

Most speed gears have a shallow groove and/or slot to let gear oil enter the gear's center bearing area. It is a good practice to open the grooves slightly to ensure an oil flow into the center of the gear (Figure 16-27). Remember that a speed gear always rotates at its gear ratio relative to the engine, and when the transmission operates in one of its other ratios, friction can occur between the speed gear and the mainshaft. Some speed gears have hardened center bores that run directly on the mainshaft, some have a steel sleeve between the gear and the mainshaft, and some use a bronze bushing or needle bearings. A reworked first gear with needle bearings can be used to replace the production first gear and sleeve in a Muncie four-speed for a freer-running combination (Figure 16-28). Occasionally, the bushing inside a gear can be replaced with a set of needle bearings, but only if the gear has a hardened bore. You can test the bore for hardness by trying to cut it with a file. If a file will cut the metal surface, it is not hardened and cannot be used as a bearing race.

The thrust surface of each speed gear and the cluster gear should be polished by working the gear over a piece of very fine emery cloth or crocus cloth that has

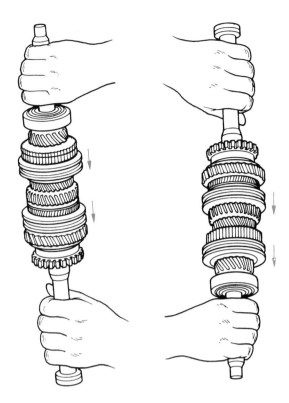

FIGURE 16-26   If the gear train were assembled without energizer springs in the synchronizer assemblies, the sleeves would drop into their shifted positions when the entire assembly was stood on end. The gears might need to be rotated to align the teeth.

been placed on a flat surface (Figure 16-29). This helps ensure accurate end-play checks as well as reduce friction and wear. To help ensure that the cluster gear thrust washers do not spin in the case, bend the tang to a 90° angle, making sure the metal does not crack (Figure 16-30). The end play of each floating gear and the cluster gear should be adjusted to the tighter end of the specifications as much as practical. When adjusting cluster gear end play, shim the end of the cluster, which moves it forward or backward into the best mesh contact with the main drive gear or speed gears. The mesh improvement is very slight, but sometimes every bit helps.

Some racers do additional gear modifications by chamfering the gear teeth and honing the bores of the speed gears. The purpose of the tooth chamfers is to remove the portion of the gear tooth that tends to chip under load. These chips can cause gear and bearing damage while the pit becomes a stress raiser, which might produce possible gear tooth breakage. Honing the bore of a speed gear is done to improve lubrication and reduce the possibility of galling on the mainshaft; it also allows the gear to move a little farther out of mesh with the cluster gear.

The inside of the case, extension housing, and any covers should be cleaned thoroughly. It is recommended

(a)

(b)

FIGURE 16-27   This gear has been reworked by grinding the lubrication grooves wider (circles) (a) and polishing the opposite thrust surface (arrow) (b) to increase end play slightly.

FIGURE 16-28   This first speed gear normally runs on a steel sleeve (lower left); it has been reworked to accept a set of needle bearings, reducing friction and the possibility of galling to the mainshaft. (Portions of materials contained herein have been reprinted with permission of General Motors Corporation, Service and Parts Operations, License Agreement #0310807)

to grit blast or glass bead them to remove any casting flash or abrasive debris that might come loose and cause wear. The cluster gear thrust washer surface should be checked carefully to ensure that it is in good condition and not worn or scored. A magnetic drain plug should be used or a magnet should be secured to the case with

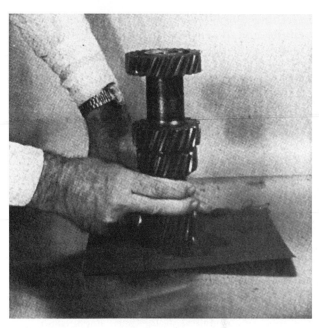

FIGURE 16-29   The end thrust surfaces of this cluster gear are being polished against a piece of crocus cloth; this will reduce friction and make setup of gear end play more accurate. (Portions of materials contained herein have been reprinted with permission of General Motors Corporation, Service and Parts Operations, License Agreement #0310807)

FIGURE 16-30   The tang of this thrust washer has been reworked with a sharper bend, which will make a more positive engagement into the groove in the case. (Portions of materials contained herein have been reprinted with permission of General Motors Corporation, Service and Parts Operations, License Agreement #0310807)

epoxy to trap any metal particles that will wear off the gears and bearings.

All of the shift mechanism should be checked to ensure that it is in nearly perfect condition: Shift forks should make good contact with the fork slots; shift rails and shafts should slide freely in their bores; and detent and interlock balls, plugs, cams, and levers should move freely and precisely. Some consider the building of a high-performance transmission as an extension of a normal, very high quality rebuild with a few additional checks to ensure that everything is working properly.

As the transmission is put into service, a good-quality gear oil should be used. If the usage will produce oil temperatures above 290°F, an oil cooler should be installed and a synthetic lubricant be used to ensure adequate lubrication. When the transmission is first operated, the vehicle should be driven under light loads in all the gears for a few miles to allow the internal parts to burnish and seat to each other.

16.4.1.1 Special Note on Stress Raisers.   When metal parts are under pressure or stress, they will often give (bend or twist) a small amount, and the elastic property of the metal will return it to its original shape after the load is removed. If the metal is not strong enough for the load, it will yield and take a permanent set or break. Ductile or malleable metals will bend; brittle metals will break.

A stress raiser is a weaker area in the metal that bends or twists easier than the surrounding metal. A stress raiser is usually something that reduces the size (thickness or diameter) of the part; it can also be a sharp corner or a step in a shaft where it changes diameter. For example, this could be an axle shaft with a serious nick in it (Figure 16-31). Normally, an axle shaft will twist slightly under load, but the twist is spread through the length of the smaller diameter of the axle. Concentrating the twisting action at one point will cause either a direct break at that point or an indirect break that will result from work hardening at that point. Work hardening, also called *metal fatigue*, causes changes in the metal's granular structure and makes the metal more brittle and prone to breaking. If possible, metal parts should never be replaced in a position that will cause the direction of stress to be reversed. In other words, if both axle shafts were identical, they must always be installed in the original position.

16.4.2   Aftermarket/Race Transmissions

Aftermarket/race transmissions fall into several categories:

- **Street four-speeds:** T10 four-speeds similar to those installed in production vehicles
- **Street five-speeds:** T5, Tremec 3550, or specially built five-speed transmissions using conventional blocker ring–style synchronizers
- **Clutch-type drag racing four- and five-speeds:** specially built transmissions using a sliding sleeve (without blocker rings) or a dog ring-type of shifter
- **Clutchless drag racing four- and five-speeds:** specially built transmissions using severely angled ramp/dog ring-type of shifters
- **Road race and circle track two-, four-, and five-speeds:** specially built transmissions using a

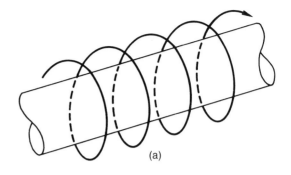

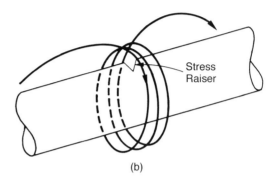

FIGURE 16-31   (a) A shaft will often twist like a torsion bar when a lot of torque is sent through it. (b) A nick can create a stress raiser and concentrate the twisting at one point, resulting in metal fatigue, or work hardening, at that point.

sliding sleeve (without blocker rings) or dog ring shifters
- **Formula car and Indy car transaxles:** specially built transaxles that include the final drive and differential

The shaft and gear arrangement in most of these transmissions is the same as in a conventional standard transmission. They have an input main drive gear driving a cluster gear and a mainshaft with the speed gears and shift assemblies. In the racing transaxles, the arrangement of the Weismann transaxle is similar to a conventional FWD standard transaxle, while a Hewland transaxle is similar to a RWD Volkswagen transaxle. The transverse Weismann transaxle uses a bevel gear at the input shaft to turn the power flow 90° to the primary shaft (Figure 16-32). This feature allows the engine and transaxle to be placed low in the car for good weight distribution while the differential is in line with the driveshafts and wheel centerlines.

In general, most racing transmissions use spur gears for their ability to transfer power with the least possible friction and power loss because they are free from any side thrust (Figure 16-33). The side thrust from a helical gear might also cause it to work its way out of mesh. The major advantage of helical gears—quiet operation—is of no concern in a race car.

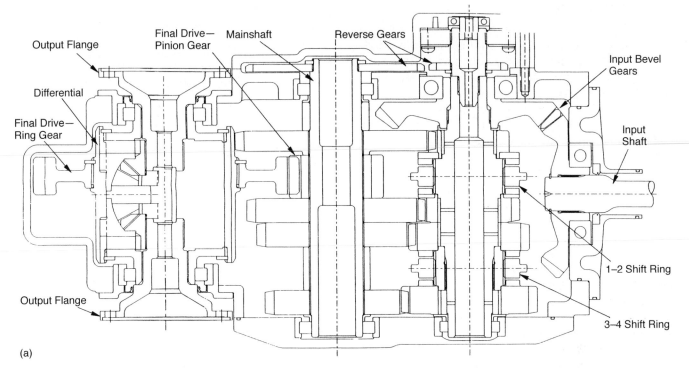

Output Flange

Final Drive—
Pinion Gear

Mainshaft

Reverse Gears

Input Bevel
Gears

Differential

Input
Shaft

Final Drive—
Ring Gear

Output Flange

1–2 Shift Ring

3–4 Shift Ring

(a)

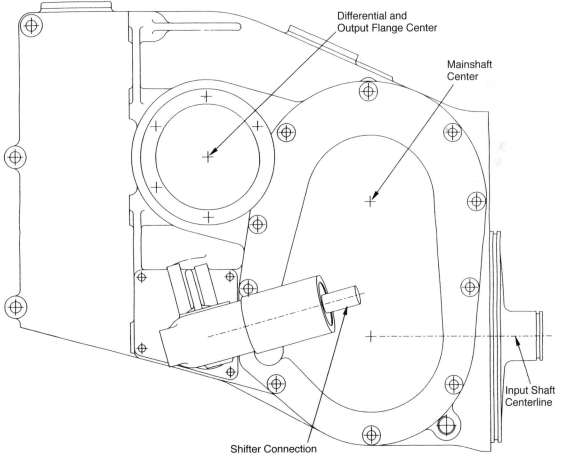

Differential and
Output Flange Center

Mainshaft
Center

Input Shaft
Centerline

Shifter Connection

(b)

FIGURE 16-32   (a) This four-speed transverse-mounted transaxle designed for a Formula I car uses a pair of bevel gears to turn the power flow from the clutch shaft to the transaxle input shaft and also dog ring shifters. In (b), note how the input shaft is lower than the differential output shafts.

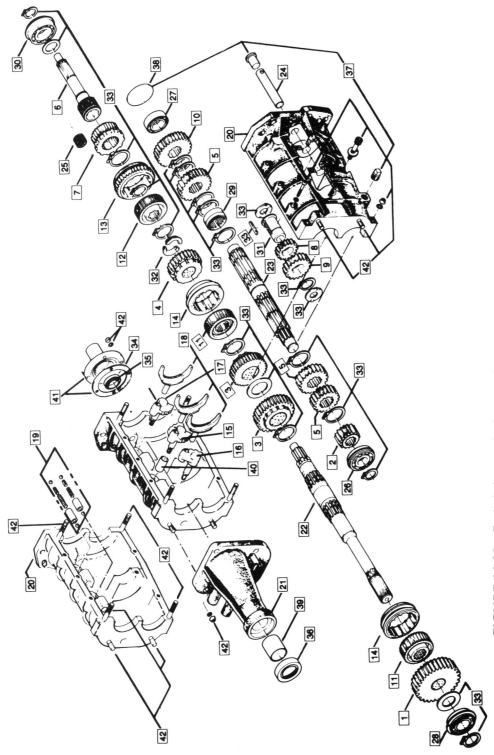

FIGURE 16-33 Exploded view of a five-speed race transmission. Some of the features include a split case for easy disassembly, the use of spur gears throughout, a cluster gear made up of individual gears for almost infinite gear ratios, and nonsynchronized sliding sleeve shifters. (Courtesy of Richmond Gear)

Main Shaft ÷ Cluster Shaft Gear	Cluster Shaft Gear ÷ Input Shift Gear (29/20 EXAMPLE) — **For Main Drive Sets**											
Main Drive Sets ↓	29/20	28/20	29/21	28/21	27/21	27/22	26/22	26/23	25/23	25/24	24/24	24/25
Main Drive Ratio ↓	1.450	1.400	1.381	1.333	1.286	1.227	1.182	1.130	1.087	1.042	1.000	0.960
Gear 34/15 (34/15 Example) ↓	3.287	3.173	3.130	3.022	2.914	2.782	2.679	2.562	2.464	2.361	2.267	2.176
33/15	3.190	3.080	3.038	2.933	2.829	2.700	2.600	2.487	2.391	2.292	2.200	2.112
34/16	3.081	2.975	2.935	2.833	2.732	2.608	2.511	2.402	2.310	2.214	2.125	2.040
33/17	2.815	2.718	2.681	2.588	2.496	2.382	2.294	2.194	2.110	2.022	1.941	1.864
32/18	2.578	2.489	2.455	2.370	2.286	2.182	2.101	2.010	1.932	1.852	1.778	1.707
1st 31/18	2.497	2.411	2.378	2.296	2.214	2.114	2.035	1.947	1.872	1.794	1.722	1.653
32/19	2.442	2.358	2.326	2.246	2.165	2.067	1.990	1.904	1.831	1.754	1.684	1.617
31/19	2.366	2.284	2.253	2.175	2.098	2.002	1.928	1.844	1.773	1.700	1.632	1.566
30/20	2.175	2.100	2.071	2.000	1.929	1.841	1.773	1.696	1.630	1.563	1.500	1.440
30/21	2.071	2.000	1.973	1.905	1.837	1.753	1.688	1.615	1.553	1.488	1.429	1.371
29/20	2.103	2.030	2.002	1.933	1.864	1.780	1.714	1.639	1.576	1.510	1.450	1.392
28/20	2.030	1.960	1.933	1.867	1.800	1.718	1.655	1.583	1.522	1.458	1.400	1.344
29/21	2.002	1.933	1.907	1.841	1.776	1.695	1.632	1.561	1.501	1.438	1.381	1.326
2nd 28/21	1.933	1.867	1.841	1.778	1.714	1.636	1.576	1.507	1.449	1.389	1.333	1.280
27/21	1.864	1.800	1.776	1.714	1.653	1.578	1.519	1.453	1.398	1.339	1.286	1.234
27/22	1.780	1.718	1.695	1.636	1.578	1.506	1.450	1.387	1.334	1.278	1.227	1.178
26/22	1.714	1.655	1.632	1.576	1.519	1.450	1.397	1.336	1.285	1.231	1.182	1.135
26/23	1.639	1.583	1.561	1.507	1.453	1.387	1.336	1.278	1.229	1.178	1.130	1.085
25/23	1.576	1.522	1.501	1.449	1.398	1.334	1.285	1.229	1.181	1.132	1.087	1.043
3rd 25/24	1.510	1.458	1.438	1.389	1.339	1.278	1.231	1.178	1.132	1.085	1.042	1.000
24/24	1.450	1.400	1.381	1.333	1.286	1.227	1.182	1.130	1.087	1.042	1.000	0.960
24/25	1.392	1.344	1.326	1.280	1.234	1.178	1.135	1.085	1.043	1.000	0.960	0.922
23/25	1.334	1.288	1.270	1.227	1.183	1.129	1.087	1.040	1.000	0.958	0.920	0.883
23/26	1.283	1.238	1.222	1.179	1.137	1.086	1.045	1.000	0.962	0.921	0.885	0.849
4th	1 to 1	1 to 1	1 to 1	1 to 1	1 to 1	1 to 1	1 to 1	1 to 1	1 to 1	1 to 1	1 to 1	1 to 1

(Left margin: Main Shaft ÷ Cluster Shaft Gear — 34/15 Example — For Speed Gears)

FIGURE 16-34 From a choice of seven input gear-to-cluster combinations and various mainshaft-to-cluster combinations, these gear ratios are available for a five-speed racing transmission. (Courtesy of Jerico Performance Products)

Another feature of most racing transmissions is the ability to change gear ratios easily. The main drive gear of some transmissions is splined onto the clutch shaft and the gears that make up the cluster are splined onto a shaft. One or more of these gears can be slid off and changed. This allows an almost infinite selection of ratios to suit the needs of a particular car or track (Figure 16-34). Having the gears splined onto their shaft also allows for replacement of only the damaged gears and removal of any unneeded gear sets.

Some racing transmissions use sliding sleeve shifters with every other tooth/spline removed from the clutch teeth and sleeve. Others use a dog ring, or face ring, shifter (Figure 16-35). There are two major styles of dog ring shifters. For transmissions in vehicles that are to be accelerated and decelerated, the shifting lugs are almost square. There is a slight reverse angle or back-cut angle on each end of the lugs (about 10°) to hold the lug into mesh under both directions of loading. Drag racing transmissions use the same face angle on the acceleration side of the lug and a very severe angle or ramp on the deceleration side. Unless it is held into mesh manually, the dog ring will jump out of gear on deceleration. Clutchless shifting transmissions use a split slider/dog ring so that the slider can be shifted into first gear with the dog ring still engaged with the first speed gear. Shifting into second gear leaves the slider engaged with first gear while the other part of the slider engages the second speed gear, and as second gear occurs, the resulting first gear speed increase kicks the dog ring out of mesh with the first speed gear. The other shifts are accomplished in the same manner.

FIGURE 16-35 Dog ring, or face ring, shifters engage the gear from the end so that shifts can be made very fast and positive. Some dog ring shifters have an angle cut on the coast side of the tooth that produces an automatic shift into neutral as soon as the speed gear tries to turn faster than the shifter. (Courtesy of Jerico Performance Products)

FIGURE 16-36 The Jerico racing transmission uses a closed case with top cover, dog ring shifters, and splined gear assemblies. This unit also includes gear oil pumps to circulate transmission and rear axle oil through coolers. (Courtesy of Jerico Performance Products)

Some performance transmissions use a split-case design. The Jerico transmission uses a top-loader design (Figure 16-36). A unique design feature of another transmission is an intermediate support collar to prevent gear forces from separating the mainshaft gears from the cluster gear. Still another transmission uses dual cluster gears (as in some heavy-duty truck transmissions), in which each cluster gear transfers half of the torque and the separation forces keep the mainshaft gears centered between them.

The Lenco transmission, which is popular in drag racing, is more closely related to an automatic transmission. It uses a planetary gear set, a one-way clutch, and a multiplate friction clutch that is applied to produce the shift. This transmission is made up of one or more two-speed units that are combined to produce the desired gear speeds.

The usual shifters used with racing transmissions are heavy-duty shifters using external linkage similar to that used on older passenger vehicle floor shifters. Clutchless transmissions use a rather complex ratchet-style mechanism or even more complex pressurized air shifters.

16.4.3   4WD and Off-Road Transmissions

Serious off-road operation usually involves fitting a different transmission or engine and transmission package into a utility vehicle, pickup, or light truck. The transmissions used are usually stock or slightly modified passenger car or light truck units. Serious off-roaders generally select light truck units because of the lower gear ratios they offer.

One of the major problems involves using a transmission that was constructed to connect to a driveshaft and fitting it to a transfer case. This is accomplished by replacing the mainshaft with one that has been shortened and machined to connect into the transfer case and by replacing the extension housing with one that connects the rear of the transmission to the front of the transfer case (Figure 16-37). Kits are available to adapt the more popular transmissions to the popular transfer cases.

When a different transmission is to be fitted behind an engine for which it was not designed, problem of adapting the transmission to the engine occurs. Special clutch housings are available that allow bolting the more popular engines to the more popular transmissions (Figure 16-38). This still leaves the potential problem of selecting or adapting the flywheel, starter, clutch, throw-out bearing, clutch release lever, pilot bearing, and transmission support. Various specialty shops have combinations of parts and guidance to help solve these problems.

Another unit developed for these vehicles is an auxiliary transmission that is designed to fit between the clutch housing and the transmission (Figure 16-39). This transmission is a two-speed unit with either a 17 percent reduction ratio or a 27 percent overdrive ratio and a direct-drive 1:1 ratio. This particular unit is 7 in. (18 cm) long, which requires the transmission or engine to be relocated.

FIGURE 16-37 This adapter is used to couple a Muncie four-speed car transmission to a 4WD transfer case. Note that the two major parts, the mainshaft and extension housing, have been machined to fit a transfer case instead of a driveshaft. (Courtesy of Advance Adapters)

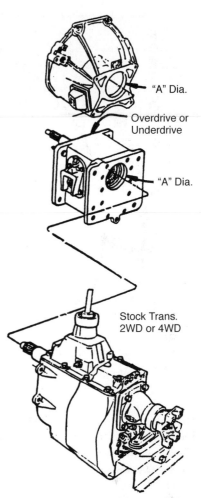

"A" Dia.

Overdrive or Underdrive

"A" Dia.

Stock Trans. 2WD or 4WD

FIGURE 16-39 This Torque Splitter transmission can be installed between the transmission and the engine, and it provides either a 27% overdrive or a 17% reduction along with a 1:1 ratio. The transmission and its mounts need to be relocated 7 3/8 in. to the rear. (Courtesy of Advance Adapters)

(a)

FIGURE 16-38 This adapter (a) allows a Chevrolet V8 engine to be bolted up to a Jeep five-speed transmission (b), making installation of this engine into the Jeep vehicle easier. (Courtesy of Advance Adapters)

(b)

Spicer U-joint sizes	Electric motor torque		Gas or diesel torque		Short duration torque		Torsional strength min. elastic limit		Max. r.p.m.	Standard tube size	Max. length ₵ -₵ installed@ max. rated r.p.m.	
	Lbs. ft.	N.m.	Lbs. ft.	N.m.	Lbs. ft.	N.m.	Lbs. ft.	N.m.			in	mm
Light-Duty												
1000	75	100	50	70	310	420	420	570	2,500	1³/₄″ × .065	55	1,397
1210	95	130	65	90	420	570	850	1,150	6,000	2¹/₂″ × .065	43	1,092
1280	140	190	95	130	570	775	1,250	1,695	6,000	2¹/₂″ × .083	43	1,092
1310	195	265	130	175	800	1,085	1,600	2,170	6,000	3″ × .083	47	1,194
1330	220	300	150	205	890	1,205	1,850	2,510	5,000	3¹/₂″ × .083	50.5	1,283
										4″ × .083	54	1,377

FIGURE 16-40 This chart can be used to determine the driveshaft and universal joint sizes required for different torque loads. (Courtesy of Dana Corporation)

16.5 DRIVESHAFTS

Driveshaft design is affected by the torque it is required to transmit and the speed at which it operates. Figure 16-40 shows the recommended joint and tubing sizes for light- and medium-duty vehicles, and Figure 16-41 shows the operating angle limits relative to speed for a Cardan U-joint. The major difference in the driveshaft design for racing vehicles is the use of aluminum or composite driveshafts, which are used in cases where rotating inertia is very important. NASCAR rules require driveshafts of magnetic steel that are similar in design to regular passenger vehicles.

16.5.1 Cautions and Considerations

In drag racing, where a high shock load is transmitted through the driveshaft, a U-joint cross can break and separate. If this happens, that end of the driveshaft will drop

Driveshaft rpm	Maximum Normal Operating Angles	Driveshaft rpm	Maximum Normal Operating Angles
5000	3°15	3000	5°50
4500	3°40	2500	7°0
4000	4°15	2000	8°40
3500	5°0	1500	11°30

FIGURE 16-41 This chart gives the maximum angle at which a U-joint should be operated for different shaft rpm values. (Courtesy of Dana Corporation)

and the rotating shaft will try to bend to the side and whip. Its travel will be limited by the underbody of the car and the ground, and serious damage or injury can be the result. Some classes of racing require driveshaft hoops to contain the driveshaft motion and make the vehicle safer to drive if a U-joint should break (Figure 16-42).

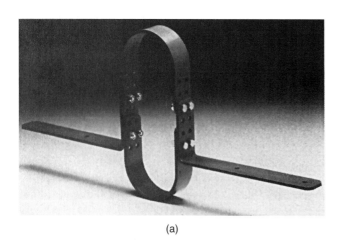

(a)

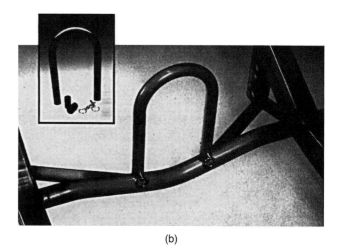

(b)

FIGURE 16-42 A hoop should be positioned at each end of a high-performance vehicle's driveshaft to prevent damage should the U-joint break. The hoop in (a) is designed to bolt under a stock-type car; (b) is for a fabricated race car chassis. (Courtesy of Alston Race Car Engineering)

16.6   DRIVE AXLES

On street-driven vehicles, drive axle modifications include changing axle ratios, differential styles, and entire axle assemblies. Axle ratio changes normally are for a lower ratio (higher numerically) (example: 3.7:1 to 3.9:1) for more torque or a higher ratio (example: 3.7:1 to 3.5:1) for better fuel economy. Remember that you can only improve one at the expense of the other. Also, manufacturers' warranties and emission standards limit the gear ratios that can be used in some street-driven vehicles.

Changing axle assemblies is normally done to get a stronger axle that is less prone to breaking under highly loaded conditions. Some of the more popular axles are the Dana 60, Ford 9 in., General Motors 12 bolt, and Chrysler Corporation 8 3/4 in. If a decision has been made to change axle assemblies, there are several factors to consider before selecting the particular axle: (1) cost of the axle assembly and its parts, (2) availability of the axle and its parts, (3) axle shaft size, (4) axle bearing type, (5) selection of gear ratios, and (6) selection of brakes. Some more basic factors to consider are housing length, which determines wheel spacing and track width; lug bolt spacing for wheel usage; brake shoe size for brake balance; spring pad or control arm bracket positioning; and driveshaft flange size and type. If the axle selected is similar enough to the original one, it can be installed without many problems; other combinations can mean a lot of additional work. Some firms market axle assembly kits to fit some of the more popular axles into certain vehicles (Figure 16-43).

16.6.1   Differentials

Besides the stock conventional open differential and limited slip differential, several aftermarket differential choices are available: the self-locking or mechanical ratcheting Detroit Locker, the TrueTrac torque proportioning differential, the ARB manually locking differential, the locked-up differential, and the spool. Each of these units has the ability to drive both wheels on an axle. It should be remembered that a vehicle cannot easily turn a corner unless the wheels on the inside of the turn go slower. A vehicle with locked front axles will go straight even if the wheels are steered at an angle.

Unlike most differentials, the Detroit Locker, also called NoSpin, does not use bevel gears. One face of a pair of dog clutches is connected to the differential case at the center (spider assembly), and the other face of each dog clutch is splined to an axle shaft (Figure 16-44). The dog clutches are spring loaded to apply and are released by a center cam. During normal driving the dog clutches transfer power to each axle. When turning a

corner, the action of the axle connected to the outer wheel allows the axle and its dog clutch to travel faster than the differential case and center cam. This action causes the dog clutch to release; it will reapply and release every few degrees of rotation relative to the differential case. This action is annoying to some drivers, as it can be heard and felt under certain driving maneuvers. Operation under poor traction conditions is quite positive with no differential action unless a wheel tries to rotate faster than the differential.

The TrueTrac limited slip differential drives the axles through a group of helical gears in the differential case. The pinion gears are intermeshed in pairs and with one of the helical axle side gears (Figure 16-45, p. 484). This differential acts like a normal, open differential under normal driving conditions. When unequal side-to-side traction conditions are encountered, the pinion gears resist rotation in the case, and more torque is transferred to the wheel with traction. The torque bias of this differential is adjusted during manufacture to suit the operating conditions for the particular vehicle. The action is smoother than that of a locker, especially while turning. A locking version of the TruTrac differential called the Electrac is available for Dana 44 and 60 drive axles. An electric solenoid mounted on the cover moves the shift fork to accomplish the shift. This unit is locked when the driver pushes a button on the instrument panel.

Manually locking differentials contain a locking mechanism to lock up differential action. The ARB Air Locker differential has an air cylinder and sliding gear inside the differential case (Figure 16-46, p. 484). This unit has normal, open differential action until the driver pushes a button on the instrument panel. Then air pressure *stops* differential action. This unit is designed for use in the front and rear axles of most popular 4WD vehicles.

A locked differential is one that has no differential action. In the past this was done by welding the differential pinion gears to the axle gears. This is not recommended because the weld can break and allow partial differential action, which produces unpredictable vehicle operation. A more securely locked rear end is accomplished by installing a minispool in the differential case or by using a spool in place of the differential (Figure 16-47, p. 484). A minispool locks the axle shafts to the differential case; the axles are splined directly into a spool. Spools are normally used in the higher-horsepower classes of drag racing and some classes of circle track racing.

Stock axle shafts should not be used in locked rear ends. If an axle shaft should break, the other axle will still drive the vehicle; this will cause the vehicle to make a very rapid turn. Stronger or oversized axles should always be installed in a unit that has a locked differential.

(a)

(b)

FIGURE 16-43 (a) This kit is used to mount a Dana 60 rear axle in a CJ5 or CJ7 Jeep; the axle housing, axle shafts, and driveshaft have been reworked or constructed to fit the vehicle. (b) A 12-bolt axle housing has been reworked to fit a Z-28 Camaro. (Courtesy of Summer Brothers)

Detroit Locker Differential Components
With New Two-Piece Differential Case Assembly

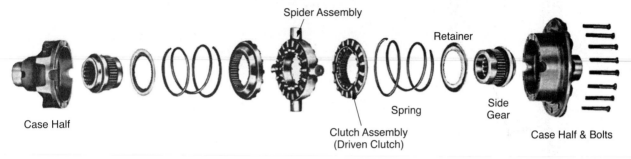

Spider Assembly

Retainer

Case Half

Clutch Assembly
(Driven Clutch)

Spring

Side
Gear

Case Half & Bolts

(a)

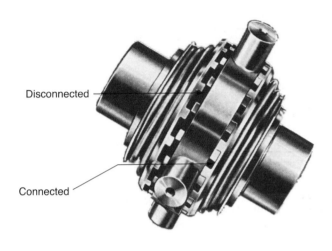

Disconnected

Connected

(b)

FIGURE 16-44 A Detroit Locker uses a center spider and two clutch assemblies to drive the side (a), and when the vehicle turns a corner, the clutch is disconnected to allow the outer wheel to turn faster (b). (Courtesy of Tractech)

16.6.2   Axle Shafts

Several features can be built into an aftermarket axle shaft (Figure 16-48, p. 486). These include:

- **A better grade of steel:** uses a physically stronger metal and forming method, usually forging.
- **Smoothed and polished surfaces:** eliminate stress raisers.
- **Increased number of splines:** gives shallower and stronger splines; this strengthens the weakest point of an axle, which is the root diameter of the shaft at the ends of the splines.
- **Oversize bearing journals:** a bearing with a larger inner diameter allows a larger-diameter shaft in this area.
- **C-clip elimination:** increases safety by converting from a C-clip to a bearing-retained axle.
- **Lightened axles:** weight is reduced by gun-drilling the shaft or by drilling the wheel flange.

- **Full-floating axle conversion:** uses the safest arrangement where the wheel is retained on a separate set of bearings; axle breakage will cause only a loss of power flow.

A changeover to full-floating axles is also popular with utility vehicles that are often towed. They can be fitted with a hub that can be unlocked so that towing motion will not rotate the axle gears or driveshaft (Figure 16-49, p. 487).

16.6.3   Drive Axle Modifications

Like a transmission, building a high-performance axle is an extension of a high-quality rebuild, taking extra care to make sure that everything is correct. All suspicious gears, bearings, or other parts should be replaced. The major modifications are to chamfer the edges of the ring and pinion gears, grind and sometimes polish the windows of the differential case to remove stress raisers,

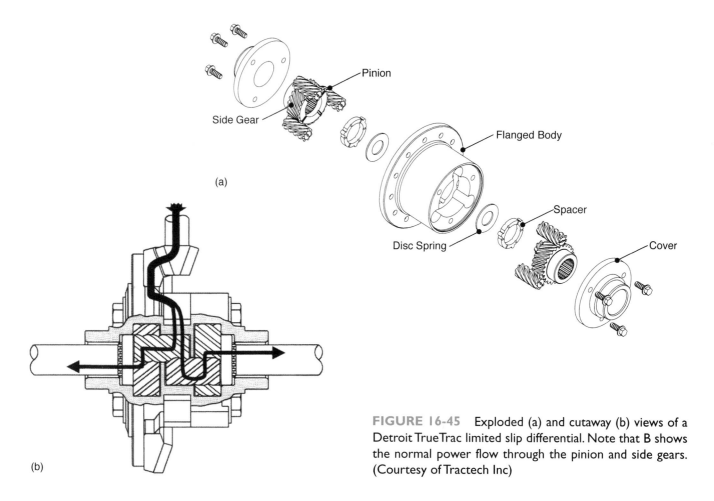

(a)

(b)

FIGURE 16-45   Exploded (a) and cutaway (b) views of a Detroit TrueTrac limited slip differential. Note that B shows the normal power flow through the pinion and side gears. (Courtesy of Tractech Inc)

shot peen the differential case and gears, and convert from a collapsible to a solid pinion bearing spacer. Shot peening tends to compress and harden the outer surface of the metal as well as remove minor stress raisers (Figure 16-50, p. 487).

Chamfering the outer edges of a gear tooth is done to reduce the possibility of chipping. Grinding, polishing, and shot peening a differential case is done to remove stress raisers, which might cause cracking and further breakage.

Many race car technicians feel that a solid pinion bearing spacer is more reliable than a collapsible spacer, which can collapse further and increase clearance at the pinion bearings. Pinion bearing preload is a little more difficult to adjust using a solid spacer. Both procedures are described in Section 12.6.7. Before starting the adjustment, some technicians will polish the pinion shaft with a plastic scouring pad; this allows the bearings to be installed and removed with less force. They will also oil the shaft and splines during assembly, knowing that the adjustment procedure involves assembling the bearings and flange into the bearing re-

tainer first with an oversize shim. After measuring the shaft end play, the assembly will have to be disassembled at least once to change the shim.

Assembly of a carrier begins with a thorough cleaning of the case and sometimes grit blasting or grinding to remove any casting flash or stress raisers at critical points. When using very high or very low gear ratios, it is sometimes necessary to grind the inside of the case to provide clearance for the larger gear. A new or very good ring and pinion gear set should be used. If a new set is used, the gear edges are chamfered, the pinion shaft is polished, and the ring gear is checked thoroughly for burrs at the mounting surface and metal chips or damage to the threads. Many technicians will run a file or a stone lightly over the back side and bore of the ring gear. It is also a good idea to run a file or stone lightly over the gear mounting face of the differential case. A light coating of oil is put on this surface to help the ring gear slide into its seated position. Many race car technicians use liquid stud and bearing locking compound on the threads of the ring gear mounting bolts, and they use a tightening

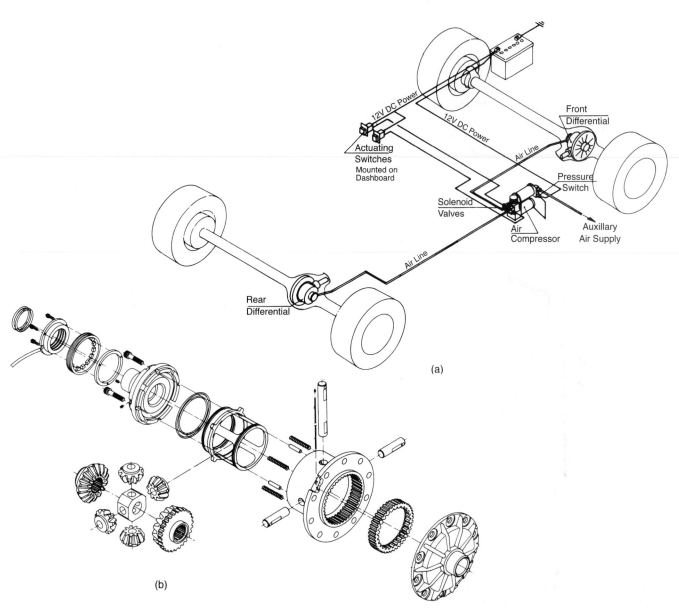

(a)

(b)

FIGURE 16-46 When the dash control (a) is actuated, air pressure is sent to the differential to shift the gear and lock the side gear to the differential case (b) of the ARB Air Locker differential. (Courtesy of ARB Air Locker)

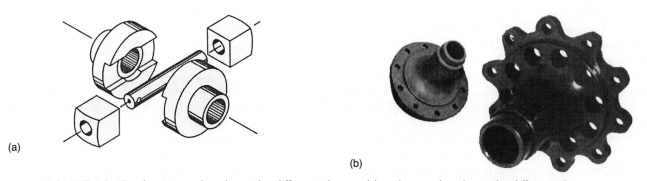

(a)

(b)

FIGURE 16-47 A minispool replaces the differential gears (a) and a spool replaces the differential case (b) so that the axle shafts will be locked to the ring gear. (Courtesy of Mark Williams Enterprises)

# Teeth	Pressure Angle	Common Application	Major Diameter	Minor Diameter	% Change in Diameter	% Change in Strength
30	45°	Basis for Comparison GM 12 bolt	1.2917	1.2083	0.0%	0.0%
28	30°	GM Buick & Pontiac '64–'70 Axle	1.1960	1.1127	−7.9%	−21.9%
30	30°	8-3/4″ Mopar '57–'64	1.2793	1.1960	−1.0%	−3.0%
31	30°	Olds/Pontiac '57–'64	1.3210	1.2377	2.4%	7.5%
35	30°	Dana 60 Strange & Lenco spools	1.4876	1.4043	16.2%	57.0%
26	45°	GM 10 bolt 7-1/2″ '82 & laer	1.1250	1.0417	−13.8%	−35.9%
28	45°	GM 10 bolt 8.5″ & 8.2″ '65-'81 & Ford 9″ & 8.8″	1.2083	1.1250	−6.9%	−19.3%
31	45°	9″ Ford	1.3333	1.2500	3.5%	10.7%
33	45°	Strange 9″ Ford spools	1.4167	1.3333	10.3%	34.4%
35	45°	Mark Williams 35 spline spools	1.5000	1.4167	17.2%	61.2%
40	45°	Mark Williams 9″ & Dana 60 spools	1.7083	1.6250	34.5%	143.2%

(a)

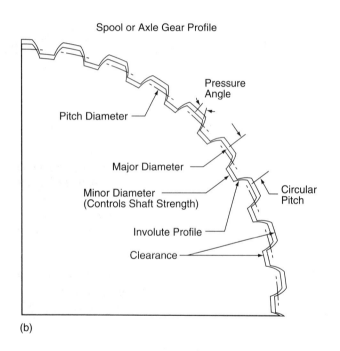

(b)

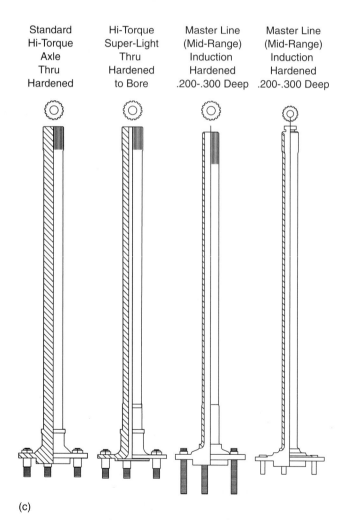

(c)

FIGURE 16-48 The shape and size of the splines between the axle shaft and spool or side gear are among the factors that determine the strength of an axle (a). Commonly used spline factors are illustrated in (b). Axle variables are shown in (c). A hardened, stock axle is at the bottom. The other axles show thicker flanges, larger bearing surfaces, larger wheel studs, and larger shafts that are fully machined. The Super-Light shaft is gun drilled. (Courtesy of Mark Williams Enterprises)

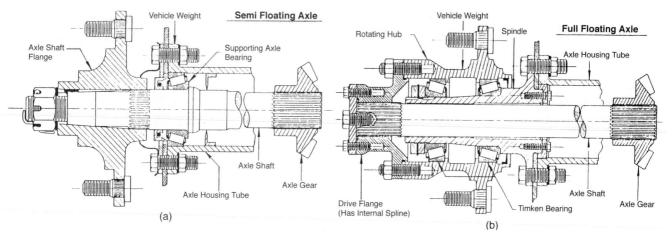

FIGURE 16-49 Kits are available to convert C-clip axle shafts to bearing retention (a) and semifloating axles to full-floating units (b). (Courtesy of Summer Brothers)

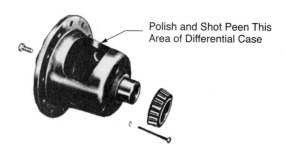

FIGURE 16-50 The rough casting provides many stress raisers around the windows; these can be removed by polishing and shot peening. (Portions of materials contained herein have been reprinted with permission of General Motors Corporation, Service and Parts Operations, License Agreement #0310807)

pattern that will draw the ring gear evenly against the flange. The bolts should be tightened carefully to the correct torque. Make sure that the bolts do not bottom out in their holes.

Pinion depth on a Ford 9-in. carrier is checked by assembling the unit with a nominal shim, adjusting the carrier, and then running a tooth contact pattern. The pinion depth shim is then changed as needed to correct the pattern. Most aftermarket pinion gears for carriers with overhung pinions will have the pinion depth marked on the gear head, and this is measured using a pinion depth micrometer.

The other gear adjustments are also made much like those to a production vehicle. Some race car technicians will adjust the pinion bearing preload a little tighter than stock (20 to 25 in.-lb) to make sure that the ring and pinion gears stay in proper mesh. Carrier bearing preload is also more critical than with a stock unit because of the increased loading. Some technicians measure the preload increase at the pinion gear as they adjust the carrier bearings; this is complicated by the

effect of the gear ratio. The amount of carrier bearing preload should be about 13 to 15 in.-lb and this is divided by the gear ratio and added to the pinion bearing preload to measure it .

◀ SERVICE TIP ▶

Assume that you have a 4.11:1 gear set with a pinion bearing preload of 10 in.-lb. The carrier bearing preload of 13 divided by 4.11 equals 3.2, and 10 plus 3.6 equals 13.1; 15 divided by 4.11 equals 3.6, and 10 plus 3.6 equals 13.6. As the carrier bearing preload is adjusted, the preload of the pinion shaft should increase from 10 to 13.1 to 13.6 in.-lb.

Other technicians use the case spread method or observation of the bearing movement as described in Chapter 12 to adjust carrier bearing preload.

The following tips can be used when adjusting a high-performance axle set:

- Oil the outside of the carrier bearing races and adjuster threads to help them seat.
- When adjusting the carrier to check pinion depth in a Ford 9-in. style, use the same ring and pinion teeth to check backlash before and after the shim change.
- If there is excessive backlash variation (over 0.003 in. or 0.07 mm), rotate the ring gear one-half turn on the differential case or spool.
- Apply stud and bearing locking compound on the threads of the carrier bearing mounting bolts and adjuster lock bolts.
- Use a contact pattern to confirm proper adjustment or problems that need correction (Figure 16-51).

A new gear set should be filled with good-quality gear oil and broken in by operating it at light to medium load for a short period of time to begin the lapping process. Then it should be run at a heavy load for a short period until the gears get hot. At this point the gears should be allowed to cool down. The object is to wear down the high-contact spots and allow them to cool before they get hot enough to produce galling and scoring.

16.6.4   Competition Axle Assemblies

Most of the axle assemblies used in drag race and some circle track cars are highly modified, production-based units. Often, the housings are shortened to place the wide tires inside the limits of the body or rules, strengthened to prevent bending, and fitted with better axle bearings or converted to full-floating axles (Figure 16-52). The most commonly used carrier is the Ford 9 in., with an aftermarket case casting of nodular iron, aluminum, or magnesium (Figure 16-53). Nodular iron is considerably stronger than cast iron, the aluminum unit is much lighter, and the magnesium unit is lighter still. These units are generally assembled using either the type of differential or spool most suited to the intended form of racing. A circle track racer will often have several carriers, each with a different gear ratio, and will use the one most suited for the particular track and conditions.

Competition axle assemblies are available for some forms of racing. Sprint cars and midgets place a high priority on light weight and fast gear changes. These axles usually include a quick-change feature (Figure 16-54). These axles have a primary shaft that is used to transfer power from the driveshaft to a quick-change gear at the rear of the housing. A second quick-change

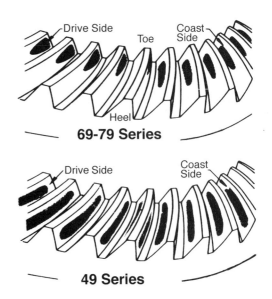

FIGURE 16-51   The ideal contact pattern on gears set up for racing is very similar to the contact pattern for a stock setup. (Courtesy of Richmond Gear)

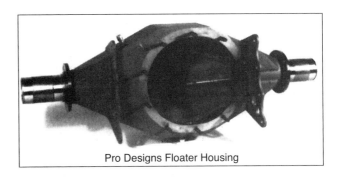

Pro Designs Floater Housing

FIGURE 16-52   Two dragster axle housings that are very narrow and use full-floating axles. (Courtesy of Mark Williams Enterprises)

gear transmits the power to the drive pinion shaft. There is a rear cover that is easily removed so that the quick-change gears can be switched or replaced with another pair of gears.

16.7 CONCLUSION

This chapter was written to introduce you to the variety, possibilities, and maybe some of the excitement of high-performance drivetrains. The development of most of these units has been accomplished through a lot of trial and some error. It is impossible to cover all the aspects of the various drivetrain components in a book like this. At this time there are several excellent books that describe the drivetrain used in special-purpose off-road and racing vehicles. Also, the component manufacturers are, in most cases, an excellent and willing source of information on their product. There are also many informative Websites on the Internet.

Drivetrain modification is not normally done in the average garage or repair shop because of the time consumed, skill required, and possible liability problems. This type of work is normally done by highly specialized shops, very knowledgeable hobbyists, and race car teams.

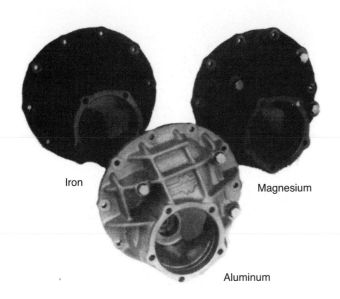

Iron

Magnesium

Aluminum

FIGURE 16-53 Besides normal cast iron, 9-in. carriers are available in nodular iron, aluminum, and magnesium. (Courtesy of Mark Williams Enterprises)

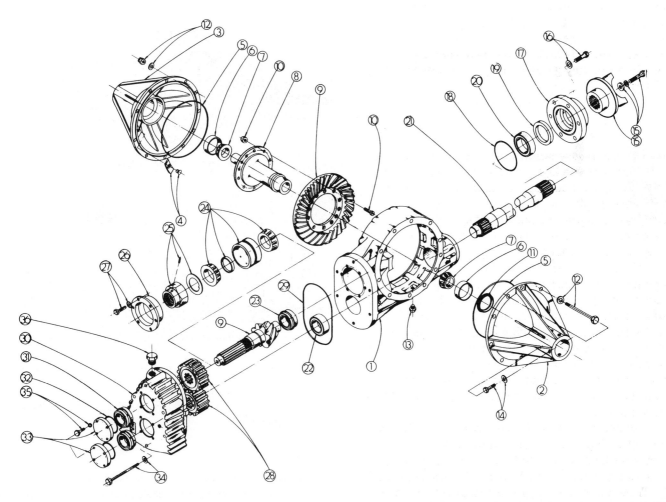

FIGURE 16-54 A quick-change rear end uses a pair of easily changed gears (28) to transfer power from the input shaft (21) to the drive pinion (9). (Courtesy of Stock Car Products)

ASE CERTIFICATION

Automotive and truck technicians have the opportunity to take National Institute for Automotive Service Excellence (ASE) certification tests voluntarily to become ASE certified technicians. Certification helps technicians prove their abilities to themselves, to their employers, and to their customers. ASE certification requires that you pass one or more tests and have at least two years of automotive repair work experience. School training can be used to substitute for part of the work experience requirement. You may take the test(s) before completing the work experience requirement. You will receive the score report, and then when the experience requirement is completed, you will receive certification.

There are eight automotive service tests, and one is A3, Manual Drivetrains and Axles. There are eight medium/heavy truck service tests, and one is T3, Drivetrain. The A3 test has 40 questions, taken from these content areas:

Content Area	Questions
A. Clutch diagnosis and repair	6
B. Transmission diagnosis and repair	6
C. Transaxle diagnosis and repair	8
D. Drive (half) shaft and universal joint/ constant-velocity (CV) joint diagnosis and repair (front and rear wheel drive)	6
E. Rear axle diagnosis and repair	7
1. Ring and pinion gears	(3)
2. Differential case assembly	(2)
3. Limited slip differential	(1)
4. Axle shafts	(1)
F. Four-wheel drive component diagnosis and repair	7

Each of the content areas are divided into groups of tasks. These are the things that a drivetrain technician should be able to do. For a current task list, call ASE and request an Automobile Preparation Guide or visit their Website at www.ase.com.

TASK LIST: MANUAL DRIVETRAIN AND AXLES

A. Clutch Diagnosis and Repair

1. Diagnose clutch noise, binding, slippage, pulsation, chatter, pedal feel/effort, and release problems; determine needed repairs.
2. Inspect, adjust, and replace clutch pedal linkage, cables and automatic adjuster mechanisms, brackets, bushings, pivots, and springs.
3. Inspect, adjust, replace, and bleed hydraulic clutch slave and master cylinders, lines, and hoses.
4. Inspect, adjust, and replace release (throw-out) bearing, lever, and pivot.
5. Inspect and replace clutch disc and pressure plate assembly.
6. Inspect and replace pilot bearing.
7. Inspect and measure flywheel and ring gear; repair or replace as necessary.

Courtesy of the National Institute for Automotive Service Excellence. For an up-to-date task list, contact ASE at (703) 713-3800 and request an Automobile Preparation Guide.

8. Inspect engine block, clutch (bell) housing, and transmission case mating surfaces; determine needed repairs.

9. Measure flywheel-to-block runout and crankshaft end play; determine needed repairs.

10. Measure clutch (bell) housing bore-to-crankshaft runout and face squareness; determine needed repairs.

11. Inspect, replace, and align powertrain mounts.

B. Transmission Diagnosis and Repair

1. Diagnose transmission noise, hard shifting, jumping out of gear, and fluid leakage problems; determine needed repairs.

2. Inspect, adjust, and replace transmission external shifter assembly, shift linkages, brackets, bushings/grommets, pivots, and levers.

3. Inspect and replace transmission gaskets, sealants, seals, and fasteners; inspect sealing surfaces.

4. Remove and replace transmission; inspect transmission mounts.

5. Disassemble and clean transmission components; reassemble transmission.

6. Inspect, repair, and/or replace transmission shift cover and internal shift forks, bushings, levers, shafts, sleeves, detent mechanisms, interlocks, and springs.

7. Inspect and replace input (clutch) shaft, bearings, and retainers.

8. Inspect and replace mainshaft, gears, thrust washers, bearings, and retainers/snap rings.

9. Inspect and replace synchronizer hub, sleeve, keys (inserts), springs, and blocking (synchronizing) rings; measure blocking ring clearance.

10. Inspect and replace counter (cluster) gear, shaft, bearings, thrust washers, and retainers/ snap rings.

11. Inspect and replace reverse idler gear, shaft, bearings, thrust washers, and retainers/snap rings.

12. Measure and adjust shaft, gear, and synchronizer end play.

13. Measure and adjust bearing preload.

14. Inspect, repair, and replace extension housing and transmission case mating surfaces, bores, bushings, and vents.

15. Inspect and replace speedometer drive gear, driven gear, and retainers.

16. Inspect, test, and replace transmission sensors and switches.

17. Inspect lubrication devices; check fluid level, and refill with proper fluid.

C. Transaxle Diagnosis and Repair

1. Diagnose transaxle noise, hard shifting, jumping out of gear, and fluid leakage problems; determine needed repairs.

2. Inspect, adjust, and replace transaxle external shift assembly, linkages, brackets, bushings/grommets, cables, pivots, and levers.

3. Inspect and replace transaxle gaskets, sealants, seals, and fasteners; inspect sealing surfaces.

4. Remove and replace transaxle; inspect, replace, and align transaxle mounts.

5. Disassemble and clean transaxle components; reassemble transaxle.

6. Inspect, repair, and/or replace transaxle shift cover and internal shift forks, levers, bushings, shafts, sleeves, detent mechanisms, interlocks, and springs.

7. Inspect and replace input shaft, bearings, and retainers.

8. Inspect and replace output shaft, gears, thrust washers, bearings, and retainers/snap rings.

9. Inspect and replace synchronizer hub, sleeve, keys (inserts), springs, and blocking (synchronizing) rings; measure blocking ring clearance.

10. Inspect and replace reverse idler gear, shaft, bearings, thrust washers, and retainers/snap rings.

11. Inspect, repair, and replace transaxle case mating surfaces, bores, bushings, and vents.

12. Inspect and replace speedometer drive gear, driven gear, and retainers.

13. Inspect, test, and replace transaxle sensors and switches.

14. Diagnose differential assembly noise and vibration problems; determine needed repairs.

15. Remove and replace differential assembly.

16. Inspect, measure, adjust, and replace differential pinion gears (spiders), shaft, side gears, thrust washers, and case.

17. Inspect and replace differential side bearings.

18. Measure shaft end play/preload (shim/spacer selection procedure).

19. Inspect lubrication devices; check fluid level, and refill with proper fluid.

D. Drive (Half) Shaft and Universal Joint/Constant-Velocity (CV) Joint Diagnosis and Repair (Front and Rear Wheel Drive)

1. Diagnose shaft and universal/CV joint noise and vibration problems; determine needed repairs.
2. Inspect, service, and replace shafts, yokes, boots, and universal/CV joints.
3. Inspect, service, and replace shaft center support bearings.
4. Check and correct propeller shaft balance.
5. Measure shaft runout.
6. Measure and adjust shaft angles.

E. Rear-Wheel-Drive Axle Diagnosis and Repair

1. Ring and Pinion Gears

1. Diagnose noise, vibration, and fluid leakage problems; determine needed repairs.
2. Inspect and replace companion flange and pinion seal; measure companion flange runout.
3. Measure ring gear runout; determine needed repairs.
4. Inspect and replace ring and pinion gear set, collapsible spacers, sleeves (shims), and bearings.
5. Measure and adjust drive pinion depth.
6. Measure and adjust drive pinion preload (collapsible spacer or shim type).
7. Measure and adjust differential (side) bearing preload and ring and pinion backlash (threaded cup or shim type).
8. Perform ring and pinion tooth contact pattern checks; determine needed adjustments.

2. Differential Case Assembly

1. Diagnose differential assembly noise and vibration problems; determine needed repairs.
2. Remove and replace differential assembly.
3. Inspect, measure, adjust, and replace differential pinion gears (spiders), shaft, side gears, thrust washers, and case.
4. Inspect and replace differential side bearings.
5. Measure differential case runout; determine needed repairs.

3. Limited Slip Differential

1. Diagnose limited slip differential noise, slippage, and chatter problems; determine needed repairs.
2. Inspect, flush, and refill with correct lubricant.
3. Inspect, adjust, and replace clutch (cone/plate) pack.

4. Axle Shafts

1. Diagnose rear axle shaft noise, vibration, and fluid leakage problems; determine needed repairs.
2. Inspect and replace rear axle shaft wheel studs.
3. Remove, inspect, and replace rear axle shafts, seals, bearings, and retainers.
4. Measure rear axle flange runout and shaft end play; determine needed repairs.

F. Four-Wheel-Drive Component Diagnosis and Repair

1. Diagnose four-wheel-drive assembly noise, vibration, shifting, and steering problems; determine needed repairs.
2. Inspect, adjust, and repair transfer case manual shifting mechanisms, bushings, mounts, levers, and brackets.
3. Remove and replace transfer case.
4. Disassemble and clean transfer case and components; reassemble transfer case.
5. Inspect and service transfer case and internal components; check lube level.
6. Inspect, service, and replace front drive (propeller) shafts and universal/CV joints.
7. Inspect, service, and replace front drive axle knuckles and driving shafts.
8. Inspect, service, and replace front wheel bearings and locking hubs.
9. Check transfer case and front axle seals and remote vents.
10. Diagnose, test, adjust, and replace electrical/electronic components of four-wheel-drive systems.

LUBRICATION GUIDE

It is usually recommended to use the manufacturer's fluid recommendations, but at times, there is still a noise or shift problem. Some of the fluid types given in this appendix are different from specifications and have cured some of these problems.

Unit Type	Specific Units	Oil Type
Transmissions:		
Asian Warner	AX5 & AX15	GM Synchromesh Fluid P/N 12346349 Only
Borg Warner	T5, T-45 & T-56	ATF Only
Borg Warner	T-18, T-19	75-90 Gear Oil
Ford	M5R1 & M5R2	ATF Only
Muncie	SM465	75-90W Gear Oil
New Process	535	GM Synchromesh Fluid P/N 12346349 Only
New Venture	4500	Castrol Syntorque Synthetic Gear Oil Only
New Venture	HM290, 5LM60, 3500	GM Synchromesh Fluid P/N 12346349 Only
New Venture	T350, A-578, Mitsubishi F5MC1	Mopar M59417 MTX Fluid P/N 4773167 Only
Nissan	FS571C	75-90W Gear Oil
Peugeot	BA10	GM Synchromesh Fluid P/N 12346349 Only
Tremec	SMOD, SROD, TOD	ATF Only
ZF Corvette Unit	S640	P/N 1062931 or Castrol IRS only
ZF Truck Units	S542, S547, S650	Synthetic ATF Only
Transfer Cases:		
Borg Warner	1345, 1350, 1354, 1356, 1370, 4401, 4405, 4406, 4407	Synthetic ATF Only
Dana	RA28	Synthetic ATF Only
New Process	136, 243, 246	Synthetic ATF Only
New Process	203, 205	75-90W Gear Oil Only
New Process	207, 208, 119, 128, 129, 219, 228, 229, 231, 233, 241, 249, 271, 273	5W-30 Motor Oil Only
New Process	247	Chrysler Part #05013457AA
New Process	435	75-90W Gear Oil

(Courtesy of Rockland Standard Gear)

◀ Appendix C ▶

ENGLISH-METRIC-ENGLISH CONVERSION TABLE

Multiply	By	To get/Multiply	By	To get
Length				
inch (″)	25.4	millimeter (mm)	0.3939	inch
mile	1.609	kilometer	0.621	

inch scale: 16th, 1, 2, 3, 4, 5, 6

mm/cm scale: mm 1 cm 2 3 4 5 6 7 8 9 10 cm 11 12 13 14 15

Multiply	By	To get/Multiply	By	To get
Area				
inch^2	645.2	millimeter^2	0.0015	inch^2
Pressure				
pounds-in.^{2}	6.895	kilopascals (kPa)	0.145	psi
Volume				
inch^3	16,387	millimeter^3	0.00006	inch^3
inch^3	6.45	centimeter^3	0.061	inch^3
inch^3	0.016	liter	61.024	inch^3
quart	0.946	liter	1.057	quart
gallon	3.785	liter	0.264	gallon
Weight				
ounce	28.35	gram (g)	0.035	ounce
pound	0.453	kilogram (kg)	2.205	pound
Torque				
inch-pound	0.113	Newton-meter (N-m)	8.851	inch-pound
foot-pound	1.356	Newton-meter	0.738	foot-pound
Velocity				
miles/hour	1.609	kilometer/hour	0.6214	miles/hour
Temperature				

(degree Fahrenheit − 32) × 0.556 = degree Celsius
(degree Celsius × 1.8) + 32 = degree Fahrenheit

°F: −40, 0, 32, 40, 80, 98.6, 120, 160, 200, 212

°C: −40, −20, 0, 20, 37, 40, 60, 80, 100

◀ Appendix D ▶

BOLT TORQUE TIGHTENING CHART

The torque that a particular bolt or nut is tightened to is determined by the diameter and grade of the bolt and nut, the type of material that a bolt is tightened into, and whether or not the threads are lubricated. Normally, torque specifications for specific bolts and nuts are printed in the vehicle's service manual. If these specifications are not available, the following charts can be used as a guide while tightening SAE and metric standard-sized bolts.

		SAE standard			
Grade	1 & 2	5	8	Wrench size	
Size				Bolt	Nut
1/4	5	7	10	3/8	7/16
5/16	9	14	22	1/2	9/16
3/8	15	25	37	9/16	5/8
7/16	24	40	60	5/8	3/4
1/2	37	60	92	3/4	13/16

These specifications are given in foot-pounds. Multiplying a particular specification by 12 will convert it to inch-pounds; multiplying it by 1.356 will convert it to Newton-meters. The values printed here are for clean, lubricated bolts.

		Metric standard			
Grade	5	8	10	12	Wrench size
Size					Bolt
6 mm	5	9	11	12	10 mm
8 mm	12	21	26	32	14 mm
10 mm	23	40	50	60	17 mm
12 mm	40	70	87	105	19 mm
14 mm	65	110	135	160	22 mm

◀ Appendix E ▶

ATTS AND NATEF TASKS

ATTS SKILLS: DRIVE TRAINS

These skills are grouped into three levels:

    Level One: Consumer or Program Entry
    Level Two: Job Entry
    Level Three: Job Entry Skills with minimum employer supervision.

Additional information and skills lists can be obtained by visiting the California Auto Teachers (CAT) website: www.calautoteachers.com.

Level I

Level I

Skill	Textbook Section	Exercise
50	8.2.1, 12.2, 14.2	E 14, E 20

Level II: Manual Drive Train and Axles

Level II, Clutch

Skill	Textbook Section	Exercise
24.9	5.3	E 6
24.10	5.2.1	E 4
24.11	5.2.2, 5.5	E 3
24.12	5.5	E 13

Level II, Transmission/Transaxle

Skill	Textbook Section	Exercise
24.13	8.2.1	E 14
24.15	8.2.4	E 18
24.16	8.2.1	E 15
24.17	8.4.1, 8.4.2	E 32, E 33, E 34

Level II, Drive Shaft & Universal Joint

Skill	Textbook Section	Exercise
24.18	10.4.2	E 34
24.19	10.4.1	E 32, E 33
24.20	10.3.2, 10.5.2	E 38
24.21	10.3.1, 10.5.1	E 35, E 36

Level II, Rear Wheel Drive Axle

Skill	Textbook Section	Exercise
24.22	12.2	E 40
24.23	12.2	E 40
24.24	E 41	
24.25	12.4.6	E 46
24.26	12.4	E 44, E 45

Level II, 4WD/AWD Components

Skill	Textbook Section	Exercise
24.27	14.2	E 54
24.28	14.2	E 55

Level III Skills

Level III, Clutch

Skill	Textbook Section	Exercise
34.49	5.3	E 4
34.50	5.2.1	E 4
34.51	5.5	E 5
34.52	5.5	E 13
34.53	5.4.2.5	E 9
34.54	5.4.2.2,.5.4.2.3	E 9, E 10
34.55	5.4.1, 5.4.3	E 10
34.56	5.4.2.1	E 9
34.57	5.4.2.4	E 9
34.58	5.4.1, 5.4.3	E 7, E 10

Level III, Transmission/Transaxle

Skill	Textbook Section	Exercise
34.59	8.2.1	E 14
34.60	8.2.1	E 14
34.61	8.2.1.1	E 15
34.62	8.2.2, 8.2.3	E 16
34.63	8.2.4	E 18
34.64	8.5.12	
34.65	8.5.1, 8.5.2, 8.5.3	E 21, E 22
34.66	8.5.4, 8.5.5	E 23
34.67	8.5.4, 8.5.5	E 23
34.68	8.5.6	E 23
34.69	8.5.7	E 23
34.70	8.5.4	E 23
34.71	8.5.4, 8.5.12	E 23
34.72	8.5.12	E 25, E 26
34.73	8.5.1, 8.5.12	
34.74	8.5.5	E 23
34.75	8.5	E 21, E 25
34.76	8.5	E 22, E 26
34.77	8.4.2	E 19, E 27
34.78	8.4.1	E 20, E 28

Level III, Drive Shaft & U-Joint (FWD/RWD)

Skill	Textbook Section	Exercise
34.79	10.4.2	E 32, E 33
34.80	10.4.1	E 34
34.81	10.3.2, 10.5.2	E 38
34.82	10.3.1, 18.5.1	E 35, E 36
34.83	10.4.1.1	

Level III, Rear Wheel Drive Axle

Skill	Textbook Section	Exercise
34.84	12.2	E 40
34.85	12.2	E 40
34.86	E 41	
34.87	12.6.4.1	E 47

34.88	12.6	E 48 to E 51
34.89	12.6.1, 12.6.2	E 48
34.90	12.6.2	E 48, E 52
34.91	12.6.4, 12.6.5	E 49, E 50
34.92	12.6	E 50
34.93	12.6.7, 12.6.8	E 50, E 51
34.94	12.6.8	E 51
34.95	12.6.9	E 52
34.96	12.6.3, 12.6.8	E 49, E 51
34.97	8.5.9	E 24
34.98	12.6.5	
34.99	12.6.2	

Level III, Limited Slip Differential

Skill	Textbook Section	Exercise
34.100	12.2	E 41
34.101	12.3.6	E 53
34.102	12.6.11	
34.103	12.6.11	

Level III, RWD Axle Shafts

Skill	Textbook Section	Exercise
34.104	12.3.5	E 40, E 42
34.105	12.4.6	E 46
34.106	12.4	E 44
34.107	12.4.2, 12.4.4	E 45
34.108	12.3.3, 12.3.4	E 46

Level III, 4WD/AWD Components

Skill	Textbook Section	Exercise
34.109	14.4.1	E 57
34.110	14.2	E 55
34.111	14.2, 14.4	E 54, E 57
34.112	14.5	E 60
34.113	10.2, 10.4.2, 10.5.2	E 34
34.114	14.4.4	
34.115	14.4.2, 14.4.3	E 58
34.116		
34.117	14.6	E 61

NATEF TASKS: AREA III. MANUAL DRIVE TRAIN AND AXLES

These tasks are assigned a priority:

90% of Priority 1 (P-1) tasks must be completed
80% of Priority 2 (P-2) tasks must be completed, and
50% of Priority 3 (P-3) tasks must be completed.

Additional information concerning NATEF certification can be obtained by calling the National Automotive Technicians Foundation, Herndon, VA (703) 713-0100.

A. General Drive Train Diagnosis

Task & Priority	Textbook Section	Exercise
1. P-1	5.3, 8.3, 10.3, 12.3, 14.3	E 3
2. P-1		
3. P-1	E 2	
4. P-1	8.2.1, 12.2, 14.2	E 5 & 14
5. P-2	8.2.1.1	E 15

B. Clutch Diagnosis & Repair

Task & Priority	Textbook Section	Exercise
1. P-1	5.3	E 6
2. P-1	5.2 , 5.3	E 6
3. P-1	5.2.3, 5.5	E 5, E 12
4. P-1	5.4.2.5	E 8, E 10
5. P-1	5.4.2, 5.4.3	E 8, E 10
6. P-1	5.5	E 13
7. P-1	5.4.1, 5.4.3	E 8, E 9
8. P-1	5.4.2.1	E 9
9. P-3	5.4.2.4	E 9
10. P-3	5.4.2.1	E 9

C. Transmission/Transaxle Diagnosis & Repair

Task & Priority	Textbook Section	Exercise
1. P-1	8.4	E 19, E 20, E 27, E 28
2. P-2	8.5.1, 8.5.2, 8.5.3	E 21, E 22, E 24, E 25, E 26
3. P-3	8.5.11	E 23
4. P-2	8.3	E 17
5. P-2	8.2.2, 8.3.1	E 23, E24, E 25
6. P-3	8.2.4	E 18
7. P-2	8.5.11, 8.5.12	
8. P-3	8.5.1, 8.5.12	E 22, E 26
9. P-2	8.5.10, 8.5.12	
10. P-1	8.5.12	E 25, E 26
11. P-2	8.5.7, 8.5.12	E 23
12. P-2		
13. P-3	8.3	
14. P-2	8.5.9	E 24
15. P-3	8.5.5	
16. P-1	Chapter 15	

D. Drive Shaft & Half Shaft, U-joint & CV joint Diagnosis & Repair

Task & Priority	Textbook Section	Exercise
1. P-1	10.3.1	E 30
2. P-1	10.3.2	E 31
3. P-2	10.4.2	
4. P-1	10.5.1	E 35, E 36, E 37
5. P-3	10.5.2	
6. P-2	10.3.2	E 31

E. 1. Ring & Pinion Gears and Differential Case Assembly

Task & Priority	Textbook Section	Exercise
1. P-2	12.3	E 42
2. P-2	12.3.5	E 40
3. P-2	12.3.4, 12.6.4.1	E 47
4. P-2	12.6.1, 12.6.2	E 48
5. P-2	12.6	E 49, E 50
6. P-2	12.6.6	E 50
7. P-1	12.6.7	E 50
8. P-2	12.6.8	E 51
9. P-1	12.6.9	E 52
10. P-2	8.5.9	E 24
11. P-2	12.6.8	E 50, E 51

E. 2. Limited Slip Differential

Task & Priority	Textbook Section	Exercise
1. P-3	12.3, 12.3.6	E 42, E 53
2. P-2	12.2	E 41
3. P-3	12.6.1	E 53
4. P-3	12.3.6	E 43

E. 3. Drive Axle Shaft

Task & Priority	Textbook Section	Exercise
1. P-2	12.3	E 42
2. P-3	12.4.6	E 46
3. P-1	12.4	E 44
4. P-2	12.3	E 45
5. P-2	12.3	E 46

F. 4WD/AWD Component Diagnosis & Repair

Task & Priority	Textbook Section	Exercise
1. P-3	14.3, 14.4	E 57
2. P-3	14.4	E 56
3. P-3	14.5	E 60
4. P-3	14.6	E 61
5. P-3	14.4.2, 14.4.3	E 58
6. P-3	14.2	E 54
7. P-3	Chapter 15	E 62 to E 64

GLOSSARY

Accelerate: To increase speed.

Additives: Chemicals added to lubricants to improve or modify certain operating characteristics.

Aerodynamic drag: The wind resistance of air moving over the size and shape of the vehicle.

All-wheel-drive (AWD): A drive system that can drive both the front and rear wheels through all phases of operation. (Also called full-time 4WD.)

Annulus gear: An internal, or ring, gear used in a planetary gear set.

Antilock braking system (ABS): A system that senses wheel lockup during braking and momentarily reduces braking forces to maintain wheel rotation.

Automatic transmission: A transmission that automatically changes forward gear speeds.

Automatic transmission fluid (ATF): The fluid designed for use in an automatic transmission.

Axial: A direction parallel to the shaft or bearing bore.

Axis: The centerline of a rotating part.

Bearing cage: A spacer to keep the balls or rollers in a bearing separated and in the proper position.

Bearing cap: A device that is bolted in place to secure a bearing in place.

Bearing cone: The inner race of a tapered roller bearing.

Bearing cup: The outer race for the needles of a U-joint bearing and of a tapered roller bearing.

Bearing race: The hardened surface on which the balls, needles, or rollers of a bearing run.

Belleville: A conical steel spring that gives a spring action because of its resistance to flattening.

Bellows-type boot: An accordion-pleated rubber cover used to protect a mechanical device inside of it.

Bleed: A procedure to remove the air from a hydraulic system.

Brinelling: Grooves worn on a bearing journal due to impact loading, vibration, or wear.

Burnish: To smooth or polish through rubbing action.

Cancelling angles: Equal and opposite angles of two U-joints, used to cancel vibrations generated by the U-joints.

Cardan U-joint: The common U-joint used in most RWD driveshafts.

Carrier: The casting section of a drive axle that contains the differential and ring and pinion gears.

Case: The rigid housing for a drive axle, transaxle, transmission, or transfer case.

C-clip: A C-shaped locking device used to retain an axle shaft.

Center section: The carrier portion of a drive axle.

Centrifugal force: The force on a revolving object that tries to push it away from the center of revolution.

Chamfer: A beveled edge on a shaft or bore.

Circlip: A snap-ring type of ring with a round cross section used to position a shaft in a bore.

Clash: The grinding sound that is heard when trying to mesh two gears that are operating at different speeds.

Cluster gear: A group of gears that are machined from one piece of metal, or individual gears combined into one group so they operate together.

Clutch: A device that controls the power transfer between two points by either allowing or not allowing a transfer.

Coast: A load condition in which the vehicle is driving the engine, as during deceleration.

Coefficient of friction: A reference to the amount of friction between two surfaces.

Constant-velocity joint: A V-joint that can transmit power without changing the velocity.

Continuously variable transmission (CVT): A transmission that varies the gear ratio in a continuous, rather than stepwise, manner.

Damper: A device that reduces the torsional vibrations between the engine and transmission.

Decelerate: To reduce speed.

Deflection: The bending or movement caused by a load.

Detent: A spring-loaded device used to position a shift fork correctly.

Dial indicator: A measuring device that indicates linear travel by a rotating needle.

Diaphragm spring: A round, conical-shaped spring; a Belleville spring.

Differential: A gear arrangement that allows the drive wheels to be driven at different speeds.

Direct drive: A 1:1 gear ratio.

Dowel: A round metal pin attached to a casting, which ensures proper alignment as a hole in another casting is placed onto it.

Drag: The resistance or friction created by one object passing by another.

Drive: A load condition in which the engine is applying power to the drive wheels.

Driveline: Another name for a driveshaft.

Driveshaft: A device that transmits power from one unit to another.

Dynamic friction: The relative amount of friction between two surfaces that have different speeds.

Eccentric: Two circles that do not have the same center.

End play: The amount of motion a shaft or gear has in a direction that is parallel to the shaft.

Energy: The ability to do work.

Engagement modulation: The ability to engage the clutch in order to produce a smooth, slip-free engagement.

Extreme-pressure (EP) lubricant: A lubricant designed to stay in place and keep parts from touching when under extremely high pressure.

Feeler gauge: Thin metal strips of precise thickness, used to measure the clearance between two parts.

Fiber composites: A mixture of fiber threads (glass, graphite, or other materials) and a resin.

Final drive: The last set of reduction gears before the power flows to the differential gears and drive axles.

Float: A load condition in which two parts are turning at the same speed with no driving force between them; also when a shaft is supported by a gear that, in turn, is supported by a bearing.

Flywheel: The rotating metal mass attached to the crankshaft that helps even out power surges and provides a mounting point and friction surface for the clutch.

Force: A push or pull measured in units of weight, like pounds or kilograms.

Formed-in-place gasket (FIPG): A gasket material that comes from a tube, which is applied to metal surfaces before assembly.

Four-wheel-drive (4WD): A drive system that can drive both the front and rear wheels.

Friction: The resistance in motion between two bodies in contact with each other.

Friction disc: A flat disc that is faced with friction materials; it is driven when it is clamped between two flat metal surfaces.

Front-wheel-drive (FWD): A drive system that drives the front wheels.

Fulcrum: The pivot or supporting point for a lever.

Galling: Wear that transfers metal and is caused by metal-to-metal contact without proper lubrication.

Gasket: A compressible material used as a seal between two mating surfaces.

Gear: A metal wheel with teeth that transmit power or motion to another gear.

Gear ratio: The ratio in the number of teeth on the driving and driven gears; it is calculated by dividing the number of teeth on the driven gear by the number of teeth on the driving gear.

Gear reduction: A condition in which the driving gear is smaller than the driven gear; the result will be an increase in torque and a reduction in speed.

Grade resistance: One hundredth of the vehicle weight times the angle of the grade in percent.

Graphite: A very fine carbon dust that is used as a dry lubricant or a fiber that is combined with resin to form very strong and lightweight objects, such as driveshaft tubing.

Half shaft: The driveshaft used to connect the differential to the drive wheels on drive axles with independent suspension.

Hat: Another name for a clutch pressure plate cover.

Heel: The outer end of a bevel or hypoid ring gear tooth.

Helical gear: A gear with teeth cut at an angle.

Hotchkiss driveshaft: A type of rear suspension that uses leaf springs to absorb drive axle housing torque reactions.

Hub: The center part of a wheel; the surface where a wheel mounts.

Hunting gear set: A gear set in which the driving gear will mesh with every tooth on the driven gear as they rotate.

Hydraulic clutch: A clutch operating system that uses hydraulic pressure to transfer motion and pressure.

Hydraulics: A branch of science dealing with the transfer of power through fluids under pressure.

Hypoid gear: A special form of bevel gear that positions the gear axis on nonintersecting planes and is commonly used in drive axles.

Idler gear: A gear positioned between two other gears such that it causes a change in the direction of rotation.

Inclinometer: A device used to measure mounting positions relative to true level.

Independent rear suspension (IRS):   A type of rear suspension in which the two rear wheels can move vertically without changing the other's position.

Index: To align two parts in the proper position before assembly.

Inertia: The physical property maintaining that a body at rest tends to remain at rest and a body in motion tends to remain in motion and travel in a straight line.

Input shaft: The shaft that carries the driving torque into a gear box.

Integral: Manufactured into; part of.

Interlock: A transmission mechanism that prevents two shift rails or forks from moving at the same time.

Internal gear: A gear with the teeth pointing inward toward the center of the gear.

Journal: A bearing surface for a shaft, gear, or bearing to rotate on.

Lash: *See* Backlash.

Limited slip differential: A differential that uses internal clutches to limit the speed difference between the axles.

Linkage: The series of rods, levers, cables, etc. used to transmit motion of force from one point to another.

Manual transmission: A transmission device in which the gear ratios are changed by manually shifting.

Marcel: A large series of wave springs between the two lining sections of a clutch disc.

Mesh: The interlocking of the teeth of two gears.

Micrometer: A precision measuring device, often called a mike, that is used to measure outside diameters or thicknesses, internal diameters, or depths.

Multiple-disc clutch: A clutch that uses more than one friction disc.

Needle bearing: A very thin roller bearing.

Neutral: A condition in a transmission where the input shaft rotates and the output shaft is not driven.

Newton-meter (N-m):   The metric measurement for torque.

Nodular iron: A type of cast iron that incorporates graphite to increase strength.

Nominal shim: A shim of designated thickness used when beginning a gauging process.

One-way clutch: An overrunning clutch that locks in one direction and freewheels or overruns in the other.

"O"-ring: A round sealing ring.

Output shaft: The shaft that carries the torque out of a gear box.

Overdrive: A gear arrangement that causes the output shaft to turn faster than the input shaft.

Passing gear: A downshift from overdrive to the next lower gear.

Pawl: A locking device that holds a gear stationary.

Peen: A process of striking a metal surface with a hammer or steel shot to upset or harden the surface.

Pinion gear: A small gear that meshes with a larger gear.

Pitch diameter: The effective diameter of a gear; midpoint of gear tooth. (Also called pitch line.)

Planetary gear set: A gear system composed of a sun gear, a planet carrier with planet pinions, and a ring gear that can produce one or more gear ratios.

Plunge joint: A CV joint that allows a driveshaft to change length.

Power: The rate at which work is done.

Power train: The mechanism that transfers and modifies the driving torque from the engine crankshaft to the drive wheels.

Preload: A load placed on parts during assembly to maintain critical clearances and adjustments when operating loads are applied.

Pressure: A force per unit area measured in pounds per square inch (psi) or units of atmospheric pressure (bars or kilopascals).

Pressure plate: The metal disc that applies pressure onto the friction disc to transmit torque.

Propeller shaft: *See* Driveshaft.

Quill: The extension from the transmission input bearing retainer that supports the clutch release bearing.

Race: A hardened surface for the bearing rollers or balls to roll on.

Rack and pinion gear set: A gear set combining a straight gear (the rack) with a pinion gear so the rack moves sideways when the pinion is rotated.

Radial: A direction perpendicular to the rotating axis.

Rear-wheel-drive (RWD):   A drive system that drives the rear wheels.

Release bearing: The bearing that is forced against the pressure plate assembly to release a clutch. (Also called throwout bearing.)

Reverse idler gear: *See* Idler gear.

Ring gear: *See* Annulus gear.

Roller clutch: A one-way clutch that uses a set of rollers and a special cam as the locking mechanism.

Rolling friction: The drag of the tires on the road plus bearing friction.

RTV: A formed-in-place gasket material; a rubberlike material that vulcanizes at room temperature.

Runout: Deviation in an item's rotation or a mounting plane.

Score: A scratch, groove, or ridge that mars a finished surface.

Sensor: An electronic device used to sense operations, such as driveshaft or wheel speed.

Shim: A thin spacer used to adjust clearance or preload.

Slider clutch: A clutch designed to slip until a certain rpm to prevent the transfer of too much torque for the drive wheels.

Slip fit: A free-running or sliding fit.

Slip joint: A splined joint in a driveshaft to allow it to change length.

Slipping: A loss in torque transfer accompanying an increase in engine rpm.

Spalling: A condition where surface metal breaks away from a bearing race.

Spline: A slot or groove cut in a shaft or bore that is used to connect to a matching spline.

Sprag: The locking element in a one-way sprag clutch.

Spur gear: A gear with teeth cut parallel to the axis of the gear.

S spring: A steel spring shaped like the letter S.

Stall: A condition where the engine is running but the transmission input shaft is not rotating.

Stall speed: A condition where the engine is running at maximum speed but the automatic transmission input shaft is not turning.

Standard transmission: *See* Manual transmission; at one time the standard equipment on a new vehicle.

Static friction: The relative amount of friction between two stationary surfaces or two surfaces that are rotating at the same speed.

Synchronize: To bring two objects to the same rotating speed; to cause two events to occur at the same time.

Throw-out bearing: Another name for a clutch release bearing.

Thrust: A motion of a gear or shaft along its axis.

Thrust washer: A bearing that is used to separate rotating parts from stationary parts or parts that are rotating at different speeds.

Toe: The inner end of a bevel or hypoid ring gear tooth.

Torque: A turning or twisting effort that is normally measured in foot-pounds or Newton-meters.

Torque converter: A type of fluid coupling that is used with automatic transmissions that will multiply engine torque. It self-releases to allow the vehicle to stop with the engine running and the transmission in gear.

Traction: The relative amount of grip between a tire and the road surface.

Traction control: A system used to sense wheel spin and reduce drive wheel torque to the amount of traction.

Tractive effort: The amount of thrust that the engine and drivetrain can generate at the road surface.

Tractive resistance: The load that the drivetrain works against.

Transaxle: A transmission that is combined with the final drive and differential and is normally used in FWD and mid-engine vehicles.

Transfer case: An auxiliary transmission used in most 4WD vehicles to divide and control the power flow to the front and rear drive axles.

Transmission: A device in the power train that provides different forward gear ratios, a neutral, and a reverse.

Transverse: A position that is across the vehicle.

Trunnion: The projecting arms of a U-joint cross that form the bearing journals.

U-joint operating angle: The angle between a U-joint's input and output shafts.

Universal joint (U-joint):   A mechanical device used to transfer power and motion at changeable angles.

Upset: The action of displacing metal with hammer blows.

Viscosity: The resistance to flow of a fluid.

Viscous: Thick; tending to resist fluid flow.

Wave spring: A spring that resembles a flat, wavy washer.

Wheel end: The outer end of the axle housing where the axle bearing is situated.

Work: The result of force that changes the speed or direction of motion of an object.

Worm gear: A type of gear with teeth that resemble screw threads.

Yoke: A U-shaped portion of a shaft that connects to a U-joint cross.

SPANISH-LANGUAGE GLOSSARY

4WD (four-wheel drive): transmisión en las ruedas delanteras.

Additive: Aditivo. Sustanicia que se añade a otro elemento, como por ejemplo gasoline en cantidades pequeñas.

Align: alinear. Ponerse al lado. Poner partes de la unidad en la posición correcta.

Alloy: aleación. Metal que consta de un elemento o más que normalmente se añaden para aumentar la resistencia del metal base o darle propiedades importantes.

All wheel drive (AWD): Traccion a cuatro ruedas.

Annulus gear: engranaje anular. Tiene dientes interiores y se utiliza en un satélite o engranaje interno. También se llama *ring gear (corona)*.

ASE (National Institute for Automotive Service Excellence): Instituto Nacional de Excellencia de Servico Automotriz.

Aspect ratio: alargamiento/relación de envergadura. Relación entre la altura y la anchura de una Ilanta. Una llanta que tiene un alargamiento de 60 (una llanta serie 60) tiene una altura (del aro de la llanta a la banda de rodamiento) de 60% de la anchura de la sección de corte.

ASTM (American Society for Testing Materials): Sociedad Americana para Materiales de Prueba.

Automatic transmission: Transmission Automatica

Axial: axial. Alineado con el eje o la línea central de un componente. Desplazamiento axial en una junta esférica quiere decir que hay flojedad en el mismo eje que tiene el espárrago de la junta esférica.

Axle: Backlash: Bearing: Bevel gear:

Baffle: plato deflector. Plato o blindaje que se utiliza para desviar el flujo de o un líquido o un gas.

Bell housing: cubierta de torus/conversor. Caja en forma de campana fijada entre el motor y la transmisión.

Bleeder screw: tornillo de purga. Válvula que se ubica en los cilíndros de rueda (y otros lugares) para purgar aire del sistema hidráulico.

Blocking ring: anillo bloqueador. Parte del aparato sincronizador que se usa en transmisiones manuales/transejes. También se llama *stop ring, blocker ring,* or *synchronizer ring (anillo de tope o anillo sincronizador)*.

Boots: fuelles/botas/cubrepolvos. Protectores de goma que se ubican en los extremos de un cilindro de rueda o calibrador que lo protegen de polvo; también cubren y protegen las juntas homocinéticas en el eje de tracción o eje propulsor.

Brinelling: brinelling. Falla mecánica que describe una abolladura en metal, por ejemplo, la que ocurre cuando se aplica una carga a choque a un balero/cojinete. Llamado en honor de Johann A. Brinell, ingeniero sueco.

Cardan joint: junta cardán. Una clase de articulación universal que Ileva el nombre de un matemático italiano del siglo dieciseis.

Center bolt: perno central/capuchino/de centraje. Perno que mantiene unidas en el centro las hojas de un elástico de hojas. También se llama *centering pin (perno centralizador)*.

Center support bearing: balero de soporte central. Balero que soporta el centro de un flecha de cardán larga/eje propulsor largo de un automóvil de propulsión trasera. También se llama *steady bearing* o *hanger bearing*.

Chassis: chasis. El bastidor, la suspensión, la dirección y la maquinaria de un automóvil.

Chatter: traqueteo/vibración. Cuando se frenan, los tambores de repente se asen y se sueltan.

Cluster gears: tren de engranaje. Engranajes que se localizan en el eje secundario. *Véase* countershaft.

Cluster shaft: *Véase* countershaft.

Clutch gear: engranaje del embrague. *Véase* input shaft.

Coast: Desembrague; deceleracion.

Coefficient of friction: coeficiente de fricción. Medida de fricción, normalmente en incrementos de 0 a 1. Un número bajo (0.3) indica una fricción baja y una alta (0.9) una fricción alta.

Cone: cono. El anillo de rodamiento interior de un cojinete.

Constant velocity joint: junta homocinética/ acoplación de velocidad constante. Comúnmente se llaman *CV joints*. Acoplaciones CV son juntas del tren de potencia que pueden transmitir el poder del motor por ángulos grandes sin cambiar la velocidad, como se ve con juntas universales convencionales tipo cardán.

Cotter key: pasador hendido/chaveta. Lazo de metal que se usa para retener tuercas almenadas por instalarlo por un hueco. El tamaño se mide por diámetro y largura (por ejemplo la octava parte de una pulgada por 1.5 pulgadas). También se llama *cotter pin (clavija)*. El nombre viene del verbo del antiguo inglés que quiere decir «cerrar» o «aborchar».

Countershaft: contraeje. Eje inferior de una transmisión manual/transeje. Los engranaje que se ubican en el contraeje se llaman *cluster gears (trenes desplazables)* o *counter gears (trenes secundarios)*.

CV (constant velocity) joints: acoplaciones CV. Juntas homocinéticas/acoplación de velocidad constante.

Diff.: Abreviatura o jerga para *diferencial*.

Differential: diferencial. Conjunto mecánico que contiene engranajes que provee desmultiplicación de engranajes y un cambio de dirección de poder del motor y también que permite que las ruedas de propulsión giran a velocidades distintas, como se requiere para doblar la esquina.

Dog: *Véase* key.

DOT (Department of Transportation): Abreviatura para el Departamento de Transportación.

Double Cardan: cardán doble. Junta universal que consta de dos articulaciones/juntas cardanes, dejando que la junta alcance mayores ángulos.

Drive plate: *Véase* flex plate.

Driveshaft: Arbol de transmission. Un tubo que tiene una junta en ambas extremidades

Dual-mass flywheel: volante de dos masas. Un volante que consta de dos componentes separados por bobinas que se usan para absorber vibraciones en la transmisión.

Dust cap: capuchón. Una tapa de metal que no deja que la grasa salga y que no permite que el polvo entre en los cojinetes de rueda. También se llama *grease cap*.

End play: Juego en la ectremidad; holgura lateral.

Energy: energia. La habilidad a trabajar.

Extension housing: retenedor de cojinete trasero. Retendor trasero de una transmisión manual o automática.

Filler vent: orificio de escape de gases. Hueco en la tapa de cilindro maestro que deja que el aire salga.

Final drive: transmisión final. Diferencial en un transeje.

Frequency: frequencia. Número de veces una onda se repite en un segundo, que se mide en Hertz (Hz), en una banda.

Galling: desgaste por friccion. El metal se transfiere de una superficie a otra.

Garter spring: muelle/bobina toroidal. Resorte usado en un cierre para ayudar mantener el labio del sello en el contacto con la parte móvil.

Gear ratio: relacion de engranajes. Al diferencia en velocidad entre dos engranaje que se calcula al dividir el numero de los dientes en el engranaje propulsor.

Grease cap: tapa de engrase. Tapa funcional de metal que no deja que la grasa salga ni que el polvo entre en los cojinetes de rueda. También se llama *dust cap*.

Grease seal: sello de engrase. Sello que se usa para prevenir que el engrase escape y para prevenir que polvo y humedad entren.

GVW (gross vehicle weight): Abreviatura para el peso bruto de vehículo. GVW es el peso del vehículo más el peso de todos pasajeros y la carga hasta el límite especificado por el fabricante.

Half shaft: medio eje. Eje de mando de un vehículo de tracción delantera o un eje que se ubica entre un diferencial estacionario y las ruedas de propulsión.

Hanger bearing: *Véase* center support bearing.

Heel: talon. Al extremidad exterior de un diente de engranaje.

Helical-cut gears: engranajes de dientes helicoidales. Engranajes que tienen los dientes cortados en un ángulo.

Hertz: hertz. Unidad de la medida de la frecuencia, abreviada Hz. Un Hertz es un ciclo por segundo. Llamado en honor de Heinrich R. Hertz, fisico alemán del siglo diecinueve.

Hunting gearset: conjunto de engranaje con diente suplementario, Cuando un diente del engranaje pinion dara la vuelta hasta que se ha puesto en contacto con todos las dientes de la corona.

Hypoid gear set: conjunto de engranaje hipoide. Engranaje de corona y conjunto de engranaje de piñón que se engranan debajo de la línea central/el eje del engranaje de corona. Este tipo del conjunto de engranaje permite que el cardán es más bajo en el vehículo pero requiere lubricante especial de engranaje hypoide.

Idler gear: engranaje de pinioon loco. Un engranaje que se usa entre dos otros engranajes, su proposito es cambiar la direccion de rotacion.

Input shaft: eje de entrada. Eje que es asegurado por cuña al eje del embrague. También se llama *main gear (engranaje principal), clutch gear (engranaje de embrague) o main drive pinon assembly (conjunto principal de piñón de mando).*

Integral: integro. Un parte que es parte con otro parte.

Internal gear: engranaje interno. Engranaje con dientes internos que se usa en un juego de engranajes planetarios. Se llama también *ring gear (engranaje anular).*

Iron: hierro. Metal refinado de mineral de hierro (óxido ferroso) en un horno. *Véase también* steel.

Key: cuña. Parte de un sincronizador que se usa en transmisiones manuales/transejes. También se llama *strut (puntal) o dog.*

Lateral runout: desviación lateral. Medida del movimiento de una Ilanta o rueda que se mueve de costado a costado mientras que se gira. Desviación lateral excesivo puede causar una vibración si las ruedas están en el eje delantero.

Lay shaft: *Véase* countershaft.

Live axle: eje vivo. Eje enterizo que se usa en las ruedas de propulsión y que lleva los ejes propulsores que propulsan el vehículo.

Lock nut: tuerca de seguridad. *Véase* prevailing torque nut.

Limited slip differential (LSD): Abreviatura que se usa comúnmente usado para diferencial de deslizamiento limitado.

Main drive pinion assembly: *Véase* input shaft.

Main gear: *Véase* input shaft.

Main shaft: eje principal. Eje principal dentro de una transmisión manual/transeje, también llamado *output shaft (eje de salida).*

Manual transmission: transmission manual. Muna transmission que cambia de velocidades manualmente.

Marcel spring: resorte Marcel. Parte de un disco de fricción de embrague que se usa para absorber el golpe instantáneo del acoplamiento de embrague.

Mesh: endentado. Cuando dos engranajes funcionan en contacto.

Mode shift: cambio del modo de conducción. Selección de impulsión de dos ruedas o impulsión de cuatro ruedas en una caja de transferencia.

Moly grease: grasa molibdeno. Grasa que contiene disulfido de molibdeno.

MSDS (material safety data sheets): hojas de datos de seguridad.

National Lubricating Grease Institute (NLGI): Instituto Nacional de la Grasa Lubricante. Generalmente asociado con la grasa. Cuanto más alto el numero de NLGI, tanto más firme la grasa: No. 000 es muy líquido mientras que No. 5 es muy firme. La consistencia más recomendada es NLGI No. 2 (suave).

Needle bearing: conjinete de agujas, Un conjinete rodamientos pequeno.

Noise, Vibration, and Harshness (NVH): Abreviatura para ruido, vibración y fricción.

OSHA (Occupational Safety and Health Administration): Instituto de Seguridad e Higiene en el Trabajo.

Overdrive: sobremarcha. Desmultilpicación/reducción de engranajes en que la rueda de transmisión se gira a una velocidad más lenta que el engranaje impulsado.

Pilot bearing: cojinete piloto. Cojinete que se encuentra en el extremo del cigüeñal del motor para soportar el extremo del eje impulsor de la transmisión manual. También se llama *pilot bushing (buje de guía).*

Pinion gear: piñón satélite. Engranajes pequeño en el extremo del mecanismo de arranque gira el engranaje anualar del volante del motor para arrancar.

Pitch diameter: diametro del paso. El punto en que se juntan lao dientes de dos egranajes.

Planet pinions: piñón satélite. Engranajes satélites fijados a un portaplanetario que rodean un engranaje solar/central en un juego de engranajes planetarios.

Plunge joint: junta profundizada. La junta CV abordo que cambia en su longitud parecido.

Preload: precargar. La carga de apriete en un partemente.

Pressure plate: placa de presion. Oprime el disco del embrague contra el volante.

Prevailing torque nut: tuerca dominante de torsión. Tuerca con un diseño especial tal como deformación o que tiene otras propiedades que permiten que la tuerca se queje fijada al fijador sin aflojarse.

Prop shaft: Abreviatura para eje/flecha propulsor.

Propeller shaft: eje/flecha propulsor(a). Término usado por muchos fabricantes que significa una flecha cardán.

PSI (pounds per square inch): libras por pulgada cuadrada.

Quill: manguito de retención. Otro nombre para el retén de conjinete delantero de una transmisión manual.

Race: pista de rodamiento. Superficie interior y exterior fresada de un cojinete de bolas o de rodillas.

Range shift: cambio de escala de la caja de cambios. Selección de escala alta o escala baja en una caja de cambios.

Ratio: ratio/tasa/relación. La expresión para la proporción. Por ejemplo, en un conjunto de eje trasero, la flecha cardán gira tres veces más rápida que los ejes traseros, lo que se expresa como una relación de tres a uno. Relaciones en un sistema de motor se expresan dividiendo la rotación del mecanismo motriz por la rotación del mecanismo movido.

Release bearing: *Véase* throwout bearing.

Ring gear: corona. Engranaje exterior en un juego de engranajes planetarios o el engranaje grande que se usa en el diferencial.

RPM (revolutions per minute): velocidad del motor que se expresa en revoluciones del cingüeñal por minuto.

RTV: El caucho de silicona que vulcanzia en temperatura ambiente.

Runout: corrimiento. La cantidad que oscila una parte.

RWD (rear-wheel drive): Transmisión por las ruedas traseras.

SAE (Society of Automotive Engineers): Sociedad de Ingenieros Automotrices.

Sensor: sensor. Un dispositivo que eleva a la computadora la informacion.

Shim: lámina de ajuste. Espaciador de metal delgado.

Society of Automotive Engineers (SAE): Sociedad de Ingenieros Automotrices. Organización profesional compuesta de ingenieros y diseñadores automotrices que establece estándares y que hace pruebas para muchas funciones qie tienen que ver con el automóvil.

Spalling: decantillado. Término que se usa para describir un tipo de falla mecánica causada por fatiga del metal. El metal agrieta luego estalla en astillas pequeñas, en los trozos o en las escalas de metal.

Speed gears: engranajes de cambio de marcha. Engranajes que se usan en una transmisión manual/transeje que son libres para mover en cojinetes en el eje

principal y están encerrado al eje por el cubo sincronizador cuando el cambio se completa.

Spindle nut: tuerca de vástago. Tuerca que se usa para retener y ajustar el espacio libre de cojinete del eje al vástago.

Spur gear: engranaje recto. Engranaje que tiene dientes recto.

Steady bearing: *Véase* center support bearing.

Stop ring: *Véase* blocking ring.

Sun gear: engranaje central/solar. Engranaje central en un un juego de engranajes planetarios.

Synchronizer: sincronizador. Conjunto que contiene la camisa/manga, el eje, las cuñas y la corona que se usan para hacer un cambio de relación de transmisión sin un choque de engranajes en una transmisión manual/transeje.

Synchronizer assembly: conjunto sincronizador. Partes que permiten que un cambio ocurra en una transmissión manual/transeje con un choque de engranajes. Las partes en el conjunto incluyen la camisa/manga sincronizadora, las chavetas de sincronización y el anillo sincronizador (anillo bloqueador).

Synchronizer ring: *Véase* blocking ring.

Throwout bearing: collarín/ballero de liberación. Cojinete que se mueve en el plato de presión y transfiere la fuerza del pie del conductor para soltar el embrague. También se llama *release bearing*.

Toe: interior del engranaje. La extrenidad interior de un diente de un enganaje.

Torque: torque/torsión. Fuerza que tuerce que se mide en libras pies (lb-ft) o Newton-metros (N-m), que pueda resultar en movimiento.

Torsen: marca de un tipo de diferencial que aplica la torsión a ambas ruedas impulsoras. El nombre es una combinación de *torque y sensing*.

Transaxle: flecha de transmission. Combina una transmission y un diferencial.

Transfer case: caja de renvío. Se usa en vehículos de impulsión de cuatro ruedas para transferir torque del motor a las diferenciales trasera y delantera.

Vehicle identification number (VIN): número de identificación de vehículo. Número alfanumérico que identifica el tipo del vehículo, la planta de ensamblaje, el tren de potencia etc.

Vibration: vibración. Oscilación, sacudida o movimiento que alterna en direcciones opuestas.

Viscosity: viscosidad: Una medida de que tal facilmente puede fluir un liquido.

Viscous coupling: acoplamiento viscoso. Artefacto parecido a un embrague que se usa en algunos vehículos de doble tracción y en la mayoría de los de tracción en toda las ruedas que usan discos finos de metal y liquido espeso de silicona para conectar los diferenciales delanteros y traseros, si hay una diferencia en la velocidad entre los dos ejes propulsores.

VSS (vehicle speed sensor): sensor de velocidad del vehículo.

Zerk: Zerk. Nombre que se usa comúnmente para una grasera. Llamado en 1922 en honor de su diseñador, Oscar U. Zerk, un empleado de la Corporación Alamite. Una grasera también se llama *Alamite fitting*.

INDEX